WATER PRACTICE MANUALS

WATER DISTRIBUT̶   ̶ ̶TEMS

EDITOR
Thomas W. Brandon, BSc, FRSC, Hon.FIWES

Compiled and Published by
The Institution of Water Engineers and Scientists,
London, England.

©Published by The Institution of Water Engineers and Scientists,
31-33 High Holborn, London WC1V 6AX,
England.

ISBN 0 901427 13 6

First published, 1984

Text photoset in 9/10pt. Times

*Printed in Great Britain
at The Lavenham Press Ltd., Lavenham, Suffolk, England.*

PREFACE

Both the former Institution of Water Engineers and the Society for Water Treatment and Examination held a well-earned reputation as learned societies responsible for the publication of authoritative works on water technology and science. In 1975 the common interests of these bodies led to their amalgamation and The Institution of Water Engineers and Scientists was formed. The new Institution has a continuing involvement in the book-publishing field with this wide-ranging series under the general title *Water Practice Manuals*.

The books will appear, over a period of several years, as a series of separate volumes and will deal mainly with the engineering and scientific elements concerned with the water cycle. They will also focus attention on more general subjects which, in England and Wales, have now become the responsibility of the Regional Water Authorities which were set up by the Water Act 1973. In recording what has become, or is likely to become, accepted current practice the books will not be confined entirely to British experience. Where relevant, references will be made to overseas practice and, in particular, to thinking and developments within the EEC. In due course the whole series will form a basic library for those concerned with the technology and science of water.

To date, three books in the series have been published:

Book 1:   **The structure and management of the British water industry**
Book 2:   **Recreation: water and land**
Book 3:   **Water supply and sanitation in developing countries**

This, the fourth book, is concerned with Water Distribution Systems.

The last decade has seen a major change in the status of the distribution engineer within the hierarchy of the water engineering profession from the Cinderella of the industry to rebirth as one of the key personnel to whom the industry is looking to help put its house in order. There are two principal reasons for this major change in direction. The first is that high distribution losses can no longer be ignored by an industry under pressure from the environmental lobby with every attempt to develop new land hungry sources; and the second is additional pressure from Government for greater operational efficiency and to obtain maximum benefits from existing facilities.

It is thus both pertinent and opportune for the first time in the memory of many water engineers to be reviving distribution engineering as an important and highly topical part of the industry.

The aims of this manual are to draw together in one reference volume all aspects of distribution systems, to give an overall view of legislation, engineering management, organization and operational practices affecting distribution, to review the current state of the art, and to look forward at developments already taking place, particularly in new technologies and techniques and the impact they will have on distribution systems in the future.

NOTE ON THE INSTITUTION OF WATER ENGINEERS AND SCIENTISTS

The Institution was established as The British Association of Waterworks Engineers in 1896 and was incorporated in 1911 as The Institution of Water Engineers. On 2nd January 1975 its name was changed to The Institution of Water Engineers and Scientists preliminary to the Institution and the Society for Water Treatment and Examination amalgamating on 1st September 1975. The combined Institution now has a membership of over 5800.

The *objects* of the Institution are set out in its Memorandum of Association. In summary these are:

1. To advance water engineering and science and education therein.
2. To promote study and research work in water engineering and science and to publish the results thereof for the public benefit.
"Water engineering and science" means the application of engineering or scientific knowledge or skill to the treatment and supply of water, the management of rivers, the treatment of sewage and its disposal, and the control of pollution in relation to water.

The corporate membership of the Institution comprises engineers and scientists, including chemists, bacteriologists, geologists, hydrologists and others concerned with the water cycle. Corporate members must be holders of approved first degrees in engineering or science and must satisfy the Council as to their practical knowledge and experience of water engineering and science. Persons in other disciplines who occupy senior positions in the water industry or who are engaged in support services can be admitted to non-corporate membership.

Most members of the Institution in the United Kingdom work for public or quasi-public authorities. In England and Wales, these are the ten Regional Water Authorities and the statutory water companies; in Scotland, the nine Regional and three Islands Councils together with the Central Scotland Water Development Board; and in Northern Ireland, the Department of the Environment for Northern Ireland (Water Services Branch).

Other members work in central government, research and teaching establishments, or as consulting engineers. Some members are concerned with the construction of civil engineering works as contractors, or as manufacturers of equipment such as pumps or treatment plant.

Nearly 20 per cent of the members of the Institution are overseas (spread in more than 90 countries throughout the world), either because they are citizens of overseas countries or because they are working there on secondment from the United Kingdom. In addition, a substantial number of members, in particular many of those employed by consultants, are extensively engaged on overseas projects even though they are United Kingdom based. The Institution has a number of Correspondents spread throughout the world, who act as focal points for the members in their areas.

The main function of the Institution is the provision of learned society activities, i.e. the sharing of experience and the dissemination of knowledge through meetings and publications. In the United Kingdom and the Republic of Ireland there are seven Local and two Specialist Sections, each with its own programme of papers and visits to works.

The publications of the Institution, besides this new range of Water Practice Manuals, include a Journal (published six times a year), Handbook, proceedings of symposia, and various reports.

ACKNOWLEDGEMENTS

The Council of The Institution of Water Engineers and Scientists acknowledges the help given in the preparation of this book by those serving the many bodies and organizations involved in the water industry and related activities.

Acknowledgements for permission to reproduce extracts from published works are included, where appropriate, in the text.

The Council also acknowledges with gratitude the work of the Manuals Subcommittee, which was set up for the planning of this series of Water Practice Manuals. The members of the Subcommittee are: T. A. Harker (Chairman); T. W. Brandon; J. D. Jepson; B. H. Rofe; H. Speight; K. H. Tattersall; and B. J. Dangerfield (Subcommittee Secretary).

CONTRIBUTORS

The Council of The Institution of Water Engineers and Scientists acknowledges the considerable debt of gratitude which is due to the following who have contributed to the writing of this book.

Book Co-ordinator

W. A. Markham,
BSc(Eng), ACGI, MICE, MIWES, (retired) formerly Managing Director, South Staffordshire Waterworks Company.

Chapter Contributors and Helpers

Chapter 1: Water Distribution Systems—Introduction

Contributed by: G. A. Booker,
BEng, MICE, FIWES, Chief Executive and Engineer, East Worcestershire Waterworks Company.

Chapter 2: The Law Relating to Water Supply

Contributed by: N. H. Bagot,
LLB, Solicitor, Company Secretary, Bristol Waterworks Company.

Assisted by:
Officials of the Scottish Development Department and of the Department of the Environment for Northern Ireland.

Chapter 3: Byelaws and Standards

Contributed by: G. Slater,
BEng, FICE, FIWES, Director and Chief Engineer, Portsmouth Water Company.

Assisted by: J. S. W. Bath,
MIMechE, formerly Head of the Fittings Testing Standards Unit, National Water Council.

R. A. Pepper,
BSc(Eng), FICE, FIWES, Director and Chief Engineer and Deputy General Manager, Sunderland and South Shields Water Company.

E. F. Young,
BSc, MICE, MIWES, Engineering Inspector, Department of the Environment.

Chapter 4: Consumer Requirements

Contributed by: G. G. Archibald,
MA, MIS, CDipAF, Principal Analyst, Policy and Planning Unit, Severn-Trent Water Authority.

T. Kitson,
BSc, PhD, MICE, MIWES, Regional Controller, Efficiency Audit, Severn-Trent Water Authority.

B. D. Waters, BSc, PhD, FRSC, MIWES, Divisional Scientist, Soar Division, Severn-Trent Water Authority.

T. J. Watson, BSc, MICE, MIWES, Assistant Operations Controller, Avon Division, Severn-Trent Water Authority.

Chapter 5: Design Philosophy and Principles

Contributed by: N. J. Curtis, BSc, MICE, MIWES, Planning Engineer, South Staffordshire Waterworks Company.

Assisted by: R. D. Foster, BSc, MICE, MIWES, Senior Engineer, Planning Unit, South Staffordshire Waterworks Company.

J. E. Thackray, MSc, FICE, FIMunE, FIWES, Assistant Director of Resource Planning, Head of Corporate Planning and Assistant Director of Finance, Severn-Trent Water Authority.

Chapter 6: Network Analysis

Contributed by: D. B. Field, BSc, MInstP, MIWES, Assistant Director, Water Research Centre.

Assisted by: J. D. Creasey, BSc, AFIMA, Project Leader, Water Research Centre (Engineering), Swindon.

G. Devine, BSc, MRSC, Senior Engineer, Water Research Centre (Engineering), Swindon.

Chapter 7: Pumping Plant

Contributed by: H. D. M. Speed, BSc, MEng, FICE, FIWES, Chief Engineer, Newcastle and Gateshead Water Company.

Assisted by: T. R. Atkinson BSc, MIEE, MIWES, Electrical and Mechanical Engineer, Newcastle and Gateshead Water Company.

Chapter 8: Mainlaying—Pipes and Ancillary Equipment and Chapter 9: Mainlaying—Planning and Construction

Contributed by: J. V. D. Banham, MBE, FICE, FIWES, Assistant Divisional Manager (Operations), Derwent Division, Severn-Trent Water Authority.

Chapter 10: Maintenance of Water Mains

Contributed by: A. L. Coe, BSc(Eng), MICE, MIWES, Group Manager (Distribution), Eastern Division, Thames Water Authority.

A. F. Elvidge,   BSc, MIWES, MIWPC(Dip), Project Leader, Water Mains Renovation Techniques, Water Research Centre (Engineering), Swindon.

Chapter 11: Water Users' Systems

Contributed by: J. A. Young   FICE, FIWES, Director of Operations, Wessex Water Authority.

F. Howarth   FIPHE, FRSH, MBIM, Regional Operations Engineer, Wessex Water Authority.

R. B. Tabor   MICE, MIWES (retired) formerly Regional Engineer (Engineering Services) Operations, Thames Water Authority.

Chapter 12: Leakage Detection and Waste Prevention

Contributed by: W. Webley,   MIMunE, MIWES (retired) formerly Assistant Divisional Controller of Operations (Distribution), Derwent Division, Severn-Trent Water Authority.

Assisted by: J. Reid,   MIMechE, MIWES (retired) formerly Divisional Manager, Western Division, North West Water Authority.

A. E. Roe,   T.Eng, Operations Room and Distribution Assistant, Derwent Division, Severn-Trent Water Authority.

T. J. Watson,   BSc, MICE, MIWES, Assistant Operations Controller, Avon Division, Severn-Trent Water Authority.

J. W. West,   MICE, MIWES, Area Controller, Supply and Distribution (South), Derwent Division, Severn-Trent Water Authority.

Chapter 13: Management and Administration

Contributed by: E. A. S. Gadsby,   MICE, MIWES, Technical Services Engineer, South Staffordshire Waterworks Company.

Assisted by: G. R. Hitchins,   BSc, MICE, MIWES, Division Operations Manager, Southern Division, Yorkshire Water Authority.

T. J. Watson,   BSc, MICE, MIWES, Assistant Operations Controller, Avon Division, Severn-Trent Water Authority.

A. R. Neve,   BSc, MICE, MIWES, Distribution Engineer, Portsmouth Water Company.

A. M. Scudamore,   BSc, MIMS, Administration Manager, South Staffordshire Waterworks Company.

CONTENTS

Chapter 12. Leakage Detection and Waste Prevention

Chapter 13. Management and Administration

LIST OF ILLUSTRATIONS
(not related to specific chapters)

Chapter 1

WATER DISTRIBUTION SYSTEMS – INTRODUCTION

1. BACKGROUND

THE last decade has seen a major change in the status of the distribution engineer within the hierarchy of the water engineering profession from the Cinderella of the industry, fighting for the financial crumbs falling from the tables of the Resource Planners and the Construction Engineers, to rebirth as one of the key personnel to whom the industry is looking to help put its house in order.

The catalogue of dereliction in the industry has been well chronicled by Pearce[1] but before the publication of that well-researched résumé engineers had begun to respond to changing social needs. In 1979, Baldwin[2] outlined the changing public attitude towards engineering works associated with water supplies and posed the question of just how much does man regard as enough in the context of a sufficient wholesome supply of water. About the same time Huntington[3] set the scene for the re-emergence of distribution engineering as a focus for some of the new techniques being taken up by the industry and since then it has increasingly become an in-vogue topic.

From being a department where no self-respecting chartered engineer willingly spent more than a year or two on his way to more lucrative "real engineering" work in planning and construction, distribution now has some of the best brains in the business, as proportionately more resources than ever before are directed towards better operational management of water functions. There are two principal reasons for this major change in direction. The first is that high distribution losses can no longer be ignored by an industry under pressure from the environmental lobby with every attempt to develop new land hungry sources; and the second is additional pressure from Government for greater operational efficiency and to obtain maximum benefits from existing facilities. In short, not only is there a shift of emphasis of management and investment from capital to revenue spending, but also a tightening of the revenue purse strings. The bewildered distribution engineer sees things he has been trying to do, and fighting for resources to do for years, now being heralded as high priority tasks and bears the brunt of criticism of matters such as high leakage and failure to introduce demand management techniques.

It is thus both pertinent and opportune for the first time in the memory of many water engineers to be reviving distribution engineering as an important and highly topical part of the industry.

The aims of this manual are to draw together in one reference volume all aspects of distribution systems, to give an overall view of legislation, engineering management, organization and operational practices affecting distribution, to review the current state of the art, and to look forward at developments already taking place, particularly in new technologies and techniques and the impact they will have on distribution systems in the future.

To put the importance and problems of distribution engineering into perspective, it is worth mentioning that in 1982 the water industry in England and Wales supplied an average of 315 litres every day to each member of the population—90 1 to metered customers, 125 1 for household use and 20 1 to other unmetered

1

customers, whilst 80 l out of every 315 l were lost by leakage and waste. For this service householders paid an average of about £32 a year or about 25p per person per week. Whilst the demands of industry for water are declining, the demands of domestic customers are increasing as more than one WC and bathroom, an automatic washing machine and a dishwasher become the objectives of many householders. Distribution operating costs in England and Wales in 1982 amounted to £200 million, whilst £130 million were spent on capital account in enhancing, extending and reinforcing distribution systems. These figures alone, however, do not show the effort currently being expended by water undertakings to pursue policies aimed at integrated distribution systems, managed and operated as entities, and at optimising the benefits to their customers in terms of the product and service supplied.

These policies embrace a wide range of technical and organizational matters, some of which are highlighted in this introductory chapter as significant developments over the last few years. Subsequent chapters contain fuller explanations of the whole range of methods, materials, techniques and designs currently available to the distribution engineer.

2. HISTORICAL

The function of the distribution system is to convey treated water to the customer on a continuous basis, meeting demand peaks and maintaining water quality as it passes through the system, and it is worthwhile recalling that during the first century AD Rome enjoyed a supply of over 900 million litres per day to its 1.2 million inhabitants[4]. Indeed, the Romans constructed aqueducts to serve their cities throughout the Roman Empire, and portions of lead pipe dated 79 AD discovered in Chester were used to distribute water to the city. There is also archaeological evidence to suggest that all earlier civilisations regarded the provision of a distributed supply of water as an essential requisite of living.

However, in Britain the decline of structured society, which followed the fall of the Roman Empire, led to the collapse of organized water supplies and the Roman distribution systems gradually fell into disrepair and disuse. The Roman plumbing skills disappeared altogether along with the bath houses and sanitation facilities they serviced. It was not until after the Norman conquest that further impetus was given to the provision of piped water supplies to monasteries and towns based on church establishments.

The renaissance of distribution systems continued in a piecemeal way until the Industrial Revolution brought together the means, the motivation and the opportunity to provide piped water to the rapidly growing communities being established.

Throughout the 18th century and the first half of the 19th century, distribution systems grew apace, and many of the great municipalities took over water supply responsibilities from some of the water companies which had mushroomed in number and size during that time. However, with the growth of distribution systems came the spread of water-borne diseases, and at their height epidemics of water-borne diseases were killing more people than all other causes of death combined. It was only in the mid 19th century that bacteria were recognised as the cause, and Parliament began to take an active overall interest in water matters with the Waterworks Clauses Act 1847 and the Public Health Act 1848. The Metropolis Water Act 1852 required that the river intakes of the London Water Companies be moved above the tidal limit of the Thames.

From that time the accent moved from the distribution of water to its treatment and subsequently to disinfection. The first chlorination plant was commissioned at Lincoln in February 1905 to disinfect contaminated river water following a typhoid outbreak in 1904, but it was the Croydon typhoid outbreak of 1937 which brought about the adoption of routine disinfection by all major water undertakers.

3. POST-WAR DEVELOPMENTS

It is worthwhile at this point noting the difference between the functions of the distribution system already mentioned, and the functions of the modern distribution engineer/manager who is required through demand management to reduce both overall and peak demands and to make value judgements on acceptable levels of supply failure, in an effort to minimise costs. These considerations even ten years ago would have been anathema to the distribution engineer/manager, whereas they are now being developed as part of his stock in trade.

THE WATER ACT 1945

One can trace many of the developments in distribution technology and practice to the legislative background which spawned them. The obvious example here is the Water Act 1945 which in many ways created the framework for post-war distribution systems, with the ability to supply pure and wholesome water at constant pressure and in sufficient quantities to meet all foreseeable demands. Under its umbrella communication pipes, and their design and installation, the requisitioning of mains, the provision of storage to meet peak demands, booster pumping and water byelaw enforcement were of paramount importance and received the appropriate attention of the distribution engineer.

This situation continued with only minor tampering with the Statute Book until the 1970s when major legislation, both in Britain and the European Economic Community (EEC), began to take effect.

THE WATER ACT 1973

The Water Act 1973 creating the Regional Water Authorities (RWAs) meant several things for distribution engineering. For customers it gave rise to the ability to interconnect former separate systems to provide better support and flexibility. It brought about uniformity in approach to problems, standards, materials and operational practices. Many matters began to be dealt with as generic policy rather than as individual unique decisions, and since the RWAs were remote bodies well removed from the customers they served, the establishment of consumer services as both a concept and a recognisable part of the organization became necessary. This in itself has brought about significant changes in distribution management philosophy, since information about system behaviour under varying constraints and conditions became recorded and brought together for top management control and policy decisions.

The change in emphasis back to distribution over the last few years since the creation of RWAs, serves to illustrate the cyclical nature of work in the water industry, reflecting the changing demands placed on the Industry by society and the environment. Action and reaction can, however, no longer be separated by 50 years. Instant solutions are demanded by Government and people alike, as instanced by the recent reaction to the Bramham pollution incident in Yorkshire[5] which gave rise both to new procedures to prevent a recurrence, and to the development of more reliable disinfection equipment for small sources. The new

emphasis on distribution is the industry's response to the needs of the late 1970s
when demands for lower operating costs and higher efficiency were translated into
efforts to reduce leakage, improve pumping efficiency, make better use of
resources and manipulate demand in a manner to produce optimum benefits from
the existing distribution system.

Financial pressure was put on the industry principally through three simple but
effective measures:

(1) external financing limits;
(2) financial targets expressed as a rate of return on current assets to increase the
self-financing of capital expenditure;
(3) performance aims expressed as operating cost targets to induce greater
operating efficiency.

The 1973 Act also gave rise to major changes in charging policy which led to
optional metering policies for domestic and commercial properties with consequent
problems for inspection, meter siting and a flurry of research activity on meter
accuracy. Changes were also afoot in plumbing with the introduction of a
mandatory requirement to install dual-flush cisterns, the encouragement given to
manufacturers of domestic unvented hot water systems through the publication of
DoE/NWC Report No. 3 on Water Regulations[6], and a most comprehensive report
on backsiphonage[7]. Entry into Europe brought about moves to harmonise byelaws,
standards, approved procedures and codes of practice but, although much work has
been done, there is little yet to show the world at large.

THE HEALTH AND SAFETY AT WORK ACT 1974

The Health and Safety at Work Act 1974 also had quite significant effects on
distribution management practices with the need to design and agree safe systems
of work which had to be built into training procedures, working practices and
supervisory controls. From that flowed the requirement to provide a wide range of
protective clothing, safety equipment and devices, better materials handling
facilities, and better amenities on working vehicles than hitherto. For the first time
design engineers had to have regard for the incorporation of safety requirements in
their projects.

INDUSTRIAL RELATIONS

Industrial relations legislation and associated training requirements have had a
less direct, but nonetheless identifiable, impact on the development of materials,
plant and equipment in distribution engineering with a clear move towards
lower-skilled, non-craft work in service and mains work.

The development and growth of incentive schemes has also had a similar impact
in the same area, with the accent on easier and quicker methods and less heavy
manual work. Similarly, the growth in the technology and application of methods
of installing pipes of all sizes underground by thrust boring or pipe jacking avoids
the need to undertake open trench excavation and the associated surface disruption
and high cost of reinstatement.

PLASTICS TECHNOLOGY

Plastics are making an increasing contribution in pipeline technology, either as
pipe material itself, lining, coating, or sleeving for other materials, or as a material
for creating watertight joints. This process has been going on for two decades and is

by now substantially completed, although there will inevitably be further developments at the margin as new synthetic materials with metal-like properties are developed. The most recent significant development is the adoption from the gas industry of medium density polyethylene pipe, which has the flexibility of other plastics together with the ability to be fusion jointed, thus avoiding all but a small number of mechanical joints and their possible leakage problems.

WATER QUALITY MONITORING

There are two well-established sources of information in the UK on the monitoring of water quality—Report No. 71[8] on bacteriological examination and WHO International Standards[9]. The 1971 edition of the Standards has now been the bible of the industry for 12 years and is again being revised. However, the Standards are in part being superseded within the EEC by a Directive concerning the methods of measurement and frequencies of sampling and analysis of surface water intended for the abstraction of drinking water, which will come into effect on 15th July 1985. This directive has a similar approach to that of the WHO Standards but, in the area of chemical constituents, covers a much wider range and uses different terminology for maximum permissible and desirable concentrations.

The implications for distribution engineering in the field of water quality lie, of course, in the maintenance of satisfactory quality throughout the system by the prevention of contamination in storage, during pumping, by backsiphonage, or from ingress during maintenance work and connections. This is undoubtedly a matter of the highest priority for distribution engineers, their staffs and operatives. Reliance has traditionally been placed on routine sampling to pick up problems, largely due to the technology available for bacteriological examination, and the time consuming and manual nature of that process has prevented 'real time' monitoring. There are, however, likely to be developments to achieve in-system monitoring of water quality, with measurements or alarms linked to telemetry to give early warning of problems of ingress, infiltration and backsiphonage.

BIOLOGY OF DISTRIBUTION SYSTEMS

One trend which has grown in importance in recent years is the interest in the biology of distribution systems. This has been in response to problems associated with the eradication and prevention of micro-invertebrate infestation. There are two categories of animal life which come within this definition, both of which pose problems of consumer acceptability. They are free-swimming types of planktonic invertebrates and larger prehensile types such as Asellus and chironomid larvae, some of which are capable of clinging to irregular surfaces. Problems are normally associated with treated surface water, originating at the treatment works where live micro-invertebrates penetrate filter beds. The necessary corrective measures to control this infestation have to be carried out at treatment works, service reservoirs, including elevated storage, and in the distribution system and, as complete eradication is difficult, may require repetition from time to time. The corrective measures required are described in Chapter 10.

TELEMETRY AND AUTOMATIC REMOTE CONTROL

A further factor which has contributed to this upsurge in activity in distribution management is the development of new technology, particularly in the telecontrol field. This has revolutionised the ability of distribution engineers to instrument, control and automate their systems, and whilst a great deal of pioneering work in this area has been undertaken over the last 15 years, it is the pressure of necessity which has been the mother of interest.

Until 1980 the development of telemetry and automatic remote control of distribution systems was rather slow and ponderous, with very few undertakings making the effort to employ the technology available. However, since 1980 the pace has increased with a significant number of undertakings making progress in this field. The pace has been hampered by lack of expertise and of appropriately experienced personnel; nevertheless, progress during the last three years has been significant and sustained, due mainly to pressure on manning levels and to take up new technology.

A variety of telecontrol facilities are available from simple systems communicating over the public telephone network to sophisticated distributed facilities under continuous control, communicating over microwave radio links or dedicated lines. One of the major contributions during the telecontrol era has come from wider use of variable-speed pumping units and development of associated speed control systems, applied to both source and distribution pumping requirements. This plant affords the possibility of varying the quantity of water pumped into the supply system as demand changes and can bring significant savings in energy costs compared with constant-speed units.

ROLE OF THE WATER RESEARCH CENTRE

The Water Research Centre (WRC) has been active in various aspects of distribution engineering for the whole of its life, but it is only in the last three years that research into engineering problems has been drawn together under a Director of Engineering and concentrated at a new purpose-built research centre at Swindon. This welcome step by the WRC means that many previously neglected areas of distribution research and development are being tackled on a co-ordinated basis, with a great deal of attention being directed to the use of new technology, particularly in the area of instrumentation, automation, and control.

The development of systems engineering is at last being accentuated and having an impact on distribution, as in other facets of the indstury. Of major importance in recent years has been Report 26[10], covering leakage control policy and practice. This report, which could not have been completed without the active participation of the WRC, creates the framework for a new look at leakage and sets out in detail a procedure for determining the best policy to adopt in particular circumstances. It is an excellent example of good applied economics which distribution engineers are finding straightforward to apply.

A number of other worthwhile developments have emanated from WRC work on leakage, including the leak/noise correlator, now firmly established for location of leaks, and the most appropriate type of valve to achieve controlled pressure reduction, with the associated control mechanisms.

The public attention which leakage has attracted over the last few years demands that it is accorded a high degree of priority by the industry, and the success or failure over the next decade or so in stemming the rising tide of leakage must depend on the willingness of distribution engineers to accept the challenge presented by Report 26 and to apply the principles outlined.

NETWORK CONTROL

The Wessex Water Authority have pioneered the development of a system comprising an eccentric plug valve, controlled by an electrically powered activator supervised by a micro-processor containing a table of possible hydraulic gradients between the valve and a critical node in the network. The table is derived from measured relationships or network analysis and is unique to the network being controlled. The system measures actual flow rate through the valve and then alters the downstream head for the appropriate hydraulic gradient.

4. CURRENT DEVELOPMENTS

RECOMMENDATIONS OF THE MONOPOLIES AND MERGERS COMMISSION

A number of peripheral activities are currently having an impact on distribution. One is the investigation and subsequent report of the Monopolies and Mergers Commission (MMC) into the services supplied by the Severn-Trent Water Authority (STWA), and the East Worcestershire and South Staffordshire Waterworks Companies. Apart from general recommendations made in the report on matters such as financial controls, investment appraisal, manpower efficiency, plant and transport utilisation and management information systems, all of which have implications for distribution managers, there were a number of specific recommendations and observations on distribution. The more important of these are outlined below.

It was recommended that the STWA should develop methods of forecasting short-term demands for operational purposes and use its simulation model to optimise day-to-day water supply operations.

It was recommended that the costs and benefits of planning and scheduling distribution maintenance work should be reviewed and appropriate procedures installed.

The work done by the STWA into components of demand to improve the reliability of long-term demand forecasting methods was recognised, but it was recommended that the WRC should co-ordinate a longer national study of demand components. It was also recommended that the companies should adopt the methods used by the STWA to improve long-term forecasting.

It was observed that the STWA should not be expected to meet nor plan to meet, all peak demands regardless of cost, and it was recommended that the Authority should investigate the effect on the capital programme of planning alternative standards of security. Consumers should be made explicitly aware of the costs of different standards, and the trade-offs between standards of service and financial resources.

On the question of demand management, it was recommended that variable-flush toilet valves should be installed free in selected areas where there is inadequate capacity to maintain supplies.

A range of recommendations were put forward on leakage control, all aimed at reducing levels of leakage to economic target levels.

It was recommended that the costs and benefits of universal metering should be kept under review, and that selective compulsory metering may be economic now. Where it is introduced, the costs of metering should be borne by the Authority and the cost spread over all consumers' charges. It was also recommended that the DoE and NWC should collaborate to eliminate any legal obstacles to selective compulsory metering, and that new houses should in future be designed to facilitate metering.

In addition to the action being taken by the Authority and the companies covered by the investigation regarding the recommendations, undertakings generally have been examining their policies and procedures in the light of the report and many are adopting the recommendations where appropriate.

CONSUMER CONSULTATIVE COMMITTEES

The MMC report was also the forerunner of another important matter affecting distribution management. The Water Act 1983, which implemented the changes in Water Authority structure and membership mooted by the Commission, also introduced Consumer Consultative Committees (CCCs) to the industry. These are likely to have a significant effect on many policies which have bearing on distribution engineering. They will, for instance, as well as dealing with the more obvious consumer worries over the structure and level of charges, billing and collection policy, and complaints handling policy, also be expected to express views and probably preferences on the construction and operation of distribution systems. These will have to include levels of service and system security, where investment choices have to be made against an objective assessment of risk of supply failure during peak demands and droughts. The concept of "willingness to pay" comes into focus in this context, and the industry will have a proper sounding board as never before. Further development of metering policy into the mandatory area will also be a matter that CCCs will expect to be consulted on, particularly where such policies will affect charges to both those being metered and the rest of the body of consumers.

HOUSE OF LORDS SELECT COMMITTEE

In December 1982 the Select Committee on Science and Technology of the House of Lords presented its report on the water industry, in particular storage and distribution of water, control of leakage and sewerage.

Some of the relevant parts of the report have been reproduced here to illustrate the interest which Parliament and the mechanisms of Government are now taking in the water industry, having stood to one side between 1974 and 1980. Indeed, these activities have been the result of deliberate policies of Government to instill efficiency into the industry, and distribution engineers must accept their share of responsibility for taking these matters to heart and implementing the necessary changes to achieve them.

The Committee chose six topics to look at in depth, three of which are relevant to the distribution engineer:

(a) Water distribution and leakage control; what is the condition of the mains and supply pipes and how efficiently is water transferred from primary storage to the consumer?

(b) Research and Development; how adequate for its purpose is the level of research and development on the engineering side of the water industry?

(c) Education and Training; does the education and training of water engineers need any improvement?

Water Distribution and Leakage Control

On this topic the Committee recommended that:

(i) The WRC's strategy for renovation of water mains, with an increase in short-term expenditure, should be refined and adopted.

(ii) Further research should be undertaken on the effects of traffic loads and speeds on underground services.

(iii) The water industry should consider how to improve its materials, specifications and construction standards.

(iv) Unlined iron pipes should not be laid.

(v) Automated operational control and telemetry should be advanced among all undertakers.

(vi) All distribution systems should be subjected to network analysis and flow surveys before capital works are undertaken.

(vii) A more active leakage control policy should be promoted, in accordance with the principles of Report 26[10].

(viii) Additional manpower should be employed for leakage control where economically justified.

(ix) The DoE should commission further research to refine the cost/benefit calculations of leakage control.

(x) Pressure control should become a standard feature of distribution systems.

(xi) Provided that research shows an extension of household metering to be practicable, the Water Authorities should make optional metering more attractive to the consumer.

Research and Development

On this topic the Committee recommended that:

(1) Water Authorities should have a statutory duty to draw up, in consultation with Ministers, programmes of research into matters affecting the performance of their functions and to secure the carrying out of those programmes.

(2) English and Welsh Water Authorities should include statements of their research activities in their Annual Reports presented to Parliament.

(3) Membership of the WRC should be compulsory for statutory water undertakers with the possible exception of Islands Councils.

(4) The DoE should assume responsibility for ensuring the existence of a long-term research strategy in the water industry, which takes into account the needs of that industry and of other interests affected by the industry's activities.

(5) The water industry should spend more on research, including an increase in subscriptions to the WRC, and the DoE should increase their commissions with Natural Environment Research Council (NERC) institutes on long-term research into the water cycle.

(6) The DoE should discuss with the water industry, the National Consumer Council (NCC) and appropriate voluntary bodies the conduct and financing of surveys to identify features of scientific interest which water authorities must conserve under Section 48 of the Wildlife and Countryside Act 1981.

(7) The Scientific and Engineering Research Council (SERC) and the NERC should create an effective liaison to promote long-term research into the water cycle.

Education and Training

On this topic the Committee recommended that:

(a) The water industry should pay attention to the case for broadening the expertise of water engineers, with particular emphasis on process and systems engineering.

(b) The water industry should support formal post-experience instruction at all levels and should look for this both in central training facilities and in the universities and polytechnics, so assisting the establishment of a career structure for the industry.

(c) Employers in the water industry should set up a programme of secondment of the more able younger engineers to full MSc courses in relevant subjects. Full advantage should be taken of the studentships available from the NERC and SERC.

Raw Water Storage

In the Section covering raw water storage the Committee made a recommendation that research should be undertaken into demand management, so that the water industry can decide how far to meet future demand for water. This must include a full economic assessment of the relative benefits of restraining demand (including leakage) and of increasing resources. Any necessary amendment of the law to permit demand management should be made.

PROBLEMS ASSOCIATED WITH CHANGING SUPPLIES

As more flexibility within the supply and distribution system is achieved through reinforcements and linking pipelines, associated problems have begun to arrive for distribution engineers. Encrustation and corrosion products which stay in place on the pipe-wall under stable water conditions become softened and displaced under changed conditions, leading to pinhole leaks and/or discoloured water.

This phenomenon is now well understood but until such time as interchangeable sources are treated to give similar characteristics in terms of pH, conductivity, and hardness, problems will continue to be produced within the distribution system which may be solved only by local *ad hoc* and pragmatic methods. The new materials being developed, and renovation of old iron mains, will tend to prevent these problems, but in the context of present spending levels on maintenance and renewal of the distribution system, such methods of prevention are not keeping pace with the spread of the problem.

PERFORMANCE AIMS AND INDICATORS

Mention has already been made of the interest which Consumer Consultative Committees are taking in levels of service and the efforts of the industry in linking them to operating costs. A further subject which has been hotly debated within the industry over the last few years is the question of performance aims and the development of appropriate indicators of performance; again as a way of placing pressure on the industry to operate effectively and efficiently. Performance indicators have been suggested by the industry and the DoE and the current state of this ongoing work, as it affects the distribution system, is covered more fully in Chapter 13.

INSTRUMENTATION, CONTROL AND AUTOMATION

Current developments in instrumentation, control and automation of the distribution system are patchy, and the industry has formed a Steering Group with the object of encouraging the growth in use of such systems in all functions of the industry, through the sharing of expertise and the creation of standards and guidelines on their implementation and use. This group is particularly concerned with the availability and reliability of suitable instrumentation for control purposes in all facets of the industry, and is currently supporting the establishment of evaluation and demonstration facilities at a number of locations, where manufacturers and suppliers will have the opportunity to install instruments and prove their viability in operational conditions.

One such facility is being promoted in a water distribution system to give more sensitive facilities than have traditionally been built into telecontrol systems. In addition to conventional arrangements to control pumping, measure service reservoir levels and pipeline flows, this system gives zonal control of pressure which is responsive to changes in zonal demand, so that leakage and demand are minimised and the situation is continuously monitored over telemetry. This will create a distribution system which responds sensitively to consumption patterns.

Another application currently being developed apace is digital recording of mains records against a background of digital ordnance survey plans, thus giving the ability to store detailed information on computer for retrieval on a common basis to visual display units (VDUs), and for transmission to distributed points including VDUs in vehicles for outside use. This information can also be supplemented by records on such matters as burst location, pipe materials, relevant details of valves, air valves and washouts etc. and maintenance information. The implications for technical management information will be far reaching in the long term but the effort necessary to set up these systems and ensure that they are religiously maintained is very demanding.

5. THE FUTURE

DEMAND MEASUREMENT AND METERING

There are a number of significant developments in prospect over the next few years which have implications for distribution. Mention has been made of the place of the new technologies in distribution engineering and the rate of take up is accelerating. On-line system simulation coupled to short-term demand prediction to give optimised operation of the system is already established in a number of locations, and this approach will grow as more telecontrol facilities are installed.

This macro view of the system will gradually be supplemented by more detailed information and control facilities to give not only control of distribution zones by monitoring and varying zonal supply to respond to demand, but also similar information and control over the supply to individual customers. Indeed the WRC sees the possible financial justification for telemetry to customer meter information being derived not from savings in meter reading costs but from the benefits associated with demand management, particularly in respect of peak daily and seasonal demands. The benefits would result principally from responsive pricing policies, reflecting the marginal costs of supplying peak demands and leaving individual customers to react to the price message. It would also be possible to assist leakage detection by the determination of legitimate night demand during minimum night flow measurement. At the present time this is a most labour intensive operation and is only rarely undertaken. In the UK at the present time less than 5 per cent of customers are metered. However, if one examines the distribution of demand, large industrial consumers of water amount to 0.05 per cent or 1 in 2000 customers and account for 20 per cent of the average demand. Thus telemetry of a limited number of customers would bring a sizeable proportion of the total demand under close scrutiny. The cut-off point on telemetering will clearly depend on the economies of the exercise and can be determined only in the light of experience.

REMOTE METER READING

There are two current contenders in the UK remote meter reading stakes. One is the Credit and Load Management (CALM) system being developed by the South Eastern Electricity Board, using the public telephone network as communication medium; the other is the Thorn EMI Mainsborne Telecontrol system using the low voltage electricity mains for communication. Both systems are designed for remote reading of electricity, water and gas meters, displaying the readings and charges at the property, detecting failure and alarm conditions (loss of supply or pressure) and remote control of valves to facilitate demand management. Time will tell which, if either, system is economically viable.

DATA-ENTRY TERMINALS

Another innovation with its roots in meter reading is the portable data-entry terminal, a device rather like a combined pocket calculator and hand held dictation machine which allows data to be entered and stored on tape for subsequent processing on a mainframe computer. Other uses in distribution engineering include generation of waste notices on site, surveying information, operatives' time or work sheets, and stock checking. In fact, the terminal is applicable to most activities which involve the recording of data on site in a standard format. There are also developments coming onto the market which allow these terminals to communicate directly with a central computer over a radio system, thus cutting out the interface problem of generating a magnetic tape.

NETWORK ANALYSIS AND COMPUTER AIDED DESIGN

Computer assisted network analysis has long been an established technique in distribution engineering and further computer help is now available for engineering design in the form of systems specifically set up to aid engineers with pipework design. These systems are in their infancy at the present time but are likely to be standard acquisitions for design offices within the next ten years.

LEAK DETECTION

Other new technology facilities in distribution as well as in other water industry functions are being fostered by the WRC through cooperative development with manufacturers. One of these is a logical extension of the demand-controlled, pressure-reduction system previously mentioned which can be linked into a primary (fast scan) or secondary (slow scan) telemetry system to continuously or regularly monitor demand into a zone of about 2500 properties for leakage detection. Examples of low cost secondary systems communicating over the public telephone system are currently in existence, measuring minimum night flow into zones on a daily basis, and on small zones of up to 500 properties are able to detect a single service burst. The economic viability of such systems looks very promising.

MULTIFUNCTIONAL TELECONTROL

In the wider context of telecontrol some Authorities are already moving towards the integration of operational control of water supply, sewerage and reclamation, and land drainage through telemetry on a common basis, operating through a single control centre. This movement towards the full concept of multipurpose water services management is interesting from an organizational structure point of view, as all telecontrol facilities are, and it remains to be seen what the effects will be for distribution engineering. It cannot be ignored and should be approached in an objective way by engineers and scientists working in this area of the industry. The opportunity to assemble a truly multi-purpose organization responding to customers' needs should not be lost.

CONSUMER CONSULTATION

Moving away from new technology, there are a number of developments coming into view in the area of customer relations. Market research, for instance, is gradually becoming accepted as a method of sounding customer opinion on policies or as a method of formulating customer service policies. Market research techniques have been used by a number of Authorities, but views as to their validity are mixed, particularly in the sphere of charging policy or standards of service. The prevalent view at present, with limited experience, is that they can at best only complement traditional public participation practices. However, market research is clearly valid as a tool to ascertain more factual information on water use habits or the frequency of use of household equipment, as witnessed by the successful studies undertaken by the STWA. These are aimed at four areas: household water use; industrial water use; major changes in tariff structure; and optional metering of non-metered customers. In each case the use of these methods proved helpful in obtaining not only information, but also reactions to alternative policies and methods of implementing these policies. As a result, the introduction of new charging policies was significantly affected by the studies and by predicting customer reaction accurately the appropriate methodology systems and resources were made available.

PRESSURE GROUPS AND WATER QUALITY

Two interdependent water quality developments may well loom large towards the end of the 1980s. They are the influence of pressure groups on water quality, and the increased use of bottled drinking water. The second seems to be directly related to the first. The prime example of the influence of pressure groups is on the question of fluoridation which is not primarily a distribution problem, but often manifests itself through the complaints machinery. Other similar quality problems relate to tastes (particularly those caused by chlorinaton), nitrates, lead and microorganics in drinking water, all of which the layman has difficulty in understanding. It is very easy for any group riding a particular hobby horse to obtain media coverage for a scare-mongering campaign about the effects of such chemicals. As society becomes more and more sensitive to environmental problems, these scares will become more difficult to resist. Indeed they appear to lead directly to the high rate of growth in the market for bottled drinking water. It has to be admitted that at least in part this is also due to bottled water being a fashionable product, but nevertheless the concern generated by water quality pressure groups most certainly does contribute. It is interesting to reflect that in some parts of Europe where bottled drinking water is well established, water undertakings are taking to advertising the high quality and low price of their own product to counteract growth in demand for bottled water.

CUSTOMER SATISFACTION

Finally, to return to the original comments in this Chapter, where the main theme was that distribution engineering is undergoing a renaissance for a whole variety of technical and historical reasons. It has to be emphasised that this process needs to be outward looking to be fruitful. It must always be borne in mind that customer service has to be at the heart of everything a distribution engineer strives for. Whilst the old adage "the customer is always right", does not always bear close scrutiny, it is nevertheless a good starting point for all engaged in distribution. The techniques, methods, aids, materials and standards covered in this volume should all be aimed in the general direction of this objective and should never be an aim in themselves. Distribution is, and will always be, a focus for achieving customer satisfaction and will be seen as a strong link in the organizational chain only when everyone working in it appreciates the full significance of that fact. Customers do not by and large expect miracles. They do expect courtesy, action on problems and sensible and proper explanations when failures occur. During strikes, droughts and freeze-ups people have always shown a strong tendency to be both reasonable and long suffering, provided they know what is happening. In the final analysis the strength in distribution has to be the understanding between the operatives on the ground and the customers. *Plus ça change, plus c'est la même chose.*

6. REFERENCES

1. Pearce, F. 1981 "Water Shed: crisis in the British water industry". Junction Books, London.
2. Baldwin, A. B. 1979 in The Institution of Water Engineers and Scientists, Water Practice Manuals, Book 1, "The structure and management of the British water industry". IWES, London.
3. Huntington, R. 1979 *J. IWES*, 33, 497, Resurrection of water supply distribution—new life for a faithful servant.
4. New England Water Works Association 1980 "The water supply of the city of Rome" (reprint). Dedham, Mass., U.S.A.
5. Freeman, L. 1980 *Water*, 10, 22, Developing trust.
6. Department of the Environment/National Water Council 1976 "Domestic unvented hot water systems" (Standing Technical Committee on Water Regulations, Report No. 3). HMSO, London.
7. Department of the Environment 1974 "Report of the Committee on Backsiphonage in Water Installations". HMSO, London.
8. Department of Health and Social Security/Welsh Office/Department of the Environment 1983 "Report No. 71—the bacteriological examination of water supplies". HMSO, London.
9. World Health Organization 1971 "International standards for drinking water". WHO, Geneva.
10. Department of the Environment/National Water Council 1980 "Leakage control policy and practice" (Standing Technical Committee on Water Regulations, Report No. 26). HMSO, London.

Chapter 2

THE LAW RELATING TO WATER SUPPLY

1. INTRODUCTION

THIS chapter is concerned solely with the statutory and common law positions governing the supply of water by a statutory water undertaker and its reception by a consumer.

The principal legislative provisions on water supply are still to be found in the Water Act 1945, as amended by the Water Acts 1948 and 1973, although the position is made more complex by the multiplicity of local Acts and statutory orders which have been inherited by the water authorities. These local enactments may incorporate certain provisions of the Waterworks Clauses Act 1847 and in the case of statutory water companies the Companies Clauses Consolidation Act 1845.

The purpose of the Water Act 1945 was to substitute the modern code contained in the Third Schedule ("the Waterworks Code") of that Act for the earlier code contained in the Waterworks Clauses Act 1847. The incorporation of the Third Schedule provisions was dependent however on the making of statutory orders by the appropriate Minister on the application of the various water undertakers, or without any such application under ss.32 and 33 of the 1945 Act. Progressively since 1945 statutory water undertakers have had the Waterworks Code and amendments thereto applied to their undertakings and by means of a "Consolidation" Order it is possible to incorporate all relevant local Act provisions into one convenient statutory document of reference.

2. INTERPRETATION

The following abbreviations where stated in the text refer to the statutory provisions or references set out alongside:

PHA 1936	Public Health Act 1936
WA 1945	Water Act 1945
	(and similarly for Water Acts of later years)
Third Schedule	3rd Schedule, Water Act 1945
PUSWA 1950	Public Utilities Street Works Act 1950
WRA 1963	Water Resources Act 1963
Undertakers	Statutory water undertakers as defined in Water Act 1973
Authority	Water authority as constituted by Water Act 1973
Water company	Statutory water company incorporated by Special Act of Parliament
The Secretary of State	The Secretary of State for the Environment and/or the Secretary of State for Wales

3. STATUTORY WATER UNDERTAKERS

MEANING AND ORGANIZATION

Prior to the WA 1973 responsibility for the public supply of water in England and Wales lay with one hundred and sixty separate statutory water undertakers, which

---

term was defined in the Water Acts 1945 and 1948 to mean any company, local authority, board, committee or other person authorised by a local enactment and any local authority or board supplying water under the PHA 1936.

On 1st April 1974 this responsibility was transferred by WA 1973 to ten new water authorities. Local authorities' existing functions to supply water ceased, as did joint water boards and committees unless their membership included a water company. The 28 statutory water companies continued in existence and have undertaken by virtue of "agency arrangements" with their respective water authorities under s.12 WA 1973 to discharge all duties relating to the supply of water imposed on their water authorities by the 1973 Act. The water authorities are under a duty to take all reasonable steps to ensure that statutory water companies have sufficient water available to meet foreseeable demands of consumers within their respective limits of supply (s.12(7) WA 1973). For all other purposes the water companies are financially independent corporate bodies with powers and duties appointed by their own local Acts and Orders.

Therefore, with one exception, the duty imposed on water companies to supply water ceased in 1974. The exception is to be found in Part VIII (ss.32-38) Third Schedule, or any similar local enactment, which imposes on water companies as statutory water undertakers the duty to fix, maintain and supply water to fire hydrants, and supply water through such hydrants for cleaning sewers, drains and highways, and for supplying any public pumps, baths or wash-houses.

The expression "Statutory Water Undertakers" is therefore defined since the 1973 Act to be water authorities, statutory water companies, joint water boards and committees (s.11(6) WA 1973). Where the term "Water Authority" alone is used (see: s.11(7) WA 1973) this can also, where appropriate, embrace water companies, boards and committees acting as the authorities' agents.

4. LIMITS OF SUPPLY

Every water authority is required, either itself or through a water company, to supply water within its area (s.11(1) WA 1973).

Supply in Bulk

This is a supply for distribution by the undertakers taking the supply. Undertakers can agree with other persons, whether statutory undertakers or not, for those persons to give, or the undertakers to take, a supply of water in bulk on any terms and conditions and, where the persons giving the supply are themselves undertakers, either within or outside the limits of supply of those undertakers (s.12 WA 1945; Schedule 4 WA 1973). The approval of the authority is required to any agreement by a water company acting as their agent in supplying such water, and such approval must be withheld if it appears to the authority that the giving of a supply would be likely to interfere with the supply of water for any purposes within the company's limits of supply. Where it appears expedient to an authority that either (a) a water company, through whom the authority is supplying water, should give a bulk supply to another company, or to the authority, and the other company or authority should take such a supply, or (b) the authority should give such a supply to the company, and such an arrangement cannot be secured by agreement, the authority may order the compulsory giving and taking of such a supply. This power may be exercised jointly by two or more authorities where a transfer of water in bulk between their areas seems expedient.

Similarly, the Secretary of State may, if satisfied that it is expedient that one authority should give to another a supply in bulk and such supply cannot be secured by agreement, order the giving and taking of a bulk supply on such terms and conditions as are provided in the Order. In giving or taking bulk supplies, either by order or agreement, the undertakers may exercise the powers relating to mainlaying and breaking open streets etc, contained in Parts V and VI of the Third Schedule.

Supply Outside Limits

This is a supply to individual premises outside the limits of supply of a statutory water undertaker. Undertakers may enter into agreement with other contiguous undertakers to supply water outside their limits of supply on such terms and conditions as may be expedient (s.13 WA 1973). Such agreements do not require approval of the Secretary of State.

Variation of Limits of Supply

The Secretary of State may by order (i) on the application of any undertaker vary their limits of supply, but not so as to include any area which is within the limits of supply of any other undertaker, and (ii) on the application of two or more undertakers vary any common boundary between their respective limits of supply (s.10 WA 1945; Schedule 8 para 47 WA 1973). If it appears to the Secretary of State expedient to vary the limits of supply of any undertaker and this cannot be secured by agreement, he may order a variation compulsorily. Such power cannot be used however to vary the boundary between two water authority areas (s.11(8) WA 1973).

5. SUPPLY FOR DOMESTIC PURPOSES

Otherwise Than in Pipes

It is the duty of every local authority (county council, Greater London Council, district council, London borough council, or common council of the City of London) to ascertain from time to time the sufficiency and wholesomeness of water supplies within their area and to notify the water authority of any deficiency.

If a local authority notify the water authority that the existing supply of water to specified premises in their area is insufficient or unwholesome such as to endanger health, that a supply for domestic purposes is required, and it is not practicable to provide a piped supply, it is the duty of the water authority to provide an alternative means of supply provided it can be done at reasonable cost.

Any dispute on account of insufficiency, unwholesomeness or cost shall be determined by the Secretary of State (s.11(2-5) WA 1973).

Normal Supply for Domestic Purposes

The duty to supply water for domestic purposes vested in each water authority and through its agents will be exercised in accordance with the powers contained in Part VII Third Schedule (ss.29-31). The undertakers are obliged to lay necessary mains for bringing water to any area within their limits of supply if required to do so by such number of owners and occupiers requiring a supply for domestic purposes whose aggregate amount of water charges payable annually will not be less than one-eighth of the cost of providing and laying the mains. Such owners and occupiers must each agree to take a supply for at least three years. If the undertakers fail to provide such a supply within three months of a valid requisition, they are liable to a fine not exceeding £50 with a daily penalty of £5 thereafter, unless they can show their failure was due to unavoidable accident or other cause (s.29 Third Schedule).

GUARANTEES BY LOCAL AUTHORITIES

Section 36 WA 1945 replaces the powers in the Rural Water Supplies and Sewerage Act 1944 (which applied only to rural areas) which enabled local authorities to guarantee any deficiency when the annual rate income for an area was less than the prescribed fraction of the cost of providing a supply.

If the owners and occupiers of any premises in any area are unable to present a valid requisition in accordance with s.29, Third Schedule because the aggregate amount of their water charges amounts to less than the prescribed fraction (one-eighth) the local authority in the area, or a combination of local authorities, may undertake to guarantee the deficit for a period not exceeding 12 years. On receipt of such guarantee the water authority is obliged to lay the necessary mains and supply water.

Note: This duty to accept guarantees given by local authorities applies to the supply of water for domestic and non-domestic purposes.

If the water authority fails to lay the necessary mains and bring water to the area within three months of receipt of such an undertaking they are guilty of an offence and liable to the same penalties as are provided in s.29, Third Schedule.

REQUISITION BY AN INDIVIDUAL OWNER OR OCCUPIER

An owner or occupier of any premises within the limits of supply who has complied with the provisions of Part X (s.40) Third Schedule regarding the laying of a supply pipe and payment or tender of the water charge is entitled to demand and receive a supply sufficient for domestic purposes for those premises (s.30 Third Schedule).

"Premises" for this purpose means property which has a sufficient degree of permanency and for example can include a permanently moored houseboat—*West Mersea UDC v Fraser (1950) IAER 990.*

There is no right to demand a supply for these purposes from a trunk main, nor if the water fittings do not comply with the byelaws or regulations applicable to the premises.

Penalties are prescribed for default by the undertakers in meeting a valid demand (maximum £25 with daily fine of £2 thereafter) subject to the defence of frost, drought, unavoidable accident or other cause, or failure to comply with any byelaw or regulation. The enforcement of such penalties is without prejudice to the civil liability of undertakers for damages—see *Read v Croydon Corporation (1938).*

Note. "Unavoidable accident . . . or cause" has been judicially considered in the case of *Industrial Dwellings Company v East London Waterworks Company (1894) 58 JP 430* (a deficiency arising from an extraordinary consumption of water during an unusually hot summer was held to be of the same nature as drought).

DOMESTIC SUPPLY FOR NEW BUILDINGS

An owner of land on which buildings are to be erected, and for which a supply for domestic purposes will be needed, may require the water authority within whose limits of supply the land is situated to construct any necessary service reservoirs, lay the necessary mains to such point or points as will enable the buildings to be connected thereto at a reasonable cost, and to bring water to that point or points—s.37 WA 1945.

Before complying with such requisition the authority may require (under a "guarantee agreement") the owner to pay each year a sum equal to one-eighth of the expense of carrying out the works, less any sums received for the supply of water from the works, until the aggregate amount of charges payable annually for the supply in respect of the newly erected buildings, and in respect of any other premises connected with the works, equals or exceeds the prescribed sum, or for a period of 12 years whichever first occurs. Except where the owner is a local or public authority, the developer may also be required to deposit as security for payment of the above-mentioned annual sums, a sum not exceeding the total expense of the works. The authority must pay interest at the prescribed rate on such a sum deposited, and also, if requested by the developer, deduct from the deposit any annual sums due under the guarantee agreement. Any question as to the point or points to which the mains must be taken to facilitate the connection of the new buildings at a reasonable cost is, in default of agreement, to be determined by the Secretary of State.

The authority commits an offence if it fails to comply within three months after receipt of a requisition and tender of any undertaking or deposit, unless it can show this was due to unavoidable accident or other unavoidable cause.

The term "necessary mains" in s.37 WA 1945 has been considered in two recent cases. In *Cherwell District Council v Thames Water Authority (1975) 1 WLR 448* the House of Lords decided that a new trunk main constructed to convey water from the Thames to an existing service reservoir was not a "necessary main" so as to enable the authority to include the cost in the guarantee sum under s.37. In *Royco Homes Limited v Southern Water Authority (1979) 1 WLR 1366* however the House of Lords had to consider the developer's contention that they could be required to meet only the cost of laying the "necessary main" from the nearest point at which water was available, even where, as was the case, the supply in the nearest main was admittedly inadequate to serve the new development. The Lords did not accept this argument—the necessary starting point must be determined in the light of sound engineering practice and this would not invariably be the nearest point to the development at which there was an existing main and supply. The Court emphasised that the purpose of the main must be to serve the development of the requisitioner, not the community at large; but the fact that once the main was laid the water in it might be used for some purpose other than supplying the developer's site did not mean the main was not a "necessary main". The circumstances in the Royco case fulfilled these requirements thus distinguishing it from the Cherwell case.

SUFFICIENCY AND PURITY OF SUPPLY

Undertakers have a statutory duty to provide in their mains and communication pipes a supply of wholesome water sufficient for the domestic purposes of all entitled to demand a supply for these purposes (s.31 Third Schedule and s.11 WA 1973). In this context it is appropriate to consider the meaning of the terms "wholesome" and "domestic purposes".

"Wholesome Water"

No definition of "wholesome" can be found in the Water Act 1945 or 1973. In the case of *Read v Croydon Corporation (1938) 4 All ER 631* it was held that the statutory duty of the corporation to supply pure and wholesome water was not absolute but was limited to the exercise of all reasonable care and skill. The Corporation was found to have failed to ensure the purity of water supplied to a consumer who had contracted typhoid. She was accordingly entitled to damages for breach of the duty of care.

In an earlier case *Milnes v Huddersfield Corporation (1886) 11 AC 511* the House of Lords had decided that the undertakers were not liable in the absence of negligence for supplying water initially pure, but subsequently contaminated by lead from the pipes—they had not failed in their statutory duty to provide and keep in their pipes a wholesome supply. However, in *Barnes v Irwell Valley Water Board (1939) 1KB.21*, also a case of lead poisoning due to plumbo-solvent water, where the undertakers were aware of the plumbo-solvency but had taken no action to remedy it, they were negligent at common law and liable in damages.

Although the judicial "reasonableness" test will still be applied, the Government has attempted to set down precautions to be applied in the day-to-day administration of water supplies[1]. Additionally, an EC directive relating to the quality of water[2] requires full compliance in England and Wales by 18th July 1985. With certain limited exceptions, such as natural mineral waters, it applies to all water regardless of origin and whether or not it has been provided by an undertaker or has received treatment. The directive lays down certain parameters which are designed to secure the wholesomeness of water intended for human consumption.

There are, of course, many private water supplies in the remoter rural areas of Britain. These are derived from springs, wells and privately owned reservoirs, the purity of which undoubtedly in many cases currently would fail to meet the EC directive on quality. Although there is provision for delays in implementation or derogations under the directive, the powers in PHA 1936 to "requisition" the provision of wholesome supplies by connection to the public distribution system would appear to be the only effective method in securing compliance with modern standards.

In conclusion it is interesting to note that whereas the original legislation imposed a duty to supply "pure and wholesome water" (s.35 Waterworks Clauses Act 1847) WA 1945 and WA 1973 only refer to "wholesome water". Scientists no doubt will argue that water can be both impure and wholesome; for instance in the case of *Attorney General of New Zealand v Lower Hutt Corporation (1964) AC 1469* the water undertaker's duty to supply "pure water" was specifically considered. The addition of fluoride to a "pure water" which was deficient in this constituent did not constitute an impurity sufficient to place the undertakers in breach of their statutory duty. It was this case which prompted the Ministry of Health to inform local authorities in an official circular that "it was the Government's view that a water supply authority has power under English law to add fluoride to the water it supplies".

Fluoridation is a subject which engenders substantial controversy, and although the Government has indemnified water authorities in respect of the fluoridation of public water supplies, it will only be added at the request of a regional health authority—only six water authorities in England were doing so in 1983, serving approximately 10 per cent of the population.

A further doubt has, however, been introduced by a recent (1983) Scottish judicial decision that it was *ultra vires* for the Strathclyde Regional Council to add fluoride. The judge said there was no evidence to suggest that fluoride had an adverse effect on health, but that he did not read in the Scottish Water Acts of 1946 and 1980 an intention by Parliament that water undertakings were to be empowered to treat water for general health improvement purposes.

The Government has announced (December 1983) its intention following the Strathclyde case to bring forward legislation which will clarify the power of water authorities in England, Wales, Scotland and Northern Ireland to add fluoride to the water supply on the recommendation of the appropriate health authorities.

"Domestic Purposes"

This term is defined in s.1, Third Schedule to mean "a supply for drinking, washing, cooking and sanitary purposes", but not for any bath having a capacity (measured to the centre line of the overflow pipe, or in such other manner as the Secretary of State may by regulations prescribe) in excess of 227 litres; and includes:

(1) a supply for the purposes of a profession carried on in any premises the greater part whereof is used as a house; and

(2) where the water is drawn from a tap inside a house and no hosepipe or similar apparatus is used, a supply for watering a garden, for horses kept for private use and for washing private vehicles:

provided that it does not include a supply of water for the business of a laundry or a business of preparing food or beverages for consumption otherwise than on the premises.

The House of Lords in *Metropolitan Water Board v Avery (1914) AC 118* held that water used by a licensee of a public house where meals were served for the purpose of cooking food and washing dishes was used for domestic purposes: "The test is not whether the water is consumed or used in the course of the trade, but whether the use of the water is in its nature domestic".

MISCELLANEOUS POWERS

Additional powers affecting new and occupied houses are vested for health purposes in local authorities under PHA 1936. By s.137 a local authority (only a district council) must reject plans deposited in accordance with the building regulations, unless proposals appear satisfactory for the provision of wholesome water sufficient for domestic purposes.

There are still properties, mainly in rural localities, which do not enjoy a piped supply from a water undertaker. The following statutory provisions are available to enforce, if necessary, the installation of piped services to such properties. By s.138 a local authority may require any occupied house to be provided with a wholesome water supply sufficient for domestic purposes. The owner may be required, where it is reasonable to do so, to provide a piped supply to the house, either by connection to the water undertaker's existing supply, or otherwise, and if there is no supply within a reasonable distance, to provide a sufficient supply within a reasonable distance of the house.

If two or more houses are insufficiently provided notice may accordingly be given to secure a joint supply. S.138 further provides for an appeal by the owner to the Magistrates' Court, and enables the local authority themselves to provide the supply and recover the cost, not exceeding £300 per house (s.5 WA 1981—this section also enables the Secretary of State by Order to increase the contribution sum).

Section 123 PHA 1936 enables a local authority to pay or guarantee payment to a water undertaker of such sums as may be agreed as consideration for providing a supply of water within any part of the local authority's district. There is provision for Government grant-aid to local authorities incurring expenditure in this way (s.1 Rural Water Supplies and Sewerage Act 1944).

6. SUPPLY FOR NON-DOMESTIC PURPOSES

Section 27 WA 1945 obliges a water authority supplying water otherwise than in bulk to supply water for non-domestic purposes on reasonable terms to owners and occupiers of premises within its limits of supply—see *Staffordshire Area Health Authority v South Staffordshire Waterworks Company (1978) 1 WLR 1387* which decided that an Agreement in 1929 whereby the water company agreed to supply the hospital authority with a daily quantity of water at a fixed concessionary rate and expressed to be payable in perpetuity ("at all times hereafter") could be terminated on reasonable notice.

This obligation is nullified if its ability to meet present obligations to provide domestic supplies, without incurring unreasonable expenditure in constructing new works for the purpose, would be endangered. Failing agreement on the terms of a supply or, in the event of a water authority refusing to supply, the Secretary of State can determine the question or refer the matter to an arbitrator. Failure to comply with an agreement, or determination, will render the authority liable (without prejudice to any civil liability) to the same penalties as are prescribed in s.30 Third Schedule.

7. SUPPLY FOR PUBLIC PURPOSES

FIRE FIGHTING

Sections 32-34 Third Schedule concerned with apparatus used for fire fighting have been applied to all undertakers by s.14(3) of the Fire Service Act 1947. At the request of the fire authority undertakers are obliged to fix and maintain fire hydrants on their mains, other than trunk mains, at such places as may be most convenient to give a supply for extinguishing fires which may break out within the limits of supply, and must maintain and renew such hydrants. Any dispute as to the number and positions of the hydrants is to be determined by the Secretary of State (s.32).

In Dawson & Co v Bingley UDC (1910) 75 JP17 the undertaker was held liable in negligence where the position of a fire hydrant had been covered by earth and was not properly indicated whereby the efforts of the fire brigade were retarded. The case of *R v Wells Water Co Ltd (1886) 55LT188* decided that the obligation to fix and maintain hydrants does not carry with it the obligation to provide at the undertaker's expense a pipe of sufficient size for an effective hydrant.

The undertakers must deposit the keys for each hydrant at fire stations and such other places appointed by the fire authority (s.33). The cost of the hydrants and their fixing, maintenance and renewal, and of providing keys, is borne by the fire authority (s.34).

The undertakers must allow all persons to take water for extinguishing fires, from any of their pipes on which a hydrant is fixed, without payment (s.36). A water company which had laid a private supply pipe for agricultural supplies to which was fixed a hydrant at the owners' request, were entitled to charge for the water used to extinguish a fire—*Weardale & Consett Water Co v Chester le Street Co-operative Society Ltd (1904) 2KB 240*.

The undertakers are obliged at the request and expense of the owner or occupier of any factory or business premises situated in or near to a street in which a pipe is already laid (not being a trunk main and being of sufficient dimensions to carry a hydrant) to fix on the pipe and maintain and renew one or more hydrants as near as possible to the premises. If required by the fire authority keys must be deposited at the fire station or other appointed place.

A fire authority must take all reasonable measures for ensuring an adequate water supply and its availability in the case of fire, and may enter into agreements for these purposes with undertakers on terms providing for payment or otherwise (for example, if the fire authority require the provision of an extra diameter main to meet fire fighting requirements). Undertakers must not unreasonably refuse to enter into any such agreement and the Secretary of State may determine any dispute. Notice must be given to the fire authority of any proposed works affecting the supply to fire hydrants (ss.13-16 Fire Services Act 1947).

Note: The obligation in s.39 Third Schedule to maintain sufficient pressure in pipes on which hydrants are fixed.

CLEANSING SEWERS ETC

The undertakers must provide a supply of water for cleansing sewers and drains, cleansing highways, and supplying any public pumps, baths, or washhouses, from any of their pipes on which a hydrant is fixed on such terms as may be agreed between the respective authorities and undertakers, or in default as determined by the Secretary of State (s.37 Third Schedule).

DEFAULT PROVISIONS

There are penalties for failure by undertakers to comply with their obligations under Part VIII of the Third Schedule, except on account of frost, drought, unavoidable accident or other unavoidable cause—maximum £50 fine with daily penalty of £5 for continuing offence (s.38 Third Schedule).

8. CONSTANCY AND PRESSURE OF SUPPLY

The undertakers must cause the water in all pipes on which hydrants are fixed, or which are used for giving supplies for domestic purposes, to be laid on constantly, and at such a pressure as will cause the water to reach the top of the top-most storey of every building within the limits of supply, provided that (a) nothing shall require them to deliver water to a height greater than that to which it would flow by gravity through their mains from the service reservoir or tanks from which the supply is taken and (b) they may at discretion determine the service reservoir or tank from which any supply is to be taken (s.39 Third Schedule).

If the undertakers fail to comply with these requirements, except when prevented by frost, drought, unavoidable accident or other unavoidable cause, or during the execution of necessary works, they are, without prejudice to any civil liability, liable to a fine not exceeding £25 and a daily penalty of £2 for each day during which the failure continues after notice given by the person aggrieved. Proceedings for recovery of other fines cannot be instituted under this section by more than one person in respect of the same period of failure.

The provisions of s.39 Third Schedule apply throughout every water authority area by virtue of s.11(7)(b) WA 1973—references to statutory water undertakers in s.39 are to be interpreted only as meaning water authorities for these purposes.

9. POWERS TO CONSTRUCT WORKS AND ACQUIRE LAND AND WATER RIGHTS

ACQUISITION OF LAND

Undertakers have powers to acquire land by agreement for any of the purposes of their undertaking, including that of erecting houses and other buildings for the use of their employees, and also land to be used for recreational purposes for persons so employed (s.24 WA 1945). The consent of the Secretary of State is no longer required.

Additionally, by s.24 undertakers may be authorised by compulsory purchase order to purchase land compulsorily for any of the purposes of their undertaking, except for the purposes of erecting houses or construction of recreational facilities for employees. The procedure for compulsory acquisition is subject to the provisions of the Acquisition of Land (Authorisation Procedure) Act 1946 and requires confirmation by the Secretary of State.

The Water Act 1973 (Third Schedule, para 2) provides that "a water authority shall have power to do anything (whether or not involving the expenditure, borrowing or lending of money, or the acquisition or disposal of any property or rights) which in the opinion of the authority is calculated to facilitate, or is conducive or incidental to the discharge of any of their functions". This apparently wide power, which is akin to those conferred on local authorities in the Local Government Act 1972 and the Town & Country Planning Act 1971, although not as specifically worded as the provisions of WA 1945 and other powers, nevertheless has a useful function in meeting any challenge that the pursuit of such a course of action was *ultra vires*.

Additionally, powers are conferred by the Town & Country Planning Act 1959, s.23, to appropriate land vested in water authorities from one statutory purpose to another.

The Minister may also by Order under ss.9 or 23 WA 1945 authorise undertakers to acquire by agreement waterworks and works associated therewith, or compulsorily any land required for the construction or alteration of such works.

POWER TO HOLD OR DISPOSE OF LAND

A specific power to hold and use land for the purposes of their undertaking is conferred on undertakers by s.25 WA 1945 and subject to the consent of the Secretary of State they may sell, lease, exchange, or otherwise dispose of such land on such terms as they think fit.

Note: The requirement for Ministerial consent to acquisition and disposal of land, subject to certain exceptions such as disposal at less than market value, was removed by the Town and Country Planning Act 1959, ss.22, 26.

Section 70 WRA 1963 enables a water authority to sell, exchange or let any land vested in it which is not required for the purpose of any of its functions. The Minister's consent is required to a disposal:

(a) of land acquired by agreement or compulsorily at a time when it was authorised to acquire the land compulsorily; or

(b) at less than the best price or rent which can be obtained having regard to any restrictions or conditions affecting the land.

ACQUISITION OF LAND AND EXECUTION OF WORKS FOR PROTECTION OF WATER

Undertakers are enabled to acquire land and construct works (including the construction and maintenance of drains, sewers, watercourses, catchpits and other works for the interception, treatment or disposal of any foul water rising or flowing on that land) for the purposes of protecting against pollution any surface or underground water which belongs to them or which they are authorised to take (s.22 WA 1945). Consent of a water authority or navigation authority is required if such works will affect a watercourse under their respective control. Similarly, consent of the highway authority is required if works required to prevent pollution of a water source affect a highway (other than under an adopted highway within the limits of supply).

Consents in such circumstances may not be unreasonably withheld and in the event of dispute the matter must be referred to arbitration.

Under s.65 WRA 1963 a water authority may acquire by agreement or compulsorily any land which they require for any purpose in connection with the performance of their water resources functions (that is, outside the scope of WA 1945).

Section 68 WRA 1963 makes special provision for the protection of water against pollution by including in the acquisition powers such land as the authority require to protect water in:

  (i) any reservoir owned or operated by them or proposed to be acquired or constructed for such purpose, or

  (ii) any underground strata within the authority's area from which they are authorised to abstract water by licence under WRA 1963.

Section 66 WRA 1963 permits the water authority to acquire interests in or rights over land by agreement or compulsorily.

POWER TO SURVEY AND SEARCH FOR WATER ON LAND TO BE PURCHASED

Undertakers may be authorised, after application to the Secretary of State, to survey and search for water on any land proposed to be acquired for the purpose of their undertaking (s.8 WA 1948; Schedule 9 WA 1973).

Notice of any such application must be given to owners and occupiers of the land who can make representations within 14 days. The Minister may hold a local or public inquiry to consider such representation before determining the application.

Authority to survey includes power to carry out trial borings to ascertain the nature of the subsoil, the presence or quantity of underground water, and the reinstatement of the land.

At least 24 hours' notice must be given to every occupier of entry on to land in order to carry out works, and if such land is held by statutory undertakers (such as railway, gas, electricity or water) who object on the grounds of detriment to their undertaking, special authorisation by the Minister is required.

Compensation is payable in respect of any damage or disturbance to land, any disputes being referred to arbitration.

MINERALS UNDERLYING WATERWORKS

The code relating to the mining of minerals is principally to be found in ss.11-18 Third Schedule where applied to water undertakings by statutory order. Contrary to the normal principles of land law that the owner of land owns, coterminous with the surface boundaries, all the land below the surface and the space above it, undertakers are not entitled to underlying minerals unless expressly purchased (s.11). The undertakers may dig, carry away or use any minerals underlying the land necessary to be removed in the construction of their waterworks, unless expressly restricted by either statute or terms of the sale of the land.

The undertakers must be given 30 days' notice of any proposal to work any mines or minerals lying under the undertakers' works, reservoirs, pipes or lying within 40 yards (36.6 m) or other prescribed distance therefrom. If the undertakers consider damage is likely to be caused to their works, they must pay compensation in lieu of working. If the undertakers are unwilling to pay compensation then the minerals may be worked in the usual manner. However any damage to the undertakers' works caused by unusual working must be made good (ss.13-14).

Note: All coal and mines of coal, and the rights to withdraw support under land, have been vested in the National Coal Board since the Coal Industry Nationalisation Act 1946. Under the Coal Mining (Subsidence) Act 1957 and the Opencast Coal Act 1958, the NCB is obliged to repair or pay compensation for any damage to buildings or works of water undertakers caused by the taking of coal.

10. POWERS TO LAY AND MAINTAIN MAINS AND PIPES

DEFINITIONS

The following definitions are to be found in s.1 Third Schedule.

Main

A pipe laid by undertakers for the purpose of giving a general supply of water as distinct from giving a supply to individual customers and including any apparatus used in connection with such a pipe.

Trunk Main

A main constructed for conveying water from a source of supply to a treatment works or reservoir, or from one treatment works or reservoir to another, or for conveying water in bulk (for distribution by the undertakers) from one part of the limits of supply to another part of those limits, or for the purpose of giving or taking a supply of water in bulk.

Service Pipe

So much of any pipe for supplying water from a main to any premises as is subject to water pressure from that main, or would be so subject but for the closing of some tap. This means in domestic premises the whole of the pipework from the main to the internal taps or cistern ballcocks.

Communication Pipe

Generally so much of the service pipe as is between the main and the boundary of the street in which the main is laid. If a stopcock lies in the premises supplied, as near as reasonably practical to the boundary of the street, then the communication pipe extends to and includes the stopcock. Where a main is laid in private land alongside and within 60 feet (18 m) of the middle of a street, s.10 WA 1948 includes in the definition of communication pipe that part of the service pipe between the main and the street or (where the premises supplied lie between the main and the street) between the main and the premises supplied. Therefore in general the boundary of the street in which the main is laid (which is not necessarily the street abutting upon the premises actually supplied with water) defines the communication pipe.

Supply Pipe

Any part of a service pipe that is not a communication pipe.

Street

Any highway, including one over a bridge, and any road, lane, footway, square, court, alley or passage whether a thoroughfare or not. Such places have been held to be included as streets "whether they are public property or private property, and whether the public have any rights over them or have no rights over them" (*Taylor v Oldham Corporation (1876) 4 Ch.D.395*). Note that: (i) s.19(5) Third Schedule expressly excludes from the definition a private street within the curtilage of a factory; (ii) Regulation 4 Walkways Regulations 1973 (SI 1973 No 686) excludes public walkways such as those found at above street level in shopping and office complexes. This wide definition of "street" means that most mains in urban areas are in "streets" even when they lie in private land, and as such are subject to the procedures of PUSWA 1950.

LAYING AND MAINTENANCE OF MAINS

The undertakers may within their limits of supply and, also, outside those limits lay a main:
(1) In any street, subject to the provisions of PUSWA 1950. This Act requires (*inter alia*) that in advance of commencing any excavations in a street, or in a bridge carrying a street, the undertakers must agree a plan and section of the proposed works with each of the authorities (highway, bridge, water or transport) concerned. However, if emergency repairs are called for, the plan and section need only be submitted "as soon as reasonably practicable" after carrying out the works.
(2) In, on, or over, any land not forming part of a street after giving reasonable notice (usually 28 days) to every owner and occupier of that land and with the consent of:
(a) the highway authority concerned if the main is to be laid within 220 feet (67 m) of any highway; and
(b) the electricity or gas board concerned if the main will be laid in, on or over any operational land of that board. "Operational land" for this purpose is defined in the Town & Country Planning Act 1971 to mean land which is used for the purpose of carrying on their undertaking, and land held (that is, not at present used, but held with the intention of use in the future) for that purpose.

The undertakers may from time to time inspect, repair, alter, renew, or at any time remove any main laid down by them (s.19 Third Schedule as amended by Local Authorities etc (Miscellaneous Provisions) Order 1977 (SI 1977 No 293).

It will be seen therefore that although the consent of other statutory undertakers is required (which may not be unreasonably withheld) the only requirement for entering on and carrying out works in land not forming part of a street is the service of the statutory notice.

Some undertakers prefer to negotiate a legal easement which has the advantage of constituting notice of the existence of the main to all subsequent owners or occupiers into whose hands the land may pass. Also conditions may be imposed, for example restricting development over the main. These forms of protection cannot be secured by service of the statutory notice. The undertakers do not in either case acquire any legal ownership of the soil in which the pipes are laid; they merely enjoy exclusive occupation of the space taken up thereby.

Compensation is payable to every person interested wherever entry under these powers is made on any land not forming part of a street in respect of damage done or for injurious affection.

Any proposal to lay a main which will cross or interfere with a watercourse or works controlled by a land drainage authority is subject to notice to that authority who may object (within 28 days). The proposal may only proceed if the objections are withdrawn or with the approval of the Secretary of State after a local inquiry.

Laying Mains Outside Limits of Supply

Where undertakers propose to lay a main outside their limits of supply, in addition to giving such notices as are required by s.19 Third Schedule they must:

(i) advertise in a local newspaper a notice describing the proposals, the land affected and naming a place where a plan may be inspected; and

(ii) serve a copy of the notice on the local authority and on the highway authority for any highway in which the main is to be laid. Any objection (within 28 days) by the local or highway authority concerned, if not withdrawn, requires determination by the Secretary of State who may approve or modify the proposals after a local inquiry (s.20 Third Schedule).

These provisions as to publication and service of notice do not apply where the main is to be laid in an adopted highway and the local or highway authority have given their consent.

Note: Additionally water companies are obliged under their agency arrangements to submit to their respective authorities an annual programme showing the works which the company propose to undertake in the following five years, including the construction of a trunk main to carry water to or from a place outside the company's limits of supply.

Indication of Water Fittings

Under s.19(4) Third Schedule undertakers may erect and maintain in any street notices (valve and hydrant plates) indicating the position of underground water fittings used for controlling the flow of water through their mains, and may fix such notices to any house or other building, wall or fence.

Laying and Maintenance of Service Pipes

The undertakers may in any street within their limits of supply lay such service pipes with stopcocks or other fittings as they deem necessary for supplying water to premises within the limits, and may inspect, repair, alter, renew or remove such pipes. Where the service pipe has been laid lawfully in or over any land not forming part of a street the undertakers must pay compensation for any damage resulting from entry on the land for inspection, renewal, etc purposes (s.21 Third Schedule).

Laying and Maintenance of Supply Pipes

An owner or occupier of any premises within the limits of supply who requires a supply for domestic purposes must (a) give 14 days' notice of the intention to lay the pipe, at the same time paying or tendering the water rate payable in respect of the premises, and (b) lay the supply pipe at his own expense with the consent of owners or occupiers of any land not part of the street. If any part of the supply pipe is to be laid in the highway this must be done by the undertakers (s.40 Third Schedule).

Responsibility for the repair of supply pipes rests with the owner or occupier of the premises supplied, save where they lie in the highway (s.44(2) Third Schedule). If the undertakers believe that a supply pipe is causing, or is likely to cause, waste of water, or injury to person or property, they may repair it and recover the cost from the owner of the premises supplied. If several buildings in the occupation of different persons are supplied by a common supply pipe the cost of repair may be recovered in such proportions as may in the case of dispute be settled by the Court (s.63 Third Schedule).

Sometimes it is difficult, for example because the owner is away, to gain entry in order to take remedial action under s.63. In such circumstances some undertakers have obtained powers, after giving not less than three days' notice to the owner or any occupier of the premises, to turn off or cut off the water supply. The supply will later be restored when the necessary remedial work has been carried out.

Laying and Maintenance of Communication Pipes

Where notice is served under s.40 Third Schedule relating to a supply pipe the undertakers must lay the necessary communication pipe, together with any part of the supply pipe which is to be laid in the highway, and connect the two. Where part of the supply pipe is to be laid in the highway the undertakers may elect to lay a main in the highway for such distance as they think fit in lieu of the supply pipe and then lay a communication pipe from the main to connect with the supply pipe (s.41 Third Schedule).

If the undertakers fail to carry out the work within 14 days of the laying of the supply pipe they are liable to a fine of £25 and a penalty of £2 for every day the default continues after the expiration of the 14 days unless they can prove unavoidable accident or other unavoidable cause (s.41(2) Third Schedule).

The expenses of executing the necessary work must be paid by the person giving notice and may be recovered in the Magistrates' or County Court as a civil debt. Where a main is laid in lieu of a supply pipe the undertakers must bear the additional cost (s.41(3) Third Schedule).

The undertakers may within 7 days after receipt of the notice require the person giving the notice either to pay the cost of the work in advance, or give security for payment, in which case the period of 14 days mentioned in s.41(2) above does not commence until the requirement is met.

All communication pipes vest in the undertakers who are responsible for their repair or renewal at their own cost (s.44(1) Third Schedule). The undertakers are also responsible for carrying out any necessary works to a supply pipe laid in a highway, but may recover the cost from the owner of the premises supplied. The undertakers are liable to a fine not exceeding £25 with a daily penalty of £2 thereafter if they fail to carry out such necessary works within a reasonable time of notice of any defect (s.44(2-3) Third Schedule).

Power to Require Separate Service Pipes

Subject to the limitations of s.4 WA 1981 the undertakers may require the provision of a separate service pipe for each house or other building supplied by them with water. If, in the case of a house or other building already supplied with water but not having a separate service pipe, the undertakers notify the owner of the house or building that a pipe is required, the owner must within three months lay so much of the required pipe as constitutes a supply pipe and is not required to be laid in a highway, and the undertakers shall within 14 days after he has done so lay so much of the required pipe as constitutes a communication pipe to be laid in a highway and make all necessary connections. If the owner fails to comply with a notice served on him, the undertakers may themselves execute the work. The expenses reasonably incurred by the undertakers in executing the work of laying a pipe in a highway and making connections, or in executing the work themselves where an owner fails to comply with a notice, shall be repaid by the owner of the house or building and may be recovered summarily as a civil debt. If the undertakers default in laying a pipe in a highway and making the necessary connections, they are liable to a fine not exceeding £25 and to a further fine not exceeding £2 for each day on which the default continues after the expiration of the 14 days (s.42 Third Schedule).

Section 4 WA 1981 provides that undertakers may not require the provision of separate service pipes for houses or buildings referred to in s.42 Third Schedule until:

(1) the existing supply pipe becomes so defective as to require renewal or is no longer sufficient to meet the requirements of the houses; or

(2) a payment in respect of the supply of water to any of the houses remains unpaid after the end of the period for which it is due; or

(3) the houses are, by structural alterations to one or more of them, converted into a larger number of houses; or

(4) the owner or occupier of any of the houses has interfered with or allowed another person to interfere with the existing service pipe or the stopcock fixed to it and thereby caused the supply of water to any house to be interfered with or the undertakers have reasonable grounds to believe that such interference is likely to take place.

Stopcocks

Section 45 Third Schedule can be applied to a water undertaking by an Order made under s.32 WA 1945. On every service pipe laid after this section comes into effect the undertakers must, and on every service pipe laid before that date they may, fit a stopcock enclosed in a covered box or pit, of such size as may be reasonably necessary. The stopcocks must be placed in the most convenient position, provided that:

(a) one placed in private premises shall be placed as near as reasonably practicable to the street from which the service pipe enters the premises;

(b) one placed in a street, after consultation with the highway authority, shall be placed as near to the boundary thereof as is reasonably practicable.

Breaking Open Streets

Reference should be made to Water Practice Manual No. 1[3] (WPM 1) ch.3, s.5 which sets out the principal powers relating to the breaking open of streets for the purpose of laying, repairing and renewing mains, pipes or other works as contained in Part VI (Sections 22, 25, 27, 28) Third Schedule and PUSWA 1950.

An important decision has recently been made by the House of Lords in the case of *Department of Transport v North West Water Authority (1983) 1 All ER 892* relating to the liability of water undertakers for damage to highways caused by burst mains. It had previously been decided in a lower court that water undertakers were strictly liable, irrespective of negligence, for such damage, on the construction of the "non-exoneration" words in Section 18(2) PUSWA 1950. The Law Lords decided that the wording of this section did not amend the general rule that no action will lie for doing that which statute has authorised if it is done without negligence—so if a water authority is under a duty to supply water under pressure it is not liable if the pressured mains burst and damage property of the highway authority.

Note: A similar exemption from liability exists in s.6 WA 1981 in relation to loss or damage suffered by "excepted undertakers"; this exemption does not apply, however, to loss or damage to private property (see Section 11 of this chapter).

Power to Break Open Streets Forming Boundary of Limits of Supply

Where premises are within the limits of supply and they abut on or are situated near to a street the width of which is wholly or partly outside the limits, the undertakers may in order to supply water to the premises exercise the same powers of laying, inspecting, repairing etc service pipes as are available under PUSWA 1950 with respect to streets within the limits of supply (s.43 Third Schedule).

TEMPORARY DISCHARGE OF WATER INTO WATERCOURSES

Undertakers carrying out the construction, alteration, repair, cleaning or examination of any reservoir, well or borehole, line of pipes, or other work forming part of their undertaking, may discharge the water therein into any available watercourse (which includes sewers). They may lay and maintain for this purpose in any street within or outside their limits of supply all necessary discharge pipes and apparatus—the statutory provisions relating to the breaking open of streets by water undertakers will apply accordingly.

Except in an emergency and as otherwise may be agreed between the undertakers and the water authority, before commencing to discharge through a pipe exceeding 9 inches (225 mm) diameter the undertakers must comply with certain provisions relating to giving notice to the water or navigation authorities and the minimising of possible injury. The undertakers must pay compensation for any damage occasioned by the exercise of these powers. If they fail to ensure that water so discharged is free from mud, silt, solid or polluting matters, or any matter prejudicial to fish, the spawn or fish food, they are guilty of an offence punishable on conviction by a fine not exceeding £200 with a daily fine of £20 where it continues (s.34 WA 1945; Schedule 8, para 52 WA 1973).

11. LIABILITY FOR INJURY OR DAMAGE

For a general statement on the liability of water undertakers in actions for nuisance or negligence arising from their operations refer to WPM 1, ch.3, s.16[3].

It will be seen that liability for the consequence of escape of water is generally dependent on proof of negligence—*Green v Chelsea Waterworks Company (1894)*—although exceptions occur as in the Reservoir Acts 1930 and 1975 which fall within the doctrine of strict or absolute liability (that is, the undertakers are liable even though damage or injury was caused without intention or negligence on their part). Section 6 WA 1981 which came into force on 1st April 1982 has now, subject to limited exceptions, made undertakers strictly liable for loss or damage caused by escapes of water from a main or communication pipe belonging to them, overruling the decision in *Green v Chelsea Waterworks Company*. It would appear that certain questions remain to be judicially resolved over the meaning of "loss" in this context, although "damage" is expressly defined to include death or injury to any person. Undertakers now therefore are committed to substantial public liability insurance to safeguard this risk. No liability is incurred if the escape of water is due wholly to the fault of the person suffering the loss or damage, or of any servant, agent or contractor of his. The liability does not extend to escapes of sewage.

Similarly there is no liability to "excepted undertakers"—this term includes railway, road transport, electricity or gas undertakers, and highway or bridge authorities. This exception appears to have been inserted in Section 6 so as to preserve the relationship which exists with other statutory undertakers under, for example, PUSWA 1950. In other words the strict liability is qualified in that "excepted undertakers" would have to prove negligence in the event of damage to their premises or equipment by an escape of water.

12. SAFETY OF RESERVOIRS

RESERVOIRS (SAFETY PROVISIONS) ACT 1930

The current law on this subject is still to be found in the Reservoirs (Safety Provisions) Act 1930, although this Act has been repealed by the Reservoirs Act 1975 which requires to be brought into effect by Order of the Secretary of State.

The 1930 Act covers the design, construction and inspection of "large reservoirs" which means ones capable of holding more than 5 million gallons (22 600 cubic metres) above the natural level of any part of the land adjoining the reservoir.

A large reservoir can only be constructed or altered in accordance with a design and under the supervision of a qualified civil engineer, who is on a panel appointed by the Secretary of State after consultation with the President of the Institution of Civil Engineers. The engineer must issue a certificate governing its filling and use. Large reservoirs must be inspected at intervals of not more than ten years, or at a shorter interval if recommended at the time of the previous inspection. Any recommendations contained in the engineer's report in the interests of safety must be complied with. A local authority or other interested person likely to be affected by an escape of water may apply to the Crown Court for an Order requiring the Act's observance. In the case of reservoirs constructed after 1st January 1931 the water undertakers are strictly liable for any damage or injury resulting from an escape of water, irrespective of negligence, under the rule in *Rylands v Fletcher (1868)*. The defence of statutory authority is not available in this case.

THE RESERVOIRS ACT 1975

The purpose of the Reservoirs Act 1975 is to strengthen the law on reservoir safety. At the time of writing the Department of the Environment have announced proposals to implement the Act in three phases with full implementation being completed by 1st January 1987.

More than half the estimated 1800 large dams or reservoirs in Britain are over 100 years old. A Government initiated survey, which reported in 1982, found that for about 600 reservoirs there are no documents certifying inspection, or the owners were unknown, or the local authorities could give no information. It is estimated there may be another 200 reservoirs of which councils have no records.

The new Act extends the reservoir safety provisions to artificial lakes. It extends to any place where water is artificially retained to form or enlarge a lake or loch, whether or not use is intended to be made of the water. The Act applies to reservoirs for water as such and therefore does not include a mine or quarry lagoon which is a tip within the meaning of the Mines and Quarries (Tips) Act 1969, or a canal or inland navigation waters.

The expression "large reservoir" in the 1930 Act is altered to "large raised reservoir" and the capacity figure in the definition is increased to 25 000 cubic metres (5.5 million gallons).

The term "undertakers" in this context means either the water authority responsible for construction or operation of a reservoir and, in any other case if intended to be used for the purposes of any undertaking, the persons carrying on the undertaking, or if not so used or intended to be used, the owners or lessees of the reservoir.

No authority was effectively charged under the 1930 Act with enforcement of the

Act. It could only be enforced through the courts on the application of a local authority or a person likely to be affected by an escape of water. Now enforcement rests with the county councils and Greater London Council in England and Wales, and the regional and Islands Councils in Scotland ("the enforcement authorities"). In view of the now stated proposals by the Government to abolish the Greater London Council and metropolitan counties, it is likely that the enforcement powers will be vested in the district councils in the metropolitan areas.

The enforcement authorities are to maintain registers of large raised reservoirs, which will be available for inspection by the public. The information to be contained on the register will merely inform whether an identifiable reservoir is at any time in compliance or not with the Act. The enforcement authorities are not required to do more than satisfy themselves that the undertakers have fulfilled their duties—no technical assessment is needed.

There is a general duty on the enforcement authorities to report periodically to the Secretary of State on action taken to comply with the provisions, both as an enforcement authority, and as undertakers owning or operating large raised reservoirs. The Secretary of State is enabled to act if the enforcement authority fails to carry out its functions, such as failing to keep a register showing the large raised reservoirs wholly or partly in its area.

The provisions contained in the 1930 Act as to constitution of panels of qualified civil engineers continue, but appointments are now to be limited to five years, and specific provision is made enabling the Secretary of State to abolish or alter a panel.

The basic requirement of the 1930 Act that a qualified civil engineer must be employed to design and supervise the construction or alteration (so as to increase capacity) of large raised reservoirs is continued, and the filling and storage of water must only be in accordance with that engineer's certificate. The final certificate must not be given earlier than three years after a preliminary certificate is first issued, and if this certificate is given more than five years after that date the engineer must give the undertakers a written explanation of his reasons for deferring the issue of the certificate.

The enforcement authority may take action where the undertakers fail in their duty to appoint a qualified civil engineer.

The Act contains safety precautions to be taken before an abandoned reservoir is brought into use again, and when the capacity of a large raised reservoir is reduced to below 25 000 cubic metres above ground level, or where a reservoir is abandoned. The enforcement authority again may take action on failure of the undertakers to carry out their obligations in this respect.

Inspections of larged raised reservoirs must in general be made by a qualified civil engineer at intervals not exceeding ten years, or within a lesser period if a report of an inspection so recommends. An inspection must also be made within two years of a final certificate.

Note: an inspecting engineer under the 1975 Act, and who is on the appropriate panel, must not be an employee of the undertaker—that is, he cannot carry out statutory inspections of reservoirs operated by his employing authority.

Undertakers are required to keep a record of water levels and other essential information and provision is made for continuous inspection by a supervising engineer between the periodic inspections referred to.

Enforcement authorities may deal immediately in emergency with an unsafe reservoir or an abandoned reservoir likely to constitute a risk, but remedial measures must be carried out under the supervision of a qualified civil engineer.

There is an obligation on undertakers to provide information to enforcement authorities of their intention to construct, alter or re-use a reservoir.

The strict liability of undertakers (under *Rylands v Fletcher*) for damage or injury caused by an escape of water from any reservoir is preserved, and additionally they are liable to criminal proceedings in respect of a breach of certain provisions (Section 22 RA 1975).

13. PREVENTION OF WASTE OF WATER

UNDERGROUND WATER

No person may:

   (i) cause or allow any underground water to run to waste from any well, borehole or other work, except for the purpose of testing the extent or quality of the supply or cleaning, sterilising, examining or repairing the well, borehole or other works, or

   (ii) abstract from any well, borehole or other work water in excess of reasonable requirements. There is a proviso that if underground water interferes or threatens to interfere with the execution or operation of any underground works (whether water works or not) it is not an offence under this section to cause or allow the water to run to waste so far as may be necessary to enable the works to be executed or operated, or if no other method of disposing of the water is reasonably practicable.

Any person who contravenes these provisions is liable on summary conviction to a fine not exceeding £200 and the court may order the well, borehole or other work to be sealed or other steps taken to prevent waste. The water authority may additionally apply to the court for authority to take such steps as are necessary to execute the court order, and recover the costs thereof from the person convicted. Any authorised officer of a water authority may on production of his authority enter any premises in the authority's area to ascertain if there has been any contravention, or to execute the court order (s.14 WA 1945; Schedule 8, para 48 WA 1973).

AGREEMENTS AS TO DRAINAGE OF LAND

Undertakers may agree with owners and occupiers of any land or with a local authority to carry out any necessary works to drain that land, or more effectually collect, convey or preserve the purity of water which the undertakers are authorised to take. If as a result of the works the water is discharged into any watercourse, other than a public sewer, the undertakers must beforehand consult either the water or navigation authority (s.15 WA 1945).

HOSEPIPE RESTRICTIONS

If any undertaker considers a serious deficiency of water for distribution by them exists, or is threatened, they may for such period as they think necessary, and in the whole or any part of their area, prohibit or restrict the use of hosepipes for private garden watering or washing private motor cars. The undertakers must advertise the prohibition or restriction in two local newspapers. Contravention of the restriction is punishable by a fine not exceeding £200. Charges made by the undertakers for use of hosepipes are subject to reduction or repayment in respect of the period of restriction. Any authorised officer of the undertaking may enter premises on proof of authority, to ascertain if there is or has been any contravention (s.16 WA 1945).

BYELAWS

Byelaws for Preventing Waste, Misuse or Contamination of Water

Undertakers may make byelaws governing waste, misuse or contamination of water, which may include provisions to regulate the size, materials, installation and repair of water fittings. Contravention may be punishable by a fine, but the undertakers may also cause the defects to be remedied and recover the costs for so doing from the person in default (s.17 WA 1945).

Byelaws for Preventing Water Pollution

Undertakers may make byelaws to protect their surface or ground water sources from pollution (a) by defining the area which they wish to control, and (b) by prohibiting or regulating certain specified acts within that area. Notice to the owner or occupier of any premises within the area to carry out works or repairs necessary to prevent pollution renders them liable to a fine in the event of breach. If the owner or occupier consider any requirement to be unreasonable they may within 28 days appeal to the Secretary of State who may decide the appeal, or refer the matter to an arbitrator.

The undertakers may carry out the required works and recover the expenses of so doing if such owner or occupier either fails to comply with any notice or to appeal.

Compensation is payable in certain circumstances for any injurious affection suffered, or expenses incurred in complying with the byelaw requirements, again determined by arbitration in default of agreement (s.18 WA 1945). The power to make byelaws for the protection of surface or underground sources contained in s.18 WA 1945 and similar powers in s.79 WRA 1963 have been repealed and replaced by the powers contained in Part II of the Control of Pollution Act 1974. Orders under the 1974 Act bringing the repeals into effect have not yet been made however.

Note: Severe penalties are prescribed by s.21 WA 1945 if a person is guilty of any act or neglect whereby any spring, well, borehole or adit, the water from which is used or is likely to be used for human consumption, or domestic purposes, or for manufacturing food or drink for human consumption, is polluted, or likely to be polluted. There is liability to a fine not exceeding £1 000 with up to £50 for every day the offence continues after conviction; or on conviction on indictment to a fine or imprisonment for a term not exceeding two years, or to both fine and imprisonment. This section is not intended to penalise farmers who unwittingly and using good husbandry, may and do pollute sources from time to time in the process of crop cultivation, nor the reasonable use of tar or oil on a public highway. There are the normal powers of entry to enforce these provisions.

The foregoing provisions are without prejudice to normal common law rights and remedies; for example, an action for damages and/or injunction for nuisance.

General Provisions as to Byelaws

The Secretary of State is the confirming authority as to byelaws made under ss.17 and 18 WA 1945 and the procedure relating to the making and confirmation is found in Part II of Schedule 7 WA 1973. It is the duty of the undertakers to enforce the byelaws, subject to any Ministerial relaxation or dispensation where enforcement is considered unreasonable. Provision may be made for a fine on summary conviction, not exceeding £400, with a daily penalty of £50 for a continuing offence (s.19 WA 1945).

By s.20 WA 1945 the Secretary of State may require any undertaker to make byelaws under s.17 of the Act with regard to waste, misuse or contamination of water, and may himself make the byelaws if the undertakers do not do so satisfactorily within three months of such requirement.

BUILDING REGULATIONS

Section 61 of the Health & Safety at Work Act 1974 substitutes new ss.61-76 PHA 1936 in extending the scope and extent of the Building Regulations. Under s.61 the Secretary of State is enabled to make regulations governing the design and construction of buildings, their internal services, fittings and equipment, and the manner in which the work is carried out. The regulations may include provisions for preventing waste, undue consumption, misuse or contamination of water.

The Housing and Building Control Bill passing through Parliament at the time of writing is likely to further amend or replace the 1976 edition of the Building Regulations currently in force.

DROUGHT

The period May 1975 to August 1976 was the driest in England and Wales since meteorological records were first kept 250 years earlier, with the result that the Drought Act 1976 was enacted "to confer fresh powers to meet deficiencies in the supply of water due to exceptional shortage of rain and for connected purposes".

General Water Shortage (Section 1)

If the Secretary of State is satisfied, due to an exceptional shortage of rain, that a serious deficiency of supplies of water exists or is threatened, then on an application by a water authority or water company he may make an Order providing as follows:

(1) Authorising an authority/company to take water from any specified source, subject to conditions.
(2) Prohibiting or limiting the use of water for any purpose.
(3) Authorising the discharge of water to any place subject to conditions.
(4) Prohibiting or limiting the taking of water from any source.
(5) Suspending or modifying any restriction or obligation to which the authority is subject.
(6) Authorising the authority to suspend, vary or attach conditions to any consent for the discharge of sewage or trade effluent.

Such an Order does not impair the right of the authority/company to charge for water supplied, despite any interruption or diminution thereof. Any authorisation prohibiting or limiting the use of water cannot have effect for longer than six months.

Emergency Water Shortage (Section 2)

In similar circumstances to the requirements of Section 1, and further being satisfied that the deficiency is such as to be likely to impair the economic or social well-being of persons in the area, the Minister may by Order provide for meeting the deficiency. The Order may include any provision which could be included in an Order under Section 1 and, in addition, may authorise the authority to supply water by means of standpipes or water tankers. An Order under s.2 cannot be effective for more than three months.

Orders under ss.1 and 2 may confer such additional powers, including entry on land, the execution of works, and payment of compensation as are requisite to discharge the functions of the Drought Act 1976.

Any person who takes, uses or discharges water in contravention of the provisions of an Order under ss.1 and 2 of the Drought Act 1976 commits an offence and is liable on conviction to a fine not exceeding £1 000 or such sum as may be substituted, taking into account the changes in monetary values, by Order made by the Secretary of State under s.61 of the Criminal Law Act 1977. The person accused may claim as a defence that all reasonable precautions were taken and due diligence exercised to avoid the commission of an offence (s.4 DA 1976).

MISCELLANEOUS PROVISIONS FOR PREVENTING WASTE

Part XIII of the Third Schedule (ss.60-70) contains the following miscellaneous but important provisions facilitating the reduction of waste.

Cisterns

Section 60 enables the undertakers to require the provision of a cistern, together with a ball and stopcock, on the pipe conveying the water to it in the case of:

(a) any building the supply of water to which need not under the special Act be constantly laid on under pressure (see s.39 Third Schedule or any other special provisions which apply); and

(b) any house the erection of which was not commenced before the coming into force of the section and to which water is required to be delivered at a height greater than 10.7 m below the draw-off level of the service reservoir.

In the case of (b) the undertakers may require a cistern capable of holding one day's supply. It is to be noted that under s.39 Third Schedule the appropriate service reservoir is in the discretion of the undertakers. If the consumer fails to provide the cistern etc, or fails to keep it in repair, the undertakers may provide it or do repairs to prevent waste of water and charge the cost to the owner of the building.

Testing Water Fittings

By s.61 the undertakers are given power to test any water fittings.

Entry of Premises

Section 62 gives an authorised officer of the undertakers power to enter premises supplied by the undertakers to detect waste or misuse of water. A person who obstructs or refuses admittance to the authorised officer is liable to a fine not exceeding £25. Powers to enforce entry on to premises by Justices' warrant are contained in s.82 Third Schedule.

Penalty for Waste etc of Water by Non-repair of Water Fittings

Section 64 provides for a fine not exceeding £200 where the owner or occupier of any premises wilfully or negligently causes or suffers any water fitting which he is liable to maintain to be out of order or repair or to be or remain so constructed or adapted or used that the water supplied to the premises is or is likely to be wasted, misused or unduly consumed, or contaminated before use, or that foul air or any impure matter is likely to return into any pipe belonging to or connected with a pipe belonging to the undertakers. If any water fitting which any person is liable to maintain is in such a condition or so constructed or adapted the undertakers may require that person to carry out necessary repairs or alterations, and if he fails to do so within 48 hours the undertakers may themselves carry out the work and recover from him their reasonable expenses. It may in some cases be a matter of much practical difficulty to discover who is liable to maintain fittings. (A modified s.64

has been applied to water authorities by the Local Government (Miscellaneous Provisions) Act 1953, as itself amended by WA 1973, though the practical effect of the original and the current form of the section is similar).

Some undertakers have obtained powers to cut off the water supply where the owner cannot readily be found, similar to the power attached to s.63 Third Schedule. Additionally, where any premises are demolished or appear to be no longer likely to require a supply, and the undertakers think a waste of water is occurring or likely to occur, they may, after notice to the owner and any occupier, cut off the communication pipe or any part of the supply pipe lying in the highway, and seal any connecting pipe, recovering the cost of so doing summarily as a civil debt.

Penalty for Misuse of Water

An owner of occupier of premises supplied with water by the undertakers who, without their consent, supplies any of that water to another person for use in other premises, or wilfully permits another person to take any of that water for such use, is liable to a fine not exceeding £25, unless such water is for firefighting purposes, or such other person is temporarily unable through no default of his own to obtain his normal supply. Further, any person who uses water supplied, other than through a meter, for a purpose for which he is not entitled (for example, using water supplied for domestic use in an industrial process) is liable to a fine not exceeding £25 (s.65). Both of these offences are without prejudice to the right of the undertakers to recover the value of the water misused.

Penalty for Fraudulent Use of Water

By Section 66 persons who fraudulently alter the index of a meter or prevent it registering correctly are liable to a fine not exceeding £25 as well as those who fraudulently abstract or use water of the undertakers (for example, by abstracting water before it has passed the meter). The onus is upon the consumer to prove absence of fraud. Where a meter has been fraudulently interfered with the undertakers are enabled to put it in order at the expense of the offender.

Penalty for Interference with Valves and Apparatus

Section 67 renders liable to a fine not exceeding £200 anyone who wilfully and without the consent of the undertakers or negligently turns on, opens, closes, shuts off or otherwise interferes with any valve, cock or other work or apparatus belonging to the undertakers. This and the next section have been amended by Schedule 9 WRA 1963.

Penalty for Extension or Alteration of Pipes etc

Section 68 renders liable to a fine not exceeding £25 any person who, without consent, attaches any pipe or apparatus to a pipe of the undertakers, or who uses any pipe or apparatus so attached or altered. This section is directed, for example, to cases where, without consent, stoptaps, hosepipes etc, are fixed or a pipe is wrongfully attached to the service pipe of one house for the supply of another house. Any person who uses the pipe or apparatus which has been so attached or altered is liable to the same fine, unless he proves he was unaware of the fact.

Meters and Other Fittings

By Section 69 a consumer must not, without consent, connect or disconnect a meter. He must give 24 hours' notice to the undertakers and they must carry out the work and are enabled to recover the expenses involved from the consumer. A consumer who contravenes the provisions of this section, and undertakers who fail to carry out the work within reasonable despatch, are liable to a fine not exceeding £25.

Section 70 enables the undertakers to break open streets to affix and maintain meters on their mains and service pipes for the purpose of measuring the quantity of water supplied or preventing and detecting waste. They may insert in the street (but as near as is reasonably practicable to the boundary of it) the necessary covers or boxes. Protection is given to telegraphic lines of the Post Office and apparatus of electricity and gas undertakers.

A more up-to-date provision regarding the installation of meters in particular is to be found in s.32 WA 1973. When charges are payable to an authority by reference to the volume of water supplied to any premises or the volume of effluent discharged therefrom the authority may install on those premises a meter for measuring that volume and, subject to the provisions of any regulations made under this section, the register of the meter will be *prima facie* evidence of the volume. The Secretary of State may by Order make regulations as to the installation, connection, disconnection, testing and maintenance of meters—up-to-date none has been made. An authorised officer of the authority may enter premises for the purposes of connection, disconnection or inspection of meters on 24 hours' notice, or earlier by agreement. Entry may be enforced by Justices' warrant in the event of refusal.

Section 35 WA 1945 enables undertakers, on request, to supply either by sale or hire, such water fittings as are permitted by their byelaws. They may also install, repair or alter (but not manufacture) such fittings, whether supplied by them or not, and make agreed charges therefore. Provided fittings hired from the undertakers have a distinguishing metal plate affixed or some other distinguishing mark which indicates the undertakers to be the owners of the fittings, they remain the property of the undertakers despite being fixed to some part of the premises in which they are situated or laid in the soil. In other words they do not become fixtures passing with the ownership of the property. Further, they are not liable to any form of distress or other annexation following court proceedings.

Any person who negligently or wilfully damages or allows to be damaged any water fitting belonging to the undertakers, is liable to a fine not exceeding £25. The undertakers can repair the damage and recover their expenses.

14. HEALTH AND SAFETY AT WORK

Reference should be made to WPM 1, ch.3, s.17[3] for a general statement of the position affecting employers and employees under the Health and Safety at Work Act 1974, together with the responsibilities of the Health and Safety Commission and Executive.

Quite apart from the statutory responsibilities of an employer for the safety, health and welfare of his employees, which render him liable to prosecution in the event of breach, there is a well established common law duty of care to ensure the safety of employees actionable in negligence.

The Social Security Act 1975 provides a form of compulsory National Insurance in respect of accidents arising out of, and in the course of, employment, or diseases or injuries due to employment (for example, pneumoconiosis contracted in mining operations). Persons qualifying for social security benefits, either on account of sickness or industrial injury under the 1975 Act, are not excluded thereby from pursuing a civil claim for common law damages.

15. WATER RATES AND CHARGES

The powers to charge for water supplied for domestic purposes in the form of water rates contained in Part XII (ss.46-48) Third Schedule have been largely repealed and replaced by the charging provisions of Part III WA 1973.

By s.30 WA 1973 a water authority may fix such charges for water services as it thinks fit, whether under a "charges scheme" under s.31 of the Act, or by agreement with any person. In so doing, and subject to any directions of the Secretary of State, they may have reference to such criteria, and adopt such system for calculation of their amount, as appears to be most appropriate. They must have regard to the cost of performing the services. They may make different charges for the same service in different cases, but must now ensure that their charges are such as not to show undue preference to, or discriminate unduly against, any class of persons.

Charges Scheme

Section 31 WA 1973 enables a water authority to make a scheme for the charges to be paid for any services performed, facilities provided, or rights made available by the authority. Such a charges scheme, which may be amended or revoked at any time, must have regard to the principles contained in ss.29 (requiring the balancing of revenue and expenditure) and 30 WA 1973. Although the authorities' general powers of charging are now clearly defined by WA 1973, the powers to demand and recover charges contained in WA 1945 and local legislation may continue to be exercised by undertakers.

Despite the principal charging provisions contained in ss.46(1), 47 and 48 Third Schedule having been repealed by WA 1973, the view is taken, so far as water companies are concerned, that these sections, being incorporated in their local enactments, have an independent existence and remain as their basic powers to charge a water rate. However it should be noted that the companies as agents under s.12 WA 1973 are obliged in fixing their charges to have regard to the principles and criteria adopted by their respective authorities, and must keep the authorities informed of their proposals. There is a saving in s.12(6) WA 1973 to the effect that the Secretary of State shall not settle or vary any "agency" arrangements so as to oblige a water company to fix their charges at a level which will endanger their ability, so long as the undertaking is managed efficiently, to provide a reasonable return on their paid-up capital.

Charges for Water for Fire Fighting

Reference has already been made to the exemption from charge of water used for extinguishing fires under s.36 Third Schedule. Section 2 WA 1981 goes further by providing that no charge may be made by undertakers in respect of (a) water taken for extinguishing fires, or testing apparatus installed, or equipment used for extinguishing fires, of (b) the availability of water for those purposes. This section is to be brought into effect by Order.

Under s.2(2) the Secretary of State may by Order provide how charges are to be calculated where water is so supplied by a service pipe which also supplies water for other purposes—such Order may provide for arbitration. An Order to this effect is likely to be coupled with the Commencement Order referred to above.

Section 2 does not prevent charging in respect of work carried out at the request, or for the benefit of any person receiving a supply of water for the purposes mentioned in (a) above. Similarly, s.2 does not prevent charging for a supply for domestic purposes where any of the water is used for the purposes mentioned in (a).

COLLECTION OF CHARGES BY LOCAL AUTHORITIES

The Local Government Act 1974 s.38 added a new section 32A WA 1973, which provides that a local authority may agree with a water authority to collect and recover on the water authority's behalf any charges payable for services performed, facilities provided, or rights made available by the water authority in the local authority's area. Such charges may be demanded, collected and recovered by the local authority in the same manner and with the general rate.

RECOVERY OF CHARGES

The liability for and recovery of water rates and charges is prescribed in s.38 WA 1945. The term "rate" for this purpose is deemed to include any reference to any charge payable under Part III (ss.29-32A) WA 1973 (Schedule 8, para 53 WA 1973).

The rate is primarily payable by the occupier of any premises, except where the owner by agreement or otherwise is made liable to pay—*West Pennine Water Board v Jon Migail (North-West) Limited (1975)*. In this case the occupiers of a shop in a shopping centre comprising over 50 shops claimed they should not be assessed to water rate as they had no piped water coming into their shop—they had only a contractual right to use communal washrooms in the centre (*inter alia* for filling kettles). It was held that they were liable to pay as occupiers of "premises" which included not only the shop but all rights and easements connected therewith—the right to use the washrooms was in the nature of an easement.

The rate may after demand be recoverable either in the Magistrates' Court or in the County Court as a civil debt. Where a person fails to pay the rate or instalment thereof within seven days after a demand, the undertakers may cut off the supply to the premises and recover the expenses of so doing. If they are given written notice within the period of seven days of any dispute as to the amount due or liability therefor, they must not cut off until settlement of the dispute by a Magistrates' Court on the application of either party.

If an owner is liable for payment of the rate and is not the occupier, the undertakers must not cut off on failure to pay. They can only recover the amount demanded, either from such owner or from any occupier by summary proceedings in the Magistrates' or County Court. Proceedings cannot be taken against the occupier until he has been given notice to deduct the amount due out of his rent and he has failed to comply.

If the undertakers cut off water in contravention of any of the above provisions they are liable on conviction to a fine not exceeding £5 for every day the water remains cut off. In the case of *Watson v Sutton District Water Company (1940) 3 AER 502*, undertakers who had assumed the duty of cutting-off a supply were held to be liable for damage resulting from an ineffective disconnection. By s.39 WA 1945 where water to an inhabited house is cut off for any reason the undertakers must give notice within 48 hours of cutting off to the local authority, failing which they will be liable on summary conviction to a fine not exceeding £25.

Restoration or Continuation of Supply

The Local Government (Miscellaneous Provisions) Act 1976 s.33 introduced a measure of protection for occupiers of dwellings by providing that where any such dwellings are cut off or likely to be cut off due to failure of the owner to pay the water rates the local authority (district council or London borough) may, at the request of the occupier, make such financial arrangements with the undertakers to ensure the restoration or continuation of the supply. The local authority may then recover any payments made from the person responsible for such payment.

Recovery of Rates and Charges—Miscellaneous

Part XII (ss.51-59) Third Schedule contains miscellaneous provisions connected with the liability for payment of water rates and charges including (s.55) the option of payment by instalments.

16. REPRESENTATION OF AND COMPLAINTS BY CONSUMERS

CONSUMER CONSULTATIVE COMMITTEES

Section 7 WA 1983 has introduced a new section (24A) into WA 1973 providing for representation of consumers' interests in water authority areas. This follows from the reorganization of the constitution of water authorities contained in the 1983 Act and the removal of direct local government representation. Consumer Consultative Committees (CCCs) are to be set up with the remit to consider and report on any matter relating to the services provided by a water authority or a water company—for example, the general principles of charging. Such committees however will not be part of the management structure of either body.

The members of the CCC will be appointed by an authority on the nomination of local authorities and other interested bodies representing domestic consumers, industry, farming and commerce. At the option of the water companies a sub-committee of the CCC may be set up specifically to deal with company matters.

Consumers' service complaints will normally be dealt with at an operational level within the authority or company, but there is provision for a CCC to consider the volume and content of complaints and effectiveness in dealing with them. The Press are entitled to attend meetings of the CCCs and any sub-committees, but not meetings of the authority or company.

OMBUDSMAN

Part III of the Local Government Act 1974 established two Commissions for Local Administration, one each for England and Wales, both with appointed Local Commissioners (Ombudsmen) responsible for investigating any claim by a member of the public to have sustained injustice in consequence of maladministration by local authorities (including a police authority) and any regional water authority. The water companies are not specifically included in these categories, although as agents for the authorities they might find it difficult to resist any complaint directed at a company and referred to the Ombudsman through the authority.

Maladministration is not defined in the Act, but is taken to cover action or inaction based on or influenced by improper considerations or conduct such as malice, bias, neglect, or failure to observe correct procedures. The complaint must be in writing to a member of the authority concerned, and generally within twelve months of the origination of the complaint. (There are a large number of matters excluded from the Ombudsman's jurisdiction). If the Ombudsman finds there has been maladministration he issues a report and requests the authority to take remedial action.

17. THE POSITION IN SCOTLAND

INTRODUCTION

The Local Government system in Scotland was reorganized with effect from 16th May 1975 under the Local Government (Scotland) Act 1973 by the creation of nine regional, three Islands and 53 district councils. With the exception of the Central Scotland Water Development Board the 1973 Act dissolved the water boards established by the Water (Scotland) Act 1967 and transferred their water supply functions, together with the sewerage and sewage disposal functions, to the regional and Islands councils. Each region was divided into a number of districts, but the district councils have no function in the public water supply or sewerage and sewage disposal services, although they are involved in respect of environmental health and building regulations.

Five of the regional councils are members of the Central Scotland Water Development Board which supplies treated water in bulk to four of them. The Secretary of State is empowered by the Water (Scotland) Act 1980 to establish new water development boards in Scotland which shall have similar functions as the Central Board. Water authorities and water development boards are charged by the Act with the duty of consulting and collaborating together in the development of water resources. There are no water companies in Scotland.

The Water (Scotland) Act 1980, which came into force on 1st August 1980, consolidated in their entirety the Water (Scotland) Acts 1946 and 1949, the Water Act 1958 so far as it applied to Scotland, and the bulk of the Water (Scotland) Act 1967.

The 1980 Act lays duties and powers on the Secretary of State in relation to the conservation of water resources and the provision of adequate water supplies comparable with those conferred on the Secretary of State for the Environment in England and Wales by the Water Act 1945. The duty imposed by Section 1 of the 1980 Act on the Secretary of State to appoint an Advisory Committee, to advise him on any of his functions under the Act, has been repealed by the Local Government (Miscellaneous Provisions) (Scotland) Act 1981.

The principal charging provisions of the Water (Scotland) Act 1980, which have no English counterpart, provide a uniform system of rating and charging throughout Scotland. The provisions are based broadly on the recommendations in the report of the Committee on water rating in Scotland (Command 6765).

The Rural Water Supplies and Sewerage Acts 1944, 1955 and 1970, under which grants are available in certain circumstances for supplies in rural areas, apply in Scotland.

PRINCIPAL STATUTORY PROVISIONS

The principal statutory provisions relating to water supply in Scotland are now:
  Reservoir (Safety Provisions) Act 1930
  Rural Water Supplies and Sewerage Act 1944
  Acquisition of Land (Authorisation Procedure) (Scotland) Act 1947
  Public Utilities Street Works Act 1950
  Rural Water Supplies and Sewerage Act 1955
  Spray Irrigation Act 1964
  Rural Water Supplies and Sewerage (Scotland) Act 1970

Local Government (Scotland) Act 1973
Health & Safety at Work etc Act 1974
Reservoirs Act 1975
Water (Scotland) Act 1980
Local Government (Miscellaneous Provisions) (Scotland) Act 1981
Local Government and Planning (Scotland) Act 1982
In addition to the above, some authorities have private Acts which are still in force.

INTERPRETATION

"Secretary of State" means Secretary of State for Scotland.
"Water Authority" means a regional or Islands council.
"The 1980 Act" means the Water (Scotland) Act 1980.

SUPPLY OF WATER FOR DOMESTIC PURPOSES

Section 6 of the 1980 Act imposes on the water authorities the duty of providing a supply of wholesome water to every part of their area where a supply is required for domestic purposes and can be provided at a reasonable cost.

Pipes affording a supply of wholesome water must be taken from such points as will enable buildings for which a supply is required for domestic purposes to be connected thereto at a reasonable cost, but the authorities are not required to do anything which is not practicable at a reasonable cost. While 'reasonable cost' is not defined in the Act, any question as to what is practicable at a reasonable cost may in cases of dispute, and at the request of ten or more local government electors, be determined by the Secretary of State. The definition of water for domestic purposes in Section 7 of the 1980 Act is similar to the English definition, but includes water for central heating and baths up to 455 litres capacity (as compared with 227 litres in England and Wales).

In carrying out their responsibilities in relation to the purity of the supply undertakers should consider the recommendations set out in Memorandum No. 13[4].

SUPPLY OF WATER FOR NON-DOMESTIC PURPOSES

Section 9 of the 1980 Act is equivalent to Section 27 of the Water Act 1945. The Section provides that a water authority may require as a condition of giving a supply an agreement to pay yearly sums for providing and laying mains and for payments for a specified period.

SUPPLY OF WATER FOR PUBLIC PURPOSES

Part V of the Fourth Schedule to the 1980 Act is equivalent to Part VIII of the Third Schedule to the Water Act 1945.

SUPPLY OF WATER IN BULK

Section 13 of the 1980 Act empowers a water authority, or water development board, to enter into an agreement to receive a supply of water in bulk from any other person whether a water authority or not. In the absence of agreement between the local water authorities, the Secretary of State may require the giving and taking of such a supply by such authorities by Order under Section 13 where it appears to him to be expedient and may in the order fix terms and conditions of supply. In an emergency the Secretary of State may make the necessary Order without following the normal procedure laid down in the First Schedule to the Act, and if the interests of public health so require may modify the provisions governing laying of mains and breaking open streets in relation to any works for the purposes of the Order.

MAINS SERVICES AND STOPCOCKS

The provisions of the 1980 Act in respect of mains, supply pipes, communication pipes and stopcocks, are similar to those in the Water Act 1945, but where the premises supplied do not abut on the part of the street in which the main is laid the term 'communication pipe' is defined to mean 'so much of the service pipe as lies between the main and the boundary of the part of the street in which the main is laid'. Section 24 of the 1980 Act (QV) is equivalent to Section 41 of the Third Schedule of the Water Act 1945. The relevant definitions are to be found in Section 109 of the 1980 Act.

PREVENTION OF WASTE

Under Section 70 of the 1980 Act the water authorities and the water development boards are authorised to make byelaws for the prevention of waste, undue consumption, misuse or contamination of water (Section 70 is equivalent to Section 17 of the Water Act 1945). Revised model byelaws for this purpose were drafted by the Scottish Development Department in 1978 and water authorities made new byelaws based on the model in the same year. Under Section 74 of the 1980 Act the Secretary of State is empowered to make regulations for any of the purposes for which byelaws may be made under Section 70 of the same Act.

The Scottish provisions for the prevention of waste etc, which are similar to those in Part VIII (Sections 60-70) of the Third Schedule to the Water Act 1945, are contained in Part VII of the Fourth Schedule to the 1980 Act. Part VII is applied by Section 28 of this Act.

POWERS TO SUPPLY WATER DURING DROUGHT

Part VII (Ss 77-78) and Schedule 5 of the 1980 Act enable the Secretary of State on the application of a water authority to make Orders authorising the taking or supply of water during times of drought. These powers are equivalent to those contained in the Drought Act 1976.

PUBLIC UTILITIES STREET WORKS ACT 1950

This Act applies in Scotland.

ACQUISITION OF LANDS AND RIGHTS

Section 15 of the 1980 Act enables a water authority or water development board to acquire land (other than water rights) by agreement or compulsorily.

The procedure for authorising compulsory acquisition is governed by the Acquisition of Land (Authorisation Procedure) (Scotland) Act 1947 and involves the making of an order by the authority and its confirmation by the Secretary of State, subject to provisions for advertising and for considering objections. The Compulsory Purchase of Land (Scotland) Regulations 1976 (SI 1976 No 820) set the forms to be used in carrying out the procedure.

Section 20 of the 1980 Act, as amended by the Local Government (Miscellaneous Provisions) (Scotland) Act 1981, is equivalent to Section 25 of the Water Act 1945 concerning the holding of land, but with certain modifications calling for the consent of the Secretary of State to its disposal.

Section 17 of the 1980 Act empowers water authorities and water development boards to acquire by agreement or compulsorily rights to take water from any stream or other source—any such acquisition, by agreement or otherwise, requires the approval of the Secretary of State by Order.

BYELAWS AND BUILDING REGULATIONS

Reference has already been made (*supra*) to Section 70 of the 1980 Act enabling a water authority or water development board to make byelaws for preventing waste, undue consumption, misuse or contamination of water supplied by them. Section 71 of the same Act further enables the making of byelaws for the prevention of pollution of water, whether on the surface or underground, which belongs to them or which they are authorised to take.

Procedures relating to the making of byelaws under these sections are contained in Part IV of the First Schedule to the 1980 Act.

Regulations relating to building standards are currently contained in the Building Standards (Scotland) Regulations 1981 (SI 1981/1596) as amended by the Building Standards (Scotland) Amendment Regulations 1982 (SI 1982/1878). Part M of the regulations deals with drainage and sanitary appliances.

LIABILITY FOR INJURY OR DAMAGE

"Nuisance" is broadly defined in Scottish law as being based on the principle that no person shall use his own property in such a way as to injure his neighbour. It should also be made clear that the rule established by the English case of *Rylands v Fletcher (1868)* is not part of the law of Scotland. Whereas English law accepted the principle of absolute liability arising from non-natural use of land, in Scottish law this is not the case. Scottish law would approach the case of an escape of water from a reservoir on the basis that the person putting the reservoir on the land had to exercise a very high degree of skill or care (as opposed to the normal standard of reasonable care). This is, of course, not absolute liability, although the very high degree of skill or care required probably means that the practical effect in the Scottish and English legal system is the same although there are differing principles. The civil and criminal responsibility for reservoirs is more particularly governed by the Reservoirs Acts.

The strict liability imposed on water undertakers by Section 6 of the Water Act 1981 for escape of water from a communication pipe or main is not applicable in Scotland. However Section 10 of the 1980 Act, as amended by Section 57 of the Local Government and Planning (Scotland) Act 1982, provides that a district council, water authority or water development board shall fully compensate any person who has sustained damage by reason of the exercise of any of their powers under the Act—a claim must be made within twelve months of the action complained of and there is provision for arbitration in cases of dispute. The amendment introduced by Section 57 of the 1982 Act excludes from liability the category of "excepted undertakers" referred to in Section 6 of the Water Act 1981 (ie highway and bridge authorities etc).

RESERVOIR SAFETY

The Reservoirs (Safety Provisions) Act 1930 and Reservoirs Act 1975 apply to Scotland. In the case of the latter Act the local authorities in Scotland with responsibility for enforcement will be the regional and Islands councils.

HEALTH AND SAFETY AT WORK

The major part of the Health and Safety at Work Act 1974 applies in Scotland.

Part III dealing with Buildings Regulations (except Section 75 and Schedule 7) does not however extend to Scotland.

EEC DIRECTIVES

Directives issued by the European Economic Community are applicable in Scotland.

OMBUDSMAN

The Local Government (Scotland) Act 1975, as amended by the Local Government (Miscellaneous Provisions) (Scotland) Act 1981, established a Commissioner for Local Administration in Scotland with powers to investigate and report on maladministration equivalent to those contained in the Local Government Act 1974. The water authorities and water development boards are within this jurisdiction.

18. THE POSITION IN NORTHERN IRELAND

INTRODUCTION

The Water Service of the Department of the Environment for Northern Ireland became the sole water supply authority in Northern Ireland on 1st October 1973, under the general reorganization of local government. Prior to that date some 76 local authorities and joint water boards had statutory responsibility for water supply, under the Waterworks Clauses Acts 1947 and 1863, the Public Health (Ireland) Act 1878, and the Water Supplies and Sewerage Act (Northern Ireland) 1945.

The Waterworks Clauses Acts, 1847 and 1863, and such parts of the Public Health Act 1878 relating to the supply of water, were repealed with effect from 1st October 1973. The Water Supplies and Sewerage Act (Northern Ireland) 1945 was also repealed from 1st October 1973, with the exception of two Sections (4 and 5) relating to the sufficiency of water supply for new or occupied houses, which transferred to the new district councils.

OPERATION AND ORGANIZATION

The Water Service operates under a divisional structure centred on Belfast, Ballymena, Craigavon, and Londonderry, with local sub-divisional offices in most of the provincial towns. A headquarters unit at Stormont, Belfast, is responsible for policy, co-ordination, finance, engineer planning, and capital programme control. The four Water Service divisions are based on the major water catchment areas.

NORTHERN IRELAND WATER COUNCIL

The Council was established under the Water Act (Northern Ireland) 1972 and consists of not more than 15 persons (including the chairman) appointed jointly by the Departments of Agriculture and of the Environment for Northern Ireland. The members are chosen to reflect a wide spectrum of opinion; industry, commerce, agriculture, angling, and the trade unions are represented. The Council advises the two Departments on the exercise of these functions under the Water Act (Northern Ireland) 1972 and the Water and Sewerage Services (Northern Ireland) Order 1973.

WATER APPEALS COMMISSION FOR NORTHERN IRELAND

The Commission was established under the Water and Sewerage Services

(Northern Ireland) Order 1973. Where an application or appeal is made to the Commission it may cause a local inquiry to be held to consider the application or appeal. The Commission is required to report its decision on an application or appeal to the Department of the Environment for Northern Ireland and the Department is required to notify the applicant or appellant of any decision so reported. The Department is also empowered to vary a decision of the Water Appeals Commission or substitute for it a new decision.

INTERPRETATION

"The Department" means the Department of the Environment for Northern Ireland. "The 1973 Order" means the Water and Sewerage Services (Northern Ireland) Order 1973.

PRINCIPAL STATUTORY PROVISIONS

The principal statutory provisions relating to water supply in Northern Ireland are now:

The Water and Sewerage Services (Northern Ireland) Order 1973 (SI1973 No 70 (N12))

The Order places a duty on the Department to supply and distribute water, and gives it responsibility for sewerage and sewage disposal. The Order also requires that water provided for domestic purposes by the Department shall be wholesome. The Department is also empowered to (a) provide and maintain such works, (b) perform such services, and (c) do such things as it considers necessary or expedient for the purposes of any of its functions under the Order.

The Water Charges Regulations (Northern Ireland) 1973 (SR & O 1973 No 158)

These regulations provide for the levying on owners and occupiers of premises of charges for the supply of water, ie metered water supplies for industry, agriculture, and commercial undertakings.

The Water and Sewerage Services Regulations (Northern Ireland) 1973 (SR & O 1973 No 344)

These regulations provide for the proper provision and maintenance of service pipes, water fittings, drains and sewage disposal facilities.

The Water Regulations (Northern Ireland) 1974 (SR & O 1974 No 143)

These regulations provide for standards for the provision of water fittings and pipes. They replaced the water byelaws of the former local authorities and joint water boards.

The Water Act (Northern Ireland) 1972 (1972 C5)

While not directly related to the supply of water, the Act provides for the conservation and cleanliness of water resources. The Act also empowers the Department to promote water management programmes and to make regulations controlling the abstraction of water. To date no regulations have been made.

RESERVOIR SAFETY

The Department have direct control of all principal reservoirs in Northern

Ireland. There is no legislation in force equivalent to the Reservoirs Acts 1930 and 1975.

ACQUISITION OF WATER RIGHTS ETC

The Department is empowered under the 1973 Order to impound or abstract water from any waterway or water contained in underground strata. The Department is required to inform statutory fisheries bodies of its proposals and take all reasonable steps to inform persons who, in its opinion, will be affected thereby. The Department is also required to give public notice in the local press of its intention to impound or abstract. Any person aggrieved by the Department's proposals may appeal to the Water Appeals Commission for Northern Ireland within 28 days.

ACQUISITION OF LAND

The Department is empowered under the 1973 Order to acquire land by agreement, or lease land, or acquire land compulsorily. The Department can also dispose of any land so acquired or taken on lease.

The Department is required to serve notice of its intention to acquire land compulsorily by vesting order, and at the same time to publish notice of its proposals in the local press. Objections may be lodged with the Department within one month from the date of service or second publication of the notice. If valid objections are received the Department may cause a local inquiry to be held to consider them. After taking all relevant factors into account, the Department may make an order vesting the land concerned. Compensation negotiations with interested parties begin as soon as the vesting order becomes operative. If agreement cannot be reached, the matter can be referred to the Lands Tribunal for Northern Ireland.

PROVISION OF WATER MAINS AND SEWERS

The Department is required under the 1973 Order to serve notice of its intention to lay a water main or construct a sewer in, on or over land not forming part of a public road, on the owner and occupier of the land concerned. Objections to the Department's proposals may be made within 28 days from the date of service of the notice. Such objections are considered and determined by the Department. After notifying the objector of its decision the Department may proceed to carry out the works specified in the notice, with or without modification.

COMPENSATION

The Department is required under the 1973 Order to make good, or pay compensation for any damage caused by or in consequence of the execution of works under the Order. Any person aggrieved by an assessment of compensation can have the matter referred to the Lands Tribunal for determination.

FINANCIAL PROVISION

Any expenses incurred by the Department under the 1973 Order are defrayed either out of monies appropriated for the purpose of defraying such expenses or, if the Department of Finance and Personnel for Northern Ireland so directs, by means of sums charged on and issued out of the Consolidated Fund.

RECREATIONAL FACILITIES

The Department may provide facilities on any land vested in it for the purposes of the 1973 Order, such as water catchment areas.

19. REFERENCES

1. Ministry of Housing and Local Government and the Welsh Office 1967 "Safeguards to be adopted in the operation and management of waterworks", HMSO, London.
2. Council of the European Communities 1980 *Official Journal of the European Communities* No. L229, 23, 11, Council Directive relating to the quality of water intended for human consumption.
3. The Institution of Water Engineers and Scientists 1979 Water Practice Manuals, Book 1, "The structure and management of the British water industry", IWES, London.
4. Scottish Development Department 1979 "Water supply hygiene, safeguards in the operation and management of waterworks in Scotland", Memorandum No. 13.

Chapter 3

BYELAWS AND STANDARDS

1. HISTORICAL BACKGROUND

A century and a half ago saw the move away from intermittent supply to continuous supply of water. At that time, there was concern about the extent of waste water which could occur under the continuous system unless controls were placed on consumers' premises. Private Acts of those days often included clauses protecting the undertaker (such as requirements for storage cisterns, the provision of efficient stopcocks, warning pipes and access for inspectors). A number of Private Acts incorporated provisions of the Waterworks Clauses Act 1847; many of these are expressed in modern terms in the Water Act 1945, Third Schedule. Particularly relevant today is Part XIII of the Third Schedule (provisions for preventing waste etc of water).

These earlier powers were not considered sufficient for preventing waste and contamination of water in the London area. The Metropolis Water Act 1871 included powers to make regulations and, following an extensive inquiry under the Board of Health, 33 regulations were confirmed and many of these are recognisable as water byelaws in the present day model water byelaws. Of these, regulation 21 was most significant as it regulated the flushing volume of WC cisterns, despite the fact that suitable designs were not available at that time. There were also requirements prohibiting the connection of boilers directly to the mains.

Towards the end of the 19th century, the situation had become chaotic as many of the country's water undertakers began to impose their own rules. This led to the setting up in 1904 of the Joint Committee on Water Regulations, the membership of which was mainly supplied by water undertakers, and this Committee subsequently published a set of model requirements in 1908. Subsequently, the British Waterworks Association set up its Standing Technical Committee on Water Regulations in 1919. The Standing Committee, which continued until reorganization of the industry in 1974, was representative of a wide range of interests and was composed of members appointed by the British Waterworks Association, the Water Companies' Association, the Institution of Water Engineers (now the Institution of Water Engineers and Scientists), the Royal Institute of British Architects, the Worshipful Company of Plumbers and the Royal Sanitary Institute, together with co-opted representatives of the National Brassfoundry Association, the British Plastics Federation, the British Standards Institution, the British Gas Corporation, the British Non-Ferrous Metals Research Association and the British Electrical Development Association.

In 1928, model water byelaws were published by the Minister of Health and thereafter successive issues were made by the responsible Departments in 1947, 1949, 1954, 1963 and 1966. The objectives have been to secure, as far as possible, uniform requirements throughout the country to avoid confusion amongst architects, builders, plumbing installers and fittings and appliance designers and manufacturers. Unnecessary variation in past years had often been the subject of complaint on that score.

Purposes and Scope of Water Byelaws

Whereas undertakers have powers enabling them to deal with waste or contamination when it actually occurs or is likely to occur, water byelaws are designed to secure that water fittings are suitable in construction, type and arrangement for minimising the possibility of such waste or contamination.

In England and Wales, water byelaws have been made under Section 17 of the Water Act 1945 (in Scotland made under Section 70 of the Water (Scotland) Act 1980). In Northern Ireland, Water Regulations made under Article 40, Water and Sewerage Services (Northern Ireland) Order 1973 apply, and are similar in their content to water byelaws.

If waste or undue consumption of water in consumers' services were not controlled or if contamination of water were not prevented, undertakers would run the risk of being in breach of their statutory duty to maintain adequate supplies of wholesome water in their mains.

Although they have powers to prosecute and to carry out repairs and alterations to water fittings and appliances in consumers' installations at the expense of consumers, wherever a case of waste, misuse, undue consumption or contamination of water comes to light, undertakers contemplate such action only in the last resort.

The incidence of subsequent cases of waste etc is considerably reduced by undertakers paying particular attention to ensure that new plumbing installations comply with water byelaws. These byelaws operate as a code of great value to water fittings and appliances manufacturers, building designers and constructors and to plumbing installers.

The procedure for making and confirmation of byelaws is set out in Part II of Schedule 7 of the Water Act 1973 and involves the water undertaking in a resolution to make the byelaws and in application to the Minister for the Environment for confirmation, following the publication of at least one month's notice of intention to apply to the Minister for confirmation, in both the London Gazette and "in such other manner as best adapted for informing persons affected".

Copies of the notice must also be served on any public authorities who appear to be concerned.

Reasonable facilities for inspection of the byelaws must be provided and any person who applies to the undertaking has to be provided with a printed copy of the proposed byelaws free of charge.

The Minister may refuse or confirm byelaws either with or without revocation.

Having made byelaws, the undertakers have a duty to enforce them—Section 19(2), Water Act 1945 (s.19(2), WA 1945).

Where the undertakers consider that the operation of a byelaw would be unreasonable in a particular case, they may, with the consent of the Minister, relax the requirements or dispense with compliance therewith (s.19(4), WA 1945).

The Minister has power to require the making of byelaws, to make byelaws in case of default and to revoke byelaws (s.20, WA 1945).

Water byelaws may not prescribe the country of origin to water fittings, their fitness for purpose, their attaining any particular quality or life expectancy in service, their manner of procurement, or manufacture exclusively to any particular standard and may not include requirements aimed at the primary purpose of securing the health and safety of consumers or the conservation of energy.

PRESENT POSITION

Since water reorganization in 1974, all water undertakers in England and Wales have made new byelaws based on the 1966 Model, with a few variations and additions. Water Authorities needed new byelaws to take over from those inherited from predecessor undertakers. Many areas became subject to byelaw control for the first time.

In normal circumstances, the 1966 Model, being technically out of date, would have been superseded by a new one. However, the Department of the Environment (DoE) was persuaded that there was need for a comprehensive investigation of the problem of backsiphonage in and from water installations and for advice to be obtained on reasonable precautions, the need for a fundamental review on byelaws controlling waste and undue consumption in consumers' services, and the desirability of future byelaws being in a detailed and more comprehensive form, supported by guidance on their application and interpretation.

CONTAMINATION CAUSED BY BACKSIPHONAGE AND CROSS-CONNECTION

In 1969, the DoE began revision of the 1966 Model with a view to a new one being published before byelaws based on that Model ran out of time. It became evident that the requirements dealing with prevention or contamination of water required a thorough overhaul. In some cases, the precautions required by the 1966 Model were thought to be not stringent enough and in others the commonly accepted air gap could be rendered ineffective. The DoE set up a technical committee and following a substantial programme of surveys, research and visits to undertakers both at home and abroad, the committee submitted a report with detailed recommendations[1], which is undoubtedly the most comprehensive and authoritative work on the subject which exists today.

Classes of risk arising from potential backsiphonage situations were identified and the appropriate categories of device were designated in numerous examples. The main recommendations of the committee were:

(1) Protection of water in the home and domestic use elsewhere should be based on protection at every point of use.

(2) Silencing pipes used in association with float-operated risers should be permitted, providing suitable protection against backsiphonage is afforded.

(3) Make-up water used in domestic boiler and central heating installations should be fed through specified backsiphonage prevention devices.

(4) The secondary circuit of a heating apparatus may be taken direct from the supply pipe providing there is no cross-connection with the primary heating circuit and that backsiphonage devices are provided at each point of use.

(5) Installations should be designed and equipped to remove the need for unprotected temporary hose connections.

(6) The over-rim type of bidet having shrouded air gaps at the hot and cold water inlets should be the only permitted type.

(7) In domestic installations, the covers of cold water storage cisterns should be rigid with overlapping edges.

(8) In installations where the risks of backsiphonage are multiplied either from heavy use of connected appliances or frequent low pressure conditions in the mains, for buildings in multi-occupation (such as blocks of flats), in large institutions (including schools, hostels), in premises where substantial numbers of people congregate and water is afforded for domestic use (such as

canteens, hotels, restaurants, sports stadia, commercial premises), there should be a "secondary backflow prevention" system.

(9) Specific requirements should apply in the protection of water in industrial, trade and commercial installations, hospitals, ports, docks, and harbours, in agricultural and horticultural use and on mobile appliances.

STANDING TECHNICAL COMMITTEE ON WATER REGULATIONS

The Standing Technical Committee on Water Regulations (STCWR) was set up in 1975 with terms of reference to keep under review and to advise the DoE and the National Water Council (NWC) on the form and content of water regulations, to identify the needs for research and to advise on the implications for the UK of draft EEC Directives.

Membership is drawn widely from the water industry, water fittings and appliance manufacturers, building designers and plumbing services contractors and installers, research bodies and from Scottish and Northern Ireland water interests and Government Departments.

As a consequence of the recommendation of the Committee on Backsiphonage that the cold feed to the secondary circuit of a heating apparatus should be permitted to be taken direct from the supply pipe providing there were no cross-connections with the primary heating circuit, the DoE set up its Committee on Pressurised Hot Water and Heating Systems to study the implications for byelaws and for safety were the recommended change taken into future water byelaws.

The report of this committee[2] was incorporated as an appendix to STCWR Report No. 3. In the event of these systems (presently not permitted under water byelaws) becoming widely used there could be consequences for undertakers in respect of reliability of service at adequate pressure and for waste of water if expansion discharge were not controlled.

As a prerequisite to making recommendations for a new Model, the STCWR undertook an evaluation of the location and relative importance of waste and undue consumption in consumers' services. Their conclusions are likely to be published as an annex to their report on a new model byelaws.

2. FITTINGS TESTING SCHEME

INTRODUCTION

Every water undertaker is empowered to test any water fittings used in connection with water supplied by them, by s.61, Third Schedule, WA 1945.

Before reorganization of the industry in 1974, one or two water undertakers operated their own testing facilities (notably the Manchester Corporation Waterworks), but most accepted the Fittings Testing Schemes operated by the BWA. These were:

(a) A joint scheme with the BSI for supervision and control of manufacturers licensed to use the joint "JCSWR/Kite mark" for fittings complying with BS 1010 and BS 1212;

(b) A small joint scheme with the British Electrotechnical Approvals Board (BEAB) for electric storage water heaters complying with BS 3456 and BS 843; and

(c) A joint scheme for type testing and listing fittings other than those in (a) and (b) above.

The work of examining and testing the above categories of fittings was carried out by inspectors at the BWA Testing Station at Staines, who also visited manufacturers' works several times a year to exercise the supervision and control required under (a) above. Test reports on fittings, and quality inspection reports on manufacturers, were presented to an Approvals Board, consisting of water industry officers and representatives of manufacturers and other bodies for decision as to their acceptability.

Until the reorganization of the water industry in 1974, the body responsible for administering and developing the central voluntary arrangements provided by the BWA for the examination and testing of fittings was its Standing Technical Committee on Water Regulations, mentioned earlier in this Chapter.

On the reorganization of the water industry the Standing Committee ceased to exist and the BWA's Testing Station staff and assets were transferred to the National Water Council (NWC), who decided to maintain the fittings testing service pending a decision on the long term arrangements; the water industry officers and others who had formed the BWA Approvals Board agreed to continue to serve on an interim basis as the NWC Approvals Board. The NWC Approvals Board, supported by a technical advisory group of expert officers, maintained the centralised service of examination by the BWA Standing Committee, except for the joint schemes referred to above, which have reverted to the BSI and BEAB, respectively.

In order to control its test methods and acceptance criteria the Approvals Board set up a Test Criteria Sub-Committee of seven members drawn from the Board and Advisory Group, with the task of recording the test methods and acceptance criteria currently employed.

DEVELOPMENT OF THE SCHEME

The NWC Approvals Board did not reflect the new structure of the water industry and could operate only as an interim body until a new scheme could be implemented. The Water Act 1973 required the Council to consult widely with a view to the establishment of such a scheme and this was done, firstly on the main issue as to whether there should be a new scheme at all; and secondly on the draft of a scheme produced and circulated for comment early in 1977.

In addition to the need to re-model the organization to fit the new pattern of the water industry, the opportunity was taken to alter the formal relationships with manufacturers and other interested bodies. Hitherto, some manufacturers' associations had taken part in the consideration of test reports on fittings submitted either by their own members or by other manufacturers; this was widely regarded as an unsatisfactory arrangement, both for those manufacturers represented and for those who were not. Furthermore, it was felt that if manufacturers were to play a full part in the operation of the scheme, albeit on a consultative basis, all manufacturers ought to be given the same opportunity to do so, either through their trade associations or individually. Finally, the view was taken that since water authorities and companies had the statutory duty to enforce their byelaws, they alone should be responsible for deciding on the acceptability or otherwise of fittings. The result was the establishment of a Consultative and Liaison Committee to provide manufacturers and others with a forum for consultation and discussion on matters affecting the operation of the Scheme; the setting up of a Management Committee and a Technical Committee composed exclusively of water industry representatives; and for the first time, the provision of arrangements to deal with complaints and appeals by those aggrieved by decisions on items submitted for test.

FUNCTION AND ROLE OF THE SCHEME

The object of the Council's Scheme for the testing and approval of water fittings is to make provision throughout the UK for the assessment and testing of water fittings to ascertain whether they comply with regulations and byelaws for preventing the waste, undue consumption, misuse or contamination of water and with such other regulations as may be made from time to time.

The Council's service, though entirely voluntary in the sense that manufacturers are not obliged to submit their fittings for test, nevertheless provides a manufacturer whose fitting passes the tests and is then entered on the Council's list, with an assurance that all statutory water undertakers in the UK will then (subject only to local requirements in certain cases because of differences in water characteristics) accept the fitting in their areas as complying with their byelaws. The advantages, both to the manufacturer and to the water industry, are obvious: the former knows that the fitting can be marketed and installed anywhere in the country without further testing or examination by individual water undertakings, while the latter are relieved of the necessity of having to test every new fitting appearing in their area. The advantage to the user of a water fitting is also obvious; he need only consult the Council's list of fittings to see whether it will meet the byelaw requirements in any area in which it is to be installed.

The scheme is administered by a Management Committee comprising a Chairman appointed by the Council, and fifteen members appointed from the UK water industry. The functions of the Management Committee are:

(i) to appoint a Technical Committee;
(ii) to establish and maintain machinery for the determination of complaints by any person aggrieved by a decision of the Technical Committee on any matter coming before it;
(iii) to be responsible to the Council for the operation of the Scheme.

The Technical Committee comprises a Chairman appointed by the Management Committee, and fifteen representatives of the UK water industry, together with a Scientific Adviser and a Medical Adviser, and observers from the BSI and the DoE. Its main functions are:

(1) to ascertain, by reference to the results of tests and examinations carried out by or on behalf of the Technical Committee, whether or not any water fitting complies with regulations and byelaws for preventing the waste, undue consumption, misuse or contamination of water and with such other regulations as may from time to time be in force, and to publish its conclusions; and
(2) to formulate, review and arrange for the publication of requirements, criteria and standards for tests.

The Committee delegates the first of those functions to its Fittings Assessment Panel consisting of five of its members, and the second function to its Test Criteria Panel, also consisting of five of its members.

Also established under the scheme is a Consultative and Liaison Committee, whose Chairman is the chairman of the Management Committee, and whose members are drawn from the Technical Committee, a variety of manufacturers' associations, professional bodies and Government Departments. Its functions are:

to consider any question relating to or arising from the operation of the Scheme and to make recommendations thereon to the Management Committee or the Technical Committee as appropriate.

The testing and examination of fittings is carried out by a small technical staff at the Council's Fittings Testing Station at Slough, supported by the necessary administrative, clerical and secretarial services.

APPROVALS

Prior to the reorganization of the water industry, water fittings submitted for examination and test and found to comply with the requirements of undertakers' byelaws were entered in the "Classified List" of fittings accepted by the BWA's Standing Technical Committee on Water Regulations. Two such lists were published, covering the periods from October 1946 to February 1967 and from February 1967 to December 1972, after which lists of accepted fittings and materials were published quarterly as supplements to the 'Bulletin' until November 1980, when the first edition of the Council's Directory of Water Fittings was published.

The Directory lists water fittings and materials which have been examined and tested and found to comply with the requirements of water byelaws during the period from 1 January 1973 to 30 June 1980, and is kept up to date for a three-year period by means of cumulative supplements published every four months. Present intentions are that the next three-year cycle will commence in December 1983, with the publication of a new Directory incorporating the contents of the previous Directory plus those of its eight supplements.

CERTIFICATION TRADE MARKS

The BWA and the STCWR were the proprietors of the following Certification Trade Marks granted under the Trade Marks Act, 1938, in respect of a wide variety of water fittings:

(a) the "JCSWR" mark
(b) the BWA "Swan" mark, and
(c) the export "Swan" mark

The JCSWR mark was applicable in association with the BSI's Kitemark under the joint BWA/BSI Licensing Scheme to fittings which were found to comply with the requirements of BS 1010 and BS 1212, and whose manufacturers were found to be exercising a satisfactory system of quality control. The joint scheme lapsed in 1979, due to the withdrawal of their support by a number of manufacturers, and reverted to an ordinary Kitemark Scheme operated by the BSI alone.

The use of the export Swan mark, which expired some ten years ago, was confined to fittings made to the old specification of the then Ministry of Health and for export only.

Both the BWA and NWC had appreciated the value, not only to the water industry but also to consumers, of a registered mark which manufacturers could apply to those of their fittings which had been found to comply with the requirements of the byelaws, and in 1970 the BWA applied for registration of its "BWAAB" mark, the initials standing for BWA Approvals Board. However, the application ran into difficulties over the lack of comprehensive written criteria against which the fittings were to be tested, and with the imminent reorganization of the water industry, the BWA suspended its application for the mark.

The application was revived by the Council in 1980, by which time the tests applicable to water fittings and their acceptance criteria had been codified, and progress has been made towards renewing the BWA Swan mark and preparing draft regulations for its use. Pending approval of these regulations by the Registrar of Trade Marks, it is the present intention to use the BWA Swan as an unregistered mark as soon as the necessary arrangements can be made.

FITNESS FOR PURPOSE

The proposition that the scope of the testing service operated by the Council, and before that, by its predecessor, should be widened to include tests for fitness for purpose has been raised on many occasions, mainly by groups of interested manufacturers who see such tests as a defence against the listing of fittings made by their foreign competitors, which, they assert, are flooding the UK market to the detriment of the sales of native products, and to a lesser extent by the water industry which sees such tests leading eventually to the listing of more robust and durable fittings for use by consumers.

However, the tests which the Council carries out at present on water fittings are those which the water industry considers necessary to assess their compliance with the water byelaws, the purposes of which are well known, and do not include fitness for purpose; therefore, any widening of the scope of the Council's tests to include such matters as fitness for purpose would entail enacting the necessary legislation either to augment the present purposes for which byelaws may be made, or to provide separate powers for carrying out the additional tests.

As regards the latter, an approach by the National Brassfoundry Association to the Department of Trade resulted in the department circulating for comment its proposals for a National Certification Scheme for Water Fittings, which would be voluntary in nature, and which embodied the following features:

   (i) the use of appropriate British Standards
  (ii) the assessment of manufacturers' quality control systems to BS 5750 or equivalent; and
 (iii) the testing of products by members of the National Testing Laboratory Accreditation Scheme (NATLAS).

Note: Following the demise of the National Water Council in September 1983, the Fittings Testing Scheme is now administered by the Water Research Centre.

3. PROGRESS TOWARDS NEW MODEL BYELAWS

INTRODUCTION

Earlier notes in this Chapter have drawn attention to the evolution of byelaws throughout the country, each undertaker in turn altering or augmenting "Model Byelaws" in the light of relevant local circumstances. The Water Act 1973 presented the then newly formed Regional Water Authorities in England and Wales with the difficult task of reconciling the differing approaches in their constituent areas inherited from earlier undertakers, and all have since adopted new byelaws which applied throughout each region. This was highly desirable and cleared the way towards more uniform interpretation.

Circumstances change, however, and there is value in reconsidering from time to time the purposes of byelaws, re-assessing the relevance of some, and strengthening others.

During the late 1970s and early 1980s the STCWR addressed itself to this task. A number of discussion documents were drafted and circulated for preliminary comments amongst the organizations represented by the members of the Committee. These were considered and enabled improved versions of the documents to be included in a "Report on proposals for a new model water byelaws"[3].

That report is based upon two important papers: the backsiphonage report (DoE[1]) and a paper on "Prevention of waste of water in water services" (Annex E to Ref. No. 3). These reviewed established practices and current byelaws, and tested them against the present needs for, and attitudes towards, the criteria for which byelaws exist.

Patterns of demand, the habits and expectations of consumers, public attitudes towards costs and accountability, and technical developments, are all changing and corresponding changes in emphasis and detail may be desirable in future editions of byelaws. Examples of the Committee's discussion points illustrate the direction some changes might take.

WASTE PREVENTION

Waste

The apparently continually rising demand for water in the domestic sector is presumed to reflect an increasing use of water-using appliances, coupled with significant changes in the pattern of use and the attitude of the public in using water without restriction. In this regard there is a difficult and ill-defined boundary between "extravagant use" on the one hand and "waste" or "undue consumption" on the other. It remains to be seen whether optional household metering available throughout many if not all undertakers' areas in 1983, with its component of a volumetric charge, will reveal that usage is sensitive to a price mechanism.

In offices, shops and other premises where numbers of people foregather, technical development now makes it possible and relatively easy and cheap to ensure that water consumption for hygiene and sanitation is minimised. A notoriously extravagant use of water has been the urinal, for which current byelaws already prescribe conditions restricting both the times of operation and the quantities which may be taken. Technical development can result in a specific objective being satisfactorily achieved with less water than hitherto (for example, WC flushing) and thus continued use of the larger quantities becomes unnecessary and could be deemed "undue consumption". Byelaws offer the possibility of requiring the adoption of such technical development, not as an aim in itself (which would be *ultra vires*), but to prevent continued unnecessary "waste".

Some of the increase in demand may be due to changes in unaccounted for water. To the extent that some of this water may be leakage from the consumer's own water services then the byelaws aimed at preventing continuing leakage from inappropriate pipework, fittings or appliances have further relevance. This is particularly so where parts of the consumer's installation are not readily seen by him in the normal day and where, even if leakage is detected, there could be reluctance to carry out repairs.

SUITABILITY

This leads in to the controversial topics of suitability and accessibility. Current byelaws endeavour to minimise the risk of failure by referring to specific British Standards. However, these become dated with a possible unfortunate effect of stifling innovation or development towards more satisfactory products. It is worth considering whether byelaws should simply state specific criteria, without identifying the mechanism, material or fitting to meet the criteria. Standards, practices and products which are "deemed to satisfy" the byelaws could appear in a complementary list. Thus British Standards and Codes of Practice relating to the water service and which are continually evolving and improving to take account of development (and on which water undertakers have a means of influence and assessment through membership of appropriate drafting and consultative committees) could be immediately accepted and adopted once they had been included in such listings.

Some products comply with present byelaws but are known to be extremely difficult or expensive to maintain. In consequence, repair or replacement might be deferred despite waste. The concept of suitability might in future include consideration of the potential waste which would arise in such cases. The byelaw criterion for this might be that replacements for parts liable to wear should be of a standard type and dimension, readily obtainable in the market place by the user.

Accessibility

Inspection, repair or renewal would be frustrated if accessibility were denied. However, the prime criterion that waste shall not occur and the need for accessibility must be tested against this. Such pipes and fittings as are essential to the provision of a water service to a property cannot in practice be abandoned in the event of leakage and therefore accessibility for the three purposes must be ensured. It could be argued that byelaws for underground pipes and fittings should be of a particularly rigorous nature because leakage through subsequent corrosion or other failure might be difficult to detect and eliminate. Thorough inspection of all new installations at appropriate stages prior to completion of a service connection is justifiable in that it helps to minimise future effort in controlling waste.

Where, however, the consumer has a pipe or fitting from which leakage is self-revealing and can be isolated without denying at least one point of discharge to the property, then the question of access for repair or replacement becomes one of convenience to the consumer, occupier or owner. Provided waste is eliminated by isolating the faulty item, byelaws would be satisfied: it is not for the undertaker to insist that any particular pipe or fitting within a water service shall necessarily exist or be replaced, only that wastage shall not occur.

Undue Consumption

Alleged wastage through excessive or extravagant use is a matter defying argument. Water-using appliances can be used by the consumer as frequently as he considers appropriate: one consumer's judgement or habits will not match those of others. Washing machines, dishwashers, sink disposal units and similar appliances will become more commonplace and they undoubtedly use a lot of water. However, the water industry has possible remedies against completely uncontrolled consumption of water through these items.

The quantity of water used per cycle of operation can be monitored. Products which have low consumption rates (measuring one product against another of the same type) can be used as a notional "standard" for acceptibility. If it can then be shown that the desired purpose of a product cannot be achieved satisfactorily other than with a high consumption rate, then the water industry could claim that the appliance was wasting water and could omit reference to it in any "deemed to satisfy" listing.

Frequency of use of water-using appliances reflects the consumer's own preference and is uncontrollable. Nevertheless, it is for the undertakers to consider whether control of consumption could be effectively obtained by introducing a byelaw such that certain water-using appliances may be connected to an installation only if the supply is metered.

CONTAMINATION

Contamination of water supplies, so far as the consumer is concerned, can arise in two ways. The first is from unwanted chemical reactions occurring within his water service; or by ingress of some foreign body or material into his installation. The second is from backsiphonage, from his own terminal fittings or from the terminal fittings of his neighbour.

For these reasons byelaws relating to the prevention of contamination through the use of unsuitable materials or substances, or backflow, or from other causes are worthy of review and strengthening.

Materials in Contact with Water

The quality of the water supplied by the undertaker is determined by national and international standards and EEC directives. Within these standards the water, whilst of a wide variety of characteristics, is considered to be "wholesome". Nevertheless the possible adverse effects of the water in supply upon pipework, fittings and appliances must be considered and, if appropriate, modified by treatment processes. There will be circumstances where adverse effects cannot reasonably be avoided and the consumer must be advised with this in mind.

The chemistry of the water supply and distribution industry has greatly improved with advanced analytical methods and a greater understanding of the interaction of various waters upon differing materials in widely changing circumstances. It is reasonable to accept that in some circumstances the selection of inappropriate materials for use in the water service should be controlled by byelaw so as to prevent subsequent contamination which in turn could lead to waste (by flushing) or leakage through corrosion.

Backsiphonage

Backsiphonage within a consumer's own water service could lead to contamination. The undertaker could take the view that this is a matter only for the consumer, providing contamination did not backflow into its mains. Nevertheless, waste through flushing would be liable to occur and must be considered.

Contamination of the undertaker's mains is potentially very serious and must be prevented. The recommendations in the backsiphonage report[1] have already been well received throughout the water industry and inclusion of these could be a valuable strenthening of new model byelaws.

SUMMARY

The Report on new model water byelaws[3] considers a number of similar matters which have influenced its two main drafts of new documents. These are:

(1) Draft "Recommendations for the technical requirements for a new model water byelaws" and
(2) Draft "Recommended guidance on the application of the proposed new model water byelaws"

The documents show clearly that the Standing Technical Committee have completely restructured the byelaws as presently applying throughout the industry. They have supported the proposals with a note on "Proposed changes in the format and content of the model water byelaws and consequences for costs" and two further documents: "Report on the enforcement of water byelaws" and "Prevention of waste of water in water services".

At the time of writing, the Report on proposals for a new model water byelaws[3] is in the hands of representative consumer bodies, manufacturers and water undertakers as part of the wide consultation process. Individual assessments and interpretation of the value of the report, its purpose and its recommendations, will no doubt vary widely and further comment here is both superfluous and unwise.

It seems possible that by 1986 the water industry will be considering the formal adoption of new byelaws which, the Committee clearly hopes, will encourage the best of current standards and practices, whilst providing a basic framework of legislation which will be precise, reasonable, understandable, and free from capricious interpretation.

The report is worthy of very careful study.

4. BYELAW ENFORCEMENT

Introduction

Under the Water Act 1945 the power to make byelaws is optional, but in fact the option was taken up by most undertakers. The Water Act 1973 created the regional authorities in England and Wales which inherited differing sets of byelaws relating to their constituent pre-1973 undertakers but they have since taken steps to achieve greater uniformity within their regions. All the water companies in England also have byelaws. There is now close conformity with the 1966 edition of Model Water Byelaws, with later variations accepted as being of general application. The Secretary of State is required to confirm the making of byelaws and variations requested by individual undertakers are likely to be approved only in exceptional circumstances.

Having made byelaws, it is the duty of undertakers to enforce them. This enforcement is carried out in parallel with the exercise of powers available to undertakers directly under the Water Act 1945. There is, however, no formal guidance as to how enforcement is to be achieved.

Current Enforcement Practice

Enforcement of byelaws is achieved by most, if not all, undertakers by employing inspectors to visit consumers' premises and to examine the water services. This covers inspection not only of such components as pipes, taps, stop-valves and other fittings but also the overall arrangement of the installation.

It is common experience that inspectors are often asked for, and are expected to be able to give, advice and guidance on byelaw matters, and this is usually given as part of the normal service provided by undertakers. Some may raise a charge for this service, particularly in the case of large industrial or commercial installations, public buildings, schools, hospitals and the like. Inspectors may take samples of water at the consumer's request or with his permission when investigating the possibility of contamination arising from backsiphonage or from the use of unsuitable materials or products in contact with the water.

New Properties

Usually new properties (where there is an application for a supply) and substantial extensions to existing services (wherever notification is given) are visited at least once and often two or more times. The incidence of inspections will depend upon the complexity of the installation, the undertaker's view of the competence of the installer and, not least, on the availability of inspectors. Particular attention is required to pipes laid in the ground before being covered over. Potential infringements in new buildings can often be identified before the water service is connected to the mains: normally there is little or no difficulty in getting these rectified. Occasionally problems arise on large building complexes (for example, schools, large public buildings and hospitals) where many specialist contractors are on site and where exact boundaries of responsibility for different parts of the water service are not always clear.

Extensions and Alterations

It is less easy to ensure that changes to existing water installations, to provide a water service to building extensions, or to accommodate the changing requirements of the owner or occupier, are equally satisfactory. It is common experience that a byelaw requiring notice to be given to the undertaker of alterations to the water service is not always complied with, and knowledge of such changes may not come to the undertaker before the extended or altered water service is brought into use. In domestic properties extensions, new bathrooms or the installation of central heating systems are not infrequently carried out by incompetent or inexperienced persons and compliance with byelaws may be fortuitous.

It follows that domestic services in existing buildings or extensions are often inspected only when access is gained for a specific purpose; for example, to follow up complaints raised by the occupier about taste, odour or noise, in connection with free rewashering services (where provided), or where leakage control operations indicate excessive flows. In some cases, local authority planning approvals and grant-aided improvements to property are brought to the attention of the undertaker.

Consumer Response

In existing properties owner-occupiers can be expected to attend quickly to repairs or renewals where damage is being caused by leaking water. They may not act so quickly where dripping taps or faulty float-operated valves discharge harmlessly into hand basins, sinks or baths, or through warning pipes, with no resultant damage.

With tenant-occupied property there is not uncommonly a delay in carrying out repairs and renewals, partly dependent upon the attitude of the tenant, and partly due to the time taken to notify the landlord and on the latter's response.

Non-domestic Services

In non-domestic services standards vary widely. As with domestic installations, extensions, alterations, additions and temporary connections are often carried out without any notification to the undertaker, and the scale of undetected infringements is probably substantial. In some cases industrial complexes and processes have great potential for waste of water and for serious backsiphonage and contamination problems.

Water services in existing non-domestic premises may warrant more attention by undertakers but, taken overall, routine inspection may be less than is desirable or recommended in the backsiphonage report[1]. High consumption shown by revenue meter readings can provide a reason for inspections, and may arise by invitation following a consumer's complaint about the size of his bill.

DETECTION OF CONTRAVENTIONS

Undertakers have no means of knowing how diligent owners or occupiers are in keeping their services in a proper state of repair, or of detecting wilful or negligent acts on the part of some persons. All that may be reasonably practicable for them is to promote an awareness of the need for adequate maintenance to be carried out by competent persons, to detect waste of water as part of their leakage control operations and to inspect periodically those services where the consequences of contamination of water in the mains could be serious.

In practical terms, the undertaker can rely only upon the vigilance of its inspectors in locating and identifying contraventions. In this task the skill and experience of the inspector can be augmented by elaborate waste detection methods but, ultimately, particular properties must be identified and detailed inspection made. Usually a tactful inspector can gain access to a property to identify a faulty fitting which is leaking, and which might have been detected by observation of water escaping from a warning pipe or by sounding techniques, but in an extreme case a magistrate's warrant can be obtained. However, random or systematic inspection of properties solely to search for contravention of byelaws is not possible. Apart from any adverse consumer reaction to such an approach, magistrates are unlikely to take kindly to such action.

Once access has been gained, there may be further difficulties to be overcome. The inspector may find fittings and appliances about which he has doubts concerning their fitness from the point of view of byelaws, or a fitting which, whilst not actually causing waste of water or contamination at the time of inspection, may be such that he suspects that it is likely to do so at any time in the future. The WRC Fittings Testing Scheme is of great help to the inspector. The "listing" of a fitting under the Scheme assures him that, provided the fitting is correctly installed, then the requirements of byelaws will not be contravened. There are, however, many fittings and appliances readily available on the market which are not "listed" and the inspector must exercise considerable judgement as to whether such items are acceptable. He has no powers to require the owner or occupier to demonstrate that a fitting is satisfactory, nor any powers himself to test or to remove a fitting for test off-site. The only testing facility normally available is to make siphon or drainaway tests on consumers' supply pipes where suspected leakage has to be confirmed prior to issue of a notice to the consumer. The ultimate recourse is limited to the issue of a warning that there could be a prosecution in the event that subsequent inspection reveals waste.

Most owners and occupiers take a view that the identification of a contravention is generally in their own as well as the undertaker's interest, and the tactful and helpful inspector usually experiences no difficulty in getting infringements attended to.

Prosecutions

Despite infringements of byelaws and the problems in identifying and resolving them, prosecution for contravention is considered by undertakers only as a last resort. There is reluctance to use the power, partly for fear that the courts would impose only token penalties and partly because of a wish to maintain a good public image. Persuasion is considered to be the best approach and is usually successful. It follows that the exact procedure for conducting a prosecution for contravention of the byelaws is not widely known. A brief note of advice is appended at the end of this section.

Inspectors

There is wide variation in the number of inspectors employed by undertakers, and even more difficulty in ascertaining the effective number employed specifically on byelaw enforcement. Many inspectors have other duties, such as waste detection and, occasionally, meter reading, and most have a public relations role in resolving complaints, promoting good customer relations, and offering a consumer service in matters which have nothing to do with byelaws. It would appear however that the notional equivalent number of inspectors employed on byelaw enforcement varies from one per 20 000 population in some undertakers to one per 175 000 in others, with an average of about one per 70 000 population. Many factors influence the number and each undertaker makes decisions based upon the circumstances prevailing in the locality.

Duty of Care

The general view is that byelaws are made and are enforced for the benefit of the undertakers and the consumers as a whole, not for the protection or convenience of the individual consumer. So far as is known this has not been tested in the courts, but it would suggest that the making of byelaws does not give rise to a duty of care to the individual. Byelaws intended to prevent waste of water cannot eliminate leakage or accidental escape or consequential damage to the property of the individual. It might be argued in particular that undertakers have a duty of care towards domestic consumers who would be unlikely to know what byelaws require, or who may be unaware of the consequences if they fail to maintain their water services, including their supply pipes. It is clear however that if consumers take the risk of failing to keep their installations in good repair or of employing incompetent persons, it is they and not the undertaker who bear the responsibility.

Undertakers have a statutory duty to provide a wholesome supply at the point at which the water is supplied to the premises, and a common law duty of care towards members of the household for whose consumption the water is supplied. But failure to enforce byelaws intended to prevent contamination of water in the consumer's pipes which connect with mains could only lead to an action for breach of statutory duty or negligence at common law if the consequence is the provision of an unwholesome supply from the mains. The byelaws intended to prevent contamination of water within distributing pipes are the first line of defence against contamination of water in service pipes. Although some forms of contamination may have consequences for the health of consumers which is of direct concern to them, other forms lead to consumers running off water to waste (which itself then contravenes the byelaws), or in the extreme case could contaminate the undertaker's mains through backsiphonage and adversely affect the quality of the public supply.

Enforcement in the Future

The enforcement of byelaws cannot be absolute; there is no way in which every single infringement can be detected and corrected.

Undertakers must therefore exercise judgement as to the amount of effort (and therefore of cost which has to be met by the consumer) which should be reasonably expended. The criteria are clear in the terms for which byelaws are made: the prevention of waste, undue consumption, misuse or contamination. Byelaws cannot prevent leakage from occurring, as pipes and fittings fail through a variety of reasons. They may, however, help to minimise waste through failure by requiring reasonable and generally acceptable standards to be adopted.

By long tradition the usual way of ensuring compliance with byelaws is by inspection by the undertaker's own employees. The possibility of discharging the responsibility by accepting reports from suitably qualified and competent persons other than direct employees has not been widely explored, but may be practicable in some cases.

The eventual outcome of the report on proposals for a new model water byelaws[3] may influence the manner in which enforcement is achieved.

5. STANDARDS

BRITISH STANDARDS

Origins

In 1901, at the instigation of the Institution of Civil Engineers, the professional engineering bodies set up an Engineering Standards Committee which in 1918 became the British Engineering Standards Association. A Royal Charter was granted in 1929 and a Supplemental Charter in 1931 when the present name— British Standards Institution—was adopted.

Function

The main function of the BSI is to draw up Standards and Codes of Practice by voluntary agreement. Finance is provided by voluntary subscription from the firms and bodies interested in the work of BSI, and Government grant based on £ for £ on subscription income.

Organization

Subject to the ultimate authority of a General Meeting, policy is determined by the Board of the Institution operating through six Councils and the Quality Assurance Council.

Standards Committees, operating under the Council's control, authorise the work of Technical Committees, of which there are about 1 000 having a total membership of 10 000 people. Full details of the organization of the Institution are to be found in British Standard 0: 1981 "A standard for standards".

Technical Committees

Membership of Technical Committees is drawn from representatives of bodies (both manufacturer and user) interested in the subject dealt with by the particular committee. These committees are responsible for drafting both British Standard Specifications and Codes of Practice. Specifications apply to the manufacture of articles whilst Codes of Practice are recommendations of good accepted practice as followed by competent practitioners. The Technical Committee concerned with water fittings and hence with water undertakers' byelaws is Committee No. SEB/2. The IWES is represented on this committee as well as the Water Companies' Association, the Association of Water Officers, the NWC and the DoE. The committee operates through several sub-committees.

Procedure for Production of British Standards

Any organization in membership of BSI can request that consideration be given to the production of a Standard covering a particular subject. In practice, such requests frequently originate from the Technical Committees of the Institution. Requests are referred to the appropriate Standards Committee, who will consider the necessity and priority for the production of the Standard and allocate the work of drafting to a Technical Committee.

When the Technical Committee has completed the draft it is passed to the editorial section of the Institution who will check that the drafting complies with the requirements of BS O, Part 3. The draft is then published for public comment. A period of eight weeks is allowed for public comment after which the Technical Committee considers comments received and recommends approval for publication as a BSS. The period of gestation of a new BSS is usually about 2 years.

Draft for Development (DD)

A Draft for Development is published by the BSI when guidance is urgently needed and can be responsibly given and it is agreed that the time is not ripe for a British Standard. An example of this is DD 82: 1983—"Specification of requirements for suitability of materials for use in contact with water for human consumption with regard to their effect on the quality of the water". This draft covers what are colloquially known as the "Burman" tests.

Amendments

Technical Committees may propose amendments to an existing British Standard. These amendments are put through the same administrative procedure, including publication for public comment, as the original BSS. After issue of five amendments, the whole Standard must be revised and, in any case, every Standard must be reviewed by its Technical Committee not more than 5 years after publication.

It should be noted that British Standards are incorporated in water undertakings' byelaws by exact identification, that is by quotation of both BSS No. and year of publication. Thus amendment and revision of relevant Standards do not affect the byelaws and the current DoE model includes only Standards amendments to 1976. In future, it would be preferable that reference to Standards in byelaws should be by undated identification, when amendments and revisions would automatically apply.

Quality Assurance and the "Kite" Mark

A product bearing the number of a BSS indicates only that the manufacturer of the product considers that it complies with the BSS.

The Certification and Assurance Department (CAD), located at Hemel Hempstead, provides an inspection service which ensures compliance with the relevant BSS and authorises the use of the "Kitemark", first used in 1903, and, since 1974 the "Safety Mark", to demonstrate compliance with a BSS in respect of safety (Fig. 3.1).

Kitemark   Safety Mark

Fig. 3.1. British Standards Institution Kitemark and Safety Mark

Reproduced by kind permission of the British Standards Institution

Manufacturers who wish to use these trade marks must apply to the BSI for a licence to do so. Licencees are subject to regular inspection of their premises and independent testing of samples by CAD, thus providing an independent guarantee of compliance with the relevant BSS.

BUILDING RESEARCH ESTABLISHMENT DIGESTS

The Building Research Establishment (BRE)—formerly the Building Research Station (BRS)—has since 1952 issued a series of Digests, some relevant to water byelaws or standards; a full list is appended.

One of the most important is No. 15 (New Series), which discusses several matters of relevance to byelaws, notably the depth of service pipes, bimetallic corrosion in plumbing systems, and insulation against frost.

The most important matter in this Digest, however, is the introduction of the "Garston" ballvalve which has been adopted by the British Standards Technical Committee and incorporated in BSS 1212, Part II Ballvalves (Brass Body) and Part III Ballvalves (Plastic Body).

BRS Digests

   8 The Use of Copper and Galvanised Steel in the same Hot Water System
 33 The Causes of Dampness in Buildings
 66 Noise in Plumbing Systems
103 Plastics for Building
110 Corrosion of Non-ferrous Metals I
111 Corrosion of Non-ferrous Metals II
118 Spray Taps

BRE Digests (New Series)

 15 Pipes and Fittings for Domestic Water Supply
 69 Durability and Application of Plastics
 83 Plumbing with Stainless Steel
 98 Durability of Metals in Natural Waters (supersedes Digest 8—First Series)
205 Domestic Water Heating by Solar Energy
253 Heat Pumps for Domestic Use
254 Reliability and Performance of Solar Collection Systems

INTERNATIONAL STANDARDS

The International Organization for Standardization (ISO), founded in 1947, comprises the national standards bodies of 88 countries, including the BSI. It operates through 160 technical committees meeting in various parts of the world and reporting to ISO headquarters in Geneva. In the technical committees, voting is by national delegation and for a Draft International Standard to be recommended for publication by a technical committee there must be a 75 per cent vote in favour. In the event of a British delegation voting in favour of an International Standard which is adopted for publication, the BSI publishes the standard as a dual-numbered BSS.

EUROPEAN STANDARDS

The European Committee for Standardization (CEN) comprises the national standards bodies of 16 European Economic Community (EEC) and European Free Trade Association (EFTA) countries plus Spain. The organization prepares European Standards which are published without variation by the national standards bodies of those countries voting in favour of them. Draft European Standards are adopted only on a vote where there are twice as many positive as negative votes. There must be at least four positive votes and the countries voting positively must represent at least two-thirds of the production and consumption of the product concerned within the representation in CEN.

6. REFERENCES

1. Department of the Environment 1974 "Report of the Committee on Backsiphonage in Water Installations". HMSO, London.
2. Department of the Environment/National Water Council 1976 "Pressurised hot water and heating systems" (Appendix to Standing Technical Committee on Water Regulations Report No. 3). HMSO, London.
3. Department of the Environment/National Water Council 1982 "Report on proposals for a new model water byelaws" (Standing Technical Committee on Water Regulations). HMSO, London.

Roman aqueduct, Nîmes (Pont du Gard)
(*French Government Tourist Office*)

Chapter 4

CONSUMER REQUIREMENTS

1. INTRODUCTION

IN 1981 the water industry in Great Britain supplied a total of 18 000 Ml/day to a variety of consumers. Chapter 12 reviews the problems of leakage from the distribution system and waste of water—parts of the total put into supply. This chapter is concerned with useful consumption: who uses water from the mains supply; what it is used for; how much is used; and when it is used. It also considers standards of service and consumer complaints.

2. CATEGORIES OF CONSUMER

Fig. 4.1 illustrates the development of water demand from 1961 to 1981 with some disaggregation into metered and unmetered supplies (including leakage). Table 4.I expands on this analysis, considering consumption according to consumer category. Each element in this table is subsequently examined to a degree of detail commensurate with its importance to total consumption.

3. DOMESTIC CONSUMPTION

Over 99 per cent of households in England and Wales receive a piped supply of treated drinking water provided by one of the 10 regional water authorities or the 28 water companies[2]. The range of uses to which this water is put is wide and varied but large parts of total household consumption are accounted for by a few important components. Analysis of household demand into these categories of use has proved valuable for developing forecasts of future household water requirements.

STUDIES OF HOUSEHOLD CONSUMPTION

A series of studies of household consumption have been undertaken by several of the RWAs since 1974[3]. These studies were prompted by the awareness that while household consumption was the largest and fastest growing element of useful consumption, little was really known about it, principally because it was unmeasured.

All of these studies have shown the high variability in household water demand. Apparently similar households sharing the same make-up in terms of family size and appliance ownership, have markedly different levels of water use. Fig. 4.2 shows the distribution of household consumption in samples of households in 1976 in the towns of Malvern and Mansfield[4].

The main determinant of household water demand is household size. Table 4.II illustrates the decrease in consumption per person with increasing household size—an important factor given the steady reduction in average household size in the UK (from 3.09 in 1961 to 2.71 in 1981).

COMPONENTS OF HOUSEHOLD WATER USE

Based on information from the various studies, household water use can now be

---

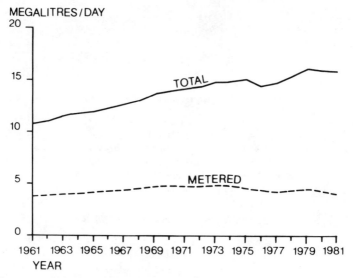

Fig. 4.1. Public water supply in England and Wales, 1961–1981

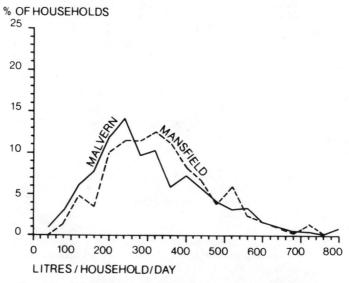

Fig. 4.2. Distribution of household water consumption
(Malvern/Mansfield study, 1976[4])

disaggregated to show the relative importance, in terms of water usage, of different household activities and this provides a forecasting framework (Table 4.III).

These are typical figures drawn from the RWA studies. The miscellaneous component covers use mainly from the kitchen and wash basin taps and thus includes some clothes washing, personal usage and other regular and occasional uses. Each of the components in Table 4.III is the product of three elements—the volume/use, the frequency of use and the proportion of households owning the appliance or fitting. Table 4.IV compares the results from the STWA and SWWA studies.

TABLE 4.I.   Analysis of Public Water Supply by Category
of Consumer
(England and Wales, 1981—excluding leakage)

Category of consumer	Ml/day	Per cent of total
Households	6 000	54
Industry	3 050	27
Commerce and Service		
Industries	1 600	14
Agriculture	500	5
Miscellaneous	50	<1
	11 200	

Source: Based on information submitted to the National Water Council (NWC) by the Regional Water Authorities (RWAs).
Note: In Scotland, metered supplies to industry and commerce are about 28 per cent of total supplies (including leakage)[1]. Total supplies in Scotland were about 2 250 Ml/day in 1981.

TABLE 4.II.   Consumption per Person by Size of Household
(litres/person/day)

Number in household	SWWA	STWA	TWA	NWWA
1	125.9	116.1	136	139.3
2	124.4	117.2	151	137.6
3	118.1	109.0	123	123.8
4	108.9	91.9	116	120.5
5	102.9	96.3	103	106.9
6	97.1	75.2	97	111.4
7+	91.7	68.9	64	124.6

Sources: South West Water Authority (SWWA), Study of Domestic Water Consumption, 1977[5].
Severn-Trent Water Authority (STWA), Mansfield Study of Domestic Water Use, 1976.
Thames Water Authority (TWA), Study of Domestic Water Use, 1980.
North West Water Authority (NWWA), Study of Domestic Water Use, 1982.
Note: The different dates of the studies and statistical estimation errors explain much of the variation in the results.

TABLE 4.III.   Components of Household Water Use
(litres/person/day)

Use	lpd
WC flushing	40
Bathing and showering	20
Clothes washing machine	14
Luxury appliances (dishwasher etc)	1
Outside use (garden, car washing)	4
Miscellaneous	40
	120

TABLE 4.IV.   Details of Household Water Use

Appliance or fitting	South West Water Authority			Severn-Trent Water Authority		
	Frequency (uses/day)	Volume (litres/use)	Ownership (per cent)	Frequency (uses/day)	Volume (litres/use)	Ownership (per cent)
Washing machine						
−auto	0.75	113	27	0.75	108	29
−other	0.27	27	45	0.32	34	50
Dishwasher	0.84	46	2.5	0.79	62	2
WC	10.60	9.4	100	10.40	9.5	100
Bath	0.56	85	95	0.58	80	96
Shower	0.55	19	25	0.51	35	21

TABLE 4.V.   Comparison of Components of Household Water Use
(litres/person/day)

Component of use	UK (1982)	Sweden (1973)	Norway (1981)	Australia (1977)	USA (1980)	Netherlands (1978)
WC	40	40	30	37	88	31
Bathing & showering	30	70	40	54	81	29
Laundry	14	30	25	33	24	24
Dishwashing	12	40	20	17	10	12
Other	24	35	15	44	17	12
	120	215	130	185	220	108

Sources: References Nos. 7 to 11.
Notes: The Australian figures[9] are for Melbourne and exclude garden watering.

INTERNATIONAL COMPARISONS

Utilising data from some of the various studies[6], part of the miscellaneous component in Table 4.III can be re-allocated to slightly redefined main uses and a comparison made between UK demand and demand in other countries (Table 4.V).

PROJECTION OF DEMAND

The higher levels of consumption elsewhere indicate to some extent the demand levels towards which UK consumption could tend. The differences may be explained by variations in habits as regards frequency of use of appliances and fittings, volumes per use, levels of appliance ownership and climatic conditions. The UK studies have suggested that increasing ownership of automatic washing machines has played a major role in the growth of household demand in the UK: the acquisition of this appliance will, on average, increase household demand by about 80 litres/day; a net increase of 45 litres/day if it replaces a twin-tub machine. If the ownership of automatic washing machines increases from the 1982 level of around 48 per cent of households to say, 60 per cent, by the end of the century, this could contribute about 7 litres/day to household demand (about 3 litres/person/day).

Projections of future levels of household demand must anticipate future ownership levels of appliances and fittings. The increasing ownership of automatic clothes and dish-washing machines is one source of growth; another is the increasing availability of fittings. For example, changes in house design with an increase in the average number of WCs per house will probably increase the size of the WC flushing component, based on observations at Malvern and Mansfield (Table 4.VI), although this effect may be countered by the growing number of dual-flush cisterns in use.

Predicting how quickly, if ever, domestic consumption in the UK will reach the levels in other countries is difficult and many methods have been advocated and tried[12]. In 1982, the RWA's forecasts for the level of demand at the end of the century were fairly consistent at around 140-160 litres/person/day. This is still well short of the US, Australian and Swedish levels.

The US consumption analysis shows a very high level of use for WC flushing—this is because the average volume/flush is 5 US gallons, twice the UK level. In addition not only is the flow rate for showers much higher (5 US galls/minute in US, 1 gallon/minute in UK), but the frequency of showering is greater (about 1 per person per day against an average 1½ baths or showers per person per week in the UK).

TABLE 4.VI. **Frequency of WC Flushing for Number of WCs in House**

Number of WCs in house	Malvern	Mansfield
	(flushes/person/day)	
1	2.91	3.44
2	3.22	3.62
3	3.76	4.65

GARDEN WATERING

Water use for garden watering is a small part of average annual household use in the UK, accounting for less than 5 per cent. In other countries, due to climatic conditions, garden watering demand through the year can exceed in-house demand[9]. However the special problem created by garden watering is that it is weather related and occurs over a short period. The profile of domestic water use through the year can still only be approximated, based on the results of RWA studies. Fig. 4.3 gives an example of the monthly profile using data from TWA.

This measure (average monthly demand) smooths considerably the shorter-term peaks (hourly, daily, weekly) and these are dealt with in more detail in Section 7.

TOURISM

In addition to garden watering peaks in the spring/summer months, there is a tourist demand in some parts of the country. The temporary resettlement of large sections of the population at certain times of year can create serious supply problems for some water authorities. For example, Southern WA (SWA)

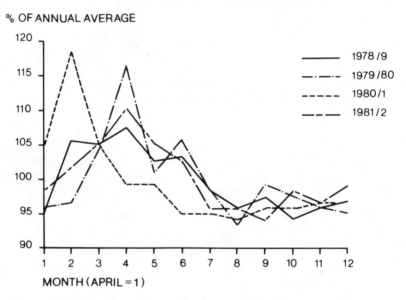

Fig. 4.3.   Monthly average household water demand
(Thames Water Authority, 1978–1982)

TABLE 4.VII.   Tourist Water Demand

Accommodation	Average consumption (litres/person/day)
Touring caravan and camping site	68
Static caravan site	71
Mixed static and touring site	84
Chalet site	108
Unclassified hotels	113
Guest houses	130
1 star and 2 star hotels	168
3 star, 4 star and 5 star hotels	269

Source: SWWA, Survey of tourist water consumption[13].

estimated that at the height of the tourist season the demand for public water supply could increase by 20 per cent over the annual average, based on a study of demand in 1978 on the Isle of Wight. SWWA found considerable variation in demand, according to the type of accommodation used (Table 4.VII).

4. INDUSTRIAL CONSUMPTION

In 1981 there were approximately 610 000 metered industrial and commercial consumers in England and Wales and the level of consumption per consumer in this sector is even more variable than in the household sector. Total metered consumption in 1981 was 4 590 Ml/day, of which 582 Ml/day were industrial supplies of a non-potable standard. As Fig. 4.1 shows, metered consumption has declined steadily from a peak in 1973; this section is concerned with the use made of these supplies and the analysis provides some explanation of the decline.

Metered consumption is mainly by industry but includes some commercial and agricultural use as well as a very small amount of domestic use. Table 4.VIII disaggregates metered consumption into the three categories, based on details from 6 of the 10 RWAs (North West, Northumbrian, Yorkshire, Severn-Trent, Anglian and Wessex) which together account for 70 per cent of RWA metered supplies.

TABLE 4.VIII.   Analysis of Metered
Demand

Consumer	Per cent of total
Manufacturing industry	69
Commerce and service industries	23
Agriculture	8
	100

Source: Various studies between 1974 and 1979; results summarised by Mr Philip Turton, NWC.

IMPORTANCE OF LARGE USERS

The general pattern of industrial water demand is for the bulk of consumption to be accounted for by a small number of very large users and the remainder spread amongst a multitude of small businesses with low levels of demand. For example, in Wessex WA, the top 20 metered consumers out of 3 400 have a 28 per cent share of metered consumption; in STWA the top 4 per cent of consumers account for over 75 per cent of metered consumption; in Anglian WA about 33 per cent of metered supplies are used by the top 20 consumers; and in NWWA the top 120 consumers use 45 per cent of metered consumption.

VARIABILITY OF USE PER EMPLOYEE

Water use expressed as a ratio per employee varies considerably among industries (Table 4.IX).

TABLE 4.IX.   Volume of Water Used per Employee by
Industry

Industry	litres/employee/day	litres/unit of output
Coal mining	540	250/tonne
Milk products	3 730	17/kg
Brewing	2 360	5/litre
General chemical	2 860	5/kg
Steel tubes	1 210	8 200/tonne
Motor vehicles	420	5 000/car
Carpets	730	34/m^2
Textile finishing	2 700	83/kg
Pottery	220	2/piece
Paper	9 730	54 100/tonne

Source: STWA, Industrial water use survey[14].

The decline in traditional manufacturing industries (metal manufacturing, textiles, etc), the emergence of new industries, particularly in the electronics field, and the development of the service industry sector will lead to a reduction in the average volume used/employee. The average in manufacturing industry is around 480 litres/employee, twice the average water demand/employee in the electronics industry. Therefore, even if employment levels are sustained by the growth of new industries of this type, industrial water demand may decline further.

COMPOSITION OF INDUSTRIAL WATER DEMAND

The relative importance of industrial sectors varies across the country and this is reflected in the structure of regional industrial water demand (Table 4.X), with the chemical industry dominating industrial water use in the North of England, while the metal manufacturing and engineering industries are the major users in the Midlands.

TABLE 4.X.   Industrial Use of Mains Supply by Region
(per cent of industrial mains supply in each area)

Sector	NWWA	NWA	STWA	YWA	Weighted average
Mining	*	*	2	5	1
Food, Drink, Tobacco	12	2	13	22	12
Coal and Petroleum Products	8	1	2	2	4
Chemicals	57	71	10	22	40
Metal manufacturing	2	19	21	11	13
Engineering	7	1	24	13	12
Vehicles	3	*	7	2	4
Textiles	3	1	9	12	5
Leather & Clothing	*	*	1	1	*
Bricks, pottery, etc	1	1	4	4	3
Timber, furniture	*	*	*	1	*
Paper	6	4	1	2	3
Other manufacturing	1	*	6	2	3

*less than 1 per cent

Within each industry, total water use can be disaggregated to show the relative importance of different categories of use (Table 4.XI). Overall water use by employees for domestic purposes (personal hygiene, catering) accounts for about 29 per cent of metered demand. In the manufacturing sectors alone, the proportion is around 20 per cent. The increasing trend to automated production processes will, of course, reduce the significance of this element of demand.

THE EFFECT OF PRICE

Unlike domestic consumers, industrialists can directly control the level of their water costs by adjusting consumption, either by good housekeeping, such as preventing waste of water on factory premises, or by changing to a production process which uses less water, or by introducing or extending water re-cycling, or by developing private sources.

The incentives required to achieve those savings may vary. For example, industry responded to requests for reduction in consumption in the 1976 drought and brought demand levels down by perhaps 20 per cent. Generally, however, the decision to change the pattern of water use will be a business decision based on commercial principles.

Industrialists consider the costs of changes, either to a new process or to extend or introduce re-cycling, against the savings in water costs (which may include both supply and effluent charges). Various estimates have been made relating the change in water price to the likely reaction in terms of demand change: recent estimates of the price elasticity of water demand by STWA[14] and NWWA put it between −0.1 and −0.3 (for a 10 per cent increase in price, water demand will decrease by 1 to 3 per cent).

SUPPLIES TO SERVICE INDUSTRIES AND COMMERCIAL PREMISES

Unlike water supplies to manufacturing industry, which are all metered, supplies to service industries and to commercial premises may or may not be metered, depending on the water supply history of the area and the attitude of consumers to the metering options now available.

Demand by service industries and commercial premises is estimated to be about 23 per cent of total metered supplies but the share of this sector is growing, not only because of the take-up of metering options but also because the service sector of industry has been less affected by the 1979-83 recession.

Table 4.XII gives some average consumption figures for service industries and commercial premises.

The allowance made for unmeasured commercial use is usually in the range 10-20 litres/person/day (lpd), as an average over the population served. The operation of the metering options is reducing the required allowance but not yet by any significant amount (in STWA it is estimated that the loss to unmeasured consumption as a result of the option is about 1 lpd).

Between 1978/9 and 1981/2 about 33 000 unmetered commercial consumers in England and Wales took advantage of the option to convert to metered charging, about 4 per cent of the total number of consumers in this category.

5. AGRICULTURAL CONSUMPTION

The use of public water supply for agricultural purposes is relatively small in terms of annual average demand (about 500 Ml/d, less than 5 per cent of the total). About 40 per cent of all agricultural water requirements are met by direct

TABLE 4.XI.   Categories of Use of Mains Supply within Sectors of Industry

Category of use of mains supply	Percentage of consumption by industrial sectors within each category of use																Percentage of total industrial mains supply used within each category
	Mining and quarrying	Food, drink and tobacco	Coal & petroleum products	Chemicals	Metal manufacturing	Engineering	Vehicles	Textiles	Leather, etc.	Clothing & footwear	Bricks, pottery, glass & cement	Timber and furniture	Paper and printing	Transport and communications	Business & professional services	All other	
Domestic	39.9	10.8	6.8	13.2	22.5	21.9	31.4	10.9	5.5	17.8	24.2	32.4	40.2	51.3	69.8	43.9	28.9
Topping-up condensate	16.3	11.3	24.4	24.2	12.6	22.7	9.8	15.3	6.1	18.4	9.8	33.3	11.8	3.7	5.4	5.8	14.6
Cooling hot metal	—	—	—	0.2	3.4	1.4	3.4	—	—	—	0.9	0.1	0.7	—	—	—	1.0
Cooling plant (re-used)	3.0	5.2	4.8	15.7	20.4	5.9	12.7	1.2	—	3.2	9.7	7.8	4.5	6.0	0.4	4.6	8.2
Cooling plant (once through)	6.2	17.4	58.0	13.6	20.7	13.7	18.5	16.3	32.9	0.9	10.9	5.2	15.5	10.0	6.1	11.4	14.6
Washing down	4.7	6.7	0.5	3.3	2.4	1.9	1.4	3.3	0.3	0.1	6.7	0.6	2.3	21.3	6.4	10.7	4.5
Washing out	0.1	10.7	0.1	2.9	1.6	1.6	2.3	6.2	—	0.1	2.5	1.0	4.7	1.6	0.5	2.0	2.9
Product rinsing	11.2	10.1	1.9	6.1	7.6	20.7	12.1	20.7	45.1	7.0	9.1	13.9	5.4	3.8	3.2	6.5	10.9
Product testing	0.2	0.2	0.1	2.2	0.9	1.1	0.5	0.1	—	—	0.5	2.2	0.4	—	—	1.6	0.7
Chemical solutions	—	0.5	0.5	9.3	3.1	5.6	6.5	24.9	9.8	52.5	2.0	2.6	9.1	0.6	0.2	2.8	5.0
Gas scrubbing	0.4	0.2	—	4.4	1.0	0.9	0.3	—	—	—	0.2	0.4	—	—	—	—	1.1
Conveying product or waste	2.2	3.1	—	0.2	1.1	1.3	0.3	0.3	0.3	—	4.1	0.3	0.4	1.1	0.1	0.2	1.0
Blanching food	—	0.3	—	—	—	—	—	—	—	—	—	—	—	—	0.1	—	0.1
Product ingredient	1.6	12.9	0.3	3.0	—	0.2	0.1	0.3	—	—	17.8	—	1.5	0.1	0.9	1.6	2.4
Sterilisation	0.2	9.4	—	—	—	—	—	—	—	—	—	—	—	0.1	1.1	0.8	1.2
Dust suppression	9.1	—	2.4	0.8	1.2	0.8	0.5	—	—	—	1.2	—	0.2	—	—	0.2	0.6
Humidifying	—	0.4	—	0.8	0.3	0.1	—	0.5	—	—	0.4	—	3.3	—	0.7	—	0.3
Other	4.9	0.6	—	0.1	0.7	0.2	0.2	—	—	—	—	—	—	0.4	5.1	7.9	2.0
Sector share of metered mains demand	1.4	9.8	1.8	7.7	15.7	17.9	5.3	7.0	<0.1	0.3	2.6	4.6	0.6	0.9	10.7	13.7	

Note: The results of the survey have been grossed up in this table to give a representative picture of water use in the Severn-Trent region.

abstraction. Table 4.XIII shows an analysis of agricultural use of public water supply.
Water demand for all purposes other than irrigation is quite constant throughout a normal year. Irrigation needs are markedly seasonal and are effectively confined to the period May-August. The ACAH survey[15] indicated that in 1977 about 130 000 hectares of agricultural land would be irrigated in a dry year (involving about 7 000 agricultural holdings). Table 4.XIV contains some details on livestock water requirements.

TABLE 4.XII. Average Water Use in
Service Industries and Commercial
Premises

Premises	Average volume
Schools	75 litres/person/dayØ
Hospitals*	175 litres/unit/day+
Laundries	5 litres/kg washing
Retail Shops	135 litres/employee/day
Offices	62 litres/employee/day
Hotels*	763 litres/employee/day

*Based on 365 working days/year (all others 250)
ØIncludes staff and pupils
+Total units = total staff + no. of beds.

TABLE 4.XIII. Analysis of Annual
Agricultural Use of Public Water Supply

Purpose	Per cent of total
Outdoor irrigation	3
Livestock	70
Domestic	20
Protected crops	6
Washing & processing	1

Source: Water for agriculture: future needs[15].

TABLE 4.XIV. Average Water
Consumption per Livestock Unit

Unit	litres/day
Dairy cow	150
Beef cow—yarded suckler	45
—yarded finishing	28
—younger	20
Sheep (drinking only)	4
Pigs—suckling sows	30
—dry sows	17
—finishing pigs	10
—others	5

Source: Water for agriculture: future needs[15].

6. MISCELLANEOUS USES OF WATER

This heading covers water required for fire fighting, mains and sewer flushing, street cleaning, etc. Some work by the Central Water Planning Unit (CWPU)[16] suggested a maximum use in this category of around 1 lpd, based on analysis of average consumption in Reading. For fire fighting, it was estimated that about 2 serious house fires occurred per week in the Borough, using between 1 000 and 4 500 litres of water to extinguish or control. Including water use for hydrant testing and fire drills increased weekly use to about 40 000 litres, less than 0.1 lpd.

Information on mains flushing obtained by CWPU suggested a rate of mains flushing of 250 litres/minute for periods of 5 to 10 minutes and a frequency of flushing of about 1 per 140 consumers per year, again a consumption of less than 0.1 lpd.

Street cleaning was also estimated as a similarly small amount and the allowance of 1 lpd for this category is likely to be generous.

OPERATIONAL ASPECTS OF MISCELLANEOUS USES

Fire Fighting

Sections 32 to 34 of the Third Schedule of the Water Act 1945 apply to water for fire fighting purposes and have been applied to all Statutory Water Undertakings by the Fire Services Acts of Parliament. All water undertakings are under an obligation at the request of the fire authority to fix fire hydrants on water mains, excluding trunk mains, to afford a supply of water for extinguishing fires. The hydrants are sited in places most convenient for fire fighting and are indicated by yellow and black plates. Ownership rests with the water undertaking which has an obligation, at the request and expense of the fire authority, to keep fire hydrants in good order and renewed when necessary.

Other hydrants on the mains system are needed solely by the water authority for such purposes as flushing or washing out the mains. These installations (often posted and plated in black and white) are provided and maintained by the water undertaking alone. Sometimes hydrants are needed for both fire and water undertaking purposes and their costs are shared. An industrial or commercial consumer (for instance a department store) may pay the water undertaking for a "fire main", to be laid up to their premises. This will be of sufficient capacity to deliver enough water for fire fighting at hydrants or sometimes through an automatic sprinkler system. Ordinary fire mains usually have a water undertaking lead seal on the control valve so that the main is used only to control fire. The seal is inspected from time to time and remade after tests or usage. Some sprinkler systems are connected to automatic valves which open to allow mains pressure into the sprinkler feed pipes.

Water undertakings must allow all persons to take water for fire fighting purposes from any pipe on which a hydrant is fixed, without payment. However, the water undertaking is not liable to provide an adequate supply of water for fire fighting. This obligation lies with the fire authority through the Fire Services Acts. The pressure requirements for fire fighting water are the same as those for domestic supplies—that is, the water undertaking is required to lay on water constantly.

CLEANSING SEWERS AND OTHER PUBLIC PURPOSES

Section 37 of the Third Schedule of the Water Act 1945 places an obligation on water undertakings to provide "a supply of water for cleansing sewers and drains, for cleansing and watering highways and for supplying any public pumps, baths or washhouses". Clearly this part of the Water Act was much more important previously than it is today. A very similar provision was made in the 1847 Waterworks Clauses Act when matters such as watering unpaved streets and bringing water to public drinking fountains were responsibilities placed on the local authority.

Sewer flushing and cleansing is still important and the amount of water and terms of payment may be agreed between the water undertaking and the local authority. However, water undertakings are generally moving towards standard charges for all their customers and a local authority will now probably pay for its water for public use at a standard metered charge for fixed installations. Water taken from hydrants is usually by means of a standpipe and thence into a manhole to flush a sewer. This facility is often charged for by renting out the standpipes at a fixed annual charge which takes account of the likely water usage.

FLUSHING AND MAINTENANCE OF MAINS

Apart from fire fighting and public purposes, water is used regularly by water undertakings themselves for a number of miscellaneous purposes, usually concerned with the care and maintenance of mains. Flushing, the most common operation, can use a significant quantity of water. It is practised to alleviate discoloured water complaints from consumers which arise from the build-up of corrosion products in the mains. Complaints tend to persist at dead-ends of mains in culs-de-sac or at a balance or null point on a system where there are no-flow conditions. The cheapest and easiest way to clean the water supply is to open the nearest hydrant and run dirty water to waste for a period (say half an hour) but care must be exercised less problems are caused elsewhere. Most distribution departments have a regular flushing programme in which teams of water inspectors flush, record and report upon mains conditions within the area of supply.

Although flushing is relatively simple it is only a palliative and the trouble frequently returns again within a few weeks. Other more effective cleaning methods involve propelling a plastic foam swab through the main by water pressure, or air scouring, using a compressed-air/water mixture. Each method in itself uses quite large quantities of water.

These methods wash out the main and on a trunk main special "wash-out" points using valved tee junctions are provided at low points along the main's route. Pipes from these points are led away to a convenient watercourse and the main can be emptied of silt and dirt.

UNACCOUNTED FOR WATER

Each of the above water uses is legitimate, although they are rarely metered or measured. When the calculation of water wastage through leakage and bursts is made, it is usual to deduct known demands (such as metered supplies to industrial consumers and assumed quantities for domestic and commercial uses) from the total quantity supplied, to arrive at an "unaccounted for" water figure. This will include actual waste water and the genuine usages described in this section (see also Chapter 12).

7. PATTERNS OF DEMAND

Demand patterns vary considerably, depending on a number of factors. These include the size of the area, its type in terms of industrial, commercial or domestic, the time of year and the weather patterns. A clear understanding of these variations is important for work scheduling and operating strategy.

AVERAGE WEEKLY VARIATIONS

Fig. 4.4 shows the average weekly variation in water consumption in the contrasting supply areas of Birmingham and the East Worcestershire Waterworks Company. For much of the year the weekly consumption is close to the average for the year. The effect of garden watering and commercial horticulture is only typically seen during June and July. The effect of holiday periods is particularly noticeable in the Birmingham pattern. There is a slight decline during April, reflecting the variable date of the Easter period, and a sharper one during the end of May Bank Holiday. A more general drop in consumption occurs from mid July to the end of August and a further notable fall from just before Christmas until mid January is a growing feature.

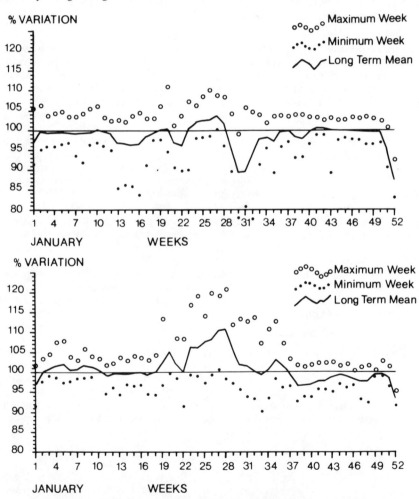

Fig. 4.4. Average weekly variation in water consumption
(Birmingham, 1961–1981 (top) and East Worcestershire, 1975–1981 (bottom))

Peak Week Consumption

Fig. 4.4 also shows the maximum and minimum percentage deviation in peak week consumption recorded in the period shown. Summer peak week percentages are considerably higher in the East Worcestershire area. This area covers part of the Vale of Evesham where horticulture has a marked effect on consumption. Because of the size of the summer peaks, the occasional high consumption that follows severe winter weather is less in this area than the summer peak. This used to be the case in the Birmingham area but in January 1982 the winter peak was about double the previous highest summer peak, when expressed in percentage deviation terms. These seasonal and often localised peaks are of particular concern in the distribution of water and are now discussed in more detail.

Winter Peaks

High consumption during winter months is particularly troublesome because it results from loss of water rather than use of water. Consequently it is not controllable by legal or financial measures and the process of stopping bursts and leaks often has to be accomplished during harsh working conditions. Whenever a drought or unusually cold winter spell occurs there is a tendency to search for a location or particular meteorological parameter that will illustrate how extreme the event has been. In fact, the water industry has to cope with difficult conditions rather frequently. The effect of a cold spell depends on the duration of the period, the relationships between maximum, minimum and mean temperatures, the underlying basic consumption and the extent to which consumers generally have taken precautions against the effects of the weather. In recent years, particularly high winter consumption has been recorded in 1947, 1963, 1979 and 1981/82. Fig. 4.5 shows the pattern of consumption and temperature in the STWA area during December 1981 and January 1982. The manner in which total water put into supply rose sharply following the end of freezing conditions on 14 December and 16 January can clearly be seen.

Summer Peaks

It is convenient to divide the causes of summer peaks into 'the tourist effect' and 'the garden watering effect'. The former is affected by fashions in holiday location, the type of holiday taken, and the weather during the holiday period. Uncertainties in these factors can cause difficult problems both in terms of planning and day-to-day operation. However, the engineers who serve areas subject to the tourist effect have been coping with the problems for many years.

Potentially more widespread implications result from garden watering. Although the 'trigger' to watering is a hot dry spell of weather, the amounts used depend on the degree of ownership of hosepipes and garden sprinklers and the attitude to their frequency of use. It may be that direct billing for water use has promoted an attitude of 'value for money' whereby some consumers on rateable value charge feel moved to use more water. There is limited information on garden appliance ownership and less on frequency of use. However, a survey of appliance ownership in Mansfield in Nottinghamshire in 1976[4] indicated that 23 per cent of households owned a hosepipe and less than 1 per cent had a garden sprinkler. A repeat survey in 1979 showed that hosepipe ownership had risen to 63 per cent and 19 per cent of households had a sprinkler. The effect on peak week summer consumption in Nottinghamshire is shown in Fig. 4.6 Some special factors could affect demand in this area such as the level of re-housing. Nevertheless, in many areas there have been two- or three-week periods in recent years when the peak consumption

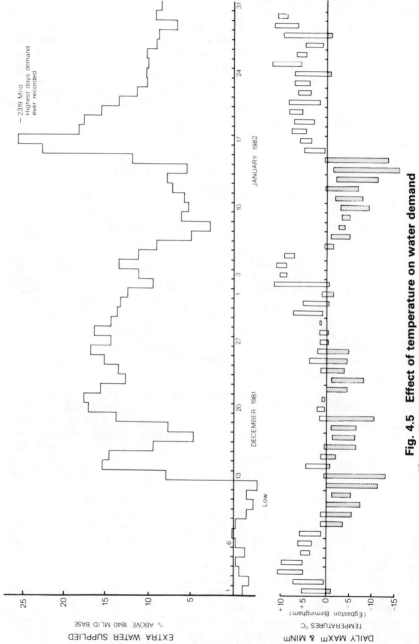

Fig. 4.5 Effect of temperature on water demand
(Severn-Trent Water Authority, December 1981–January 1982)

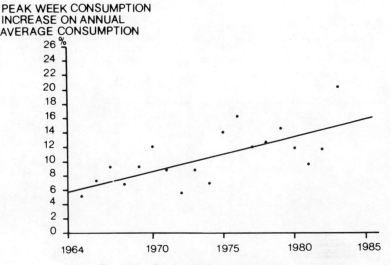

Fig. 4.6. Peak week consumption
(Severn-Trent Water Authority, Nottinghamshire, 1964–1983)

recorded has been particularly high. This has considerable implications for expansion of the capacity of the water distribution system and it is important that an appropriate level of service is fixed for this activity.

WEEKLY AND DIURNAL FLUCTUATIONS IN DEMAND

Variation in demand within the day and within the week is very much dependent on the characteristics of the system and there are wide differences between urban and rural areas. In most places the critical period is the evening hourly rate during hot weather. Demand management at this time is becoming increasingly important. The House of Lords Select Committee[17] recommended that more research was necessary into demand management so that the water industry might decide the extent to which it met future demand for water. The committee suggested that any necessary amendments of the law to permit demand management should be made.

8. QUALITY REQUIREMENTS

QUALITY FOR DOMESTIC CONSUMPTION

The various Water Acts impose a duty on water authorities to supply "wholesome" water without defining the meaning of this term. Most interpretations acknowledge that this means that the water should not be injurious to health and that it should not offend the senses unduly. Monitoring and control of known toxic constituents and harmful bacteria that could be present in water (due to pollution or to geological sources) is practicable and in many cases there are accepted standards by which quality can be judged. The control of some of the factors that affect the aesthetic quality of the water is often more difficult. Consumers' perceptions of

TABLE 4.XV. Summary of the Chemical Requirements of the EEC Directive Relating to the Quality of Water Intended for Human Consumption

Parameters	Units	Guide level	MAC†	Comments	
Organoleptic parameters					
1 Colour	mg/l Pt/Co scale	1	20		1
2 Turbidity	mg/l SiO$_2$	1	10		2
3 Odour	Jackson units / Dilution number	0.4 / 0	4 / 2 at 12°C / 3 at 25°C		3
4 Taste	Dilution number	0	2 at 12°C / 2 at 25°C		4
Physico-chemical parameters					
5 Temperature	°C	12	25		5
6 Hydrogen	pH	6.5–8.5	*		6
7 Conductivity	µS/cm at 20°C	400	*		7
8 Chlorides	Cl mg/l	25	*	See Article 8 of Directive	8
9 Sulphates	SO$_4$ mg/l	25	250		9
10 Silica	SiO$_2$ mg/l		*		10
11 Calcium	Ca mg/l	100			11
12 Magnesium	Mg mg/l	30	50		12
13 Sodium	Na mg/l	20	175	90 percentile; 80 percentile of 150 after 1987	13
14 Potassium	K mg/l	10	12		14
15 Aluminium	Al mg/l	0.05	0.2		15
16 Total hardness				See Directive, Table F concerning softening	16
17 Dry residue	mg/l		1500		17
18 Dissolved oxygen	Per cent saturation			Saturation 75 per cent except for groundwater	18
19 Free carbon dioxide	CO$_2$ mg/l			Water should not be aggressive	19
20 Nitrates	NO$_3$ mg/l	25	50		20
21 Nitrites	NO$_2$ mg/l		0.1		21
22 Ammonium	NH$_4$ mg/l	0.05	0.5		22
23 Kjeldahl nitrogen	N mg/l		1		23
24 KMnO$_4$ oxidizability	O$_2$ mg/l	2	5		24
25 Total organic carbon	C mg/l			Investigate any increase in concentration	25
26 Hydrogen sulphide	S µg/l		*	To be undetectable organoleptically	26
27 Substances extractable by chloroform	mg/l	0.1	*		27
28 Hydrocarbons	µg/l		10		28
29 Phenols	µg/l		0.5	Excluding natural phenols	29

TABLE 4.XV. (Continued)

Parameters		Units	Guide level	MAC†	Comments	
Physico-chemical parameters (continued)						
30 Boron	B	µg/l	1000	200		30
31 Surfactants		µg/l	1	*		31
32 Organochlorine compounds		µg/l			Excludes those covered by 55. Trihalomethane concentrations must be as low as possible	32
33 Iron	Fe	µg/l	50	200		33
34 Manganese	Mn	µg/l	20	50		34
35 Copper	Cu	µg/l	100		3000 µg/l after 12 hours	35
36 Zinc	Zn	µg/l	100		5000 µg/l after 12 hours	36
37 Phosphorus	P_2O_5	µg/l	400	5000		37
38 Fluoride	F	µg/l		1500 700	8–12°C 25–30°C	38
39 Cobalt	Co	µg/l				39
40 Suspended solids		µg/l	None			40
41 Residual chlorine	Cl	µg/l				41
42 Barium	Ba	µg/l	100	*		42
43 Silver	Ag	µg/l		10		43
Parameters concerning toxic substances						
44 Arsenic	As	µg/l		50		44
45 Beryllium	Be	µg/l			No values quoted	45
46 Cadmium	Cd	µg/l		5		46
47 Cyanides	CN	µg/l		50		47
48 Chromium	Cr	µg/l		50		48
49 Mercury	Hg	µg/l		1		49
50 Nickel	Ni	µg/l		50		50
51 Lead	Pb	µg/l		50**		51
52 Antimony	Sb	µg/l		10		52
53 Selenium	Se	µg/l		10		53
54 Vanadium	V	µg/l			No values quoted	54
55 Pesticides		µg/l		0.1 0.5	Individually Total	55
56 Polycyclic aromatic hydrocarbons		µg/l		0.2		56

Notes:

† Maximum admissible concentration

* The Government have yet to set MAC values

** MAC value quoted for running water or after flushing. Where lead pipes are present and a sample is taken directly or after flushing and the lead either frequently or to an appreciable extent exceeds 100 µg/l, suitable measures must be taken to reduce the exposure to lead on the part of the consumer.

This table has necessarily been abbreviated. The full Directive includes microbiological parameters and limits to softening and should be consulted for the full details and additional comments on the individual standards.

what is acceptable vary, especially with regard to matters such as taste and odour (see Section 13).

For practical purposes water authorities have adopted two categories of standards for assessing quality: bacteriological and chemical.

Bacteriological Quality

Bacteriological quality is usually measured against the recommendations in Report 71[18]. The 1969 edition was revised during 1982 and the main requirements of the new edition are:

(1) *E. coli* should not be detectable in any sample of 100 ml;
(2) no sample of 100 ml should contain more than three coliform organisms;
(3) coliform organisms should not be detectable in any two consecutive routine samples of 100 ml from the same location;
(4) for any given distribution system, coliform organisms should not occur in more than 5 per cent of routine samples, provided that at least 50 samples have been examined at regular intervals throughout the year.

The rationale for the standards can be examined in the standards themselves. The main point to emphasise is that regular and frequent bacteriological examination of water samples is the most important safeguard of the quality of water supplies. Contamination by sewage, due to inadequate treatment or to infiltration in distribution, presents the greatest risk to the health of consumers and samples indicating such potential contamination should be the cause of immediate further investigation and remedial action.

Chemical Quality

Chemical quality has traditionally been compared with the WHO European Standards[19]. Again, a major revision took place during 1982, the 1970 standards being replaced by WHO Guidelines[20]. To complicate the picture further, the EEC has produced a directive[21] which will come into effect during 1985. These standards for chemical quality are summarised in Table 4.XV.

The adoption of WHO standards by the UK water industry has been voluntary but has provided a practical measure by which to assess performance. Many supplies do not comply with all of the standards, especially for such parameters as iron or manganese. This is mainly because removal at source would be expensive and in many cases unjustified if the concentrations are not causing problems to consumers. Adoption of the EEC directive, however will be a legal requirement and a DoE circular[22] has indicated that compliance with the terms of the directive will be "a necessary characteristic but not a complete definition of any water that is to be considered wholesome". The directive does make provisions for derogations and for delays in implementation, but, long term, the consequences are likely to be a gradual improvement in the quality supplied.

Another significant change associated with the adoption of the directive is that it applies where the water is made available to the consumer (whereas WHO standards were mainly concerned with quality at source). Under the terms of UK legislation this means that the directive applies to the water authority at the curtilage to the property. Responsibility for quality at the consumer's tap rests with the owner of the property and this will not always be the consumer himself. The directive therefore will impose additional responsibilities on water and local authorities to monitor quality at consumers' taps and makes the problem of compliance more difficult with respect to some parameters such as iron and lead. Quality at consumers' taps has been monitored in the past but the requirement to do so and the need to take action was less well defined.

It should be added that the WHO standards and guidelines and the EEC directive include bacteriological standards but the revised edition of Report 71 takes account of these.

QUALITY FOR SPECIFIC PURPOSES

The standards referred to above are for the protection of the health of consumers and water that complies should be suitable for normal domestic purposes. It will also be suitable for many industrial and other purposes but there are special applications for which additional treatment is required. The water undertaker is not expected to provide water suitable for non-domestic purposes. He should be aware however of the sensitive users in his area of supply, so that he can advise them of a change in quality when distribution areas are switched from one supply to another, or when new sources are brought into use.

The hardness of the supply prompts most enquiries to water suppliers. Over the last two decades the concept of what is acceptable has slowly changed. This is partly a reflection of the reality that naturally soft supplies were virtually fully exploited in the areas that could economically benefit, partly a move away from centralised softening on grounds of economy, and partly as a result of indications of an association (not necessarily causal) between soft water and cardiovascular disease. However, in some areas of use hardness is no longer a major problem. Detergents for industrial and domestic use that are insensitive to water hardness have largely replaced natural soaps. Textile processing was initially largely located in areas supplied with naturally soft water but dyes and other chemicals have been developed which can be used with different quality waters. Chemical treatment for scale and corrosion control has meant that many waters can be used unsoftened for cooling and heating.

There are applications for which softened or demineralised water is still necessary, the commonest being in steam boilers. Water of much higher quality than that for domestic use is also required for process applications in many industries. The manufacture of electronic components and pharmaceuticals probably have the most stringent requirements but chemical manufacture, plating, textile processing and photographic development are examples of industries generally requiring water of much higher quality than that typically supplied for domestic use. Such industries are also the most susceptible to changes in water quality that can affect their own water treatment plant or the process itself (for example sudden changes in hardness or discoloration due to iron).

Water for food manufacturing is subject to the EEC directive [21] but compliance with the directive does not necessarily imply that the water is suitable for all applications. The brewing industry makes extensive use of private boreholes, but where public supplies are used the quality of the final product can be affected by changes in water quality. Water that is to be carbonated or otherwise acidified can be a source of difficulty if it contains algal metabolic products that precipitate at low pH values.

The medical use of water is another area sensitive to quality. For many uses potable supplies are adequate but some consumers are on special diets which may limit, for example, sodium intake. Water used in pharmaceutical manufacture (including that for injection) has already been mentioned. Home dialysis is gradually becoming more common and as its use has extended the problems associated with water quality have become more apparent. Water is generally softened prior to preparation of the dialysate but the renal unit should be advised of the full analysis of the water. In particular, aluminium has been found to cause serious complications in dialysis patients and softening will not reduce the concentration below the currently recommended maximum concentration of 30 μg/1[23].

9. PRESSURE REQUIREMENTS

The Water Acts are very careful not to prescribe a fixed pressure for supplies to consumers. They do not specify a hydraulic head of pressure to be delivered, although a definite value of residual pressure often has to be used in mains design calculations. Rather, the Water Acts refer to constancy of supply (see Chapter 2, Section 8).

It is interesting to note that when the great waterworks supply schemes of the mid-nineteenth century were designed there was fierce debate between water engineers on whether to provide an intermittent supply or one of constancy. The case for a constant supply won the day and has been incorporated in the Water Acts since that time.

Section 39 carries the very important proviso that water undertakings cannot be required to deliver water at a height greater than that to which it will flow by gravitation through their mains from the supplying service reservoir or tank—and the undertakings are entitled to determine from which service reservoir or tank the supply will come. This effectively saves the water undertaking the disproportionate expense of, for example, supplying a single new housing estate to be sited high up on a distribution zone close to the water levels of the service reservoir supplying it. If application to build these premises were made and it was determined by hydraulic calculation that pressures in the existing mains were not sufficient to allow water to flow by gravity from the supplying reservoir to them, then new necessary mains (or a booster station or even a new reservoir if the development were large) would be required. Funding of the new mains could then be arranged under ss.36 or 37 of the Water Act 1945 with a mains guarantee or contribution to the cost of the mains by the developer as necessary.

The provisos concerning gravity flow and chosen service reservoirs in Section 39 of the Third Schedule of the 1945 Act would also be applied in the case of very tall buildings situated in an otherwise low-lying distribution zone. Here the mains pressure would be insufficient to reach the higher storeys and a booster pump or hydro-pneumatic pumping set would be installed in the building at low level. These would be privately owned and funded but would need to comply with water undertaking byelaws to ensure that backsiphonage pollution from the high-head storeys of the building could not contaminate the lower mains pressure.

As demand grows in a particular distribution area, or as mains age and their flow carrying capacity deteriorates, then water pressure to existing consumers will decline. Section 39 protects their interests in these cases when the water undertaking has a duty to maintain or restore that pressure so that it will reach "the top of the top-most storey". The obligation however is interpreted to be a sufficient pressure to reach the top storey as measured at the water undertaking's stop tap. If this is achieved, but by reason of corroded and constricted private service pipework in the consumer premises there is low pressure at the consumer's tap, then the water undertaking would still be meeting its statutory requirements.

Similarly if a non-domestic consumer significantly increases his demand for water, with the result that pressure in his premises becomes too low, then the water undertaking has not failed in its duty. Again it may be that the private pipework is causing the pressure drop or that the main feeding the premises is only sufficient to carry the original demand. In the latter case a new main or greater site storage at the non-domestic consumer's expense might be necessary.

Although the Water Act does not quantify pressure values for sound legal reasons, they are necessary for design and testing of mains systems. Most mains design engineers use a minimum distribution pressure in the mains of about 15 to 20 m head. Whilst there are many consumers being supplied below this level at times, particularly at the extremities of mains systems, pressure readings below these values are indicative of problems and the need to take remedial action (for example providing a new booster station or a reinforcement main—see Chapters 5 and 6).

Maximum distribution pressures are usually designed to be of the order of 40 to 60 m. However there are circumstances where perhaps by reason of the contours of the land much higher values have to be tolerated, giving pressure of up to 100 m head. Excessive pressures are undesirable and uneconomic. Wear on valves and fittings is exacerbated, water usage increases and waste levels and leakage go up. Indeed leakage has been shown to vary exponentially with pressure, resulting in a doubling of leakage from an increase by half in pressure.

Desirable pressure ranges in a distribution system are frequently achieved by dividing it into pressure zones, each valved such that it is separate from other zones on the system or linked by pressure controlling valves. Desirable pressure ranges in each zone are about 30 to 50 m but this is sometimes unobtainable if the zone covers a scattered rural area or if the district is hilly. Properties in a valley might have to tolerate high pressures at night, those on hills low values during peak demands. Domestic storage is desirable for houses on high land and can be required on properties built since 1945 and at a height within 35 feet (10.7 m) of the service reservoir draw-off level—Section 60, Third Schedule, Water Act 1945.

It should not be forgotten that pressure control valves are energy destroying devices and energy is expensive to impart to water. For the reasons discussed above pressure zoning is desirable but it needs careful introduction and monitoring. Automatic microprocessor control of pressures close to their optimum can now be achieved and is a concept with good potential.

10.   OTHER REQUIREMENTS

FLOW RATES

Pressure and flow parameters are linked to each other through fundamental hydraulic principles. As with pressure, the Water Act 1945 (Section 39) refers only to constancy of flow as a duty rather than to particular values.

Distribution mains systems work to well established demand rates per head and per property but what is an acceptable flow for consumers is often a subjective matter. A flow rate sufficient to fill a kettle slowly might be considered to be quite adequate by an elderly consumer living alone but equally would not be acceptable to meet the needs of a growing family.

British Standard CP310:1965 gives recommended rates of flow at fittings in this respect (see Table 4.XVI) and points out that, at the domestic pipework design stage, an allowance must be made for some fittings to discharge water simultaneously.

DIALYSIS UNITS

There are an increasing number of home kidney-dialysis machines in Britain and the number in use within a water undertaking's boundary depends partly on the policy of the health authorities in that region and partly on population (in STWA in 1982 there were about 400 in use). Each machine depends upon a steady minimum positive water pressure to operate it and is used three days a week on average.

Water undertakings have no extra-statutory duties with respect to supplies to dialysis machines. In the case of a burst water main occurring because of ground movement or frost, there would be no case of negligence against the undertaking if pressure to the dialysis machine fell and it ceased to operate.

Nevertheless, water undertakings work closely with health authorities in this respect and it is usual for distribution departments to keep an up-to-date list of the locations of all dialysis machines in their area and to ensure that local water inspectors each have details of the installations within their district. In this way, the health authority can be informed in good time of any necessary maintenance work on the mains system which might affect the supply to the dialysis machine.

TABLE 4.XVI. Recommended Flow
Rates at Various Fittings and Appliances

Fitting or appliance	Rate of flow (litres/min)
WC flushing cistern	7
Wash basin tap	9
Basin spray tap	2
Bath tap, 19 mm	18
Bath tap, 25 mm	36
Shower (with nozzle)	7
Sink tap, 13 mm	11
Sink tap, 19 mm	18
Sink tap, 25 mm	36

Based on British Standard CP310 : 1965

11. ADVISORY SERVICES

Consumer services staff offer a number of important advisory functions, including:
   (a) Interpretation of byelaws (see Chapter 3) made under Section 17 of the Water Act 1945. Each water undertaking issues its own byelaws which are based on a national set of Model Byelaws. The consumer needs to know what those byelaws mean in his own particular circumstances. For instance, whether pipework may be boxed or not, what access is necessary, whether plant processes may be connected directly to the mains or whether a risk of backsiphonage exists.

   Water undertakings often produce illustrated guides to the byelaws which a byelaw inspector can then describe and interpret for the consumer.
   (b) Advice on waste detection and prevention (see Chapter 12). Prevention in this case is very much better than cure so it is good practice to promote the message to consumers to use water wisely and to repair or report leaks quickly. Undertakings offer advice in this respect and visit major industrial consumers to explain how leakage may best be prevented.
   (c) Early warning of possible supply problems. Periods of hot, dry weather or of frost are when water supply is at its highest and when the distribution mains system is stretched to its capacity. Advice in good time—for instance, the

issue of frost precaution publicity before the winter, and an appeal for sensible usage of garden sprinklers given in late spring—does much to alleviate these troubles.

(d) General advice, through talks and visits, about the industry's services and operations.

12. DEMAND MANAGEMENT

The 1975-76 drought heightened awareness of the practical difficulties of maintaining water supplies. The control of the frequency, duration and intensity of shortage in supply is just one aspect of demand management, which may be defined as the deliberate application of policies to influence the quantity and timing of the demand for water. The aim is to achieve an appropriate balance between the level of expenditure and the level of service to the consumer.

Certain aspects of demand management have been practised by the water industry for many years, including the use of byelaws to control wasteful use and the inspection of appliances through the NWC Approvals Scheme. Advice is also given to industrial consumers on efficient use of water. Other aspects of demand management, notably through charging policy, have hardly been touched.

It is appropriate to make a distinction between restrictions on consumption made necessary by droughts—a shortage of rainfall and runoff lasting perhaps for several months—and restrictions in shorter periods of high demands caused by a warm dry spell during the growing season. The former situation leads to a deficiency of water in sources, the latter leads to very high demands which it may be impossible to meet through existing distribution systems. Although a ban on the use of hosepipes may form a part of a package of measures taken during a drought to reduce consumption, it is much more common for this restriction to apply when demands exceed the treated water storage and/or carrying capacities of the supply system. The problem can be particularly acute in two types of area. The first occurs in rural communities where centres of population may be served from long small-bore mains and where, because of increased demands, pressure falls to unacceptable levels at the end of the delivery main. The second occurs in those areas served by old unlined iron pipes, where internal corrosion of a main can reduce the carrying capacity to unacceptable levels.

Powers to prohibit or restrict temporarily the use of hosepipes are contained in Section 16 of the Water Act 1945. There is some debate as to whether a shortage of water at source is necessary before this power can be used. Often the more pragmatic viewpoint has prevailed, which argues that a deficiency of water at any point in the distribution system *from whatever cause* is sufficient grounds for using this power. A standard of a 1 in 5 to 1 in 10 year chance is usually assumed for the frequency of hosepipe bans. Encouraging public cooperation in limiting water use at certain times can reduce peak demand problems. There remains the question of how to control and suppress surges in demand over short periods. The other methods available to reduce peaks of demand fall into three categories: legal, financial and technical. A legal solution might strengthen the powers to prohibit the use of hosepipes and, more especially, garden sprinklers. This would tend to be rather a coarse instrument, requiring notice and involving fairly widespread application over several weeks. A financial solution could be more promising if the use of a hosepipe and sprinkler were linked to a requirement to take a metered supply. However, to be really effective a rate of flow charge on a short time base would probably be needed. A technical solution is, in the longer term, most promising, with more supply zoning and pressure control being used to suppress intermittent short-lived increases in demand.

13. CONSUMER COMPLAINTS

In the context of water distribution the relevant complaints concern inadequate supply and water quality. The importance of dealing quickly and effectively with consumer complaints has always been a main element in the industry's standards of service. The Water Act 1983 provides for setting up Consumer Consultative Committees to consider and report on any matter relating to the services provided by a water authority or company (see Chapter 2, Section 16).

INADEQUATE SUPPLY

Sudden complete loss of supply or poor pressure can usually be traced to a burst, either in a distribution main or a service pipe. The development and nature of the problem may give a clue to the cause if a burst is not immediately obvious. Tracing and dealing with bursts is dealt with in detail in Chapter 12.

Defects on the consumers' own premises can sometimes be the cause of the problem. Most undertakers provide an advisory service, for example, on the causes of frost damage and the action that can be taken. In some cases, water undertakings will assist in dealing with emergencies.

Gradual deterioration of the supply may be due to a number of causes. A steadily worsening leak could be to blame or poor pressure in the main may be a symptom of other causes. For example, a local increase in demand may mean that there is a supply problem. A closed valve or other obstruction could be to blame or deterioration of the internal surface of the main or supply pipe could have reduced carrying capacity. These topics are covered in other chapters.

QUALITY OF SUPPLY

Complaints concerning the quality of the supply can be split into seven main categories: illness, discoloration, taste and odour, animal infestation, aeration, excessive hardness and corrosion. Although these are the main types, there are always miscellaneous complaints that do not fit neatly under any heading.

All complaints should be taken seriously, dealt with sympathetically and referred to chemists and bacteriologists for investigation. Consumers who are not satisfied with the quality of their supply are often genuinely worried about possible effects on their health and may be reassured by a report on a chemical and bacteriological sample, even if the cause of complaint has not been eliminated. Complaints can be the first indication that something is seriously wrong, for example pollution of the supply at source or by backsiphonage. On the other hand, complaints about taste or hardness often reflect a consumer's awareness of a change of quality of supply from that to which he is accustomed and all that is required is reassurance.

Detailed information on the causes of complaints and how to deal with them is given in a WRC publication[24].

ILLNESS

Allegations of illness due to the water supply are not common but should always be taken very seriously. Sickness and diarrhoea are not usually caused by water in the UK but may be an indicator of serious pollution. Samples of water should be taken for bacteriological and chemical analysis and the environmental health officer informed of the circumstances and results. Storage tanks are often the cause of substantiated contamination and, although not immediately the responsibility of the water undertaking, they should not be overlooked.

Remedial measures depend on the extent and cause of the problem. If the supply is at fault, effective and rapid response is essential. If the problem is contained in the household the environmental health officer should again be advised and arrangements made for a remedy. Often all that is required is cleaning and disinfecting of a storage tank and the provision of a cover or other means to avoid contamination in the future. Although consumers should be advised not to drink water from storage, this can obviously not be enforced; in any case it is unavoidable in some tall buildings but in these circumstances special storage arrangements should have been made, in accordance with the Model Byelaws, to protect quality.

Some illnesses alleged to be caused by water usually involve allergies. Although these are rarely substantiated, the only action available is to provide a full analysis to the consumer's doctor, as for all illnesses, and rely on him to deal with the problem.

DISCOLORATION

Discoloration is usually the commonest cause of complaint and often the most difficult to deal with. There can be a variety of causes and analysis of samples of water from the household and from other points in the distribution system may give an indication as to the most likely. Poor treatment resulting in inadequate removal of solids, iron, manganese or aluminium may have resulted in flocculant material settling in the distribution system only to be subsequently disturbed. A sudden reversal or increase in flow may disturb these sediments. On the other hand they may just build up until the quantities are excessive.

Microbiological activity and corrosion on the internal surfaces of pipes may be another cause of discoloration. Microbial activity can take place in any water supply, the bacteria obtaining nutrients from the water or from materials in the distribution system. The bacteria are usually fixed to solid surfaces but periodically some of the growth will break away and appear as flocculant material or small shreds at consumers' taps. Bacteria are also usually associated with corrosion of iron pipes. This is described more fully in Chapter 10. The consequences of corrosion, in the form of iron-containing precipitates and bacterial matter, eventually become apparent at the consumer's tap. Solid material can also be released from the corrosion of galvanised service pipes and tanks. In this case the discoloration is caused by sand-like grains of zinc and salts.

A change of water quality, especially the substitution of a supply by another of a very different nature, can result in widespread discoloration. Although not well understood, the most likely causes are a change in flow pattern and a disturbance of the equilibrium between the water and the deposits and corrosion products on the internal surfaces of the mains. Usually the disturbance rapidly settles down but sometimes the system never returns to its original stable condition and a continuing higher level of complaints persists.

Animals can also be a cause of discoloration and are considered further later.

Complaints of discoloration tend to be seasonal, the highest incidence being between April and October. The numbers also vary from year to year. The higher incidence in the summer is due to a number of factors, including higher flows (leading to increased disturbance), higher temperatures (resulting in increased microbiological and chemical activity), and seasonal changes in water quality (resulting in increased nutrient levels in the water).

Remedial measures obviously depend on the cause of the discoloration. Flushing or air-scouring may provide temporary relief by removing loose material but a long-term solution may require improvements in treatment, or scraping and relining, or replacement of mains. Relatively simple measures such as control of pH or the addition of silicates or polyphosphates can help in some cases by complexing iron or manganese in solution or by inhibiting corrosion. An increase in chlorine residual or a change to the more persistent chlorine dioxide can help to inhibit microbiological activity. Corrosion and other activities are also worst at dead ends and other areas of low flow so that system design can have a role.

Taste and Odour

Taste or odour may be the subject of complaint but both are intimately connected and often have similar causes so that they can be considered together. In this section the use of the terms taste or odour can be taken in most instances to refer to both types of complaint.

Chlorinous tastes are a common source of complaint, particularly in areas close to a treatment works or served with groundwater supplies. In these cases the consumer must be reassured that the chlorine residual is under proper control and at the level specified for that works.

Earthy and musty tastes and odours are frequently encountered in surface-derived supplies. The incidence is seasonal, higher levels being encountered in summer months, when warm weather causes an increase in biological activity and an increased likelihood of the consequences being noticed. Matters can be made worse by low turnover in distribution so that system design and regulation to minimise dead-ends and low flows can be beneficial. Apart from that, the only other proven remedial measure is treatment at source with activated carbon. Powdered carbon can be used as a temporary measure to get over the worst periods but if usage is prolonged the cost will be high. If permanent treatment with carbon is required, granular carbon filtration is likely to cost less but the choice needs a careful economic and financial appraisal.

Earthy and musty tastes and odours are a natural phenomenon and not a potential risk to health. Any other sort of taste or odour warrants detailed investigation as it may indicate pollution. Chlorophenolic tastes are due to the reaction of chlorine with various, usually industrially-derived, phenols. Investigation and elimination of the source of pollution is one remedy but some relief can be obtained by substituting chlorine dioxide for chlorine as the disinfectant. The use of chlorine dioxide has not been without its own problems, however, being the cause of tom-cat like odours and the release of polynuclear aromatic hydrocarbons from coal tar linings in rare instances[25].

Animal Infestation

The appearance of "animals" or their products at the consumer's tap sometimes provokes the most outraged reaction. Fortunately, in the UK none of the animals commonly found is known to be a risk to health, although a large number of different types have been found. It is unlikely that many distribution systems exist without some form of infestation; the main problem is keeping it under control.

The commonest animals reported are Asellus, Gammarus, Nematodes, Nais worms and Chironomids. They can feed and breed in the distribution system, so that high numbers in the mains are not necessarily an indication of high numbers passing through treatment. Complaints are seasonal, higher temperatures increasing the growth and breeding rates. As well as feeding on each other's debris, animals feed on algae and other biological material in the water and on microbiological growths and organic debris in the mains. Effective water treatment and a clean distribution system can therefore help to control the numbers.

Removal by flushing can alleviate the worst situations, provided that the water's velocity is high enough to dislodge the animals. More effective removal of Asellus and Gammarus can be obtained by chemical treatment of the distribution system with pyrethrin or permethrin and is described in Chapter 10.

Aeration

The milky appearance of aerated water sometimes results in complaints. The cause is usually the release of pressure of supersaturated water as it leaves the tap, supersaturation possibly being caused by an increase in temperature. This is harmless. Air entrainment due to a venturi effect at valves, pumps etc, should be the cause of investigation and remedial action as this is a potential source of backsiphonage.

Hardness

Scaling of kettles and heating systems are more frequent causes of complaint now than that of excessive soap usage due to hard water. Less common complaints are due to the film formed on tea or the precipitation of solids when ice is made. Centralised water softening is less widely practised now and is unlikely to be reintroduced. Consumers can be advised to fit a domestic water softener but to leave the supply to drinking water taps unsoftened. Direct heating systems and immersion heaters are the most vulnerable to scaling but the conversion to indirect systems will be costly for the consumer. Some control of scaling and of the effects of hardness on washing machines and dishwaters can be effected by the use of polyphosphates in the cold water storage tank or by the use of rinse aids in the machines.

Corrosion

The consequences of corrosion of iron and galvanised pipes, in the form of discoloured water, have already been discussed. Other aspects of corrosion also occur on domestic premises. There is a large potential source of problems; some common ones are mentioned here.

All iron and galvanised fittings are prone to corrosion and eventual failure. The lifetime of any fitting is determined partially by water quality. The use of copper, brass and plastics for pipes, fittings and tanks has resulted in much extended lives but not all of these are without their own problems.

Pinholing of copper tube is a problem specific to groundwater within a well defined range of qualities. It is caused only if a residual carbon film is left behind during the manufacture of the tube and responsibility rests with the manufacturer or supplier of the tube[26]. The pinholing may become apparent only after a change of water from a groundwater to another of different quality that does not itself cause pinholing [27]. The speed with which a tube pinholes is mainly affected by the water quality but pinholing often appears within one to two years. The only remedy is to replace the tubing with clean new tube.

Dezincification of brass fittings is another phenomenon confined to areas of specific water quality. The main consequence is blockage by the corrosion products, although failure of the fitting is also a possibility. Water treatment to avoid blockage and even to prevent dezincification is possible[28] but, in areas known to be prone to dezincification, inhibited brass or gunmetal should be used and other brasses banned.

Corrosion of copper tubes and fittings can also cause other problems apart from failure. Common problems are staining of baths and other sanitary ware, astringent tastes, and corrosion of aluminium kitchen ware. These can all be due to copper picked up from the service pipe and fittings (or present from another cause), especially where the water has been static or in contact with long lengths of pipe at high temperatures for long periods of time. Some waters are more likely to cause these problems than others and, if widespread, treatment may be possible.

Corrosion of fittings can be accelerated by mixed metal combinations of pipes and fittings. As an example, copper in the water from a copper service pipe can accelerate the corrosion of galvanised tanks; generally, a mixture of metals should be suspect whenever corrosion is found unexpectedly.

Trends in Consumer Complaints

A variety of causes of complaints have been briefly outlined and it is already clear that the factors that affect the level of complaints are a combination of seasonal influences, the state of the distribution system and the effects of changing quality of waters. As the distribution system gets older and corrosion and other problems take a wider toll, it is possible that the levels of complaint about discoloration will increase unless advance remedial action is taken. However, publicity of a problem, the reaction to higher water charges, even the more widespread availability of telephones, are factors that can just as easily affect the level of complaints.

A system for recording complaints which should enable not only periodic statistics to be collated, but also an analysis by type, area and cause, will enable improvements in the distribution system or treatment works to be planned for maximum benefit.

LEVELS OF SERVICE

The volume of complaints received by the industry is relatively low, considering the difficult and complex nature of the service. By way of an example, Severn-Trent Water Authority received approximately 35 200 complaints during 1982 concerned with its supplies. Analysis of the complaints is shown in Table 4.XVII.

TABLE 4.XVII.   Analysis of Complaints
Received by STWA, 1982

Cause of complaint	Number	Per cent of total
Supply cut-off	15 415	44
Low pressure	8 360	24
Discoloured water	8 285	23
Taste or odour	2 270	6
Presence of animals	260	1
Other	610	2
	35 200	100

The figure of 35 200 complaints compares with 6 618 200 people who receive a piped supply and 2 674 690 properties connected in this area. When commenting on similar figures for 1980 the Monopolies and Mergers Commission concluded "This (level of complaint) does not seem to us to be excessive".

The industry is moving towards greater quantification of levels of service. This has resulted in clearer definitions and a split into factors that the consumer can sense and express an opinion on and those which the consumer must rely on the industry to secure and maintain on his behalf. The former category includes:

(i) Availability — whether the service exists or not.
(ii) Connection — the response time to a request for connection.
(iii) Interrupted service — the frequency and response time to restore a supply.
(iv) Pressure — the adequacy to operate appliances and the time taken to provide the service needed.
(v) Taste, odour, animals, discoloration — the response time to provide the service needed.

The latter category includes the extent of compliance with chemical, bacteriological and virological criteria.

The National Working Party of the NWC Panel on Performance Measurement has collected information on the level of service indicators from 1981. These include the following:

(1) Number of new supply connections to all properties.
(2) Number of supply connections for which the job ticket has been issued and the work has not been completed.
(3) Number of properties receiving water at an inadequate pressure.
(4) Total number of bursts.
(5) Estimated number of bursts not rectified in 12 hours.
(6) Estimated number of properties affected by bursts for 12 hours or more.
(7) Number of properties receiving water which is undesirable on organoleptic or aesthetic grounds.
(8) Number of connected properties experiencing foul flooding.

In addition, authorities now produce a series of indicators based on the speed of response to contact from the consumer. Quantified information on these aspects is difficult to obtain but the Government has asked for generalised assessments. The categories are shown in Table 4.XVIII.

TABLE 4.XVIII. Categories of Response to Consumer Complaints

Nature of contact by consumer	Type of complaint	Units	Response Time†		
			Level 1	Level 2	Level 3
			Less than		More than
Emergency*	Lack of supply	hours	3	3-5	5
	Poor water quality which alarms the consumer	hours	4	4-6	6
	Burst mains	hours	3	3-5	5
Correspondence**	Complaints of quality	days	2	2-5	5
	Requests for analysis	working days	5	5-10	10
	Complaints of low pressure	days	2	2-5	5

Notes: *An emergency contact is regarded as one that is genuinely urgent and received by telephone.
**A correspondence contact is not urgent and usually but not always raised by letter.
†Response times are categorised as follows: level 1, good; level 2, acceptable; and level 3, requiring improvement. A response means that positive action has started, although the problem may not necessarily have been put right in the time indicated.

14. REFERENCES

1. Scottish Development Department 1980 "Water in Scotland—a review".
2. National Water Council 1982 "The water industry in figures".
3. National Water Council 1982 "The components of household water demand", Occasional Technical Paper No. 6.
4. Thackray, J. E., Cocker, V. and Archibald, G. 1978 *Proc. ICE*, 64, 37, The Malvern and Mansfield studies of domestic water usage.
5. South West Water Authority 1978 "Study of domestic water consumption".
6. International Water Statistics Committee 1982 "International water statistics".
7. Ministry of Agriculture, Sweden 1977 "Water in Sweden", Report to the National Water Conference.
8. Wedum, K. and Johanson, S. S. *Vatten*, 38, 231, Water consumption and water demand in Norway.
9. Power, N. A., Volker, R. E. and Stark, K. P. 1981 *Water Resources Bulletin*, 17, 1042, Deterministic models for predicting residential water consumption.
10. Clouser, R. L. and Miller, W. L. 1980 *Water Resources Bulletin*, 16, 453, Household water use: technological shifts and conservation implications.
11. Ardon, G. W. 1981 *H$_2$O*, 14, 599, Development of domestic water consumption (in Dutch).
12. Archibald, G. G. 1983 *Journal of Forecasting*, 2, 181, Forecasting water demand—a disaggregated approach.
13. Hooper, B. D. 1981 "Survey of tourist water consumption", South West Water Authority.
14. Thackray, J. E. and Archibald, G. G. 1981 *Proc. ICE*, 70, 403, The Severn-Trent studies of industrial water use.
15. Advisory Council for Agriculture and Horticulture in England and Wales 1980 "Water for agriculture: future needs".
16. Males, D. B. and Turton, P. 1979 "Design flow criteria in sewers and water mains", Central Water Planning Unit, Technical Note No. 32.
17. House of Lords Select Committee 1982 "Report on the water industry".
18. Department of Health and Social Security, Welsh Office, Ministry of Housing and Local Government 1983 "Report on public health and medical subjects No. 71, The bacteriological examination of water supplies, 5th ed", HMSO, London.
19. World Health Organization 1970 "European standards for drinking water, 2nd ed", WHO, Geneva.
20. World Health Organization 1984 "Guidelines for drinking water quality" WHO, Geneva.
21. European Economic Community 1980 "Council directive relating to the quality of water intended for human consumption (80/778/EEC)".
22. Department of the Environment and the Welsh Office 1982 Joint circular, refs. 20/82 and 33/82.
23. Department of Health and Social Security 1982 Letter ref. DIA/57 to Secretaries of Boards of Governors with dialysis units.
24. Water Research Centre 1981 "A guide to solving water quality problems in distribution systems", Technical Report TR 167.
25. Howells, V. W. and Pound, B. R. E. 1982 "Problems with the use of chlorine dioxide at a small groundwater source", presented at IWES symposium on chlorine dioxide.
26. Lucey, V. F. 1974 "Pitting corrosion of copper in supply water: summary report", British Non-ferrous Metals Technology Centre.
27. Mackett, N. J. F. 1977 "Exposure of pitting corrosion in copper tubes after a change of water quality", presented at Water Research Centre seminar on the effect of water quality on pitting corrosion in copper.
28. Oliphant, R. 1978 "Dezincification by potable water of domestic plumbing fittings: measurement and control", Water Research Centre, Technical Report TR 88.

Chapter 5

DESIGN PHILOSOPHY AND PRINCIPLES

1. INTRODUCTION

IN the past, distribution system design has often had to rely on rules-of-thumb and the adoption of 'best practice'[1,2] rather than on detailed and logical analysis. The use of engineering judgement has been strongly advocated[1,3].

The aim of this chapter is to draw attention to the techniques available for optimal design and operation of systems, in the context of total system costs, and the achievement of reasonable levels of service (Chapter 4). The emphasis is upon design philosophy rather than technical procedures, which are well covered in standard texts.

The extent to which optimising approaches can be applied to particular systems is often dictated by the historic arrangement of demand and supply, and previous design and operating philosophies. Engineers will be expected to prepare best-value justifications for their proposals to obtain funding and satisfy consumer bodies and external criticism[4]. Integrated system design and development requires an unblinkered approach to all components of the water supply function, from tap to source. No single parameter need be regarded as fixed.

FUNCTIONS OF DISTRIBUTION SYSTEMS

It is the statutory function of the distribution system to meet all demands placed upon it within the legal framework (see Chapters 2-4 and 11-13). Design and construction (Chapters 4-9), operation (Chapters 5, 7, 10 and 12), maintenance (Chapters 5 and 10) and administration (Chapters 2, 3 and 13) of the system all represent costs of fulfilling this function, and must be incorporated, with the funding procedures, in system design for least total cost.

Water legislation does not define 'reasonable' limits on the demand which should be met, despite the non-potable nature of many peak demands. This has been commented upon by the Monopolies and Mergers Commission[5] and is discussed later in this Chapter, in Chapter 4, and elsewhere[6,7]. The challenge for the designer is to provide a system which meets reasonable levels of service, whilst controlling excess use in proportion to the payment made for it, at true marginal costs[5,8]. The distribution function can now incorporate demand management as well as provision for future demand, looking at sources, trunk mains, service reservoirs, distribution mains and services as an integrated system.

BASIC FLOW FORMULAE AND DATA COLLECTION

Considerable attention has been given to the development of simple, practical flow charts and tables for manual computation of pipe friction losses, and reduction of carrying capacity with age[1,3,9-13].

Use of computers for the iterative solution of dimensionally correct expressions does not necessaily improve the accuracy it is possible to obtain when measuring parameters in the field, and so for most design purposes, empirical formulae within their known ranges of accuracy are suitable. This is particularly so for the computation of flows in networks, where assumptions for pipe roughness are rarely made to an accuracy greater than 5 or even 10 per cent.

Field flow measurement is desirable, otherwise precision is limited by the accuracy of measurement of pressure differentials. For small mains, artificially high flows and pressure losses can be arranged by temporary re-routing of supplies, or by hydrant operation. For larger mains this is not generally possible, and greater accuracy is required. For example, for a large main working at (say) 60 metres head of water, with an hydraulic gradient of 4 per 1000, to obtain the pressure difference between two gauge points one kilometre apart within 10 per cent accuracy, the gauges would have to be read to 0.3 per cent of the indicated pressure, or about 200 mm water head.

Further comments on the useful ranges of flow formulae and data collection are made in References 14-16, and elsewhere in this Manual. Care must be exercised in applying any flow formulae to analysis. Colebrook has commented upon this in explanation of the decision not to include a factor for reduction of area in his flow equation[17]: "When dealing with 3″ pipes in which the diameter was reduced to 1″, the problem was not one for the scientist or engineer, but rather for the scrap-iron merchant."

BASIC COSTING INFORMATION

Topography, and source and demand inter-relation influence the comparative expenditure on individual components of a supply system, and it is recommended that unit costs are derived which reflect local conditions. Comparisons can be based upon published component cost information which has been collated at a common base date[18-22] otherwise the use of indices is necessary. Historic costs can be modified using published information[23-27] or standard estimating procedures.

2. CONSUMER SYSTEMS

The purpose of this section is to provide a broader overview of some consumption parameters which could be of significance for design of local capacity to meet future demands.

INDUSTRIAL USE

The demand of industrial users is already 'managed' to a large degree, irrespective of the proportion of industrial use which is domestic in character (see Chapter 11). Also the pattern of industrial use of water in the UK is changing. Local knowledge is essential for system design, particularly in older urban areas experiencing decline in traditional water-using industries. Individual consumers who cease trading release capacity which can be used for new occupiers of the same site. Small-scale adjustments of this type can be ignored for forecasting purposes, but should be included for local analysis.

Water costs form a small part of average industrial costs, but water conservation schemes are often viable for customers[28,29], particularly when they also lead to reduction of trade effluents, which are always charged for by volume. Conservation within premises could release local system capacity (or delay system extension), but this can only be relied upon if the peak flow rate of the industrial site is permanently reduced. Over larger areas the global effects of conservation measures on demand can be used with more confidence. Shifts in demand pattern could occur when an industrial user ceases trading, and the domestic fraction of industrial use (which can average 30 per cent of total demand[28]) is transferred with the newly unemployed to housing areas. Effects must be estimated locally. Trend forecasting for industrial use in areas of recent unemployment is of little value. Land use planning and local economic policy influencing industrial location can guide an assessment.

INDUSTRIAL LOCATION

The effects of changes in patterns of employment over the past twenty years vary locally and regionally. Several factors have overlapped but some broad trends have emerged in recent studies[30-34].

Industrial location in the period of rapid growth at the turn of the century tended to follow the distribution of coal, and population growth then followed the distribution of industry. After 1920, new industry concentrated in urban areas with the best transport facilities, particularly London and the West Midlands. The older infrastructure of the less prosperous regions has been retained over the past twenty years of continuing decline of primary industries, and the more recent decline of manufacturing industry.

A marked urban-rural shift in location of new manufacturing industries can now be observed, adding to population migration from urban areas due to lower density redevelopment. New growth has occurred at smaller centres, and also in peripheral regions. Eligibility for UK and European Regional Aid, and some regional growth of state industries, have slowed down the earlier decline of peripheral regions to the extent that the greatest fall in manufacturing employment over the past twenty years has been experienced in Greater London. Large companies have taken advantage of grant aid for location of production centres in the peripheral regions, whilst retaining headquarters and development units in the more accessible and attractive regions. The distribution of the electronics industry in the UK illustrates the new pattern; development units are located along the 'silicon valley' of the M4 motorway, and other attractive 'high-tech' areas of southern England (e.g. Cambridge), but many production centres are in Scotland.

New industries with large demands for water, and producing a lot of effluent are more likely to be located in the lower reaches of rivers and other situations where effluent disposal is simplified.

Areas ineligible for aid, whose prosperity depended upon manufacturing in the recent past, such as the West Midlands, could experience permanent decline in manufacturing demand for water. New high-technology industries are not generally heavy water users, even if they take root in these regions.

The agricultural policies of the European Economic Community (EEC) have had some impact on the irrigable crops of the UK. Cereals have replaced dairying activities in some areas (e.g. Hampshire), and beet production has been increasing (East Anglia). Because of the UK climate and the costs of obtaining suitable water, irrigation is only increased significantly during drought conditions, and tends to occur chiefly in the south east[31].

Waterlogging is more of a problem in the UK than drought, and irrigation requires good drainage, which depends upon local soil conditions. In general, vegetative crops require more irrigation, and it can be economic to design irrigation to obtain maximum yields when such crops are to be harvested. Calculations of irrigation requirements based upon potential evapotranspiration and soil moisture deficits can be made[31,35-40]. The same techniques have been used in calculation of garden watering requirements (see later). Calculation by the Penman method[35-38] has been questioned[41] in respect of over-irrigation, but the drier areas of the UK could usefully adapt the technique. Irrigation demand will also depend upon stability of agricultural pricing, influenced by the European Common Agricultural Policy.

DOMESTIC USE

Studies of water use disaggregated into components (Chapter 4) are useful, but at present, work has concentrated upon average demands[28,42,43]. Of more significance to system designers would be a study of peak demands, but published information is largely empirical (see later).

Table 4.3 (Chapter 4) confirms that the bulk of domestic use is volumetric in nature, bearing in mind that most miscellaneous use (40 per cent of the total) results from the filling of bowls of fixed dimensions. If domestic storage is small (see later for discussion), peak demands which occur on 'normal' days are produced by the propensity of consumers to use water at the same time. If the time taken to fill volumetric fixtures is small compared with the duration of peak demands, then peak flow reductions can only be achieved with smaller fixture volumes (see Section 4).

It is common for the largest peaks on distribution systems to be caused by 'discretionary' non-potable uses of water such as car-washing and garden watering. If fixture volumes are reduced in future, such 'open-tap' uses will assume even more importance in their effect on design capacity.

In all plumbing systems, at least one tap will be on direct mains feed for potable purposes. An acceptable flow rate for such taps (see Chapter 4 for CP 310 figures) can exceed the average demand of the property by a factor of 30. Simultaneous tap use in several properties could thus produce much higher peaks than presently occur. However, for larger groups of consumers, peak rates are much closer to the average, and hence it could be deduced that there is little likelihood of simultaneous use increasing. Average use apparently increases with the number of toilets (see Chapter 4), and hence may increase with the number of direct head taps. The effect of fully pressurised systems (see Chapters 2 and 3) on peak flow rates will require careful study.

Statistical methods have been used for design of service pipe capacities and consumer meters, and are incorporated in Codes of Practice and design guides[44-47] (see also Chapter 11). Similar US work has used much higher minimum flows for fittings[48,49], but they also use pressurised hot water systems.

In respect of 'open-tap' usage, most published information on peak flows comes from the US which experiences extremely high peaks in some areas[50], with up to 95 per cent of maximum hourly demand rate attributable to garden watering[51]. Predictive models of garden watering demands have been developed[51], based upon the potential evapotranspiration methods of agricultural irrigation (see earlier[35-41]). Although doubts have been expressed over the universal application of such models[52], they may have some relevance for calculation of ultimate demands for drier areas of the UK.

3. DESIGN PHILOSOPHY

The design process is the iterative analysis of a series of ideas intended to achieve predetermined standards, in a range of criteria chosen to be representative of the expected function of a final scheme. In respect of structural integrity and safety, such standards may properly be regarded as absolute, and factors of safety are used to guarantee that shortfalls in performance do not combine to violate standards.

In the UK water industry, statutory standards are open-ended, requiring the exercise of professional judgement to set quantitative targets for design. Substantial progress in refinement of the most appropriate standards can be expected during the next 10 years (see Chapter 4).

Financial resources for the maintenance of an ageing system may continue to be scarce in future, and so it is appropriate to question whether constancy of supply is a just or equitable statutory requirement[7] and whether installed capacity can be minimised by fiscal or physical controls (the carrot or the stick), before committing design to the ground. It would be unwise to assume that all current practices will continue to offer the best compromise between standards, value, and equitable treatment over the lifetime of new and renovated mains. The expected function of system capacity (supply of potable water) may be overtaken by non-potable domestic use.

Since so many of the parameters are inter-related, integrated design assumes the proportions of an infinite problem. Simplification is possible, using the numerical analysis technique of decomposition (parallel to partial differentiation and disaggregated demand forecasts). Judgement must be exercised to decide which parameters are best selected as fixed, when investigating relationships between the others. Iterative testing of the outcome of changes in parameters, usually termed sensitivity analysis, can be further refined by the application of probability distributions to the ranges of parameters assessed (risk analysis). This may not appear worthwhile at the level of mains' design, but with computing assistance, could become viable in the near future.

Designers should be aware of the records required to undertake this sort of analysis, and ensure that 'standard' designs are genuinely 'risk-free' decisions. At least, the weight attached to each parameter should be tested, including the apparent economic advantage of standard designs. ('Standard' design in this context implies that sizes are selected by policy, not as a result of detailed one-off analysis).

When expenditure is necessary on existing systems to support new developments or general growth in demand, the opportunity to re-appraise the balance between sources, storage and mains' sizes should be taken. Like-for-like replacements could financially prejudice improvements in system efficiency, particularly pressure optimisation. It is important to study the supply characteristics of existing systems, and to understand how they have developed, to guide the choice between simple extension and full revision (see Section 5).

It is not possible to produce an economic or financial justification for a design standard without being able to assess the cost of failure to meet it, and the likelihood of different margins of error. Objectives and 'failure' strategies have been proposed which balance resource expenditure against different levels of demand restraint[4,53-55] (see Chapter 4).

Most demand management studies have been motivated by a desire to restrain resource development, yet resource failure is infrequent in the UK. Except for areas of limited storage (such as South Wales and South-West England), most supply difficulties stem from an inability to satisfy peak demands on the distribution system, at consistent quality.

Some proportion of 'spare' capacity within supply systems is essential for practical reasons of construction of phased extensions. If the design capacity is used for such short durations that peak demand served has no effect on the annual demand, as is generally the case for summer peaks, then management of peaks may be economic, since it can defer system expansion. The highest peak to average demand ratios are experienced for small groups of consumers, and peaks become less pronounced, and more predictable, as larger numbers are served. The replacement cost of local supply mains generally much exceeds that of source and trunk works (see Section 5). Thus management of local peak demands potentially offers greater savings in system investment than demand management biased to resource savings.

At the end of an analysis, each system designer may arrive at a different decision, and some may confirm the validity of standard designs, or reject demand management, but confidence in the design will be enhanced.

4. DEMAND MANAGEMENT

VOLUNTARY CONTROLS

Voluntary controls on demand during resource deficit periods have been favoured in the UK up to the present. The drought experience of 1976 demonstrated that demand can be modified to match available resources, provided that there is public perception of scarcity. The concept of limited distribution capacity as a constraint on supply has yet to be understood and accepted by the UK public. (For US experience, see Refs. 56, 57). Response to appeals for restraint in garden watering when a hot summer follows a wet spring (such as in 1983) has been negligible, but this could also be attributable to the level of publicity exercised in the absence of resource deficit. Infra-red photography from helicopters or low-flying aircraft can now be used to monitor violations or restrictions, and major leakages, during drought conditions. (The gas supply authorities already 'fly' major gas main routes).

Early discussion of the relative merits of different conservation measures in 1953[58] suggested that publicity could save 17-28 per cent of total consumption, and this was borne out in 1976. The voluntary use of physical controls appears less successful. In one conservation exercise carried out in the UK three-quarters of consumers who opted for water metering (presumably on grounds of cost savings) did not fit a reduced-flush device supplied free with the meter[29]. The issue of conservation kits ('retro-fit' kits) has been tried in several areas of the US[57,59,60-63] and 3 to 10 per cent permanent savings have been reported (if fixed to new dwellings, 9 per cent was expected), which is similar to the UK response.

PHYSICAL CONTROLS

The emergency use of standpipes can result in savings of 50-80 per cent of average domestic demand[58] and peaks become almost non-existent, but their use is confined to resource deficits, or occasionally, penalties for violation of drought restrictions.

Reduction of Water Used in Toilet Flushing

Unless the rate of fill of volumetric fittings, including recharge of storage, can be dropped very close to the average domestic rate of demand, the proportions of peak demand attributable to such fittings (whatever these are—research is needed) can only be modified by reduction of volumes[64]. Reduction of toilet flushing, (the major component of domestic demand—see Chapter 4) which is essentially a non-potable use, is attractive, but should not proceed in isolation from the other elements of the engineered water cycle, often ignored in the design assumptions of functionally separated disciplines.

Public health is not necessarily enhanced by the flushing of large volumes of water for toilet cleaning, and dual-flush, variable flush, and low-volume alternatives to the customary British two-gallon flush have been developed[65-67] with forecast savings of 25, 40 and 10 per cent of average demand, respectively. Unfortunately, the addition of concentrated sterilising agents to flush volumes is common practice in the UK (with the assistance of implied standards of cleanliness in advertising), and is likely to continue. With low-volume flushing, it is possible that increased disinfectant loads on sewage works in dry weather could be detrimental to treatment processes. Although self-cleansing of sewers may not be affected[63,68,69] blockages could occur, and the 'first-flush' received at sewage works following rainfall could be of higher strength. It could cost more to relay sewerage systems at steeper gradients, and improve treatment methods for shock loadings, than to construct larger capacity water supply systems. US research has been proposed[63].

Advantages of Storage

The use of stored rainfall from roof drainage to supplement piped supplies has been studied[67] and it is estimated that ten thousand litres storage could meet one third of normal domestic demand (roughly equivalent to present toilet flushing). Because of the very high household peaks (30 times average) generated by the 'acceptable' flow to a single tap, peak flows in mains caused by simultaneous use of potable taps cannot be practically reduced[64]. However, greater volumes of storage could ensure that multiple use of fixtures within premises has a reduced peaking effect. The 'South of England' plumbing system has only one directly supplied tap, and is found to be more tolerant of low mains pressures and interruptions to supply. Storage would have to be large to balance out hosepipe peaks (more than 500 litres can be used in an evening's garden watering, and 200 litres for car washing[70]), and connection of hosepipes to direct supply would have to be prohibited and policed, for storage to be effective in peak management.

Throttling of Services

Deliberate throttling of services by the installation of small orifices has been tried successfully in the US to assist supplies in rural areas[71], though the flow rates were higher (30 litres/minute) than would be effective for the UK, and orifices were easily fitted to consumer meters. Design of orifices for head loss, reversing the usual design procedure[72] could produce larger openings for the same flows, or constant-flow devices could be used.

Self-throttling of supplies particularly through common service pipes and also through fittings is significant. Suppose that a 15 m hose is connected to a direct feed tap which is an equivalent length of 15 m in 12 mm bore, plus 10 metres in 19 mm pipe, away from a main carrying 30 m head of water. Assuming free discharge, the flow to the tap would be around 23 litres/minute (about double the CP 310 recommendation), and flow to the hose would be 16 litres/minute. Sprinklers would reduce this further. When 23 litres/minute is taken at the tap, 90 per cent of the total head loss occurs in the 15 m of 12 mm pipe. Stop-tap losses can be very high (ignored here).

Pressure Reduction

Pressure reduction in distribution mains is a cheaper alternative than throttling of services, and for the hosepipe example above, a drop in mains pressure by 10 per cent (3 m) would reduce flows by around 6 per cent. Clearly this would have no effect on volumetric uses, since fill times would extend, but fixed duration, open-tap consumption could be reduced. A study by East Bay Municipality, US suggested that a residual mains pressure of 10 m head on a 25 mm service would still satisfactorily supply a 19 mm hose[73]. Increases in service size, associated with demand management measures, might allow reduction of supply pressure.

FISCAL CONTROLS

Fiscal controls can operate on both peaks and throughput. Often it is more important to operate on peak or excess demand, than average throughput.

If consumers were charged according to orifice size, or peak flow rate, the system designer would have to establish the overall effect of the measures, since addition of allowable flows would produce peaks of more than 30 times the average. Allowing unrestricted use of a single tap for potable use, prohibiting hose connection to it (by tap design, perhaps) unless licensed, and throttling a separate branch to larger non-potable storage would be more practical. It would ensure that excess 'discretionary' use penalised the consumer rather than his neighbour, equivalent to the 'polluter pays' principle. Both metered and unmetered supplies in the Midlands of England and in Wales are already subject to a peak-capacity-related 'cover' or 'minimum' charge. Refinement for effective sizes below 15 mm is needed. Potable tap peaks are very likely to be lower than present peaks (particularly if water needed for toilet flushing were supplied from storage).

Hosepipe and Other Metering

The effect of hosepipe bans (subject to fines) is not well documented, and their use is biased towards resource deficiency. More information may be available in future from the South-West of England, where hosepipe metering has been tentatively introduced. A survey[74] in the US found only 10 per cent reduction in maximum daily demand from hosepipe metering, though it was recognised that further study was required. The same survey found that flow restricters and pressure reduction resulted in only 5 per cent savings, but, again, based upon maximum daily totals. Metering of services, whilst carrying the highest cost, was found to produce mean savings of 40 per cent of maximum daily demand. Since resource peak factors in arid regions of the US can exceed 15 to 1, this would not be repeated in the UK, and UK studies of the effect of metering on peak demands would be useful.

The throttling action of a correctly-sized meter is significant, since head losses of up to 3 m are possible at peak flows, which for the hosepipe example would produce 6 per cent savings in peak flow rate.

Operational control of a throttled system which does not rapidly register the occurrence of peak demands would be made more difficult, with more reliance on demand prediction.

Price Response of Domestic Demand

Price elasticity of industrial demand has been referred to in Chapter 4. Equivalent price response of domestic demand could be expected, though it has often been reported that water costs, and consumption, are too low in the UK to produce sufficient savings to recover the extra costs of meters, reading, extra billing, and installation. Several UK papers cover this topic[5,8,66,67,75-79]

Remote Metering and Meter Maintenance

Trials of more sophisticated metering arrangements, including remote interrogation of meters by telephone, are in progress in the UK at Milton Keynes, and at Kingswinford in the West Midlands. The case for telephone interrogation has been supported several times in the US[80-82] but UK field trials are necessary for the remote controls which could be applied by other utilities. A talking meter has now been developed in the US which 'nags' occupiers when their flow rate increases, using its 3 200 word vocabulary[83].

The physical arrangements of meters are described in Chapters 6 and 11. From the design point of view, it would be useful to record—and hence charge—service pipe leakage, but telephone interrogation will be better accomplished from within the premises with a common site for utility metering. Conflicting philosophies for maintenance or replacement of domestic meters have been equally successful in the US, with advocates of replacement of parts[84,85] and planned maintenance[86] each finding economic justification for the chosen policy. The latter course finds more favour in the UK[87] though some European countries have justified renewals[88].

Metering in Developing Countries

In developing and third world countries, lower incomes and scarcity of funds create the price elasticity which can justify metering[89] and rapidly growing consumption has been checked by its introduction[90]. However, it is essential to be sure that the local administration is sufficiently effective and free from undue pressure, to enable meter reading and charging to be reasonably accurate and reliable. The World Health Organization recommended metering in 1971[91], both as a control on use and to provide equitable charging. Unmetered water supply projects are not generally financed by the World Bank, which has sponsored the publication of a cost-benefit approach to metering which includes social factors such as the 'foregone benefit' of water not taken[92].

Metering in North America

Low prices for water in the US[93] prevent it acting as a constraint on industrial location or housing development[94], but low price allows little control over peaking. Large increases in cost of 45-70 per cent have permanently reduced arid area demands, but in temperate areas, the effect has been temporary[95]. In exceptionally dry areas (Colorado), demand from metered properties is 60 per cent lower than for unmetered properties. The most interesting description of the effect of metering comes from Canada where the 81 per cent unmetered city of Calgary in 1981 had demands 30-40 per cent higher than the fully metered—and in most respects similar—city of Edmonton, though unaccounted-for water was also believed to be high[96]. Metered residential demands in the two locations were identical, but of course much greater than in the UK.

Alternative tariffs have been tried in the US which reverse the usual utility bulk-discount tariffs, in that as total use exceeds a threshold, the whole of the water taken is charged at a higher unit rate to reflect the higher costs of pumping and system capacity. A decrease in demand of between 1 and 8 per cent has been recorded[97]. The impact on peak flow rates was not observed. Recovering the marginal cost of excess use in this way is a genuine alternative to controlling peak demands, provided that resources are cheap and plentiful. There is US evidence of public acceptance of such tariffs[57].

Charging Based on Local Cost

Demand management in the UK will probably have to combine recovery of costs with control, depending on access to resources. There appears to be no reason, with direct computer interrogation and billing, why separate charging based on local cost of supply could not be developed. The social consequences of such policies for remote areas would require political rather than engineering judgements.

5. SYSTEM CHARACTERISTICS

The figures used in this section are presented to illustrate the supply characteristics of a particular undertaking. Each supply unit will have its own characteristics and constraints which dictate least-cost design. It is to be expected that the optimum balance between pumping head and mains capacity will be different for each supply zone, because of these constraints. Appraisal techniques have advantages over standard designs for extensions to existing systems, since they can accommodate such variations.

Spatial Characteristics

Comparisons between water undertakings would require classification of different types of supply area, but some guidance can be obtained from published information[98]. Geographers will recognise that Fig. 5.1 has some similarities to the primate rank-size distribution of UK urban populations[99-101]. Other spatial parameters may be of use in adapting performance indicators, including the interaction between population and resource distribution. Population distribution is not uniform across water supply units; predominately rural areas will have greater lengths of main *per capita* than urban areas. The positions of individual units reflect the proportions of urban and rural supply within their boundaries. Population density is analogous to demand density, subject to local housing occupancy and water use information. If all undertakings have adopted similar nominal design standards, then regions with greater mains' length *per capita* might be expected to benefit more from pressure optimisation. It is interesting to note that the Bristol Avon Division of Wessex W.A. lies on the upper extreme of the

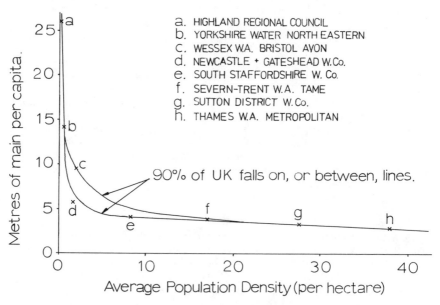

a. HIGHLAND REGIONAL COUNCIL
b. YORKSHIRE WATER NORTH EASTERN
c. WESSEX W.A. BRISTOL AVON
d. NEWCASTLE + GATESHEAD W.Co.
e. SOUTH STAFFORDSHIRE W. Co.
f. SEVERN-TRENT W.A. TAME
g. SUTTON DISTRICT W.Co.
h. THAMES W.A. METROPOLITAN

90% of UK falls on, or between, lines.

Fig. 5.1. Lengths of main per capita—UK water undertakings
Source: Water Services Handbook

envelope, and this is one of the supply units which has reported success with microprocessor-controlled pressure reduction valves, but factors of topography and source location also influence their application (see later).

HISTORIC CHARACTERISTICS

Fig. 5.2 illustrates the changes in lengths and sizes of mains laid since 1910 for a Midlands water company. From around 1920, it appears that it was decided to adopt 4-inch size in preference to 3-inch size for most local mains. About 80 per cent of total mains length has been 6-inch size or less throughout the seventy years

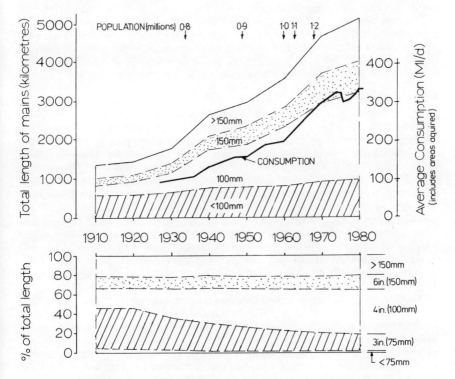

Fig. 5.2.   Development of a distribution system, 1910-1980
Source: South Staffordshire Waterworks Company

illustrated. The only proportionate capacity increase over this period has been the transfer from 3 to 4-inch size though some much larger trunk mains have been constructed since 1960 for a major new source. Under the same hydraulic gradient, the capacity of similar new mains can be related by:

$$\frac{Q_2}{Q_1} = \left(\frac{d_2}{d_1}\right)^{2.63} \qquad \text{(from Hazen-Williams equation)} \qquad (1)$$

where Q = flow and d = diameter

From this, 4-inch (100 mm) and 6-inch (150 mm) mains have respectively 2.13 and 6.2 times the capacity of a 3 inch (75 mm) main. Since peaking factors for design have appeared to stay in a fixed ratio to average demands, being affected only by climatic factors[70], it is initially surprising to observe that between 1930 and 1980 total demand has trebled, yet local capacity (6-inch and less) has not even doubled overall.

The answer to this apparent puzzle is that the system still has adequate capacity, for which consumers pay historic financing cost, because there has been plentiful head available to deliver more water. This is partly because of the separation of sources from demand by the watershed of the Severn and Trent catchments, and partly because of gravity flow flexibility decisions taken in the 1930s and maintained into the late 1950s. The designers could not have envisaged oil-based economies and the fuel crisis of the 1970s at the time, and so consumers are now suffering some penalty in higher pumping costs (revenue) which offsets the earlier capital advantage. For this company, design attention since the early 1970s has focused upon energy saving and general reductions in pumping heads.

FINANCIAL CHARACTERISTICS

The relative proportions of an undertaking's assets attributable to source works or mains will also depend upon the nature of the sources utilised (i.e. whether full or partial treatment is necessary). Undertakings with a high proportion of lowland abstraction and treatment might expect source investment to be around one-third to one-quarter of the value of mains[102]. For the water company illustrated in Figs. 5.1 and 5.2—which has a higher than average pumping lift, and a high proportion of borehole sources (55 per cent of average demand)—the current asset value of sources represents one-sixth of the value of mains. The historic asset value (unadjusted purchase price) is between 5 and 10 per cent of the (1982) replacement value of assets. Of this company's water charges, financing cost for assets represent less than 10 per cent, abstraction payments around 4 per cent, and pumping and treatment costs around 19 per cent. Electricity represents three-quarters of pumping and treatment costs. Costs for other undertakings could be much different.

Distribution mains are designed to accommodate much larger flow ranges than source and trunk works. If it could be assumed that financial constraints have forced undertakings to stretch their systems to their limit, then a decision to expand sources to meet unrestrained growth in demand implies system expansion too, which could (eventually) incur mains costs 3 to 6 times greater than the source expansion costs. Demand restructuring to reduce peak hour demands could allow resource expansion alone to meet higher off-peak demand by maximising use of existing system capacity. An all round appraisal of options is required (see Section 10).

6. QUALITY

Quality requirements have evolved in conjunction with research into essential constituents, and impurities, in treated water supplies. The development of more sophisticated measurement techniques and equipment has allowed standards to be set for a wider range of parameters, and international standards are more frequently being superimposed upon national ones. Chapter 4 details quality standards; the interaction of water quality with system materials and procedures for locating and dealing with problems are covered in Chapter 10. This section provides a brief description of quality parameters to consider, for design purposes. Although system events such as burst mains cannot be foreseen, the behaviour of the system when they occur is predictable, using network analysis. If all lengths of a pipework system are operating at an average velocity of 1 m/s, the water can travel around 86 km in a day, yet the average daily demand of one person can be stored in a 15 m length of 100 mm main (c.f. Fig. 5.1). A velocity of around 1 m/s ensures self cleansing of sewers, hence where lower velocities occur in water mains, it could be expected that heavier debris will accumulate, whether or not the slow moving sections are themselves corrosion-free. For this reason, dead legs and quiescent lengths (null-points in the system) should be eliminated as far as possible at the design stage. Burst mains and system operations can alter flow régimes and dislodge deposits.

Automatic quality monitoring within distribution systems is now developing, but not yet to the level of a fifteen parameter 1972 prototype[103]. Mathematical modelling of the effects of mains on quality[104] could guide selection of locations for automatic and manual sampling. The effectiveness of sampling routines[105-107] is enhanced by the separation of supply systems into single-route feeds of around 5 000 population, which do not coincide with usual waste meter district sizes (see Chapter 12). Direct hydrant sampling to represent distribution quality is preferred[106] since, for example, aged copper pipe has been observed to fully remove a chlorine residual of 1 mg/l in 2 hours[108]. A comprehensive description of distribution quality problems[109] and other technical[106] and critical summaries are available[4]. In particular, transfers from ground water supplies to surface water supplies should be treated cautiously. Flushing of mains[110] is helpful, but cannot cure problems related to initial quality, particularly those arising from transient blending within the system.

Corrosion and deposition can reduce the capacity of mains. Growth rates have been given by Lamont[11], who also advised reduction of the corrosive power of the source water, but caution in the use of the Langelier Index[1,106,111-113] to measure corrosive power. Recent work has identified sources of error[106,114]. Preventive measures[109,115] are discussed in Chapter 10. Treatment can aggravate some problems. Manganese can be precipitated by post-chlorination, if not removed in treatment[1], creating a higher chlorine demand, and perhaps permitting micro-biological agents to survive in deposits. Tuberculations can harbour anaerobic micro-organisms[106,109,116-120] as can some common materials (coal-tar to BS 4164: 1967 and flexible PVC tube, for example[121]). Air-scour techniques used for removal of deposits have been suggested[122] for removal of macroorganisms such as Asellus, as an alternative to treatment with pyrethrum[123] or synthetic pyrethroids[124,125].

Taste Complaints

It has been reported that up to 50 per cent of consumer quality complaints relate to taste[121]. Human taste sensations are sharpest if substances are at body temperature. Some individuals are more sensitive than others, and tasting panels have been proposed[126]. 'Musty' tastes can be removed with slow sand filters[1], which can still be economic in some locations[127]. Alternatives are activated carbon and ozone, generally regarded as expensive[128], to the extent that pre-chlorination has been used to reduce ozone demand[129]. Chloramine reactions can offset chlorine taste problems[1,109] but larger contact tanks are necessary. Chlorine dioxide can combat phenolic (medicinal) tastes, but system residuals may not be persistent[130].

Ozone also suffers this disadvantage[1] and is less effective for high turbidity, manganese, and iron[131]. Chlorination following ozonisation can produce more haloforms than chlorine itself[132,133], hence blending of differently disinfected water could cause problems. Ozone costs are forecast to fall with new production techniques[132,134].

Medical Problems

Hypothesised links between some medical conditions and water quality have been tested, with full water industry co-operation, but causal relationships have not been established. Some correlations which can be demonstrated are modified by other parameters. From time to time, health 'scares' occur which can bring about immediate tightening of standards, and it is prudent to allow for more rigorous standards when carrying out scheme appraisals, since a finite risk of loss of source capacity exists. Examples of UK 'scares' are Legionella, dialysis encephalopathy[135,136] (from high aluminium residuals) and toxic haemolytic uremic syndrome. In the US the Environmental Protection Agency proposed inclusion of a total ban on asbestos pipes in the Toxic Substances Control Act (due July 1984)[137], despite absence of hard evidence[138], and in the UK asbestos hazards from asbestos cement mains have been implied on Breakfast Television (Dec. 1983). Removal of natural asbestos from source waters has proved difficult in the US[139].

The most frequently researched health risks have been cardiovascular disease (CVD), blood pressure, blood-lead concentrations, and perinatal deaths. The presence of magnesium is thought to lower CVD mortality, and the presence of calcium reduces lead, cadmium and zinc absorption[140]. Softening of water has been alleged to lift CVD mortality rapidly[140] but the location cited (Scunthorpe) still had water hardness higher than some naturally soft waters[141,142] and other socio-economic factors apply. Statistics are further confused since some softening processes result in increased sodium levels[108] known to be linked to high blood pressure[140,143]. Also, foods cooked in soft water taste less strongly and there is a tendency to add more salt, in turn perhaps offset by the addition of magnesium to table-salt for 'free running'. Sodium has also been linked to cot deaths, in conjunction with the higher sodium levels of cow's milk, suggesting increased fluid loss as a mechanism[144]. Risks to infants from high nitrates have been recognised for a longer period[1].

Plumbosolvency is well understood[1] and can be corrected by pH balancing of source waters[145]. Contamination of sources with traces of heavy metals or radioactive substances will probably result in removal from supply, although some methods of treatment for radioactive substances have been partially successful[1,146]. The World Health Organization has revised its standards, and extended its range of parameters, several times in the past twenty years, and the EC has been following the same pattern. Designers should check compliance of sources with current standards before circumscribing continued use with system design.

7. DESIGN FRAMEWORK

A compromise is required between two extreme design philosophies: unrestricted demand or managed demand within the installed capacity of the system. A model of the first would have to predict consumer behaviour in peak periods when no resource deficit exists, and the second would have to predict the willingness of consumers to economise on water use in response to some combination of voluntary, physical, or fiscal controls[57].

Demand management measures can only be taken into account in so far as they represent physical, or predictable tariff-based controls over future peaks. While rateable value continues to levy consumers in rough proportion to their water use[5] and capacity is available at reasonable cost, then it would be difficult to justify such measures. If standard system capacity 'runs out' in the near future then pressures must be increased at peak periods, or wholesale reconstruction undertaken. Any element of option which is available to the consumer, such as whether or not to continue with an 'option meter' on taking up residence in a property[147], or freedom to install domestic storage, must be discounted at present. If a case for changes in byelaws and adoption of metering can be justified on improved value-for-money for the consumer, then the designer must decide how far in the future these measures can be implemented. The latest model byelaws (1984) for example, allow fully pressurised systems which could limit opportunities for flow-rate charging and control. Further revision may not be practicable before 1990.

It is customary to segregate distribution mains from trunk mains at some selected diameter between 200 and 400 mm, and it is common to find standard designs below the threshold, and one-off designs above. Standard designs may prove cost effective in terms of simplification of both design and operation, repair and renewal, in dense urban areas with similar street layouts. In rural areas, or infill development, an arbitrary threshold based on diameter could result in substantially the same expenditure being made on an inefficient system. One division between distribution and trunk mains which could still be valid relates to statutory definitions (see Chapters 2 and 4).

The choice which must be made before local sizing is considered is whether to have minimum 'trunk' mains losses and make local systems 'work' harder, or minimal local losses, and make 'trunk' mains work harder. In practice (since systems develop over many years) a mix of the two extremes occurs but, because of the longer timespan for future demand provision and the addition of links to form loops, the local losses are minimised in the first instance.

Design for least installed cost would be expected to allow greater head loss in local mains to reduce sizes, and recover head in the more cost-efficient larger sizes, where capacity can follow demand more closely because demand is more predictable when larger areas are served.

Larger sizes of some local mains are still funded from private sources (subject to revenue guarantee agreements, for example—see Chapter 2), and so there is no apparent impact on water charges until repair or renovation becomes necessary. If an undertaking's performance is measured on throughput against asset values, high local capacity is an advantage. With relatively large local mains, there has been no incentive to determine the magnitude of local peaks, or the reasons behind them.

PRESSURE AND LEAKAGE

There is no reason why high pressure mains, properly constructed and maintained, should be any less efficient than low pressure mains[148]. Excess pressure can be turned to advantage as spare hydraulic capacity, and design for daily use of any spare capacity to improve levels of service and security, or to make savings in operating costs, may assist arguments for early expansion of main sizes.

The relationship between pressure and leakage could be assumed to be equivalent to the orifice flow equation with only small changes in flow for large changes in pressure, as pressures increase. Some recent energy-saving papers have included this assumption[149]. More recent work has demonstrated empirically that the reverse is true[150]. The results of a study of burst records (over five years) for typical areas of a Midlands water company reflect the latter form in a similar relation between pressure and burst frequency (Fig. 5.3). This relationship is not believed to be causal.

Pressure surge is discussed in Chapter 7, but designers of PVC mains might also find of use two papers on the development of standards for this material[151,152]. Several papers detail analysis of pressure transients, design for rate of valve closure and so on, and include computer programs[153-157].

Since leakage is known to diminish with a fall in system pressures, the assumption that it forms a constant proportion of average demand is inaccurate. Also, since it is generally assessed at times when system pressures are at their highest, its value could be overestimated. Automatic pressure control is discussed later.

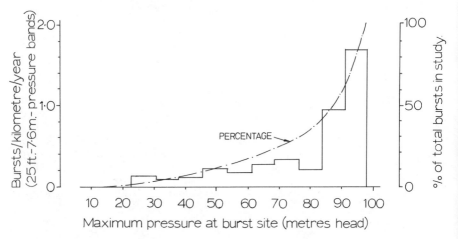

Fig. 5.3.   Relationship between mains pressure and bursts
Source: South Staffordshire Waterworks Company

The Use of Network Analysis

Procedures for network analysis are described in Chapter 6, with optimal solutions being obtained from trials of possible improvements, and the application of simple cost models.

First attempts to design optimal layouts directly from demand information with a computer appear to have been made in Japan in the early 1960s[158]. Least-cost branched networks were designed using standard pipe sizes, resulting in cost savings of up to 20 per cent.

Other methods for optimal design of networks have incorporated a simple tree structure for purposes of solution. References are suggested at the end of this Chapter for those engineers who may wish to follow the mathematical development of the most recent programs[159-172], including that of the Water Research Centre (WRC). Further references are suggested for techniques of optimal design using more complex methods of analysis, including non-linear optimisation models[173-184]. Many other papers can be found in the ASCE journals, and further UK references follow Chapter 6.

The use of standard network analysis programs can lead to some misinterpretation of the location of hydraulic losses. The errors in application of the results arise from the continuity assumptions necessary for convergence of computation, as against the real variation in flow factors through the system.

If a full system is being modelled there is a temptation to factor demand characteristics up or down, or to change roughness values, to recreate the real total head loss to a given node. Even where roughness values have been determined from field tests, errors will arise from the application of uniform peaking factors to ensure flow continuity. Peaking factors vary through the system, based on the area served. Hence it is nonsense to assume that the hydraulic gradients obtained from analysis with a uniform peak factor can be correct anywhere but on a single short length of main, where the modelled flow happens to coincide with the real flow. The mathematically inclined might seek to use Monte Carlo simulation to allocate local peak flows, but most peak demand behaviour is non-random, being conditioned by social and climatic factors.

The collection of local supply systems onto single route feeds can assist modelling of otherwise ill-conditioned networks, since they can be separately modelled at higher peaks. Inclusion of isolated small areas on trunk models, to model indicator node pressures, might overcome the difficulty of full analysis at uniform peaking factors.

DESIGN FLOWS

The prediction or forecasting of demands will be more fully detailed in the forthcoming IWES Water Resources Manual. A designer should be aware of any pitfalls there may be in the validity of forecasting data. Spectral analysis[185] and time series methods[186] have been proposed for forecasting of residential demand, but water use studies are required[43] for any disaggregated approach.

Recent UK demand experience has made forecasting future demands more complex. The drought year of 1976 has been followed closely by two years with dry, hot summers which can be described from the demand response viewpoint as less than once in fifty year events, in 1980 and 1983. A demand model is required which can explain such responses, but this would not be relevant for the design of local mains.

Sizing of local mains could be based on the probability methods of plumbing services design[44,64] (see Section 2), but this would require fairly detailed studies of demand behaviour. It is also possible to look at local sizing on the basis of practical limits on demand and head loss. In many respects the potential demand of older, smaller properties is finite. Population growth has stabilised over the past few years, but household formation has continued, resulting in lower occupancy ratios, falling to levels around 2.7 persons per household. Together with lower density redevelopment, this has resulted in net out-migration from urban areas, aggravated by urban industrial decline (see Section 2). The increase in average *per capita* consumption has generally offset the effect on demand of the decline in urban population, but some forecasts project saturation of ownership of water-using devices in the near future, and stabilising demand. Insufficient information is available to predict saturation levels at the moment.

With this uncertainty, it is usual to find sizing based upon ratios of average demand, as for network analysis. The simplest form of calculation is to add maximum estimated metered demand to the product of a peaking factor, estimated population, and the average *per capita* unmetered demand. The peaking factors used will depend on whether or not leakage is subtracted from unmetered totals, but should reflect the demand characteristics of the area, with an allowance for future demands (see Chapter 4 and Section 2 of this chapter).

Some standard peaking factors have been produced over the years, ranging (for local distribution mains) from three times average demand in 1905[187], which was based on an average total *per capita* demand in manufacturing areas of 115 litres/h/d, to a higher factor of up to six times winter demand quoted in 1979[70]. It has also been observed[70] that the ratios of peak week, peak day and peak hour to average (or winter) demands have not changed as *per capita* unmetered demand has risen.

Use of peaking factors greatly simplifies local design. Detailed design could commence at a point where intermediate sized mains are required, and peak factors or observed flow rates are more reliable, or can be determined from published design recommendations[1,188].

Care is needed in interpretation of what 'average' demand is. Pressure reductions can reduce local demands, hence peak factors are only universally valid if all areas receive broadly the same pressure, and leakage is uniform. It is not clear whether any of the elements of demand which make up peak hour flows replace other uses. The proportion of summer peak demands attributable to garden watering is not known.

There is no definition of what peak factor design is intended to include. The future adoption of failure standards will require a more accurate knowledge of how and why peaks occur. It is difficult to reconcile deferred source expansion at the expense of demand restrictions, with the provision of distribution capacity to meet unrestricted future demands. There is no reason why distribution system capacity should exceed consumer requirements by any greater margin than resource system capacity. Nevertheless, it is probable that supplies to older property will 'fail' before those to new properties, because existing system capacities are less favourable. Control at household level will ensure equitable treatment.

Provision for Fire Fighting

Water for fire fighting is free of charge in the UK, but there is no statutory duty to provide any particular head or capacity for firefighting. Fire authorities pay for the provision and maintenance of public fire hydrants.

Design of mains in the US has often been for firefighting requirements, with investment charged to consumers as hydrant rental[189], since fire protection accounted for up to 75 per cent of the installation costs. Fire flow rates[190] are based on the Insurance Services Office[150] recommendations, and storage requirements[191] on the 10 hours fire demands of the American Insurance Association. Either fire flow or potable supply could be taken as the basic installation cost, and the other as marginal use, or allocation of costs between functions could be according to design flows.

A survey in the US[192] concluded that potable use was the primary cost, which is equivalent to UK practice. In the UK the definition was unimportant pre-1974, when water supply was frequently the responsibility of the same Local Authority as the Fire Service, and there was little point in moving funds around a common purse. It is possible, with 'managed' peak demands in future, that fire flows could become critical for design of capacity.

FREQUENCY OF DESIGN EVENTS

There are some problems of interpretation when considering probabilities such as the dry spells of 1980 and 1983, following so closely after the 1976 drought. If a failure standard is adopted, then it should be applied even if three years in a row qualify. If the tests applied are valid for these years, the standards remain valid, even though consumer reaction may occur.

The issue raised by this is independence, not randomness. If all of the observed factors which explain a peak even are in effect 'reset' after it, then it is subsequently no more or less likely to occur than it was before. Since this is generally true of annual variations in climate, the chances of a one in fifty year dry spell next year are still one in fifty, even if one happened this year, and the year before, provided that the test was based on sufficient trials (years) in the first place. It is usually assumed that each year is independent of the next, though longer-term climatic cycles are believed to exist. Consequently any climate-related water activity whose magnitude can be related directly to the climatic factors analysed will follow the same pattern. Provided that a potential response to climate from (say) increased hosepipe ownership could be assessed, a ceiling would be placed on future total demands for years within the failure criterion.

The danger to avoid is in combining rare events which should really be independent of one another, and consequently whose coincidence is rarer still. Also some events will be mutually exclusive—for example, garden watering would not normally be combined with car washing unless more than one hosepipe is owned. If two independent events have the same probability of one in fifty, then the chance of their simultaneous occurrence is one in two thousand five hundred, if the events are of similar duration.

What is more important to assess for such rare coincidences is the cost of failure. If this were merely curtailment of unreasonable demand, then perhaps it would be no bad thing. If it were a failure of standby plant already in use, leading to total loss of supply for long periods, then perhaps it would not be acceptable. If it only occurred once in a hundred years, and all other risks to supply were even smaller, then perhaps it should be allowed in the interests of economy.

It is not very efficient to construct mains which may only be used over 90 per cent of capacity for well under 5 per cent of the time (see Fig. 5.4). Fortunately on the wider scale there is considerable scope for energy savings from daily use of spare capacity. Bulk transfer systems and emergency transfer capacity would be more cost-effective if similar arrangements could be made for daily use (see later for energy-saving design).

Design for Head Loss or Velocity

Design limits on hydraulic gradient or velocity result in different pipe sizes for flow increments. Using Hazen-Williams equation:

$$\text{from Section 5,} \quad \frac{Q_2}{Q_1} = \left(\frac{d_2}{d_1} \right)^{2.63} \quad \text{subject to} \quad \frac{H}{L} \text{ constant} \tag{1}$$

$$\text{also} \quad \frac{Q_2}{Q_1} = \left(\frac{d_2}{d_1} \right)^{2} \quad \text{subject to} \quad V \text{ constant} \tag{2}$$

The hydraulic gradient constraint is more flow-efficient, and the velocity constraint is more head-loss efficient with respect to a given increase in design flow. Larger mains are in general flow-efficient, and construction cost-efficient with respect to flow.

Extensions to capacity to meet increased flows will be required earlier if the test applied is allowable velocity (to avoid disturbance of deposits, for example), rather than head loss (to maintain pressures). The use of both tests is to be preferred.

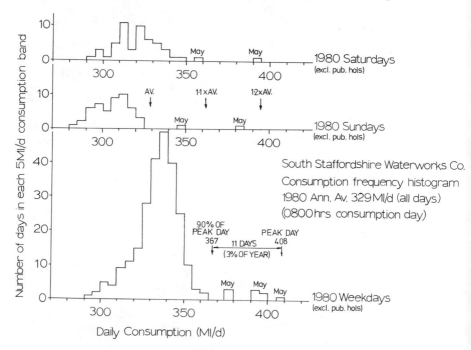

Fig. 5.4 Consumption frequency histogram

Source: South Staffordshire Waterworks Company

ELECTRICITY TARIFFS

Social habits with respect to electricity usage are unlikely to alter in the future unless there is widespread use of private generation, and so, in general, night consumption of electricity can be made at less than half of the unit cost of daytime use, for periods of 6-8 hours (at present, 7). A typical high voltage units tariff is shown in Fig. 5.5 (see also Chapter 7).

Additional charges based on maximum power requirements are usually levied, and for constant output sources could represent 10 per cent of annual electricity costs, with around two-thirds of this being payable for the period November to March, and highest costs being December to February (inclusive months between meter readings).

The power input for pumping water can be simply expressed in metric units as:

$$\text{Water power} = Q \cdot \frac{10^3}{3600.24} \cdot \varrho.(H+h). \frac{1}{\eta_m \, \eta_p \, f} \text{ kW} \qquad (3)$$

$$(1 \text{ kW} = 1 \text{ kNm/sec})$$

where:

Q is pump flow Ml/day (converted to m^3/s by $\left(\dfrac{10^3}{3600.24} \right)$)

ϱ is water mass (9.81 kN/m^3)
H is static lift in metres
h is system pressure loss in metres head

η_m is motor efficiency ⎫
η_p is pump efficiency ⎬ can be combined as station efficiency where
f is power factor ⎭ there is more than one pump

Hence, collecting constants and expressing static and dynamic power requirements separately:

$$\text{Static power} = 0.1135 . Q . H . \frac{1}{\eta_m \, \eta_p \, f} \text{ kW} \qquad (4)$$

(independent of diameter of pumping main)

and, substituting for h from Hazen-Williams equation:

$$\text{Dynamic power} = 0.315 . Q^{2.85} . \frac{L}{d^{4.87} . C^{1.85}} \cdot \frac{1}{\eta_m \, \eta_p \, f} \text{ kW} \qquad (5)$$

where:
Q, H, h, η_m, η_p and f are as before
L is pipe length in kilometres
d is pipe diameter in metres
C is Hazen-Williams roughness value.

The daily units used per megalitre of output can be obtained by multiplying the last two expressions by $^{24}/Q$. For existing plant, curves of units per megalitre against output are sometimes obtained from test running, to be used as an indication of least cost per unit of output and a measure on continuing performance. It is necessary to be cautious here, since deterioration of the pumping main, or the partial closing of valves (such as a reflux valve jamming), will also increase the power requirement. Flow measurement accuracy is also of importance. The tariff structures are easily incorporated in pump-scheduling programs with reservoir operating constraints[194].

Larger users of electricity may be able to negotiate special tariffs, such as load-shedding arrangements, which could offer cost advantages.

8. SIZING OF SMALL MAINS

Whatever methods are used to determine the 'normal' flow in a given local main, its size can only be selected from a very limited range with large increments of capacity (See Section 5).

There is a good deal of 'might as well' economics associated with local mains design, since it is possible to lay a 100 mm diameter main for only a small extra expenditure over a 75 mm main. With the same available head, the capacity is more than doubled. If greater capacity costs little more, it would usually be economically justified to argue that larger capacity should be installed, since no hydraulic problems have been attributed to excess capacity.

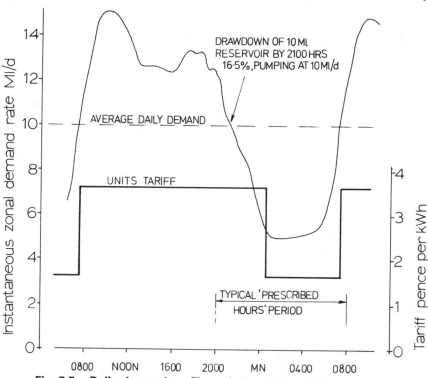

Fig. 5.5. Daily demand profile and electricity tariff arrangements
(for notional 10 Ml/day supply zone)

However, if 'standard' design sizes as large as 150 mm diameter are to be considered, then the effect on the quality of water supplied becomes paramount as a design constraint. For systems with low retention times, that is with short lengths of mains per consumer (as for Thames Metropolitan area—see Fig. 5.1) or very high *per capita* consumptions, such as for large modern high-value houses, then these problems may not arise. However, for an average undertaking the 'age' of water received could be increased by up to half a day if 150 mm diameter were used, instead of 100 mm diameter. Designing and analysing local systems only for peak flow rates will overlook this problem. Small mains may also cause problems, since deposits could be disturbed by higher velocities. A good case could be made for the manufacture of a size intermediate between 100 mm and 150 mm diameter, taking advantage of the techniques used for the manufacture of modern plastic materials.

If head loss is critical, then housing layout is of major importance to main sizing. The greater the distance between cross-connections, the larger are the necessary main sizes to provide alternative supplies in the event of failure of the primary route. The number of valves available to limit the numbers of properties involved in shut-offs is also important. Logically, the more valves, the smaller the main sizes, but policy on valve locations (usually at junctions) tends to dictate numbers of valves for modern housing layouts. (See later for discussion of fittings).

For minimum installation costs, design results in a dendritic (tree-shaped) structure, if single-route feeds are available. The use of spare distribution capacity for transfer to assist other areas is limited to off-peak periods, and the number of supplies affected by mains failure could be very large. The lower installation cost is partly offset by higher running costs, and quality problems could arise from a greater number of dead legs (assuming minimum-sized links in the alternative looped system).

Non-loop systems are necessarily used in some circumstances, such as in rural areas, and optimal design will then approximate to those for pumping main designs[1,149,194-199]. Some simplified manual methods specifically for rural areas have been developed[71,200,201] and also for network analysis[202].

Trends in housing layouts, such as the Radburn vehicle/pedestrian separations, have also had a major influence on local design. Pedestrian walkways which link dead ends are not always adopted by Highway Authorities (see Chapters 2 and 9). The installation of common services from mains laid in distributor roads, has caused problems with definitions of ownership when maintenance has been required. The provision of consumer meters will be more difficult with such arrangements unless installation is internal to the property.

Council housing sales were not envisaged when common services were being installed in the post-war estates, and low first cost was the prime consideration. Common services are now best avoided, and existing ones are being replaced with separate services by many undertakers as the opportunity arises.

Normal standards of minimum pressure in distribution mains (see Chapter 4) may not meet the peak demands on common services, and the cost to the supplier of preserving higher pressures, to get over the problem, could be considerable.

CAPACITY OF LOCAL MAINS

The example which follows illustrates the capacity which is available to individual consumers from distribution mains, rather than representing a realistic design procedure. Similar calculation methods[203] could be useful for checking pressure losses during peak demand periods.

Assume that a cul-de-sac, served by a 100 mm main (Hazen-Williams C-value 100) at 30 m pressure, has houses on both sides with 6 m frontages. In general, the head loss from the end of the cul-de-sac (ignoring fittings losses) can be summated as:

$$H_n = KD^{1.85} \sum_{r=1}^{n} r^{1.85} \qquad (6)$$

(from Hazen-Williams equation)

D   = demand of 2 houses
n   = number of house pairs
H_n total head loss after n pairs of houses
K   = constant including diameter, C-value, frontage, and conversion factor for units.

The head losses along the cul-de-sac resulting from simultaneous demands of 16 litres/minute at each property are given in Table 5.I (this is the hosepipe flow from

TABLE 5.I.   Sequential Head Losses in Cul-de-sac

Number of houses	Distance from end of road	Total head loss	Largest hydraulic gradient
	m	m	m/1000 m
2	6	0.0008	0.14
20	60	0.237	9.8
40	120	1.59	35.3
60	180	4.95	74.8

Section 4). The assumption that 30 m head would be maintained fails after 40 houses are passed, and if 60 houses completed the cul-de-sac, the hosepipe flows at the closed end of the road would be around 10 per cent lower (because of the 5 m loss from the main road). The velocity in the main outside the sixtieth house is just over 2 m/s.

Simultaneous use of 16 litres/minute represents a demand of 50 times average, even if it is assumed that typical leakage is occurring exclusively on the consumers' apparatus. The head losses in a 75 mm main would be four times greater, and for a 150 mm main would be seven times smaller than for a 100 mm main. An improvement in C-value to 120 would recover 40 per cent of the head losses. It would appear that a 75 mm main is adequate for peaking factors of 50 on groups of 40 houses, provided losses of 6 m head can be tolerated. A 100 mm main normally fed from both ends with 30 m pressure could be more than 360 m long (120 houses, 320 population) without head losses exceeding 5 m at the halfway point for 50 to 1 peak flows. Adams[188] suggested a peak hour factor of around 3 for this size of area.

The addition of a 160 litres/minute throughput (equivalent to average demand, with leakage, of 1200 population) would increase the head loss for 40 houses from 1.59 to 3 m at 50 to 1 peak demand. (This flow could alternatively be regarded as the output of a single fire hydrant).

It would take 6 minutes for water to reach the end of the cul-de-sac from the sixtieth house at 50 to 1 factor without throughput, and at average demand, 5 hours. If the frontages were around 11 m (representing the average length of main, 100 mm and less, installed in an average undertaking—see Figs. 5.1 and 5.2) then the local time of travel, and local losses, would nearly double. Under these circumstances, if a 150 mm main was used, the age of water just from the end of the road (300 m away) would be 30 hours.

An alternative method of assessment is to determine the number of properties which can be served beyond a given point in the system. For example, if peak velocity were limited to 1 m/s (low for large mains), a 100 mm main (C = 120) could meet 7 times average demand for a population of 600 without exceeding 15/1000 hydraulic gradient.

9. LARGER MAINS, SOURCES AND STORAGE

SYSTEM LAYOUT

Practical design should attempt to develop a viable range of options for appraisal which, subject to real constraints, as nearly as possible conform with the following common sense principles:

(1) Service reservoirs should be as near to demand centres as possible. In the event of source failure, depending on source location, the whole of peak demand is applied to the reservoir outlet mains. Consequently the shorter they are, the better, for both cost and head loss reasons.

(2) Sources which are hydraulically closer to demand centres are cheaper than those at a distance, subject to relative costs of acquisition.

(3) There will be an economic balance between main sizes, and pumping or repumping requirements, depending on the shape and topography of the supply area, and electricity tariff.

(4) Provision of standby capacity which is used frequently is a more efficient use of funds. Inter-zonal water transfers can be more economic than self-sufficient zonal standby.

(5) Pressures made available by the distribution system should be as low as possible consistent with defined levels of service (which will include emergency arrangements and economic provision for future demands). Direct supply at minimum pressure is preferable to pressure reduction.

Any number of corollaries could be expressed. Study of simplified systems is useful for generating ideas on layout[204] before 'leaping into computer optimisation'[205].

Service reservoirs balance daily and seasonal fluctuations in demand, and provide security of supply against failure of trunk mains[1]. Storage requirements for tariff advantage pumping could be added to the list, but may not result in an increased volume (see later).

Considerable dilution is available at the service reservoir in the event of quality failure, and blending of waters away from the distribution system could avoid sloughing-off of deposits which might otherwise occur, with changes of distribution quality (see Section 6). Source waters must pass through the service reservoir or blend in 'trunk' mains before going into supply to satisfy this condition, and this arrangement is assumed in standard texts[1].

There are many circumstances where it is more economic to pump through supply areas towards service reservoirs, and least-cost design will depend on the relative locations of sources, reservoirs, and demand centres. The risks to supply from quality failure continue to diminish with improved quality-monitoring automation, and this should not be overlooked when planning system extensions. Continuous throughput of fresh water is desirable to prevent reservoir stagnation, consequently inlet and outlet arrangements must be separated to prevent refluxing of old water, where consumers are situated between sources and the reservoir.

Reservoir outlet mains must be designed to meet all demands in the event of source failures. Duplication is an advantage for security and maintenance reasons, but is costly, and preserves higher than optimum system pressures, because of reduced head loss. Reservoir inlet mains need only be designed for maximum source pumping.

The pressure 'seen' by the source station when pumping through demand areas to storage is lower during the day because of head losses from reservoir outflows, and higher at night during re-filling, in the cheapest tariff period. The system characteristic is much closer to that of a fixed speed pump (see Chapter 7), except that higher output during the daytime is the reverse of the expected tariff advantage pumping regime. It is possible to combine a base output fixed-speed pump with a variable 'top-up' pump to match the system curve, as well as running at lower daytime output, and retaining flexibility for continuous pumping at high rate during high demand periods. The viability of such arrangements will depend on local conditions.

SERVICE RESERVOIR SIZING

The reservoir must be sited at least that distance above the highest property served equal to the minimum level of service envisaged (say 15 m), plus an allowance for head losses in mains under normal peak operating conditions. The shape of the reservoir for construction economies largely governs the available depth[1,206] above this minimum level. A survey of storage volumes in use is possible from published data[98] but the range is so great (1-4 days' average demand) that no conclusions can be drawn.

The demand-balancing element of storage can easily be determined as the area of the design demand graph (see Fig. 5.5) which lies above a line representing source input.

Security Storage in Service Reservoirs

The provision of security storage (against burst mains, source failure, or pump failure) is notionally based upon the time taken to restore the system to normal operation, such as (say) 12 hours at average demand[1]. Provisions for exceptional fire demands have dictated security sizing in the US[191] and early recommendations for UK sizing also included fire protection[187,207].

Clearly the provision of pump standby and security storage are to an extent mutually exclusive, with the extreme condition of no storage at all when automatic diesel start up on pump failure is installed (see Chapter 7). The availability of pump or reservoir capacity in adjacent zones should also be taken into account since some risks can be shared, and thereby diminished. There will still be some potential regional catastrophes which ought to be considered, such as the widespread loss of power lines, but it would be a misuse of probability to assume that all risks were coincident.

If failures took 24 hours to repair, then all times of day would be equally secure, whatever volume of security storage was adopted. However, if shorter horizons are sufficient for most frequent repairs, then times of greatest security can be derived. Using the example of Fig. 5.5 and a 12-hour repair period, Table 5.II reveals that the service reservoir is most vulnerable just as it is full, since the quickest drawdown follows it immediately.

Hence repair efforts would be concentrated on trying to complete repairs before the morning peak if storage had been minimised. Outside frost or high demand periods (i.e. 90 per cent of the time) water transfers, preferably by gravity, would be the cheapest design option.

TABLE 5.II. Relative Security of Supply from Service
Reservoirs

Time	1. Storage at beginning of period (Ml)	2. Succeeding 12 hour demand (Ml)	Security Ratio 1 ÷ 2
0800	10	6.5	1.54
2000	8.5	3.5	2.43

SOURCES

Design of resource provision for daily peak periods is simplified to some degree by the balancing effect of service reservoirs, and only general trends in gross use need to be considered for year-to-year forecasting (see forthcoming IWES Water Resources Manual).

Some resource expenditure could be saved by more flexible use of sources to meet peak demands from short-duration increases in output in non-drought years. The progressive development of small-scale sources (usually groundwater) has been recognised [5,208] as being more flexible economically.

If sources can sustain short periods of continuous operation at the higher output by 'resting' for other periods, then gross source output need only be designed for average demand (plus some margin for growth). Some savings in deferral of capital expenditure will result.

Direct abstraction not undertaken when sources are plentiful may be lost. Conjunctive use of borehole and river sources relies upon maximum uses of rivers/impounding schemes in wet periods, in order to 'rest' groundwater sources for use in dry periods. The subject of conjunctive use will feature in the IWES Water Resources Manual but some points are relevant here.

For boreholes, yield determinations have been understood as maximum continuous output. For flexible economic use of sources, far more information is required on aquifer behaviour, since yields higher than the algebraic sum of source output can be demonstrated. Various US examples of regional resource development have been published[209-211] and UK work has proceeded in parallel for groundwater specifically[212-218] and conjunctive use in general[219-225]. Groundwater recharge schemes to safeguard existing abstractions, and to provide water for stabilising river flows, could make use of the techniques developed overseas[225-229].

Determination of the availability of additional groundwater requires extensive exploratory work, including the construction of test bores and observation boreholes, using standard procedures[229-232]. Some preliminary quality information can be obtained[233], and methods of operation and treatment can be developed to overcome quality problems[234-238].

Use of multiple boreholes can add to the flexibility of output for short periods (subject to aquifer conditions) without costs increasing because of drawdown (i.e. higher 'static' lift). Inclined wells have also been claimed to produce higher yields, but some interaction is inevitable[239-241]. Flexible use of groundwater has been tried successfully in West Germany[242].

The flexibility of upland impounding reservoirs, or river abstractions balanced by storage, is more obvious. Availability of higher rates of output will commonly be due to the early construction of works to accommodate future demands, on the basis of economies of scale. The use of spare capacity for tariff-advantage pumping can generate large savings of operating expenditure, which although diminishing as capacity is absorbed by demand, could be utilised. Depending upon land available for future work, bankside storage may have been constructed for ultimate station output. Where abstraction pumping is necessary, night pumping could be maximised, using any excess of capacity above the recommended minimum[243].

Where full treatment is necessary, individual treatment units could be limiting the overall capacity, particularly when a works has been extended in stages over a long period. Certain designs of settlement tanks are capable of more rapid adjustment of dosing and throughput than others, and may be preferred if flexibility is to be designed-in[244,245]. Few, if any, full treatment works could tolerate very large sudden increases in output. Staged increases (as additional output pumps are brought into use) will be more common, but where output pumping is to high pressure, some financial anomalies can be observed.

The ideal tariff advantage pumping schedule would use maximum output overnight, and daytime output at plant minimum flow, or as necessary to pump the daily total, whilst minimising units cost and electrical power employed outside prescribed-hours periods (see Section 7). Where output must be increased in stages, extra daytime units are incurred to allow maximum night pumping at high rate. Since the stages are required for treatment purposes, there is no reason why the water treated should be pumped to high lift (supply pressure). Because night units cost less than half the daytime rate, at any works on which abstraction and treatment unit costs are less than half the daytime high lift electricity costs, money is saved by throwing away the excess treated water of intermediate stages of output, assuming that the daily requirement can be met from night pumping at maximum output. Even when night units are fully used, the single-violation, winter-month penalties associated with maximum power outside prescribed hours, can justify the technique, for pumping at less than minimum plant output, or to defer pumping increments. (It is assumed that trade effluent charges for returning treated water to watercourses are minimal. At the present time there are no such charges in the UK, but discharge charging is practised in some parts of the US and Europe). Design for recirculation could avoid wastage, but dosing residuals in circulation could cause treatment imbalance.

LEAST-COST DESIGN

Some general principles can be illustrated in a worked example. Suppose that the 10 Ml/d supply area of Fig. 5.5 is served by a 10 Ml service reservoir, 5 m deep, from a source 5 km away, pumping through a 400 mm main with a C-value of 140 (Hazen-Williams equation). The static lift for source pumping is 35 m (quite low, for the purposes of this example), and the maximum output of the source is 12 Ml/d, but station efficiency drops from 70 per cent at 9–10 Ml/d to 65 per cent at 12 Ml/d. Two pumping patterns can be compared: constant 10 Ml/d and a combination of 12 Ml/d night pumping and 9.2 Ml/d daytime pumping to produce the same total.

From Section 7:

	Day only	Constant	Night only	Tariff pumping
Output Ml/d	9.2	10	12	9.2 day/12 night
Static power (kW)	52.21	56.75	73.34	52.21/73.34
Dynamic power (kW)	11.65	14.78	26.77	11.65/26.77
Total power (kW)	63.86	71.53	100.11	63.86/100.11
Daytime units costs (£) (17 hours)	38.00	42.56	—	38.00/ —
Night-time units costs (£) (7 hours)	—	7.51	10.51	— /10.51
Daily total units costs (£) (including 10 per cent maximum power)	—	55.08	—	53.36

The calculation of 10 per cent maximum power charges assumes that prescribed hours are used, and that maximum output is necessary during summer peak demands. In practice, power charges require up to six or more separate calculations for daily and seasonal variations, depending on the tariff structures. Most weekends are de-restricted, for example.

The tariff advantage savings from this low-lift example are equivalent to £630 p.a., despite a drop in efficiency at higher output. This represents only 3 per cent of the annual costs, but 20 per cent dynamic losses.

Additional reservoir drawdown for the tariff pumping pattern would be around 4.5 per cent of the 10 Ml reservoir storage, at 2100 hours. If the storage is considered to have been designed to meet peak week, when 20 per cent extra demand is taken (say) wholly within 13 of the 24 hours (for which the pumps would run continuously at 12 Ml/d) the extra drawdown compared with 10 Ml/d pumping, and average demand, would be just over 9 per cent at 2100 hours. Examining Fig. 5.4, 95 per cent of days in a year might be expected to record demands of less than 90 per cent of the peak (with 4½ per cent drawdown). Consequently tariff pumping would be available at no loss of security for 95 per cent of the year.

It may appear that no saving can be made against static lift, but in fact the calculations presented ignore reservoir levels. Based on its assumed depth of 5 m, the permanent reduction of its operating level by 20 per cent would also produce savings of 3 per cent of annual costs.

Selection of pumps to maintain 70 per cent rather than 65 per cent station efficiency at 12 Ml/d would save an additional 1½ per cent of annual costs (on night units).

Overall savings of 5 per cent of total costs (£1 000 p.a.) could alternatively finance (say) £10 000 of capital expenditure. The higher the dynamic losses, the greater the capital advantage from tariff advantage pumping. If the C-value in the example was 110, then the dynamic costs and savings would be higher, being multiplied by a factor of:

$$\frac{1}{\left(\dfrac{110}{140}\right)^{1.85}} = \frac{1}{0.45} = 2.2 \quad \text{(from Hazen-Williams equation)}$$

Hence tariff advantage pumping on an older main with the same configuration could capitalise £22 000. Dynamic costs would be higher by around 15 per cent of annual totals, or about £3 000 p.a., hence total capitalisation could exceed £50 000 (or about £10 per m of the pumping main). Savings could help to offset scraping and relining expenditure for improved 'C' value.

10. AN OUTLINE OF PROJECT APPRAISAL

It is common for water undertakings to apply standard methods, based upon their own financial structures, so this section is limited to discussion of alternatives. Whatever methods are adopted, appraisal is a prerequisite of optimised design.

There is some basic confusion over terminology. Economic appraisal generally includes placing monetary values upon intangibles such as loss of supply, the inconvenience of low pressure, and so on, and embraces the field of cost-benefit analysis. It has no regard to whom derives the benefit from an improvement, whether it is the undertaking, customers, or a third party. Financial appraisal is simpler and merely looks at costs to the undertaking. It is probably best thought of as the construction of a mathematical model of the real cash flows which would be associated with a project, and thus the effect which the project will have upon, for example, water rates. Neither method can be practised to the exclusion of the other, and standard procedures are usually an unsatisfactory hybrid of both economic and financial appraisal. The objective determination of levels of service is an economic appraisal, but if the selected levels are used as design standards, then financial appraisal of projects can follow. It is preferable to test a range of possible variations in parameters to see if this affects the selection of projects.

With capital rationing, dissimilar projects are in competition with one another, and a procedure for selection of priorities is required. Where loans or grants are involved, the procedures of the lending body (e.g. the European Development Fund) may be prescribed. For commentary upon UK governmental procedures see the Treasury publications 'The Test Discount Rate and the Required Rate of Return on Investment' (January 1979), and 'Investment Appraisal in the Public Sector' (June 1982). The Monopolies and Mergers Commission[5] has also made some observations about appraisal procedures in its recommendations. Chapter 4 of the first Manual in this series[246] amplifies many of the points that follow.

THE TIME VALUE OF MONEY

Whichever methods are adopted, all are based upon the premise that immediate benefits have higher value than future benefits. In financial terms, money not spent will have acquired greater value by investment and the addition of interest. If money is spent on a project and repaid in equal annual instalments, then the relative value of the payments in future years will be less than that of the same amount retained. This is the familiar mortgage type of annuity repayment. To compare the payments made in future years with present ones, they are reduced by 'discounting' their value relative to the value of money not spent; in fact, dividing by the proportion by which unspent money would have increased over the same period. (It is important not to confuse this procedure with the treatment of inflation, which is described later).

Discounting at the 'Social Time Preference Rate' (see later) of around 3 per cent or the real return on a risk-free investment (around 3 per cent) allows projects with differently phased expenditure to be compared.

Internal rate of return (the discount rate at which the net present value of a project is zero) is an alternative where resources are restricted.

Simplified procedures have been included in standard texts[1,246,247] (see also the Treasury documents referred to earlier). Unfortunately, real problems cannot be solved in so straightforward a fashion, and some interpretation of techniques is necessary. Annual cash deficits in the early years of projects with positive net present values have caused bankruptcies. The impact of capital projects on annual cash flows is of some importance, and graphical presentation of cash flow will assist decisions.

ALTERNATIVE DISCOUNT RATES

There is some debate over the treatment of inflation. Some authors advocate its exclusion from appraisal, but it can equally well be included, provided that the treatment of all costs and benefits is consistent. Most difficulties arise from inflation occurring (or forecast to occur) at different rates for each parameter and those whose standard procedures are inflation-free are tempted to adapt discount rates for part of the appraisal calculations, which would be inconsistent. If inflation is to be included, all money cash flows must be corrected for inflation to become real cash flows based on purchasing power. If revenues or costs are governed by market forces such as for debt-financed works, with benefits as energy savings, then real values will be more accurate. If future payments are fixed by present decisions (longer term annuities etc.) then inflation-free money values will better represent the cash flows[248-252]. (Note that if two separate rates of change are considered to act, their effects are multiplied, not added).

These simple 'rules' do not assist analysis on annuity-financed, energy-saving projects when differential inflation is forecast[149]. Different discount rates for different streams of benefits[253] could more accurately represent financial conditions, but would not facilitate selection of projects in a capital-rationing environment. Because high discount rates diminish future benefits rapidly, cost-saving activities are difficult to justify, particularly if procedures take some time to develop, such as for waste control[148]. Both the Monopolies and Mergers Commission[5] and the House of Lords Select Committee[7] have made comments about cost-saving schemes.

It is sometimes argued that cost-saving schemes should be treated differently, such as by allocation of fixed budgets. This procedure is not recommended but it has the advantage that it reduces appraisal to a simple question of timing[254]; however, it should not ignore the impact of short-term increases in cash outflows before longer-term benefits are accrued.

Implicit in the application of uniform rates with or without inflation is the assumption that resource distribution is constant and that all schemes are so small that social welfare is unchanged by them. When very large projects are under consideration (e.g. Kielder Reservoir Scheme) then the diversion of resources to particular schemes could be significant. The alternative application of funds could be considered in calculating future purchasing power, particularly following a period of recession. The use of global indices of inflation for non-standard collections of commodities is dubious, and other parameters could justifiably be corrected for differential inflation (e.g. relatively cheaper electronics, falling proportions of labour, and so on). The concept of discounting the value of future manning requirements has been questioned[255] on the basis that labour involvement in tasks was thereby assumed to grow with time. Provided that labour costs form a constant proportion of total costs, there would be no error in this.

Alternatives to the use of quasi-financial discount rates have been advanced. Recognising that individuals accept present expenditure for future benefits (the basis of savings and investment), then what is referred to as a social time preference rate could be used to discount back the future benefits of schemes[256]. Shorter life expectancies and scarcity of funds would require higher rates of discount[249] to represent the (assumed) desire for more rapid benefits, or greater benefits, from viable schemes. The benefits generated from expenditure in this economic procedure are assigned the value accorded to them by the investor/recipient, on the basis of the utility of the additional benefits.

Assuming that resources are not scarce, and supply is at (say) adequate pressure, then a consumer would perceive less benefit from an improvement above this pressure than one below it. The marginal utility has diminished. Consequently it would be inconsistent to appraise projects which achieve minimum standards (or statutory duties) on the same basis as improvements in levels of service. Some methods of appraisal attempt to reconcile social time preference rates with market systems, including the effects of taxation and debt-financing[257].

STAGED DEVELOPMENT OF WORKS

It has been customary in the UK water industry to ensure that gross capacity has exceeded gross demand. Technically this implies that the marginal benefit of water foregone in the event of shortages is infinite, becuase of the continuity requirements of legislation. Advanced construction of larger works has been justified in the past on the basis of economies of scale, but as long ago as 1905 it was suggested that: ". . . the accumulated interest of any capital outlay upon such parts of the works as are only partially used during a long period of time, should not exceed the additional cost of equivalent new works, if constructed when the need for their actual employment arises[187]". Expressions for economy-of-scale factors for staged development were proposed initially on the basis that capacity exceeded demand[258-260]. If deficits are allowed, which could be accommodated by demand management or by water transfers (imports) then an opportunity cost method can be developed for optimal phasing of extensions[261].

It is attractive to commute expenditure between capital and revenue if full appraisal is undertaken. Thus leakage control could defer the next stage of source expenditure. Progress towards new technology is often 'bought' with manpower savings. Does this imply that current levels of service are adequate, or so nearly so that automation cannot be justified except as an economic substitute for existing arrangements?

The benefits associated with proposed expenditure should truly arise from it, rather than occur simultaneously. More effort put into costing of intangibles in an economic appraisal could be fruitful for expenditures which would otherwise have to proceed as a 'gesture of faith' in their validity.

Subject to the law of diminishing returns, increased leakage control effort can bring about net savings from capital deferral, but the higher the discount rates, the closer to imminent deficit the justification would occur[148,253,262]. Buried assets with lives greater than (say) fifty years need not necessarily be regarded as repaying any capital at all, since the difference between annuity for repayment (mortgage type payments) and the value of a perpetuity (interest only) becomes negligible over such periods at higher rates. For example, at 10 per cent rate the difference is less than 1 per cent for 50 years, and seven times smaller than this for 70 years. Similarly, since replacement costs are discounted to such low values, it does not appear to be worth constructing equipment with lives longer than fifty years or so, if high rates still apply in fifty years. The operating environment is also unlikely to remain stable over such periods.

If assessing a two year advance of capital works to take advantage of lower prices in recession, then, if financed by annuity methods over a lifetime of seventy years (say) at 10 per cent, the present value of the two first annual payments (assuming payments starting a full year after completion) would be 174 per cent of the annual payments calculated at day one. The present value of the whole project payments over seventy years starting immediately can be approximated as a perpetuity, i.e. the reciprocal of discount rate, which is 10 times the annual payments. If deferred two years, the present value of a seventy-year annuity would be 8.26 times the annual payments (i.e. $10 - 1.74$). Hence current costs would have to be 17.4 per cent lower in real terms to justify two years advance of a project, at 10 per cent discount rate. At lower rates, and shorter financing periods, advancing projects which could be cheaper in real terms now (rather than waiting) becomes progressively better justified.

Projects with declining real costs (for example, automation) are less favourable unless offset by benefits with increasing real costs. In a climate of declining real costs of automation, and static or marginally increasing money costs of labour, it is difficult to see how the two can be linked, unless financial appraisal of efficiency (N.B. not double-counting any labour savings) and improved levels of service (bearing in mind diminished utility) can confirm net savings from early automation. It has to be borne in mind that if high rates of unemployment persist, then the real money costs of employment, particularly of unskilled labour, may reduce as a result of either lower real wages or changes in government taxation policy.

UNCERTAINTY

If all conceivable outcomes were equally likely, then there would be no meaning in producing a 'best' estimate, and for selection between projects, the decision areas would overlap. Since estimates can generally be produced, they present the most likely financial out-turn of a project, and a probability distribution can be used to describe the likelihood of occurrence of values away from the 'central' estimate. Projects with a preponderance of contract payments, perhaps with predetermined targets, could be limited to quite narrow ranges, whereas a good deal of uncertainty could be present in (say) forecasting consumptions or energy costs.

Whilst it could be expected than an individual investor might require a forecast of greater present value of benefits from high-risk schemes, because of potential losses, and would use a higher discount rate to test for validity, it is better practice to assess separately the consequences of failure to achieve given levels of benefit and assess the impact of these on the investor. Hence a default-free discount rate could be used initially[252].

Where a sufficiently large number of projects is in progress, it has been argued that the risks are diminished effectively to zero, for large public corporations, and consequently default-free rates should always be used[263]. How far this is applicable to individual water undertakings must be a matter of policy, but a case can be argued for allowing for uncertainty for projects such as ground-water development. Dorfman[264] develops the use of probability for some water resource system.

11. OPERATIONAL REQUIREMENTS

Earlier sections have concentrated on satisfying consumers' needs. Most other aspects of design relate to the suppliers' needs, for reliable and economic management and control of the system. The costs of management and control can exceed the annual financing costs of assets, plus abstraction, treatment and pumping of water (see Section 5). Some of these operational costs cannot be directly reduced by engineering design, though of course indirect effects could be taken into account in an economic appraisal.

For least-cost operation of any system, an economic balance must be sought between the first cost and service life of apparatus, its maintenance and manpower requirements. These could be combined under the general term serviceability. Specifications for conventional equipment will often refer to British Standards and Codes of Practice, which have been developed in conjunction with manufacturers and users, but maintenance and manpower requirements are frequently left to manufacturers, particularly for long-life apparatus. The consequences of failure of apparatus, and provision of standby arrangements (not necessarily duplication), should be taken into account in serviceability specifications. Frequency and causes of failure must be recorded to enable specifications to be adapted.

The importance of service records for efficient management of systems cannot be over-emphasised. Nevertheless, despite the information explosion of recent years, and cheaper equipment for data manipulation, manpower is involved in its recording, (particularly failure statistics) and all costs must be set against the usefulness of comprehensive record-keeping. For monitoring of performance, standard procedures can be developed using sampling techniques, in a similar fashion to water quality monitoring. Continuous recording can thereby be reduced to representative parameters, supplemented by intensive sampling in areas where failure (to meet levels of service) is imminent.

Serviceability criteria for individual items of equipment should not be used universally to justify replacement. It is the degree of risk to the local level of service which is important. For example, a valve which proves inoperable could be ignored, and a greater number of consumers would in future be shut off with the nearest available valves, provided that the expected frequency of shut-off remained within the accepted level of service. If this were the case, the valve could be regarded as superfluous for the time being. However, it could be that the value of a few extra valves to cover occasional failure is still less than that for the installation of the absolute minimum number of high performance valves.

Preventative maintenance has been shown to have financial and reliability advantages over breakdown maintenance for short-life, high value plant, but it is very difficult to justify for long-life, low value equipment, if subjected to financial appraisal. There are factors which can balance the effects of rigorous financial appraisal, based upon manpower and workload planning. The likelihood of failures of equipment is not constant. It may vary seasonally, it will certainly increase with age, and it may depend upon the service conditions (cyclic loading, high pressure, etc.). Thus there will be spatial and seasonal peaks in workload to maintain levels of service during extreme conditions, and annual peaks which depend upon the age-profile of an ageing system.

Manpower requirements can be calculated with or without peak-lopping from outside sources, depending upon the flexibility of skills, and the opportunity for temporary restructuring of workloads. Continuity of employment for a stable workforce can then be calculated from a combination of breakdown and preventive maintenance programmes, provided that system performance and levels of service are monitored. Behind this are the aims of smoothing of manpower requirements, and smoothing the impact on consumers of peaks in construction and renovation expenditure. The justifications for continuity arise from reduced supervision (through training) of a skilled and well motivated workforce with security of employment, and are thus economic as well as financial. Whilst recession has forced reappraisal of traditional procedures in many areas, operations controllers have a professional duty to ensure that workforces will not diminish to the point where the mains systems will deteriorate at an uneconomic rate.

In view of the dominance of non-supply expenditure in the make-up of water charges, it is surprising that so little advice on organization and methods is published which is specficially relevant to "one of the UK's largest industries"[4]. Huntington [265] gives guidance on the adoption of standards, and the first Manual in this series[246] describes the initial organizational structure of the industry from 1974. Recent major reorganizations of management structures are largely undocumented. Parliamentary interest in water industry management appears to concentrate on performance indicators, rates of return, and remuneration (see the Advisory and Information Section of 'Water Bulletin'[266]).

The new Consumer Consultative Committees should be concerned with levels of service, and the opportunity they have to bring about a wider public understanding of the management problems of the industry should be welcomed. Clear systems for using consumer contacts as feedback on performance need to be developed.

SERVICE RESERVOIRS

Maintenance procedures are detailed in Chapter 10; this section relates to design provisions (which must allow for future maintenance).

Reservoirs will 'short-circuit' readily, as model testing can demonstrate, and elimination of quiescent zones is important. Facilities for sampling potential stationary areas of a new reservoir must be included at the design stage. Since the turn of the century, the provision of internal baffles to assist flow patterns has been recommended[207] and the use of modern PVC materials offers a much cheaper method of construction than structural walls. For maintenance purposes, it should be possible to subdivide the reservoir volume safely (with a full or partial height) division wall) and safe illuminated access for cleaning equipment and personnel is required. Air venting arrangements must be designed such that air flows do not pull in any foreign matter, insects, etc.

Internal equipment should be maintenance-free as far as is economic. Glass reinforced plastic fittings can be used as alternatives to metallic components. The more steeply inclined the reservoir floor, the deeper will be the required holding level for first, undisturbed inspection by water quality staff, and it would be preferable to limit it to one 'wellington' per half-width, which could dictate drainage layout for a larger reservoir. Spacing of drains should be uniform for safety reasons, particularly for the first inspection, which may have to be conducted by torchlight if only temporary lighting is available.

High-level inlet pipes will minimise water loss on mains failure, and a reflux valve can be omitted, but the energy-saving advantages of pumping to lower reservoir head are lost, as is the case for inlets controlled by ball valves.

Structural integrity of reservoirs is essential for reasons of public safety. Direct responsibility for failure has rested upon reservoir owners since the time of Hammurabi, the sixth King of the Armorite dynasty of Babylon (circa 1760 BC) whose civil code included: 'if any one be too lazy to keep his dam in proper condition and does not keep it so; if then the dam breaks and all the fields are flooded, then shall he in whose dam the break occurred be sold for money and the money shall replace the corn which he has caused to be ruined'[267]. Designers have been liable for the consequences of design errors in Europe and the US, and Health and Safety legislation in the UK has a similar basis. The 1975 Reservoirs Act will in future define the UK position on inspection for structural condition, but internal inspection is likely to be more frequent for quality reasons in service reservoirs.

Structural arrangements for different styles of design and construction are available in published literature for conventional reinforced concrete designs[268-272] and for the circular, prestressed types found most commonly in the US[273-275], though there are recent UK examples.

Construction cost savings are claimed for circular prestressed reservoirs, particularly for precast assembly, and for self-supporting domed roof structures. Roof costs have been estimated to be 50 per cent of the cost of conventional construction[271] but may be dictated by post-constructional use of the roof area, particularly in urban areas where there is considerable pressure for development of open space. In the US service reservoirs have been combined with car parks, and the largest (45 Ml) restrained-based circular prestressed reservoir at Arvada has basketball and tennis courts on its roof.

General maintenance procedures are described in Chapter 10 and in standard texts[1,276]. Particular problems can be experienced in prestressed concrete reservoirs[277] which could be prevented at the design stage.

Maintenance costs will always be greater for water towers than for the equivalent surface reservoir, but their use can nevertheless be economic, particularly in flat rural areas, where mainlaying and boosting costs could be high.

Mains Systems

A recent international survey of water losses[278] cited ground movement as the major factor in leakage from mains (mains' leakage represents around 55 per cent ot total losses in the UK). Selection of pipe and joint materials, and construction methods, as described in Chapters 8 and 9, will help prevent future failures from movement, and also from corrosion, the second most frequent cause of leakage. The only other major factor which is generaly within the supplier's control is pressure. This leaves around half of the potential causes of leakage to be corrected by breakdown maintenance, even if design and construction of new mains could be made leak-free. There have been problems reported even on the new potentially leak-free polyethylene (PE) materials and some service pipes in Memphis, US have been replaced with copper[279], though UK experience of failures has been limited to jointing problems[280,281].

Since mains failure cannot be fully prevented and if disruption for consumers is to be minimised (based on agreed levels of service), valves are an essential operational requirement. Nominal spacing of (say) 'every hundred metres' should be tested against anticipated maintenance requirements, and control requirements.

All fittings contribute head losses, usually ignored in design and network analysis. However, the cost of these losses can be significant for larger mains. It is common practice to reduce the diameter of trunk mains through cross-connections to reduce the valve costs. Losses in tapers are negligible with appropriate design (7° side angles are used for venturi tubes) but the increased velocity results in higher head losses even at fully open valves. For example, suppose an 1 150 mm diameter main has cross-connections along its length (for duplication) in reduced size cast pipework, with two valves and a tee-piece on line at each cross-connection chamber. If the main velocity is 1 m/s, C = 140, and the valves and cross-connection sizes are made 750 mm diameter (two-thirds of the trunk diameter), the fittings' head losses at the connections—if installed every kilometre along the main—will be 11½ per cent of the main's losses, compared with 5 per cent if installed full size. If velocities are increased to 1.5 m/s (equivalent to 135 Ml/d) the lost energy (at current tariffs) is worth over £1 000 per annum, which at real finance rates could have paid for full size fittings, and still retained operational savings.

Comparing this with a 100 mm distribution main, with valves and fittings (say) ten times more frequent, fittings losses are only 3 per cent of total losses at 1 m/s velocity, since the hydraulic gradient of the small main is more than 16 times greater. This is another area where the balancing of computer models requires careful interpretation. Use of equivalent lengths of fittings to adapt models where frequent connections exist will indicate the significance of the local losses. Ultimately, the installation of excess fittings and connections on larger mains will lead to earlier addition to the system capacity though, again, this can appear insignificant if financial appraisal at higher discount rates is applied.

(Values for 'k' used to calculate fittings losses as $\dfrac{kV^2}{2g}$ are available from tables[1,3]).

Selection of the most appropriate type of valve is well described in other publications[282-287], and control applications are discussed later.

Reflux valves are used chiefly on larger diameter mains, in effect as automatic leakage control devices, but they may cause surge problems which can nevertheless be designed-out[283,284]. Their potential for energy-saving operation associated with service reservoirs has been referred to earlier but the head losses can be very high. Pump application is covered in Chapter 7.

Water can contain above 2 per cent of dissolved air by volume, equivalent to 20 m of empty pipe per km run. This air will remain in solution provided that pressure and temperature conditions are stable.

Where mains are laid parallel to the hydraulic gradient, or rise towards it, air valves must be installed, at each end in the case of parallel mains. Air can also collect at sudden changes of slope. Small orifice valves (up to 10 mm diameter orifice) are used to vent air in working conditions. Larger diameters are required to allow charging-up of mains. Charts for sizing of valves are available[288]. An attempt has been made to determine air-purging velocities, as an alternative to air valves, but it was concluded that velocities would be impractically high[289].

Air valves can fail open. If chambers become flooded, contaminated water may be pulled into the main on failure of supply pressures, unless chambers are designed to drain.

Specialist civil engineering design is required to deal with practical problems of mainlaying across major structures, or unstable ground. It is useful to study previous solutions to these types of problems—for example, for the Erskine bridge[290], Tinsley viaduct[291] and a congested area of West Bromwich[292]. The effects of subsidence on mainlaying[293] and service reservoir construction[294] have also been the subjects of papers.

Frost Protection

Frost protection is usually provided by ground cover of apparatus, though some foil frost-protection tapes are available. Many failures are due to ground movements rather than direct freezing of water, which tends to affect only services and consumers' apparatus. Consequently a large number of freeze-thaw cycles will tend to produce more mains' failures than continuous cold weather, though the reverse is true for consumers' services.

Formulae are available for the rate of freezing of still water in pipes which enable insulation calculations to be made, and tables of electric current requirements for low-voltage (110V) thawing of service pipes have been published[206].

Severe winter weather in recent years (the lowest temperatures since records began) did not result in widespread freezing of mains, though some local problems were experienced. Nevertheless, relations between the numbers of bursts and the number of degrees of frost are regularly established[295].

Renovation of Mains

Details of alternative methods of renovation, and the financial justifications are given in Chapter 10. There are some operational needs which must be taken into account before certain types of renovation are contemplated. For longer rural mains, and more generally in 75 mm diameter sizes, reduction of diameter by relining can be significant, and partial relaying could be worthwhile to preserve capacity. For example, a 75 mm diameter main with an apparent 'C' value in Hazen-Williams equation of 80 (outside the normal range of the flow formula), after scraping and lining with a 5 mm thick mortar to give a new 'C' value of 120 will have exactly the same carrying capacity as before. If the lining thickness were 7 mm (within normal tolerances[115]), the carrying capacity would be reduced by 15 per cent. On small mains, spare capacity made available may not meet future demands within the extended life of the main, and duplication may be required sooner.

Similarly, the sleeving of larger diameter mains with polyethylene tube, particularly in rural areas, must also be carefully considered. If the available diameter after sleeving is around 75 per cent of the original, the Hazen-Williams 'C' value of the original main would have had to be lower than 70 for there to be any improvement in carrying capacity.

Renovation decisions are taken upon various criteria, chiefly burst frequency[278] for renewals, and quality or preservation for reconditioning. Systematic pressure testing has been practised in the US[296] and analytical procedures for scheduling of pipe replacement have been developed based upon burst frequency[247,298] and for renovation based on energy savings from improved carrying capacity[299]. These American papers are comprehensive in respect of financial appraisal methods.

12. CONTROL

DATA ACQUISITION AND APPLICATION

Operation and control of any system, of manpower or machines, rely upon data acquisition to monitor performance. In this respect, there are many similarities between control theory for electro-mechanical equipment, and organization and methods theory for management within organizations. The analogy cannot be extended too far, but certainly feedback of information is required before control can be contemplated.

Natural divisions may exist because of the operation of separated pressure or quality zones (say between 'soft' and 'hard' waters), or historical or spatial arrangements of sources and reservoirs. Subdivision into comparably sized zones facilitates identification of system anomalies. Hierarchies of sizes might range from large source zones of 100 Ml or more, subdivided to 10 Ml and 1 Ml levels for zonal and local control. Subdivision to the 1 Ml level would not normally require continuous monitoring (unless it happened to be a discrete supply zone for pressure or quality reasons), though with progressively cheaper telemetry (and limitless funds) all things are possible. Local control for waste and quality purposes is usually subdivided below the 1 Ml level, as low as perhaps a few hundred houses depending upon mains arrangements, but recording is usually limited to periodic sampling to detect changes.

Observation and prediction of local demand behaviour require that as a minimum, flows are recorded as totals for recognised demand cycles, i.e. daily (and hence seasonally and annually).

Reliable instananeous flow recording is considerably more expensive than integrated flows, and without telemetry, requires manual intervention for rapid feedback. Chart recorders are available for this type of duty, and are often installed in source stations to monitor instantaneous output.

Permanent installation of flow recording is otherwise generally limited to locations from which confirmation of remote system control instructions is required (in the same way as installation at sources is used for output control). Cheap solid-state data-logging devices are now available which can economically be used to record flows and pressures for smaller areas than before, but local demand fluctuations ultimately limit the value of continuous flow sampling of small areas.

Pressure is equally important for cost control at source stations, since plant performance can then be fully monitored. For reasons of safety, it is usual to set flow and pressure limits for the normal operation of pumping equipment, as well as heat and sometimes vibration monitoring, together with electrical protection systems. Where immediate manual fault-finding and intervention is possible, warnings could be used, backed up by automatic trips at wider operating ranges but, for remote stations, automatic trip-out subsequently requires manual intervention. Recording of the nature of faults is essential for future improvements of specifications.

Continuous monitoring of quality remote from sources is in its infancy. The development of improved electrodes (some now have ultrasonic cleaning) will assist practical application.

Distribution system monitoring for pressure alone, at representative nodes determined by network analysis (on balanced networks) will be sufficient to indicate the onset of hydraulic problems.

The time allowable for checking and correction of anomalies dictates automation requirements. Response time may be seasonally variable, allowing for the difficulties in getting emergency repair gangs to remote locations in winter, for example.

Some control responses will be immediate, such as station trips due to faults, or perhaps pumping control on reservoir level or delivery pressure. The response time for manual or mechanical intervention following shutdown of plant will depend upon risks to supply or safety. If genuine failure is not identified, repairs are delayed, and risks to supply from coincident failure elsewhere are increased.

Direct local feedback for control purposes is required at pumping installations, and modern intelligent outstations can be programmed to follow expected demand behaviour, with exclusion reporting of anomalies. Intelligent programming of this sort requires knowledge of system behaviour, and expected future behaviour (to assess re-programming intervals). System records are essential for this work, otherwise control bands are very coarse, and substantial intervention is necessary. Direct line control of pumping based on predicted demand behaviour for cost control has been in operation in the UK in recent years.

Some direct feedback systems are unrecorded. Reflux valves and pressure-reducing valves operate in this way, as do pressure relief valves and other fail-safe fittings.

INSTRUMENTATION, CONTROL AND AUTOMATION

Instrumentation, control, and automation (ICA) techniques do not represent the whole spectrum of distribution control. Nevertheless a systems approach to daily operation of distribution networks can simplify analysis of the necessary management arrangements. The development of microchip technology has paralleled management development in that exclusion reporting is practised, and responsibility for normal functions can now be delegated to remote locations, referred to by Jaggard[300] as the 'supervised autonomy' of intelligent outstations.

Instrumentation for flow measurement is described in Chapter 8, but for more g. ~eral descriptions of the theory behind instrumentation for flow and pressure, see references 301-305.

To complete monitoring of local demands, continuous recording of reservoir levels is required. Reservoir levels also provide a check on the behaviour of the system, and modern telemetry systems with intelligent controllers can rapidly detect unusually high or low rates of rise and fall. Total source and system control can include groundwater table and drawdown monitoring if desired[306]. Level monitoring equipment has developed from bubble tube, airbell and hydro-pneumatic equipment to ultrasound and infra-red reflection devices capable of resolution to 1 mm.

Calibration of meters is most convenient in laboratory conditions, but some locations require *in situ* calibration, for which chemical tracer techniques can be extremely accurate[305]. For open-channel flow, fluorimeters can detect concentrations of 0.01 parts per billion.

Intelligent control loops have recently been used to minimise the output pressures of PRVs and savings in overall flows of 10 per cent have been reported[150,307,308]. Simpler diaphragm valves are also in development[309].

The cost savings from waste control of this kind are attractive, but not as great as optimised pressure control at sources, associated with tariff advantage pumping. PRVs themselves add to the supply pressure requirement because of their high head loss at full flow (if correctly sized for low-flow control).

Nevertheless, there will be areas of supply, perhaps shielded from source pumping by a controlling reservoir, where no other form of pressure control is possible, and no opportunities for supplying small high ground areas with separate boosters are available. Pressure control can be applied equally to any supply zone which has a significant range of pressures throughout the day, and not just to existing PRV installations. (Details of PRVs are given in Chapter 8).

If the pressure range is sufficient for operation of variable reduction valves, then it can almost certainly be permanently subdivided into a greater number of pressure zones with cheaper, conventional PRVs, though of course this would depend upon system layout. Self-throttling (i.e. smaller diameter) mains could also be considered for feeding of night lines, with primary (tree-structured) feeds being closed down overnight. System instability can occur with PRVs sited too close together and feeding the same area, unless control pressures are well separated.

The physical arrangements of other types of control valves are described in Chapter 8 and elsewhere[282,310,311]. Cavitation can occur in valves at high throttling settings. Appropriate valve design and selection of materials can help to overcome this potential cause of erosion of surfaces[311,312]. Actuator design will normally require specialist advice, and if rate of closure could create surge problems, additional interrupter timing devices or different gearing may have to be arranged.

Installation of remote operation for valves is generally for flow or pressure changes in trunk mains systems, and except where simple motor-open, motor-closed actions are sufficient, they will normally be associated with flow or pressure monitoring for feedback.

Where additional source or transfer capacity is available, or where blending is allowed and large differences in total source costs exist (including abstraction charges), the design becomes too complex for manual solution. To develop systems for least total cost, marginal costs must be available, together with network models, to allow dynamic modelling of the removal of constraints, such as limits on existing mains or transfer capacities. Decomposition techniques are necessary to simplify the problem, and it is convenient to develop separate archives of system information, and merge them as necessary with a master control program[313]. The data requirements to develop total control systems commence with data acquisition for demand prediction[186] and proceed to dynamic programming. The general mathematical procedures have been described for the East Worcestershire Waterworks Company[314], and dynamic programming has been referred to earlier. The argument about closing the control loop and doing away with 24-hour manual intervention continues. Verification of the best control response at each decision stage by rapid forward simulation of outcomes of alternative responses has been proposed, though initially as an aid to intervention[315].

On-line control with total data capture would require immense storage, unless parallel hardware, or exclusion reporting from intelligent programmable outstations, was available. Local intelligence has been used in this way to transmit the results of local 'Penman' calculations (see Section $2^{35,38}$) in an hydrometric data retrieval system[316].

It is common for telemetry installations to be associated with manpower reductions (see Section $10^{306,317-320}$). Following manpower pruning most recent schemes concentrate upon new applications for system managment, such as for waste control[321].

The detailed operation of telemetry systems has been set out in several general papers[314,319,320,322-327] and some installations have been fully described[300,317-320,328-330]. The hardware available from various manufacturers has also been presented in the literature[331-343].

13. REFERENCES

1. Twort, A. C., Hoather, R. C. and Law, F. M. 1974 "Water Supply" (2nd Edition) Edward Arnold (Publishers), London.
2. Rowell, W. F. and Barnes, J. W. 1982 Introduction to Ref. 184.
3. The Institution of Water Engineers 1969 "Manual of British water engineering practice", Vols I, II and III, 4th Edition, IWE, London.
4. Pearce, F. 1982 "Watershed—the water crisis in Britain" Junction Books, London.
5. The Monopolies and Mergers Commission 1981 "Report on water services supplied by Severn-Trent Water Authority, East Worcestershire Waterworks Company and South Staffordshire Waterworks Company", HC 339, HMSO, London.
6. Kitson, T. 1983 *J. IWES,* 37, 74, Reply to Communication on Ref. 225.
7. House of Lords Select Committee on Science and Technology—"The Water Industry 1982, Volumes I and II, HMSO, London.
8. National Water Council 1976 "Paying for water" and 1980 "Charging households for water", NWC, London.
9. Lamont, P. A. 1969 *Wat. and Wat. Engng,* 73, 9, The choice of pipeflow laws for practical use.
10. Colebrook, C. F. and White, C. M. 1937 *J. ICE,* Nov., 99, The reduction of carrying capacity of pipes with age.
11. Lamont, P. A. 1954 *J. IWE,* 8, 53, The reduction with age of the carrying capacity of pipelines.
12. Lamont, P. A. 1977 *Water Services,* 81, Feb., 60, Mar., 131 and 201, Metrication: hydraulic data and formulae.
13. Barr, D. I. H. 1978 *J. IWES,* 32, 19, A new approach to the fully graphical (dimensional) solution of the Colebrook-White function.
14. O'Garra, R. W. and Stuckey, A. T. 1970 *Wat. and Wat. Engng,* 74, 109, Hydraulic considerations in the design of pipelines.
15. Stuckey, A. T. 1967 *J. IWE,* 21, 237, The evaluation of pipe constants from field measurements and their significance in the solution of distribution problems.
16. Collins, R. P. 1974 *ibid,* 28, 332, Notes on the collection of field data for mains network analysis.
17. Colebrook, C. F. 1954 *ibid,* 8, 80, Discussion of Ref. 11.
18. Gregory R. *et al.* 1977 Technical Report 61. "Cost information for water supply and sewage disposal", Water Research Centre, Medmenham.
19. Miller, D. G., Burley, M. J. and Mawer, P. A. 1970 *Chemy Ind.,* 673, A Survey of water supply costs.
20. Whitlatch, E. E. and Asplund, P. L. 1981 *Wat. Resources Bull.,* 17, 310, Capital cost of rural water distribution systems.
21. White, R. J. and Gregory, R. 1976 *Proc. ICE,* Part 1, 60, 259, Informal discussion: cost estimating data for the water industry.
22. Bradley, R. M. and Isaac, P. C. G. 1969 *Wat. Pollut. Control,* 68, 368, The cost of sewage treatment.
23. HMSO publications: "Monthly digest of statistics" and "Annual digest of statistics" for the Central Statistical Office; "Construction cost indices, housing and construction statistics" for the Department of the Environment (further details in Ref. 18).
24. HMSO "Bulletin of constructional indices: Civil Engineering" (Baxter Indices).

25. HMSO "Price adjustment formulae for building contracts (Series 2)" (Osborne Indices).
26. *New Civil Engineer* (The magazine of the Institution of Civil Engineers) publishes Refs. 24 and 25 monthly, Thomas Telford, London.
27. "Measured Rates" appears quarterly in *Civil Engineering* magazine, Morgan-Grampian Construction Press, London.
28. Thackray, J. E. and Archibald, G. G. 1981 *Proc. ICE*, 79, Pt. 1, Aug. 403, The Severn-Trent studies of industrial water use.
29. Thackray, J. E. 1983 Paper presented to CIPFA-IWES Joint Seminar, Managing Water More Efficiently, London, "Demand management".
30. Manners, G. et al. 1980 "Regional development in Britain" 2nd Edn. John Wiley and Sons, Chichester.
31. "The U.K. space resources, environment and the future" Ed. J. W. House, 2nd Edn. 1977 (especially Chapter 3—Environment and land use), Weidenfeld and Nicholson, London.
32. Hugget, R. and Meyer, I. 1981 "Geography: theory in practice. Book Three—Industry" and 1980 "Book Two—Agriculture" Harper and Row, London.
33. Bale, J. 1976 "The location of manufacturing industry" Oliver and Boyd, Edinburgh.
34. Dunford, M. 1983 "Exploring Europe, Number 1—industry and development in Europe" The Schools Unit, University of Sussex, with assistance from the Commission of the European Communities (London Office).
35. Penman, H. L. 1948 *Proc. R. Soc., Ser. A*, 193, 120. Natural evaporation from open water, bare soil and grass.
36. Penman, H. L. 1950 *Quart. J. R. Met. Soc.*, 76, 372, Evaporation over the British Isles.
37. Penman, H. L. 1962 *Quart. J. R. Met. Soc.*, 88, 209, Weather and crops.
38. Penman, H. L. 1968 Proceedings of Ninth International Congress on Soil Science, Adelaide, 29, "Available and accessible water".
39. Thornthwaite, C. W. and Mather, J. R. 1955 *Publications in Climatology*, VIII, 1, The water balance, Centreton, NJ.
40. Thornthwaite, C. W., and Mather, J. R. 1957 *Publications in Climatology*, X, 3, Instructions and tables for computing potential evapotranspiration and the water balance, Centreton, NJ.
41. Edwards, K. A. 1970 in Taylor, J. A. (Ed.) "The role of water in agriculture"; "Sources of error in agricultural water budgets", Pergamon Press, London.
42. Thackray, J. E., Cocker, V. and Archibald, G. G. 1978 *Proc. ICE*, 64, Pt. 1 Feb. 37-61, The Malvern and Mansfield studies of domestic water usage.
43. Evans, D. and Cook, R. G. 1979 *J. IWES*, 33, 580, Water use studies as a basis for demand forecasting (Summary only—full paper available from IWES).
44. Howick, H. A. 1981 *The Public Health Engineer*, Oct., 9, 4, The theory of probability applied to plumbing services design.
45. British Standards Institution 1965 "Code of Practice 310".
46. Institute of Plumbing 1973 "Design guide and data book".
47. Institute of Plumbing 1977 "Plumbing services design guide".
48. Moodhe, N. S. 1967 *J. AWWA*, 59, 43, Correct meter sizing.
49. Francis, J. L. 1970 *ibid*, 62, 85, Designing residential water services.
50. Wolff, J. B. and Loos, J. F. 1956 *Public Works*, Sept., Analysis of peak water demands.
51. Linaweaver, F. P. Jr., Geyer, J. C. and Wolff, J. B. 1967 *J. AWWA*, 59, 267, Summary report on the residential water use research project.
52. *Ibid*, 1973, 65, 300, Review of John Hopkins University project methods for estimating residential water use.
53. Multidisciplinary Group No. 3 (MGD3) Dec., 1977 "The water industry—a system of management accounting". Directors of Finance Working Party 1.
54. Harley, M. J. 1979 *Water Services*, 83, Aug. 653, and Sept. 677, PPBS and the water industry (PPBS = Planning, Programming and Budgeting System).
55. Young, J. A. 1976 *J. IWES*, 30, 313, Public relations and consumer service in a crisis economy.
56. Wiley, R. D. 1983 *J. AWWA*, 75, 320, Denver's water conservation program.
57. Lord, W. B., Chase, J. A. and Winterfield, L. A. 1983 *ibid*, 75, 324, Choosing the optimal water conservation policy.
58. *J. IWE*, 1953, 7, 497, Discussion topic "Drought restrictions and water conservation".
59. Maddams, W. O. and Feurstein, D. L. 1979 *J. ASCE, Wat. Resources Div.*, 105, WR2 Sept. 343, Effect of water conservation on water demands.
60. Morgan, W. D. and Pelosi, P. 1980 *J. AWWA*, 72, 131, The effects of water conservation kits on water use.
61. Palmini, D. J. and Shelton, T. B. 1983 *ibid*, 75, 336, Noncrisis use of household water saving devices.
62. Maddams, W. O., Parker, D. S. and Hunt, A. J. 1983 *ibid*, 75, 330, Reducing water demand and wastewater flow.

63. Siegrist, R. L. 1983 *ibid*, 75, 342, Minimum-flow plumbing fixtures.
64. Field, D. B. 1978 Technical Report No. 94 "Effects of domestic storage on demand patterns", Water Research Centre, Medmenham.
65. Sobolev, A. and Lloyd, C. J. 1964 *J. IWE*, 18, 53, Trials of dual-flush cisterns.
66. Rump, M. E. 1979 *J. IWES*, 33, 173, Demand management of domestic water use.
67. Rump, M. E. *et al.* 1978 Building Research Establishment, Watford, CP.65/78 "Potential water economy measure in dwellings: their feasibility and economics".
68. Swaffield, J. A. 1980 *The Public Health Engineer*, 8, 126, A study of the effect of water conservation on WC discharge and drainage system transport efficiency.
69. Webster, C. J. D. and Davidson, P. J. 1981 Building Research Establishment "Current experience of new water economy measures".
70. Males, D. B. and Turton, P. S. 1979 Central Water Planning Unit Technical Note No. 32. "Design flow criteria in sewers and water mains".
71. Hughes, T. C. 1978 *J. ASCE, Wat. Resources Div.*, 104, WR1 Nov., 129, Management of rural water supply peak flow rates.
72. Constantine, T. and Medley, P. R. 1962 *J. IWE*, 16, 464, Head losses across isolated ridges or grooves in a pipeline.
73. Eide, O. F. 1972 *J. AWWA*, 64, 295, Minimum service standards.
74. Stone, B. G. 1978 *ibid*, 70, 483, Suppression of water use by physical methods.
75. *Wat. and Wat. Engng*, 77, 379, Comment—effect of water metering in U.S.A.
76. Phillips, J. H. 1972 *J. IWE*, 26, 337, Domestic metering—an interim review.
77. Smith, R. J. 1974 *ibid*, 28, 47, Some comments on domestic metering.
78. Phillips, J. H. and Kershaw, C. G. 1976 *J. IWES*, 30, 203, Domestic metering—an engineering and economic appraisal.
79. Water Research Centre 1975 Technical Inquiry Report No. 361 "Domestic water metering".
80. Kullman, D. J. and House, E. A. 1970 *Wat. and Wastes Engng*, Jan., 44, Automatic meter reading and billing.
81. O'Leary, T. V. 1971 *J. AWWA*, 63, 481, Meter reading revolution.
82. Utilities Telecommunications Council 1973 *ibid*, 65, 99, Automatic meter reading using existing telephone circuits.
83. *Aqua* 1983 No. 5, 243, IWSA, London.
84. Gallagher, R. E. 1972 *J. AWWA*, 64, 143, Meters: replace, repair or modernise?
85. Lacing, W. 1974 *Wat. and Sew. Wks.*, Nov., Meter replacement program pays for itself.
86. Hembrae, J. W. 1976 *J. AWWA*, 68, 504, Planned measurement of meter repair and maintenance costs.
87. Jenkins, J. D. 1976 *J. IWES*, 30, 446, Pumping plant.
88. Coe, A. L. 1973 *J. IWE*, 27, 345, Communication on Ref. 76.
89. Tomon, S. 1975 *J. IWES*, 29, 46, Letter on Ref. 76.
90. Berry, N. S. M. 1972 *J. IWE*, 26, 375, The effect of metering on water consumption in Honiara—British Solomon Islands.
91. World Health Organization 1971, Third Regional Seminar on Environmental Health, Manila, Phillipines.
92. Middleton, R. N., Saunders, R. J. and Warford, J. J. 1978 *J. IWES*, 32, 111, The costs and benefits of water metering.
93. *Aqua* 1983 No. 5, International costs survey, IWSA, London.
94. Lord, W. B. 1982 *Wat. Resources Bull.*, 18, 271, Municipal water supply restrictions as urban growth constraints.
95. Report of the Water Use Committee of AWWA 1973 *J. AWWA*, 65, 285.
96. Gysi, M. 1981 *Wat. Resources Bull.*, 17, 956, The cost of peak capacity water.
97. Young, C. E., Kinsley, K. R. and Sharpe, W. E. 1983 *ibid*, 19, 81, Impact on residential water consumption of an increasing rate structure.
98. *Water Services Yearbook* 1983 "Waterworks statistics", Fuel and Metallurgical Journals, Redhill, England.
99. Haggett, P. 1972 "Geography: A modern synthesis". Harper and Row International, London (Chapter 12 'Chains and hierarchies').
100. Everson, J. A. and Fitzgerald, B. P. 1969 "Concepts in geography—settlement patterns". Longman Group Limited, London.
101. Tidswell, V. 1976 "Pattern and process in human geography". University Tutorial Press, London (Chapters 10 and 11, 'Spacing of settlements').
102. Cox, G. C. 1983 Presentation to CIPFA-IWES Joint Seminar on managing water more efficiently, London.
103. McClelland, N. I. and Mancy, K. H. 1972 *J. AWWA*, 64, 795, Water quality monitoring in distribution systems: a progress report.

104. Gotch, K. 1983 Paper to IWSA Conference, Brussels, "Numerical analysis of water quality change in the distribution network—pipe path analysis and water quality matrix, Vol. 2, B 65" Pergamon Press/IWSA.
105. Short, C. S. 1980 *Water Services*, 84, Aug., 529, Sampling programme design for water quality in distribution.
106. Ainsworth, R. G., Oliphant, R. and Ridgway, J. 1980 Technical Report No. 146, "The introduction of new water supplies into old distribution systems", Water Research Centre, Medmenham.
107. Ainsworth, R. G. (Ed.) *et al.* Technical Report No. 167 "Guide to solving water problems in distribution systems", Water Research Centre, Medmenham.
108. Westendorf, J. R. and Middleton, A. C. 1979 *J. AWWA*, 71, 417, Chemical aspects of the relationship between drinking water quality and long-term health effects: an overview.
109. Water Research Centre 1978 Conference on Water Distribution Systems: Maintenance of Water Quality and Pipeline Integrity, Oxford (23 papers).
110. Pattison, P. L. 1980 *J. AWWA*, 72, 88, Conducting a regular main flushing program.
111. Langelier, W. F. 1936 *ibid*, 28, 1500.
112. Thomas, J. F. and Trussell, R. R. 1970 *ibid*, 62, 245, Computer application to water conditioning calculations (see also *ibid*, 1971, 63, 49).
113. Morton, T. H. 1977 *J. IWES*, 31, 26, An algorithm for the Langelier index of process waters.
114. Large, M. 1982 Paper presented to IWES Scientific Section Symposium on Internal Corrosion of Iron Mains and Copper Services, London, "Misconceptions in the use of some water quality parameters to control corrosion in cast iron water mains" (Summary of papers: *J. IWES*, 1982, 36, 246).
115. Parkinson, R. W. and Giles, R. G. 1977 Technical Report No. 38. "A survey of renovation techniques for water mains", Water Research Centre, Medmenham.
116. Water Research Centre, Reading List No. 36, 1975 "Iron, manganese, organic and miscellaneous deposits in pipes carrying raw and potable water".
117. Bays, L. R. 1975 Sept., at IWES Symposium on Maintenance of Water Quality, Cambridge.
118. Allen, M. J., Taylor, R. H. and Geldreich, E. E. 1980 *J. AWWA*, 72, 614, The occurrence of micro-organisms in water main encrustations.
119. Tuovinen, O. H. *et al.* 1980 *ibid*, 72, 626, Bacterial, chemical, and mineralogical characteristics of tubercles in distribution pipelines.
120. Lee, S. H., O'Connor, J. T. and Banerji, S. K. 1980 *ibid*, 72, 636, Biologically mediated corrosion and its effects on water quality in distribution systems.
121. Burman, N. P. and Colbourne, J. S. 1979 *J. IWES*, 33, 11, Effect of non-metallic materials on water quality.
122. Merckx, G. and Van Alsenoy, J. 1983. Paper to IWSA Conference, Brussels, "Le nettoyage intérieur des conduites de distribution d'eau", Vol. 2, B145, Pergamon Press/IWSA.
123. Holland, G. J. 1956 *J. IWE*, 10, 221, The eradication of *Asellus aquaticus* from water supply mains.
124. Abram, F. S. H., Evins, C. and Hobson, J. A. 1980 Technical Report No. 145, "Permethrin for the control of animals in water mains", Water Research Centre, Medmenham.
125. Mitcham, R. P. and Shelley, M. W. 1980 *J. IWES*, 34, 474, The control of animals in water mains using permethrin, a synthetic pyrethroid.
126. Zoeteman, B. C. J., Piet, G. J. and Postma, L. 1980 *J. AWWA*, 72, 537, Taste as an indicator for drinking water quality.
127. Visit to Blackbrook reservoir and treatment works (S-TWA Soar Division), associated with IWES Midland Section paper "Reservoirs Act 1975 and spillway design", Kegworth, 1981.
128. Richards, W. N. and Shaw, B. 1976 *J. IWES*, 30, 191, Developments in the microbiology and disinfection of water supplies.
129. Barker, M. R. and Palmer, D. J. 1977 *ibid*, 31, 109, Persistent odour and taste removal using ozone and microcoagulation.
130. IWES 1982 Joint Midland and Scientific Sections Symposium on "Chlorine Dioxide", Telford.
131. Campbell, R. M. and Pescod, M. B. 1965 *J. IWE*, 19, 101, The ozonization of Turret and other Scottish waters.
132. Sankey, K. A. and Whatmough, P. 1980 *J. IWES*, 34, 435, Experiences in the use of ozone.
133. McConnell, G. 1976 *ibid*, 30, 431, Halo-organics in water supply.
134. Majumdar, S. B. and Sproul, O. J. 1974 *Water Research*, 8, 253, Technical and economic aspects of water and wastewater ozonization: a critical review.
135. Report on studies at Essex Water Company 1982, *Water Research News*, Sept., 6.
136. Report linking bone pains, slurred speech and aluminium protein complex build-up in bones of dialysis patients. 'Tomorrow's World' BBC TV, 31.3.83.
137. *World Water* 1983, Nov., 8, Thomas Telford, London.
138. Commins, B. T. 1983 "Asbestos fibres in drinking water, May 1983" B. T. Commins, Maidenhead.
139. McGuire, M. J., Bowers, A. E. and Bowers, D. A. 1983 *J. AWWA*, 75, 364, Optimizing large-scale water treatment plants for asbestos-fiber removal.

140. Robertson, J. S. 1979 *ibid*, 71, 408, Minerals and Mortality. Reprinted from *Community Health* 1977, 8, 227.
141. Pocock, S. J. *et al.* 1980 *Br. Med. J.*, 24th May, 280, 1243 The British Regional Heart Study: geographic variations in cardiovascular mortality, and the role of water quality.
142. Shaper, A. G., Packham, R. F. and Pocock, S. J. 1980 *J. Envir. Path. and Tox.*, 4-2, 3: 89, The British Regional Heart Study: cardiovascular mortality and water quality.
143. Calabrase, E. J. *et al.* 1980 *J. AWWA*, 72, 645, Elevated levels of sodium in community drinking water.
144. Robertson, J. S. and Parker, V. 1979 *ibid*, 71, 413, Crib deaths and sodium in water. Reprinted from *Lancet*, 1978, 2: 1012.
145. Richards, W. N., Britton, A. and Cochrane, A. 1980 *J. IWES*, 34, 315, Reducing plumbo solvency—the effect of added lime on the Loch Katrine supply to Glasgow.
146. White, S. K. and Bondietti, E. A. 1983 *J. AWWA*, 75, 374, Removing uranium by current municipal water treatment processes.
147. Phillips, J. H. 1983 *J. IWES*, 37, 325, Water usage and the quantification of unaccounted water in a universally metered supply area.
148. Speed, H. D. M. 1983 Paper presented to CIPFA-IWES Joint Seminar, Managing water more efficiently, London, "Water losses".
149. Patton, J. L. and Horsley, M. B. 1980 *J. AWWA*, 72, 315, Curbing the distribution energy appetite.
150. Ratcliffe, B. 1983 *The Surveyor*, 161, 20th Jan., 12, Cutting down on leakage.
151. Hucks, R. T. Jr. 1972 *J. AWWA*, 64, 443, Designing PVC pipe for water distribution systems.
152. Walters, G. Z., Jeppson, R. W. and Flammer, G. H. 1976 *J. ASCE, Hyd. Div.*, 102, HY7 July 831, Water hammer in PVC and reinforced plastic pipe.
153. Streeter, V. L. 1967 *ibid*, 93, HY3 May, 81, Valve stroking for complex piping systems.
154. Streeter, V. L. *ibid*, 93, HY5 Sept., 185, Water-hammer analysis of distribution systems (includes program for 3-4000 pipes).
155. Driels, M. 1974 *ibid*, 100, HY11 Nov., 1549, Valve stroking in separated pipe flow.
156. Driels, M. 1975 *ibid*, 101, HY5 May, 437-448, Design of pressure transient control system.
157. Fok, A. T. K. 1978 *ibid*, 104, HY9 Sept., 1289, Design charts for air chambers on pump pipe lines.
158. Nakajima, S. 1975 *J. AWWA*, 67, 390, Improved design of distribution networks by minimum route.
159. Lam, C. F. and Wolla, M. L. 1972 *J. ASCE, Hyd. Div.*, 98, HY2 Feb., 335, and HY3 Mar., 447 Computer analysis of water distribution systems.
160. Wood, D. J. and Charles, C. O. A. 1972 *ibid*, 98, HY7 July, 1157, Hydraulic network analysis using linear theory.
161. Williams, G. N. 1973 *ibid*, 99, HY7 July, 1057, Enhancement of convergence of pipe network solutions.
162. Donachie, R. P. 1974 ibid, 100, HY3 Mar., 393, Digital program for water network analysis.
163. Salkin, H. M. 1975 "Linear programming" Addison-Wesley Publishing Co., Reading, Mass.
164. Jeppson, R. W. and Tavallaee, A. 1975 *J. ASCE, Hyd. Div.*, 101, HY3 Mar., 576, Pumps and reservoirs in networks by linear theory.
165. Chandrashekar, M. and Stewart, K. H. 1975 *ibid*, 101, HY4 Apr., 341, Sparsity-oriented analysis of large pipe networks.
166. Fox, J. A. and Keech, A. E. 1975 *J. IWES*, 29, 183, Pipe network analysis—a novel steady-state technique.
167. Jeppson, R. W. and Davis, A. L. 1976 *J. ASCE, Hyd. Div.*, 102, HY7 July, 987, Pressure reducing valves in pipe network analysis.
168. Bradley, S. P., Hax, A. C. and Magnati, T. 1977 "Applied mathematical programming" Addison-Wesley Publishing Co., Reading, Mass.
169. Rao, H. S., Bree, D. W. and Markel, L. C. (2nd paper) 1977 *J. ASCE, Hyd. Div.*, 103, HY2 Feb., 97, and HY3 Mar., 281, Extended period simulation of water systems.
170. Chandrashekar, M. 1980 *ibid*, 106, HY1 Jan., 133, Extended set of components in pipe networks.
171. Isaacs, L. T. and Mills, K. G. 1980 *ibid*, 106, HY7 July, 1191, Linear theory methods for pipe network analysis.
172. Coulbeck, B. and Orr, C. H. 1980 "Computer control of water supply. Interactive network analysis and simulation program", Research Report No. 8, School of Electronic and Electrical Engineering, Leicester Polytechnic. Also 1982 "A simplified user guide to the graphical interactive network analysis and simulation program (GINAS)".
173. Shamir, U. and Howard, C. D. O. 1968 *J. ASCE, Hyd. Div.*, 94, HY1 Jan., 219, Water distribution system analysis.
174. Jacoby, S. L. 1968 *ibid*, 94, HY3 May, 641, Design of optimal hydraulic networks.
175. Karmeli, D., Gadish, Y. and Meyers, S. 1968 *J. ASCE, Pipeline Div.*, 94, PL1 Oct., 1, Design of optimal water distribution networks.
176. Kally, E. 1971 *Wat. and Wat. Engng*, 75, 148, Automatic planning of the least-cost water distribution network.

177. Deb, A. K. and Sarkar, A. K. 1971 *J. ASCE, San. Eng. Div.,* 97, SA2 April, 141, Optimisation in design of hydraulic network.
178. Deb, A. K. 1973 *Wat. and Wat. Engng,* 77, 18, Least-cost pipe network deviation.
179. Cembrowicz, R, G. and Harrington, J. J. 1973 *J. ASCE, Hyd. Div.,* 99, HY3 Mar., 431, Capital-cost minimisation of hydraulic network.
180. Flam, C. 1973 *ibid,* 99, HY6 Jun., 863, Discrete gradient optimisation of water systems.
181. Yang, K. P., Liang, T. and Wu, I. P. 1978 *ibid,* 104, HY1 Jan., 187, Design of conduit system with diverging branches.
182. Cenedese, A. and Mele, P. 1978 *ibid,* 94, HY2 Feb., 237, Optimal design of water distribution networks.
183. Rowell, W. F. 1979 PhD Thesis, University of Texas, "A methodology for optimal design of water distribution systems".
184. Rowell, W. F. and Barnes, J. W. 1982 *J. ASCE, Hyd. Div.,* 108, HY1 Jan., 137, Obtaining layout of water distribution systems.
185. Sterling, M. J. H. and Autcliffe, D. J. 1974 *J. IWE,* 28, 413, A technique for the prediction of water demand from past consumption data.
186. Hanke, S. H. and deMare, L. 1982 *Wat. Resources Bull.,* 18, 621, Residential water demand: a pooled time-series cross-section study of Malmo, Sweden.
187. Tudsbery, J. H. T. and Brightmore, A. W. 1905 "The principles of waterworks engineering". 3rd Edn., E. and F. N. Spon, London.
188. Adams, R. W. 1955 *J. IWE,* 9, 540, The analysis of distribution systems and the design of reinforcing mains.
189. Wilson, J. B. 1967 *J. AWWA,* 59, 29, Hydrant rental charges.
190. Carl, K. J., Young, R. A. and Anderson, G. C. 1973 *ibid,* 65, 335, Guidelines for determining fire-flow requirements.
191. Proudfit, D. P., Collins, G. B. and Murray, H. K. 1970 *ibid,* 62, Oct., 629, Balancing needs, responsibility and costs in the distribution system.
192. Cote, D. R. and Goodman, A. S. 1970 *ibid,* 62, 407, Costs of providing water for protection.
193. Reid, J. 1970 *Wat. and Wat. Engng,* 74, 147, Paper presented to Second Symposium on Pipeline Engineering in Waterworks Practice, Department of Civil Engineering, University of Salford, 1969 "Planning considerations in design and layout of distribution mains".
194. Coulbeck, B. and Orr, C. H. 1981 "Computer control of water supply—optimised pump scheduling for water supply systems", Research Report No. 12, School of Electronic and Electrical Engineering, Leicester Polytechnic.
195. Lamont, P. A. 1974 *Water Services,* 78, Nov., 438, The economics of pumping mains.
196. Stephenson, D. 1978 "Pipeline design for water engineers" Elsevier Scientific, Amsterdam.
197. Davies, G. 1968 *J. IWE,* 22, 281, Trunk pipeline selection—what size when?
198. Paine, N. and White, J. K. 1969 *ibid,* 23, 435, Water transport costs.
199. Greenwood, R. H. 1978 *J. IWES,* 32, 509, Optimal sizing and staging of pumping mains.
200. Robinson, R. B. and Austin, T. A. 1976 *J. ASCE, Hyd. Div.,* 102, HY8 Aug., 1119, Cost optimisation of rural water systems.
201. Wright, F. B. 1977 "Rural water supply and sanitation" 3rd. Edn. McGraw-Hill U.K.
202. Pocock, J. S. 1969 *J. IWE,* 23, 571, Simplifying network analysis by the concept of specific diameter.
203. Cornish, R. J. 1972 *ibid,* 26, 298, The loss of head with abstraction of water along a pipe.
204. Camp, T. R. 1939 *Trans. ASCE,* 104, 190, Economic pipe sizes for water distribution systems.
205. Lischer, V. C. 1979 *J. ASCE, Hyd. Div.,* 105, HY1 Jan., 113, discussion of Ref. 182.
206. Babbit, H. E., Doland, J. J. and Cleasby, J. L. 1962 "Water supply engineering" 6th Edn., Mc.Graw Hill International.
207. Burton, W. K. 1907 "The water supply of towns and the construction of waterworks." 3rd Edn., Crosby, Lockwood and Son, London.
208. Institution of Geologists 1982. Memorandum submitted in evidence to House of Lords Select Committee: published in Ref. 7 Volume II Evidence pp. 446-449, 6, and referred to in Ref. 7 Volume I Report, para. 2.31.
209. Chun, R. Y. D., Mitchell, L. R. and Mido, K. W. 1964 *J. ASCE, Hyd. Div.,* 90, HY4 July, 79, Ground water management for the nation's future—optimum conjunctive operation of ground-water basins.
210. Aron, G. and Scott, V. H. *ibid,* 97, HY5 May, 705, Dynamic programming for conjunctive water use.
211. Hamdan, A. S. and Meredith, D. D. 1975 *ibid,* 101, HY10 Oct., 1343, Screening model for conjunctive-use water systems.
212. Ineson, J. 1970 *J. IWE,* 24, 155, Development of groundwater resources in England and Wales.
213. Richards, H. J. 1972 Paper presented to symposium of IWE River Engineering Section at Birmingham, "River basin groundwater development—principles and the national practice".

214. Water Resources Board 1973 "Water resources in England and Wales" Vols. 1 and 2, HMSO. London.
215. Rushton, K. R. 1975 *J. IWES*, 29, 373, Aquifer analysis of the Lincolnshire limestone using mathematical models.
216. Birtles, A. B. and Nutbrown, D. A. 1976 *Water Services*, 80, Sept., 533, Use of groundwater modelling techniques in water resource planning.
217. Rofe, B. H., Durrant, P. S. and Egerton, R. H. L. 1977 *J. IWES*, 31, 47, Some aspects of the use and management of groundwater sources.
218. Swinnerton, C. J. and Hillyer, M. A. 1983 *ibid*, 37, 421, Malmesbury groundwater scheme.
219. Buchan, S. 1962 Paper given to ICE Symposium on Conservation of Water Resources in the UK, 181, "Conservation by integrated use of surface and groundwater".
220. Law, F. 1965 *J. IWE*, 19, 413, Integrated use of diverse resources.
221. Armstrong, R. B. and Clarke, K. F. 1972 *ibid*, 26, 11, Water resource planning in South-East England.
222. O'Neill, P. G. 1972 *ibid*, 26, 47, A mathematical programming model for planning a regional water resource system.
223. Hilson, M. A. 1978 *J. IWES*, 32, 537, Treatment of mixed raw waters.
224. Rushton, K. R. and Tomlinson, L. M. 1981 *Wat. Resources Bull.*, 17, 406, Operating policies for a surface/ground water system.
225. Kitson, T. 1982 *J. IWES*, 36, 257, Development and operational strategies for water resource and supply systems.
226. Zoeteman, B. C. J., Hrubec, J. and Brinkmann, F. J. J. 1976 *ibid*, 30, 123, The Veluwe artificial recharge plan—water quality aspects.
227. Edworthy, K. J. and Downing, R. A. 1979 *ibid*, 33, 151, Artificial groundwater recharge and its relevance to Britain.
228. Jones, H. H. 1983 *ibid*, 37, 9, Investigations for artificial recharge of the Triassic sandstones aquifer near Stourbridge, UK.
229. Synopsis of joint IWES and Geological Society Meeting on Well Construction and Development 1979 *ibid*, 33, 41, (Full report in *Quart. J. Eng. Geol.*, June 1979).
230. Brereton, N. R. 1979 Technical Report No. 103 "Step drawdown pumping tests for the determination of aquifer and borehole characteristics", Water Research Centre, Medmenham (see also BS 6316, Test pumping of water wells).
231. Final Reports, Research Panels. 1969 *J. IWE*, 23, 369, Panel 9, "Observation boreholes—construction and use", 355-368, Panel 6, "Well screens and ground packs".
232. Shaw, A. P. 1976 *J. IWES*, 30, 61, Water supplies for Warrington.
233. Thornton, I. and Webb, J. S. 1977 *ibid*, 31, 11, Regional geochemical maps.
234. Fried, J. J. and Ungemach, P. O. 1971 *Water Research*, 5, 7, July, 491-495, A dispersion model for a quantitative study of groundwater pollution by salt.
235. Prakash, A. 1982 *J. ASCE, Hyd. Div.*, 108, HY4 April, 572, Ground water contamination due to vanishing and finite size continuous sources.
236. Edwards, A. E. J. 1972 *J. IWE*, 26, 170, Salinity control on a borehole source in Bunter sandstone.
237. *Engineering News-Record* 1982, 209, July 22nd, 16, Coal seams mined for water.
238. Bouchardeau, H. 1983 *Technique de L'eau*, 438/439, 54-55, Inauguration of the first plant for the elimination of nitrates in drinking water (see also WRC Research Programme 1984/5).
239. Sternberg, Y. M. and Scott, V. H. 1967 *J. ASCE, Hyd. Div.*, HY4 July, 169, Mutual interference of water wells.
240. Day, J. B. W. *et al.* 1978 *J. IWES*, 32, 329, The use of inclined boreholes for well development.
241. Stow, G. 1978 *ibid*, 32, 517, Communication on Ref. 240.
242. Poss, C. 1983 *Wasserwirtschaft*, 3, 169 and 175 (in German) Meeting peak demands in drinking water supply by means of groundwater storage.
243. Steering Committee on Water Quality 1972 Joint circular 22/72 (First annual report of Committee) Department of the Environment, London.
244. Lamont, J. and Holland, G. J. 1974 *J. IWE*, 28, 155, Extensions to Hampton Loade works.
245. Sweeting, F. W. and Brignal, W. J. 1976 *J. IWES*, 30, 91, Uprating of accentrifloc clarifiers.
246. The Institution of Water Engineers and Scientists 1979 Water Practice Manuals, Book 1, "The structure and management of the British water industry", IWES, London.
247. Institution of Civil Engineers 1969 "An introduction to engineering economics".
248. Hanke, S. H., Carver, P. H. and Bugg, P. 1975 *Water Resources Research*, 11, 511, Project evaluation during inflation.
249. Balmer, R. 1975 *J. IWES*, 29, 390, Discounting—its use in project appraisal.
250. Rouse, M. J. 1976 *ibid*, 30, 112, Discussion of Ref. 249.
251. Pogson, C. H. 1976 *ibid*, 30, 379, Discussion of Refs. 249 and 250.

252. Bierman, H. Jnr. and Smidt, S. 1975 "The capital budgeting decision" 4th Edition, Collier Macmillan, London.
253. Smith R. J. and Males, D. B. 1978 *J. IWES*, 32, 423, A theoretical approach to the optimisation of waste control expenditure.
254. Lauria, D. T. 1973 *J. AWWA*, 65, 583, Water supply planning in developing countries.
255. "Comment" 1973 *Wat. and Wat. Engng*, 77, 479, (on Ref. 221).
256. Feldstein, M. S. 1964, in "Cost-benefit analysis" 1972 (Ed. R. Layard) 245 'The social time preference rate'. Penguin Books, England.
257. Feldstein, M. S. 1972 in "Cost-benefit analysis" (Ed. R. Layard) 311, 'The inadequacy of weighted discount rates'. Penguin Books, England.
258. Manne, A. S. 1961 *Econometrica*, 29, 4, Oct., 632-649, Capacity expansion and probabalistic growth.
259. Manne, A. S. (Ed.) 1967 "Investments for capacity expansion, size, location and time phasing". MIT Press, Cambridge, Mass.
260. Law, F. 1972 Paper presented to ICE Symposium on Management of National and Regional Resources, "Management of water storage, treatment and distribution under new regional authorities".
261. Erlenkottler, D. 1967 Optimal plant size with time-phased imports (in Ref. 259.
262. Balmer, R. 1979 *J. IWES*, 33, 277, Communication on Ref. 253.
263. Arrow, K. J. and Lind, R. C. 1970 in "Cost-benefit analysis" 1972 (Ed. R. Layard) 335, 'Uncertainty and the evaluation of public investment decisions'. Penguin Books, England.
264. Dorfman, R. 1962 in "Design of water resource systems" (A. Maass *et al.*) 129, 'Basic economic and technologic concepts; a general statement'. Harvard University Press. (Excerpt published in "Cost-benefit analysis" 1972 (Ed. R. Layard) 360, 'Decision rules under uncertainty', Penguin Books, England.
265. Huntington, R. 1979 *J. IWES*, 33, 497, Resurrection of water supply distribution —new life for a faithful servant.
266. *Water Bulletin* is published weekly by the Water Authorities Association, London.
267. Biswas, A. K. 1967 *J. ASCE, Hyd. Div.*, 93, HY5 Sept., 115, Hydraulic engineering prior to 600 BC.
268. Manning, G. P. 1967 "Reservoirs and tanks" Cement and Concrete Association.
269. Tattersall, F. 1959 *J. IWE*, 13, 21, Design, construction and maintenance of service reservoirs.
270. Risbridger, C. A. 1947 *ibid*, 1, 337, Design and construction of Perry Barr service reservoir.
271. Final Report, Research Panel 4 1967 *ibid*, 21, 607, Standardised techniques in covered service reservoir construction.
272. Lane, V. P. and Mascarenhas, I. 1974 *ibid*, 28, 228, A computer-aided design system for service reservoirs.
273. Mansfield, C. S. 1972 *J. AWWA*, 64, 284, Construction of precast, prestressed concrete storage tanks.
274. Woodside, R. D. 1972 *ibid*, 64, 289, Prestressed concrete storage tanks: design and construction.
275. American Concrete Institute, Report of 344 Committee 1972 *ibid*, 64, 809, Design and construction of circular prestressed concrete structures.
276. Kenmir, R. C. 1969 *ibid*, 61, 145, Periodic inspections of tanks and reservoirs.
277. Hertzberg, L. B. and Westerback, A. E. 1976 *ibid*, 68, 652, Maintenance problems with wire-wound prestressed concrete tanks.
278. Reed, E. C. 1980, *Aqua*, 8, 0178, Report on water losses, IWSA, London.
279. *Engineering News Record* 1982, 208, Mar. 11th.
280. Gill, D. A. 1959 *Wat. and Wat. Engng*, 63, 757, The use of low-density polyethylene tube in United Kingdom water supply.
281. Batchelar, T. G. 1960 *J. IWE*, 14, 383, Polythene water pipes.
282. Bridges, F. L. 1969 *J. NEWWA*, Sept., 270, Why the butterfly valve?
283. Miller, E. 1968 *J. IWE*, 22, 91, Developments in valve engineering for water supply.
284. Livesey, R. J. 1972 *ibid*, 26, 430, A note on waterworks sluice valves.
285. Cooney, A. 1983 *Water Services*, 87, July, 301, Butterfly valves—a modern alternative.
286. Lupton, H. R. 1960 *J. IWE*, 14, 209, Rate of closure of a single-flap reflux valve.
287. Kane, R. S. and Cho, S. M. 1976 *J. ASCE, Hyd. Div.*, 102, HY1 Jan., 57, Hydraulic performance of tilting-disc check valves.
288. Lescovich, J. E. 1972 *J. AWWA*, 64, 457, Locating and sizing air-release valves.
289. Wisner, P. E., Mohsen, F. N. and Kouwen, N. 1975 *J. ASCE, Hyd. Div.*, HY2 Feb., 243, Removal of air from water lines by hydraulic means.
290. Stevenson, G. 1978 *J. IWES*, 32, 141, The laying of 24 inch (outside diameter) mains over the Erskine bridge.
291. Godden, H. C. 1970 *J. IWE*, 24, 209, The design and construction of the twin 24 inch water main crossing of Tinsley viaduct.

292. Burgess, D. E. 1973 *ibid*, 27, 365, The design, planning and construction of a 45 inch diameter water main across a congested area of West Bromwich.
293. Summerton, J. R. and Findlay, G. E. 1972 *ibid*, 26, 359, The design of a trunk main, with particular reference to the long-term effects of ground settlement.
294. Lackington, D. W. and Robinson, B. 1973 *ibid*, 27, 197, Articulated service reservoirs in mining subsidence areas.
295. Serpell, C. A. 1960 *ibid*, 14, 214, Recent developments and current practice in a distribution department.
296. Kocol, R. J. 1972 *J. AWWA*, 64, 430, Pressure testing the distribution system in Milwaukee.
297. Shamir, U. and Howard, C. D. O. 1979 *ibid*, 71, 248, An analytical approach to scheduling pipe replacement.
298. Clark, R. M., Stafford, C. L. and Goodrich, J. A. 1982 *J. ASCE, Wat. Resources Div.*, 108, WR3 Oct., 243, Water distribution systems: a spatial and cost evaluation.
299. Walski, T. M. 1982 *ibid*, 108, WR3 Oct., 296, Economic analysis of rehabilitation of water mains.
300. Jaggard, S. P. 1979 *Water Services*, 83, Dec., 925, New telemetry system allows more precise network planning.
301. Dean, J. and Thurley, B. L. 1968 *J. IWE*, 22, 205, Transducers for operation with telemetry networks.
302. Wolfner, J. P. 1971 *J. AWWA*, 63, 117, Flow metering in water works.
303. 1977 *J. ASCE, Hyd. Div.*, 103, HY8 Aug., 889, Bibliography on discharge measurement techniques.
304. Creasey, J. D. and Sanderson, P. R. 1978 Technical Report No. 84 "The accuracy of venturi-type bulk meters". Water Research Centre, Medmenham.
305. Committee Report 1979 *J. AWWA*, 71, 428, Automation and instrumentation: a compendium of articles on distribution system instrumentation.
306. *Engineering News-Record* 1981, 207, Dec. 3rd. Feature: Computer-aided everything.
307. Marshall, R. W. 1981 *J. IWES Supplement*, 35, 77, Micro-electronics in the water industry: remote management of a water authority region.
308. Mulready, J. 1983 *The Surveyor*, 161, 20th Jan., 14, Maximising waste reduction.
309. *World Water* 1983 Nov., 37, Thomas Telford, London.
310. Hore, D. L. 1975 *Waste Services*, 79, Aug., 327, Valve operation and control.
311. Miller, E. 1968 *J. IWE*, 22, 512, Flow and cavitation characteristics of control valves.
312. Grandage, R. E. 1978 *Water Services*, 82, Aug., 503, Experiences with cavitation in waterworks valves.
313. Cesario, A. L. 1980 *J. AWWA*, 72, 508, Computer modelling programs: tools for model operations.
314. Burch, R. H. *et al.* 1979 *Water Services*, 83, Oct., 761, Energy saving by optimal control of water supply.
315. Gilman, H. D., Goodman, M. Y. and DeMoyer, R. Jr., 1973 *J. AWWA*, 65, 255, Replication modelling for water distribution control.
316. Walker, S. T. 1982 IAHS Publication 134 "Advances in hydrometry" (Proceedings of Exeter Symposium, July 1982) 229, Hydrometric data capture using intelligent solid-state logging systems.
317. Pepper, R. A. and Banks, W. 1969 *J. IWE*, 23, 299, The telemetry installation for the central control of the Sunderland and South Shields water system.
318. Burch, R. H. and Marlow, K. C. 1978 *J. IWES*, 32, 443, Seven years' operational experience of computer-based telemetry and control applied to a water supply network.
319. Marlow, K. C. and Fallside, F. 1980 *ibid*, 34, 517, Mini-computer, microprocessor and telecontrol applications to a water supply network.
320. Andrews, J. 1977 *Water Services*, 81, Feb., 79, Data transmission system's role in automated pumping system.
321. Hughes, L. J. *et al.* 1983 Paper to IWSA Conference, Brussels, "Distribution problems in water supply—Dial-line—a secondary telemetry system for leakage detection" Vol. 2, B13-16. Pergamon Press/IWSA.
322. Dickinson, G. C., 1968 *J. IWE*, 22, 176 (Abridged), The relationship between users' data handling requirements and the capabilities of multiplexed telemetry systems.
323. Tattam, M. J. 1970 *Wat. and Wat. Engng*, 74, 15, An introduction to telemetry for water engineers.
324. Brooks, M. J. 1971 *ibid*, 75, 63, Specifying telemetry for a water authority.
325. Day, L. J. 1971 *ibid*, 75, 229, Operational facilities for water supply schemes.
326. Cox, H. 1972 *ibid*, 76, 14, Control system design, software and flexibility.
327. The Institution of Water Engineers and Scientists 1981 *J. IWES Supplement*, 35, Micro-electronics in the water industry.
328. *Wat. and Wat. Engng*, 1972, 76, 251, Compton supervisory scheme of the Thames Valley Water Board.

329. Burch, R. H. *et al.* 1973 *ibid,* 77, 335, 397 and 453, A computer-based telecontrol and communications system for a water supply network (full version of earlier paper: *ibid,* 1971, 75, 371).
330. Clark, D. 1977 *Water Services,* 81, Nov., 671, Micro telemetry for Bristol.
331. *Wat. and Wat. Engng,* 1970, 74, 51, Post Office facilities for telemetry.
332. *Ibid,* 1970, 74, 105, Privately owned land lines for telemetry use.
333. *Ibid,* 1970, 74, 155, UHF radio equipment for telemetry use.
334. *Ibid,* 1970, 74, 198, Kent telemetry systems for data transmission.
335. *Ibid,* 1970, 74, 240, Ferranti telemetry equipment for data transmission.
336. *Ibid,* 1970, 74, 286, Westinghouse telemetry systems for the water industry.
337. *Ibid,* 1970, 74, 379, Plessey remote control and telemetry systems.
338. Rose, J. 1971 *ibid,* 75, 12, ML telemetry and telecontrol systems.
339. Walton, A. 1971 *ibid,* 75, 184, STC telemetry systems.
340. Barclay, D. 1974 *Water Services,* 78, June, 202, Low-cost telemetry can trim costs at all levels.
341. *Water Services* 1976, 80, April, Telemetry feature.
342. *Ibid,* 1977, 81, Feb., 94, Telemetry in the water industry: microprocessors in telemetry.
343. Davies, H. B. 1981 *J. IWES Supplement,* 35, 69, Micro-electronics in the water industry: programmable controllers.

Chapter 6

NETWORK ANALYSIS

1. INTRODUCTION

NETWORK analysis is the general term used to describe the process of constructing a model of a water distribution network and using that model to investigate the complex relationships between consumptions, flows and pressures.

A typical water distribution network comprising sources of supply, interconnected looped pipes, pumps and valves is a complex physical system. Understanding the behaviour of such a system under varying demand conditions is beyond the reach of most people's engineering intuition or ability with a pocket calculator. In all but the simplest cases the relationships between the many variables can be investigated only with the aid of a model to simulate the behaviour of the real system.

All items of plant and equipment commonly found in a water distribution system can be modelled to produce a 'snapshot' simulation at a particular time or, with sufficient time-based data (demand, pump status etc) can be extended to cover a time interval such as 24 hours, in which the analysis can additionally simulate the behaviour of reservoir levels etc.

Network analysis is a tool to help the engineer understand the behaviour of a distribution network and the information it provides can be an aid to almost every aspect of distribution management. Examples of applications are:
(1) Assessment of the capacity of an existing network.
(2) Investigation of the operation of a network to control pressures or reduce pumping costs.
(3) Design of new systems.
(4) Comparisons of different possible reinforcements to existing systems.
(5) Provision of information for investigations of deterioration in water quality, consumer demand, deterioration of pipelines, etc.
(6) Alleviation of problems under emergency conditions—for example, burst mains.

Whilst the impetus to undertake a network analysis usually results from a specific need as listed above, few engineers having undertaken such an exercise feel that they have wasted their time. Indeed many engineers agree that the discipline imposed upon them in rationalizing their distribution networks to provide the data for a model has in itself been a beneficial exercise.

2. HISTORICAL BACKGROUND

The calculations associated with network analysis are difficult for two reasons: firstly, the relationship between flow through a pipe and the pressure drop across its length is non-linear; and, secondly, most networks contain a number of loops, making it impossible to solve the network one component at a time. A mathematical solution to a network is based on two principles. These are: that at each node flow is conserved; and that the algebraic sum of headlosses around any *closed* loop is zero. These laws can be expressed as non-linear equations in either pressures (nodal formulation) or an independent set of flows (loop formulation).

Numerical solution methods are iterative. The methods involve making a preliminary estimate of pressures (or flows) and calculating a series of corrections to these values until a satisfactory balance is achieved.

The first numerical methods for solving the fluid networks to be widely known are those associated with Hardy Cross[1,2]. The Hardy Cross analysis was particularly amenable to programming and hence soluble using digital computers. The first attempts to do this appear to have been made simultaneously by workers in North America, Europe and Australia during the period 1955 to 1960. It is often claimed that the Hardy Cross method does not always reliably lead to a solution.

At about the same time McIlroy[3] found that the relationship between current and voltage of a tungsten filament lamp was sufficiently similar to the fluid pipe flow relationship to enable a direct analogue to be developed.

In 1963 the British Aircraft Corporation built a direct analyser[4] (*Wanda*), which modelled the head flow relationship by a series of straight lines. Most network analysis performed in the water industry during the 1960s was undertaken using an electric analogue.

From 1970 onwards there has been a gradual increase in the use of digital computers for network analysis and analogues are seldom used today. The reason for this change is probably because digital computers have become cheaper, more versatile and widely available, removing the need for the special purpose device. Also the computer programs for use on digital computers have become more versatile and enable complex situations to be modelled which would have been difficult, if not impossible, on analogues.

Even with digital computation there is still no consensus on the choice of numerical method which should be used to solve the network. The main divisions of opinion have been whether to centre the equation solving[5] on loops or on nodes, since they have relative advantages and disadvantages in terms of computational storage, time and reliability. The latest method to be devised and probably the most efficient[6] combines the greater reliability of a loop formulation with the greater efficiency of nodal solution methods.

3. NETWORK ANALYSIS PROGRAMME

Computer programs for water distribution network analysis are readily available from most large computer bureaus, from the larger manufacturers of computers, from a number of consulting engineers and from the Water Research Centre[7].

From the user's viewpoint the formats used for entering data and displaying results, together with the features that can be modelled, are more important than the knowledge of the detailed method by which the solution is obtained, although the cost of each computer run should not be overlooked.

The latest computer programs can be used interactively and enable a diagram of the network to be produced and annotated with the results of the analysis. This enables an engineer to sit in front of a terminal and design, manipulate or otherwise examine the behaviour of the network without the need for a pen, calculator or a drawing. However, he can—whenever he desires—produce a permanent record of his work at the touch of a button. Many programs offer the user a choice of either Hazen-Williams or Colebrook-White flow formulae.

4. CHOICE OF FLOW FORMULAE

Over the years a number of empirical flow formulae have been devised for calculating the head/flow relationships of water pipes. Each formula has been developed to adequately model the flow behaviour for a range of flow and pipe conditions. Only one formula, Colebrook-White, adequately covers a wide range of turbulent flow conditions and this is the most difficult formula to use in normal hand calculations. Traditionally, most engineers in the British water industry have used the Hazen-Williams formula for calculating pipe flow and this is perfectly adequate for normal design purposes, where velocities are likely to be around 1 m/s and pipes relatively smooth. There is, however, a gradual trend to the use of the Colebrook-White equation for network analysis. The main reason for this is the need for more accurate simulation of network behaviour when network analysis is used to solve operational problems which may involve simulation of flows very much less than 1 m/s. The DoE/NWC Standing Technical Committee on Sewers and Water Mains recommends the use of Colebrook-White for all pipe flow calculations.

5. DATA COLLECTION

SIMPLIFICATION OF NETWORK AND PRODUCTION OF SCHEMATIC DIAGRAM

For the purposes of network analysis, a water supply distribution network is considered to consist of a number of pipe lengths interconnected at node points. Water can enter or leave the network only at these node points. Experience has shown that networks can be represented in this way without significant loss of accuracy or generality[8,9]. An analysis will usually be undertaken to investigate the behaviour of a network in a certain set of circumstances or to determine the best design to supply new or increased demands. In these circumstances, only the pipes that transfer water from one part of the network to another will be of interest, and those which supply a local demand, estate or individual consumers can be ignored. It is convenient therefore to simplify the network. This will not only make the task of analysing the network that much easier, but will also reduce the time and cost of the computer analysis. There are no exact rules to be followed when simplifying a network. Each network must be considered on its merits. It is possible, however, to give some general guidelines as follows:

(a) Any pipe that does not form part of a loop and which is in a limb containing no source can be ignored. The consumers supplied by that pipe should be represented as extra consumption at an appropriate place in the simplified network.

(b) Small diameter pipes which feed into the areas of demand, such as housing estates, and which do not transfer water from one part of the network to another can be ignored. Note, however, that in some networks, particularly rural networks, a 4 inch (100 mm) diameter pipe or even a 3 inch (80 mm) diameter pipe can form a vital link and then the pipe must not be ignored.

(c) Small diameter pipes in parallel with a much larger diameter pipe, whether laid along the same route or taking a slightly different route, can be ignored.

(d) Short lengths of pipe, particularly of large diameter, need not be modelled individually. There is no precise rule on this. The aim should be for a model hydraulically equivalent to the real network but not necessarily geometrically identical.

If there is any doubt about the importance of a particular pipe length, then in general it is better to leave it out and include it at a later stage if necessary, thus keeping the network size to the minimum.

The task of simplifying and analysing a network will be made very much easier if a schematic diagram of the network is produced. Ideally the schematic drawing should include all the fixed information and, as far as possible, follow the geographical layout of the real network. It can best be produced by following the procedure below:

   (i) On a scale drawing of the network, mark the node points: (intersections of two or more pipes), sources of water, groups of consumers, individual consumers, individual consumers of large quantities of water.

  (ii) Draw the nodes on a separate piece of paper in roughly the same configuration as the original but leaving sufficient space between adjacent nodes to draw an information box, and moving the relative positions of certain nodes so as to prevent pipes from crossing one another.

 (iii) Draw in those pipes which are to be included in the analysis, and construct on each an information box of the type shown in Fig. 6.1.

 (iv) Record in the boxes the diameter and length, scaled from the drawing, of each pipe in the network. It may be found that further simplification can be made at this stage.

  (v) Number or name the nodes on the schematic drawing in some logical sequence. This will be found helpful later.

 (vi) On each node, construct a flag as shown in Fig. 6.1, and in the lower space insert the ground level. For system design purposes, this is normally the level of the highest ground supplied from that node. However, for other purposes, particularly comparison with pressure measurements, actual ground levels should be used.

(vii) Produce a negative of the schematic drawing so that copies using dyeline or other suitable process can be made for subsequent use.

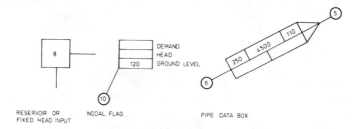

Fig. 6.1. Recommended data boxes for network schematic diagram

When an interactive graphics program is used the diagram is constructed, by the user, on the graphics terminal and stored in the computer for future reference.

HYDRAULIC ROUGHNESS VALUES

Each pipe section in the network model must have assigned to it an initial estimate of roughness value. These estimates will be later reinforced by the field test measurements and if necessary modified. Table 6.I lists typical C-Values for use in the Hazen-Williams formula for pipes of different ages and materials. Lawson[9] gives typical K-values of roughness for use in the Colebrook-White formula.

TABLE 6.I.   C-Values for Use in the Hazen-Williams Formula *(from Ref. 2)*

Type of pipe	Values of C for pipes of diameter:—					
	1 in	3 in	6 in	12 in	24 in	48 in
Uncoated Cast Iron: Smooth and New		121	125	130	132	134
Coated Cast Iron: Smooth and New		129	133	138	140	141
30 years old:–						
Trend 1: slight attack		100	106	112	117	120
„ 2: moderate attack		83	90	97	102	107
„ 3: appreciable attack		59	70	78	83	89
„ 4: severe attack		41	50	58	66	73
60 years old:–						
Trend 1: slight attack		90	97	102	107	112
„ 2: moderate attack		69	79	85	92	96
„ 3: appreciable attack		49	58	66	72	78
„ 4: severe attack		30	39	48	56	62
100 years old:–						
Trend 1: slight attack		81	89	95	100	104
„ 2: moderate attack		61	70	78	83	89
„ 3: appreciable attack		40	49	57	64	71
„ 4: severe attack		21	30	39	46	54
Miscellaneous:–						
Newly scraped mains		109	116	121	125	127
Newly brushed mains		97	104	108	112	115
Coated Spun Iron: Smooth and New		137	142	145	148	148
Old:– Take as coated cast iron of same age						
Galvanised Iron: Smooth and New	120	129	133			
Wrought Iron: Smooth and New	129	137	142			
Coated Steel: Smooth and New	129	137	142	145	148	148
Uncoated Steel: Smooth and New	134	142	145	147	150	150
Coated Asbestos Cement: Clean		147	149	150	152	
Uncoated Asbestos Cement: Clean		142	145	147	150	
Spun Cement Lined and Spun Bitumen Lined: Clean ...		147	149	150	152	153
Smooth Pipe: (inc. lead, brass, copper, polythene, smooth						
P.V.C., etc): Clean	140	147	149	150	152	153
P.V.C. (Wavy): Clean	134	142	145	147	150	150
Concrete:– (Scoby)						
Class 1 ($C_s = 0.27$) Clean		69	79	84	90	95
„ 2 ($C_s = 0.31$) Clean		95	102	106	110	113
„ 3 ($C_s = 0.345$) Clean		109	116	121	125	127
„ 4 ($C_s = 0.37$) Clean		121	125	130	132	134
Best ($C_s = 0.40$) Clean		129	133	138	140	141
Tate Relined Pipes: Clean		109	116	121	125	127
Prestressed Concrete Pipes: Clean				147	150	150

NOTE:– The above table has been compiled from an examination of 372 records. It is emphasized that the Hazen-Williams formula is not suitable for values of the coefficient C appreciably below 100, but the values in the above table are approximately correct at a velocity of 3 ft/sec.

NETWORK CONTROL VALVES

Pressure reducing valves (PRVs), pressure sustaining valves (PSVs) and non-return valves (NRVs) can all be modelled directly by most computer programs. Usually the inlet and outlet nodes must be specified to model the direction of flow.

An NRV need be included only if there is uncertainty about the operating status under particular network conditions. An NRV which is known to be open can be omitted for analysis purposes.

Some programs allow the user to optionally specify the likely status of any control valve in the network. Whilst this information is not strictly necessary it may reduce computation time.

FLOAT-VALVES

Many service reservoirs and water towers are fitted with float-valves on the inlet pipe to prevent overflow. These valves gradually close as the level of water in the reservoir rises, and have the effect of apparently increasing the resistance of the inlet pipe or raising the effective head of the reservoir. If the computer program does not specifically model float-valves they can be modelled by the user in one of three ways:

(1) The network can be divided and the reservoir replaced by two reservoirs. One is placed at the outlet of the actual reservoir with a head set to the level of water in the reservoir, and the second is placed on the inlet to the actual reservoir with the head set at some higher level to simulate the effect of the valve.

(2) The reservoir and float-valve are modelled by a reservoir and a demand. The network is split at the reservoir and the valve is simulated by a reservoir at the outlet, set to the appropriate head, and a consumption on the inlet, set to the appropriate inflow rate.

(3) A dummy pipe is inserted in the inlet to the reservoir and the resistance of this pipe is adjusted to simulate the resistance imposed by the ball-valve.

SOURCE INPUTS

For the purposes of network analysis, any point where water can enter the network must be considered as a source. Consequently, service reservoirs, water towers and bulk supply inputs, in addition to boreholes and treatment works, are considered to be sources.

For non-pumped sources, either the head of the incoming supply (relative to a common datum, usually OD) or the rate of input is required. For the field test, which will be discussed later, both head and flow are required for every source. If the behaviour of a service reservoir or water tower is to be studied over a 24-hour period, then the surface area and depth or the volume/depth characteristic, if the reservoir is of non-uniform cross-section, will also be required.

For pumped sources, the information required will depend upon whether the pump is fixed-speed or variable-speed.

Fixed-speed pumps

Fixed-speed pumps will normally have a characteristic head/flow relationship of the type shown in Fig. 6.2a. Pairs of lift and flow readings are taken from the curve and input to the program. If the pump has a fairly flat characteristic, care should be taken in reading points at the extremities of the curve to ensure that it does not dip, giving rise to two flow values at the same head.

Variable-speed pumps

A variable-speed pump with constant flow control can be modelled by specifying a negative consumption of the appropriate flow rate. A variable-speed and constant-head pump can be modelled by specifying a reservoir set to the appropriate head.

In-line boosters

A fixed-speed booster is dealt with in exactly the same way as a fixed-speed source pump.

A variable-speed booster can be modelled by specifying a pump with straight line

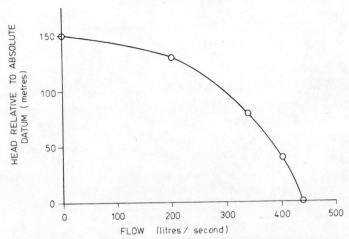

Fig. 6.2a.   Head/flow relationship for fixed-speed pump

characteristic. With some network analysis programs care must be taken to ensure that this line is not exactly horizontal (constant lift—Fig. 6.2b) nor exactly vertical (constant flow—Fig 6.2c) otherwise a solution will not be obtained.

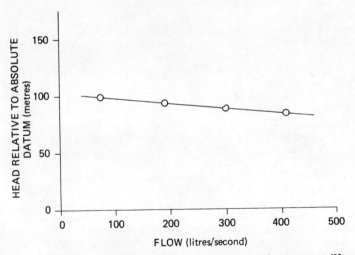

Fig. 6.2b.   Head/flow relationship for variable-speed, constant lift pump

ESTIMATION OF NODAL CONSUMPTION

The next stage is to determine the area around each node which can be considered to be supplied from that node. This again depends upon the skill and judgement of the engineer, and there are no definite rules to follow. In general, however, it will be a simple matter to determine a large proportion of the area

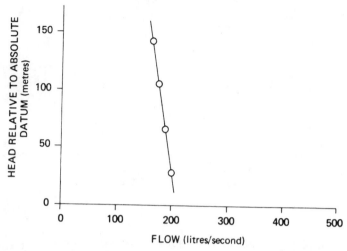

Fig. 6.2c. Head/flow relationship for variable-speed, constant flow pump

supplied by each node, and hence it is only the determination of the precise position of the boundary between demand areas which might cause difficulty. Fortunately, most networks are insensitive to small changes of demand between one node and another, and moving, say, one-tenth of the demand from one node to an adjacent node, will have an insignificant effect on pressures. This is not, however, always the case, particularly in networks with a large number of small diameter pipes flowing near their maximum capacity. Caution is therefore necessary. The results of the preliminary field measurements can often be useful for determining boundary positions. Demand areas should be shaded on a suitably scaled map of the distribution system using coloured pencils. This approach is illustrated in monochrome shading in Fig. 6.3

When the area supplied from each node has been decided, the next step is to determine the average consumption within each area. This is usually achieved by counting the number of houses or unmetered connections within the area and multiplying by the annual average demand per unmetered connection. It is therefore implicitly assumed that the average annual consumption for non-metered connections is constant throughout the network and that all leakage in the system is equally divided between all non-metered consumers. The total number of metered consumers within each area should then be ascertained and their average consumption obtained from meter records. If the total metered consumption is small, or if the average consumption per metered consumer is similar to the average consumption per non-metered consumer, then all consumers can be considered in the same way as non-metered.

Any metered user that consumes a very large volume of water, takes a high flow rate for a short period of time, or consumes water, say, during the night should be noted and possibly dealt with individually.

The following steps summarise the procedure for estimation of consumption at each node:

(a) On a suitably scaled map, mark the area supplied from each node and shade using coloured pencils.

(b) Determine the number of metered connections in each shaded area.
(c) Determine the number of non-metered connections in each shaded area.
(d) Note the details of the users of large quantities of water or high flow rates for short periods.

From measurements of total supply and from quarterly meter readings, it will be possible to obtain the average consumption per non-metered connection, and the average consumption per metered connection. Consequently, the average demand for each node is given by:

(Number of houses × average consumption) +
(Number of meters × average consumption) +
(Consumption of users to be dealt with individually).

It is often convenient to convert average metered consumption into an equivalent number of unmetered connections. The consumption for each node can then be given as a number of connections.

When undertaking network analysis, it is normal to assume that demands vary *pro rata* from one load condition to another and a factor can be used to increase or decrease the average demand, depending upon the condition to be analysed. If the user has a program with this facility, the consumption per node can be input as a

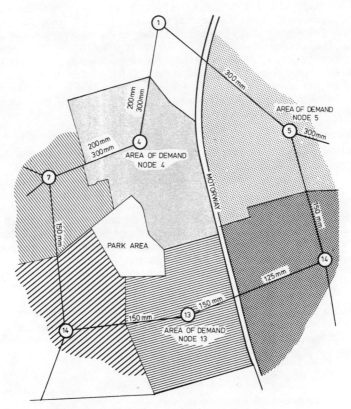

Fig. 6.3. Allocation of demand areas to nodes

number of connections and the scale factor arranged to give the particular flow rate desired. Any demands, such as large users, that do not vary *pro rata*, can be dealt with separately. This procedure not only saves some manual arithmetic, but also makes it easy to transfer consumers between nodes, or to vary the number of connections or the average demand at some future stage in the analysis.

Bulk supplies to an adjacent zone or network not included in the model are also treated as demands.

DIURNAL VARIATIONS IN DEMAND

The total demand in a network varies throughout the day. In a completely homogeneous system the percentage variation in demand at any node, from one hour to the next, is the same and equal to the percentage variation in total demand and all demands can be changed *pro rata*. In some networks, however, particularly those with separate industrial and domestic estates, this is not the case and percentage changes in one part of the network can be quite different from those in another. Most programs for network analysis allow differing variations in model consumption to be accommodated.

For normal network design purposes, factors for peak, average and night demand conditions will usually suffice. For other purposes, such as investigating the behaviour of a service reservoir over a 24-hour period, factors which represent the changing demand throughout the day may be required. Careful thought must be given to the purpose of the analysis and hence to the most appropriate factors. For example, if the purpose of the analysis is the future design of the system, then factors for the peak hour on the peak day or peak week will be most appropriate, whereas for examination of the behaviour of the system under emergency conditions it will be more appropriate to use factors for peak hour on the average day. Further discussion on the selection of demand factors and their component points is given in Chapter 4.

GROUND LEVELS

The use of ground levels (and the problems of which figures to use in different applications) causes confusion and is discussed separately below.

All pressures in the network model must be related to some common datum, usually OD. The pressure is the sum of the hydraulic head above ground and the ground level. For many applications it is useful to specify the nodal ground level as the highest ground supplied from that node. In any subsequent design it is then a simple matter to check that all consumers in that nodal area have sufficient hydraulic head by simply subtracting the ground level from the computed pressure, a task performed automatically by most programs.

For pressure measurements, the gauge reading must be added to the height of the gauge above datum. The depth of the main at the point of measurement is not relevant.

The height of reservoirs should be taken as the height of the bottom water level (BWL) above datum plus the height of water in the reservoir above BWL.

The set pressure for PRVs and PSVs is the height of the valve above datum plus the valve setting.

6. FIELD MEASUREMENTS

PRELIMINARY PRESSURE MEASUREMENTS

When a network is being analysed for the first time, it is recommended that preliminary pressure measurements be made whilst initial data are being collected. This is achieved by putting out pressure recorders close to nodes shown on the simplified diagram and taking 24-hour pressure recordings. The next day the recorders are put out on the next set of adjacent nodes and the process repeated. Thus, if there are sufficient pressure recorders to measure pressures at 10 per cent of the nodes, then it will take ten working days to cover the network. At the end of each 24-hour period, the recorder charts should be examined and the pressure measurements read at three different time periods, usually from 0800 hours to 1000 hours, 1200 hours to 1400 hours and 0100 hours to 0600 hours, corresponding approximately to peak, average and minimum night conditions. These results should be tabulated and recorded on a simplified diagram of the network. The charts should also be examined for any large changes in pressure occurring in short time periods, possibly caused by consumers taking water at a high flow rate or by valve closures. Any such pressure fluctuations should be investigated.

(Note: the height of each gauge AOD should be measured and added to the gauge reading for comparison purposes).

Pressures shown on the simplified schematic diagram of the network should be examined and compared for consistency. Pressure should gradually decrease as the distance from the source increases and the algebraic sum of headlosses around any loop should be about zero. Headlosses at night should be very much less than during the day, with pressures rising towards those of the incoming source or service reservoir. Any large losses in single pipe sections, or other anomalies, should be investigated. By adopting this procedure, many of the inconsistencies in the data will have been discovered and investigated before any work is undertaken on the computer. Consequently, shut valves, incorrect pipe work connections, mistaken diameters or lengths and open bypasses, should have been found.

Preliminary measurements can be useful for deciding the position of boundaries between demand areas and whether or not a particular pipe section should be included in the analysis. They may also be used to determine whether PRVs, pumps or boosters are working as designed and whether ball-valves need to be simulated. In practice it will not be possible to measure pressures at all of the nodes on the network and perhaps achieving reliable measurements at half of the nodes will be nearer the norm. Note that since the preliminary pressure measurements cannot all be made on the same day, and because demand can vary from one day to the next, it may not be possible to compare directly one day's readings with the next. It is advisable therefore to have one pressure measuring position common to two consecutive days' measurements, thus allowing differences between one day and the rest to be measured directly.

FIELD TEST

The data collected so far consist partly of factual data, such as pipe diameters and lengths, and partly of estimates of quantities such as roughness values and demands. In order to check that there are no gross errors in the factual data, and that the estimates are reasonable, the flows and pressures predicted by the model are compared with a known situation within the real network. To achieve this a field test is undertaken. Information required for the field test consists of the head (AOD) and inflow from each source in the network and simultaneous measurement of selected pressures within the network. It is normally sufficient to measure pressures at approximately 10 per cent of the nodes within the system and the results of the preliminary pressure measurements will indicate which nodes are preferable for this purpose. If the network contains metered consumers who take water at a high flow rate, then it may also be necessary to read those meters during the field test. Ideally the field test data should be obtained from recordings taken over a 24-hour period.

MAKING FIELD MEASUREMENTS

Whenever possible field measurements should be made with accurate and reliable recording instruments. Unfortunately this is not always possible and it will be found necessary to make a series of spot measurements or manual recordings. There are a number of problems that can be encountered whilst making field measurements and the more common are discussed briefly below.

Reservoirs

For the field test, the inflow, outflow and water level of every reservoir and water tower in the network will be required. In practice if any two of: (inflow, outflow and the rate of change of level) are measured, then the third can be calculated. If the test is made during the peak period, then in many cases there will be no flow into the reservoir and the measurement of rate of change of level will produce both the height and the outflow. In other cases it will be found that the inlet to the reservoir can be turned off for a few hours, if no flow measurement is possible.

Reservoir level measurements are best made with a recording depth-gauge, but in many cases it may be necessary to make manual measurements, using a dip-stick or hook-gauge, every five or fifteen minutes, depending upon the surface area of the reservoir and the outflow rate. The level measurement by sight tube is an alternative method of obtaining manual readings. If the sight tube is tapped into the outlet pipe of the reservoir, then changes in headloss in that pipe section can lead to inaccurate measurement. Measurements of flow rates into and out of the reservoirs are dealt with in the next section.

Measurement of Flowrate

Measurements of rate of flow are required for all sources in the network. Many of the meters associated with the sources will not provide a measurement of flow. These are usually meters of the Helix type. In order to obtain rate of flow measurements on this type of meter, it will be necessary either to fit a Leeds recorder or to record the meter reading manually every five minutes or so.

If there is no existing meter at a source, then the most convenient way of obtaining flow measurements will be to use an insertion meter. This may be either a Pitot tube or an insertion turbine, although it will be found that the latter is the more convenient since a recording of the output can readily be obtained.

There are a number of checks that should be made before making any measurements at all. These are as follows:

(i) Make sure that the meter bypass is closed.
(ii) If a chart recording is to be made, then make sure that the chart is in the right units and the appropriate scale for the meter is being used.
(iii) If an insertion meter is being used, then make sure that the operator has had a chance to familiarise himself with the instrument before making the field test measurement.

Manual Recording

Whenever manual recording—making specific measurements at set time intervals—is required, it is important to impress upon the operator the need for an accurate reading, since recording flow or levels every five minutes over a two- or three-hour period is extremely boring. The measuring units of different meters can give rise to errors, particularly if the person making the measurements is used to units other than those being read. The danger is then that the flow is recorded in the wrong units or, more seriously, that the last two digits of the reading may be ignored, when in fact they represent a considerable proportion of the flow.

Pressure Measurements

Pressures within a distribution system are usually measured with mechanical pressure recorders. These instruments are undoubtedly very good for normal waterworks use, but for network analysis they must be pushed to their limits of accuracy. To achieve the best possible accuracy, the recorders should be calibrated before and after making the measurements and a zero pressure line should be scribed on the chart, by rotating the chart in the appropriate direction, after the recorder is installed but before the connections are tightened or the hydrant opened.

The current trend in the UK water industry is to use pressure transducers and solid-state pressure loggers for pressure measurement. These instruments are very much more accurate than mechanical recorders and generally are more reliable. This increased accuracy is particularly important when models are produced to investigate operational problems, because close agreement between the behaviour of the model and the real system is essential.

Erroneous pressure measurements can result from a variety of causes, including:

(1) Use of an instrument with an unsuitable pressure range.
(2) Using the wrong scale of chart on a particular instrument.
(3) Connecting the recorder to a loose jumper hydrant. (Characteristic trace is a pressure which rises during the day but does not fall).
(4) Gauge connected to a hydrant but hydrant not opened.
(5) Pressure measured on the wrong main. This is likely to occur when mains in different pressure zones are laid in the same road.
(6) Pumping station losses.

It has been the author's experience that pressures measured inside a pumping station can be between 3 m and 30 m higher than those measured in the distribution system immediately outside the station. The pressure differences are caused either by manifold losses or by throttling the pump to keep it on its duty point. It is therefore recommended that, whenever a pumping station is included in an analysis, the pressures should be measured outside the station and as close to the network as possible. Where large differences are encountered they should be reported to the engineer responsible for pumping.

All pressure measurements should be referred to some common datum, usually OD. The level of each gauge must be determined using normal surveying techniques.

7. CALIBRATION OF NETWORK MODEL

In order to calibrate the network model, field test data are used for comparison between computed and measured flows and pressures within the network for some given consumption pattern. A time is chosen, usually a peak flow period where the flows and headlosses are high, but also when demand is stable. All readings are then made at this time. From the flow measurements it is possible to determine the total demand of the network at that particular time and, from the pressure recordings plus ground levels, it is possible to determine the pressures at the selected nodes within the network. The average demands calculated earlier for each node are then increased *pro rata* so that their total equals the total measured input. The program is then run and the computed flows and pressures compared with the measured flows and pressures. If the two sets of readings do not agree, the data must be re-examined for possible error and perhaps the estimates revised so that the two sets of readings come into line. There are a number of reasons for disagreement between measured and computed flows and pressures, and some of the more common are tabulated below:

(*a*) Incorrect assumptions regarding hydraulic resistances.

(*b*) Dimensions and units are a common source of errors. These may be either in the field test information or in the basic pipe data. It is not uncommon for pipe lengths or diameters to be either measured wrongly or recorded wrongly.

(*c*) Unsuspected cross connections may exist or the actual connections may be different from those assumed. Fig. 6.4 shows common situations.

(*d*) Shut valves that were assumed to be open or valves where the gate has dropped from the spindle are not uncommon.

(*e*) Bypass valves around PRVs, NRVs or meters left open.

(*f*) Valves between pressure zones left open or leaking.

(*g*) Making pressure measurements on rider mains (small diameter mains in parallel with a large diameter main) may give rise to apparently large headlosses that do not occur in the larger main.

(*h*) Obstructions in the main causing high headlosses over short lengths of pipe have been caused by a variety of debris ranging from bottles and planks of wood to a wheelbarrow.

(*i*) Large pressure losses in a pumping station have been encountered in many networks. Consequently, in any network containing a pump, it is recommended that the relationship between pumphouse pressure and distribution pressure close to the distribution system be measured and compared. If the station losses are high, then all future pressure measurements should be made in the distribution system.

Changes are made to the data, initially on a trial and error basis, until the computed and measured flows and pressures are in agreement. All changes to data must, however, be justified and all but small changes in roughness value or demand should be verified by either field inspection or further field measurement.

The preliminary pressure measurements will prove extremely valuable during this model-making stage and can be used to justify changes in the data. It should be remembered, however, that one day's pressure readings are not necessarily exactly

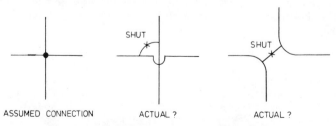

ASSUMED CONNECTION   ACTUAL ?   ACTUAL ?

Fig. 6.4. Possible modes of connection

comparable with another day's readings, since they may have been made under different flow conditions. The relevance of a batch of preliminary measurements can be assessed by comparing the field test measurements with the preliminary measurements made at the same nodes.

Once good agreement between measured and computed flows and pressures has been achieved for one particular demand period (peak) the total of the demand should be adjusted to a second period (average) and the computed and measured pressures compared. A further comparison may be made for night conditions.

If poor agreement is obtained when comparing measured and computed pressures for night flow conditions, this may be partly due to the fact that the Hazen-Williams equation if used is not particularly accurate at low flow velocities; this should be less of a problem if the Colebrook-White equation is used.

When good agreement between measured and computed flows and pressures has been obtained, the schematic negative should be modified to incorporate any changes made, together with the final roughness values inserted in the pipe boxes.

If a calibrated model has been produced using the Hazen-Williams formula and the user wishes subsequently to use Colebrook-White, conversion is best made by calculating the appropriate K-value of each pipe from the flows and headlosses obtained from the model relating to peak flow conditions.

8. APPLICATION OF THE MODEL

SHORT TERM IMPROVEMENTS

Most networks have a small area or a number of small areas which give rise to operational problems during the year. These may be caused by poor pressure at certain times of the day or year, reservoirs or towers remaining full or drawing down too quickly, or areas of high pressure giving rise to increased leakage. These problems can often be overcome by laying short lengths of main, valving, re-zoning, or removing obstructions within the system. Network analysis enables various changes to be simulated and the corresponding costs and advantages to be determined.

DESIGNING FOR THE FUTURE

Most network analyses are undertaken to determine the long term forward design of a network. Determination of the reinforcement size, location, the effects of introducing new supplies, the positioning of new service reservoirs, and the effects of zoning can be determined by network simulation. The steps necessary to achieve this are to some extent self evident and have been adequately covered elsewhere[8]. However, an outline of the basic steps is as follows:

   (i) Determine design period, typically 20-30 years.
   (ii) Calculate projected demand of existing consumers in, say, five-year steps up to the final design year. Add to each demand step all anticipated new development.
   (iii) Determine design criteria, such as maximum and minimum allowable pressures, maximum velocities, preferred diameters, storage requirements etc. See Chapters 4 and 5.
   (iv) Put the predicted demand for the final design year into the model and add to the model any new nodes necessary to account for future development. Suitable pipe routes for supplying these new developments must be determined and the lengths of the proposed pipes scaled from a map. Where more than one possible route exists then this fact should be noted.

The new nodes should then be connected to the model with pipes of a diameter likely to be adequate—these will be refined later—laid along one of the suitable routes. The introduction of other new works is dealt with in a similar way.

(v) The program is then run and the results inspected to determine how the pressures and velocities compare with the design criteria. Changes are then made to the model, typically reinforcements, new sources, boosters etc, and the initial estimates of diameters of pipes supplying new demand, until the design criteria are met. Normally there will be a number of different ways in which a network can be reinforced to supply future demands. These should all be investigated separately and the results recorded.

(vi) The various design options are then compared on the basis of cost (using a simple cost model), reliability (removing key mains to simulate bursts) and any other local factors such as whether any of the routes go through the town centre.

(vii) Having determined the final design the demand in the model is progressively reduced, in the five-year stage previously calculated, and at each step as many reinforcements as possible are removed whilst maintaining the design criteria. This is repeated back to the present day and results in a mainlaying programme working towards the final design.

The model can be used in a similar way to investigate the effects of any design or operational changes. For example, effects of installing boosters or PRVs, the ability of the network to withstand bursts or to meet firefighting needs or to determine suitable sites and levels for new service reservoirs. In this latter case it will be necessary to simulate demand over a 24-hour period under different conditions to check that the reservoir fills and empties.

9. NEW AND FUTURE DEVELOPMENTS

The use of interactive graphics computer facilities is likely to increase in the future. Programs already exist which enable the schematic diagram of the network to be drawn, stored, displayed and printed, together with the results of the analysis. Programs also exist which enable automatic 24-hour simulation and the results of, say, nodal pressure to be displayed as a graph of pressure against time of day.

The general use of computerised records and maps will enable the collection and maintenance of data for network analysis to be achieved more readily and is likely to result in the increased use of network models for operational problems, such as dealing with bursts and planning mains maintenance such as relining.

Modifications will have to be made to network analysis programs to allow modern developments in distribution control equipment to be modelled. The area where most changes are currently taking place is that of pressure control. Future computer programs should be capable of modelling remotely sensed PRVs, the pressure at one node being fixed by controlling the pressure in some other part of the system. The second development, that has yet to be proven, is a demand-controlled PRV. With this device the outlet pressure of the valve is related to, and raised, with increased flow through the valve.

The Water Research Centre is currently investigating the use of network models linked to a distribution telemetry system to enable continuous surveillance comparison of real and predicted flows and pressures to allow continuous regulation of the network.

10. REFERENCES

1. Cross, H. 1936. Bulletin 286 "Analysis of flow in networks of conduits or conductors". University of Illinois Engineering Experiment Station, Urbana, Illinois.
2. The Institution of Water Engineers (now The Institution of Water Engineers and Scientists) 1969 "Manual of British water engineering practice" (Fourth edition, volume II).
3. McIlroy, M. S. 1950 J. AWWA, 42, 347, Direct-reading analyser for pipeline networks.
4. Williams, R. W. 1964 Wat. & Wat. Engng, 68, 12, A new water.network distribution analyser.
5. Martin, D. W. and Peters, G. 1963 J. IWES, 17, 115, The application of Newton's method to network analysis by digital computer.
6. Stimson, K. R. and Brameller, A. 1981 J. IWES, 35, 186, An integrated mesh-nodal method for steady-state water distribution network analysis.
7. Creasey, J. D., Stimson, K. R. et al 1982 Water Research Centre Technical Report TR 177 "A guide to water network analysis and the WRC computer program WATNET, Parts I, II and III".
8. Lawson, W. R. 1969 Wat. & Wat. Engng, 73, 144, The art and philosophy of network analysis.
9. Lawson, W. R. 1970 J. IPHE, 69, 160, Some practical aspects of water distribution network analysis.

Continuous monitoring of distribution system (*Bristol Waterworks Company*)

Pumping plant (*Bristol Waterworks Company*)

Chapter 7

PUMPING PLANT

1. INTRODUCTION

AS with almost all engineering design, successful selection and installation of pumping plant entails achievement of some best compromise. The processes necessarily involve iteration but the chapter has been laid out as far as possible as a logical series of steps. Thus Section 2 below is a general guide to the process of designing and locating pumping plant and is followed by Sections giving more details on plant selection; pump construction and specification; buildings; and finally control, operation and maintenance.

2. DETERMINATION OF DUTY

GENERAL

This Section deals with those matters which are necessary prerequisites to the selection of the type of pumping plant and its motive power.

HYDRAULIC INVESTIGATION

Clearly the more accurately the hydraulic characteristics of the system into which the pumping plant is to be introduced can be determined, the more successful will be the completed work in terms of cost and efficiency.

Existing Mains

The first requirement is to determine the conditions at the chosen site. A record of suction pressures should be obtained since these will determine both the ouput of any given unit and the strength of casing required. Careful assessment of the effects of sudden start up on the system should be made, both for the effects on consumers of reduced pressure and the possibility of damage due to surge; this latter problem is discussed later.

Accurate records should be obtained of the mains system on the delivery side and flow/pressure tests should be carried out using pressure recorders at as many locations as possible in order to determine accurately the hydraulic characteristics of the system. More information upon the conduct of such tests is given in Chapter 5. It is worth taking a good deal of care over this operation since not merely will overall friction loss in the system be determined, but also the individual losses in sections of (say) different diameter, age, material etc. can be studied. This information may indicate a need for relaying a particular section or for improving its frictional characteristics by scraping and relining. Whether such changes are carried out immediately or deferred for a period of years, their likely effect upon pump performance must be assessed.

New Mains

It is an oversimplification to state that the aim must be to minimise pipe friction; whilst this would minimise running costs, the capital cost of the resulting pumping main would be uneconomic. It is necessary, therefore, to find some best compromise and ideally this will be achieved by comparing the capital and operating costs of pumping plant over the assumed life of the plant with those for mains of differing sizes and (perhaps) materials. Where fairly constant pumping is envisaged, a main giving a flow rate of about 1.5 m/s is likely to provide an economic choice. Guidance on the carrying out of such an economic assessment will be found in Chapter 5.

Suction Lift

Where it is not possible to guarantee a positive suction head at all times, then the required suction lift must be specified most accurately. The performance of the pump will be found to reduce dramatically where suction lift is increased beyond a certain critical amount, due mainly to separation in the liquid in the suction pipe.

A further consequence of such separation is erosion of the metal surfaces due to collision of the separated particles.

Thus suction valves and suction pipes must be designed to ensure velocities and accelerations such that the absolute residual pressure shall nowhere fall as low as the vapour pressure of the fluid.

Whilst the variation of atmospheric pressure with elevation in the UK is not sufficient to cause difficulty, it should be remembered that height above sea level when working in overseas countries may cause a significant reduction in atmospheric pressure and hence available suction lift. It is important, also, to specify fluid temperature and specific gravity.

Factors which depress absolute pressure are therefore:
(1) elevation above the level at which the pressure is atmospheric;
(2) hydraulic friction through suction pipes and suction valves;
(3) velocity, v, which for its generation absorbs a head not less than $\dfrac{v^2}{2g}$;
(4) acceleration, f, which requires a force of $\dfrac{f}{g}$ per unit mass accelerated, or $l\dfrac{f}{g}$ head in a pipe of length l.

Where the absolute suction pressure is liable to be small:
(a) location of the pump should be as low as possible;
(b) suction pipes should be large and bend-free;
(c) columns of fluid to be accelerated should be short;
(d) good bellmouthed suction entry with an immersion depth of at least $\dfrac{v^2}{g}$ should be provided if possible.

DEMAND AND PUMP CHARACTERISTICS

'The matters to be dealt with under this heading are quantity; pressure requirements, including residual head; capacity, both installed and standby. These are considered separately under five categories of pumping duty later but, in general, it is obviously most important to be sure both of the suction flow and pressure conditions, as has been explained above, and also of the delivery requirements; this is particularly so in distribution pumping and in boosting, where the demands on the system will vary. Some guidance on the assessment of such flows and their peak rate variation is given in Chapter 5.

Assuming, therefore, that data are available as to the projected increases in demand (if any), it is necessary to decide how much spare accommodation should be included in the pumphouse and what the initial installed capacity of plant should be. These are complex matters and much must depend upon the degree of

confidence that can be placed on the demand projections; however, it is not usual
to provide spare accommodation for plant beyond a period of 20 or 25 years, nor to
install plant whose capacity will not be fully required within ten years.

The capacity of standby plant, or the degree of overcapacity, relates to whether
and for how long periods of outage can be tolerated, taking account of reservoir
storage and other pumped supplies. A starting point will be the provision of one
spare machine for each size of pump installed: however, in the case of boosting and
possibly in distribution and borehole pumping, it may be possible to hold one or
more spare pumps or motors only in central (dry) storage.

The following general classifications will be discussed:
  (i) Pumping from wells and boreholes.
  (ii) Pumping into supply at base stations.
  (iii) Repumping to higher elevation zones.
  (iv) Boosting along trunk and distribution mains.
  (v) Pumping to local high areas.

The main factors which will be discussed for each of these categories are:
  (1) The degree of reliability required.
  (2) Load factor, i.e. the ratio

$$\frac{\text{mean w.h.p. throughout the year}}{\text{maximum w.h.p. at any time during the year.}}$$

  (3) Hourly variation of flow and head during any one day.

Pumping from Wells and Boreholes

Impeller pumps for wells and boreholes, of both the surface-driven and
submersible-motor types, are briefly described in Section 3. For such duties
continuity of running is usually of great importance, or at any rate interruptions
must be of short duration: adequate stand-by capacity is therefore essential. The
load-factor is in most cases high, so the highest attainable efficiency is to be sought.

Where drive by purchased electric power is adopted, it will usually be found that,
with a careful choice of pump characteristics, constant speed will be preferable to
variable speed; however, widely varying demand pattern or other particular local
conditions may justify the extra cost of the latter. Unattended running under
automatic control should be the aim and this is discussed in Section 6. It is vital to
include low-level protection to guard against abnormal fall of the water level in well
or borehole.

Where water is not only to be raised from below ground but also pumped either
into supply or to a reservoir above the surface, best efficiency will be obtained by
applying the full head required by means of the underground pumps. It will be
necessary, of course, to arrange for chemical dosing pumps which are capable of
injecting against the full system pressure. Where more complex treatment is
involved, it may prove necessary to break the duty, in which case some balancing
storage must be provided before the suction of the surface (centrifugal) pump(s) to
avoid hunting since matching of duties is virtually impossible.

Pumping into Supply at Base Stations

Such pumping may be to a service reservoir, in which case brief interruption may
be tolerable. However, in some cities (Chicago is perhaps the best example)
topography militates against provision of service storage, so base stations must
operate continuously. Not only must machinery of high reliability be chosen, but
also much thought should be devoted to stand-by provision. There should be spare

units at least for each size or type of pump employed and a good case is arguable for going beyond this to at least 50 per cent spare capacity. Where electric power is purchased, dual feeds as far as possible from different supply sections should be laid in with automatic switch-over. When this is not possible, or where there is insufficient service storage, it will be prudent to provide either alternative drive by diesel engines or stand-by power from diesel-driven alternators. Direct mechanical drive of pumps by diesel engines is more economical in fuel than the alternative diesel-electric generation, but the greater flexibility of the latter, as to use and layout, and the existence of standard generating units, usually cause it to be preferred.

Diesel engine drive avoids the constraints of constant speed, but is usually subject to somewhat high labour and maintenance costs. On the other hand, where the stand-by plant is to be used to lessen the demand upon the grid at times of peak demand, thus effecting a saving in maximum demand charges, the higher efficiency of the direct-drive diesel engine may give it the advantage.

Since base stations usually have a high load factor, it is, in general, economic to go to considerable expense to ensure the highest efficiency, over the working range and throughout the expected useful life-period, of the units carrying the normal load. Most base stations perform a complex range of duties. Such multiple duties are easily arranged when the drive is by purchased electric power; using diesel drive, they can be performed by a number of engines and pumps without serious loss in efficiency.

In a large station driven by purchased electric power the constant speed of the ordinary induction motor presents some difficulty. The variations in head in most base stations are, however, generally not sufficient, in view of the wide range of head over which a good impeller pump will give a high efficiency, to justify the use of the variable-speed motor, with its lower efficiency and extra cost. Variations in rate of flow are covered by the use of multiple units, usually of graded size. In some cases (for example, where a variable rate of flow imposes considerable variations in friction head) it may pay to reduce the range of head required of the main pumps by installing low-lift pumps, acting as inlet boosters, for use during times of high head.

Plant design should aim for unmanned automatic running under remote supervision and control (Section 6).

Repumping to Higher Elevation Zones

Much of what has been written for base stations applies equally in this case. Pumping implies in this instance that there is a storage reservoir or water tower to which the pumps deliver and control will normally be arranged from water level or pressure sensors. If such storage is adequate (24 hours or more) it may be found worthwhile to install extra pumping capacity (or provide generous stand-by plant) so that off-peak tariffs may be used overnight for the major part of the supply. The extra pipe friction created by pumping at increased velocities should be checked lest this nullify overall cost savings.

Variable-speed pumps normally have no place in this type of station, since pumps of graded size should simply cover any required output variations.

Boosting along Trunk and Distribution Mains

Boosting may be applied:
  (a) to increase the carrying capacity of a main and to avoid, or postpone, replacement or duplication.
  (b) to overcome local deficiencies in pressure.

(c) to maintain or increase output of a pumping station with increasing friction-head or demand.

Boosting can often be restricted to times of peak demand; moreover, the desired boost head is generally variable, from almost zero up to that needed to impel the maximum required flow. The load-factor is therefore usually a low one. Since the boost head increases rapidly with the flow, the range of duty is such as can be covered by a variable-speed impeller pump with good efficiency (Section 3), but in many cases the complication of variable speed is not justified. Where it is justified, it is no longer necessary to go to the expense of the commutator motor, as thyristors and inverters are now being applied to speed control of ordinary squirrel cage motors.

Control is best effected in accordance with the pressure at the locality where it is liable to be deficient. With variable speed the difference between the settings of the stopping and starting pressure-limits must, to avoid hunting, exceed the resulting changes in the pressure: with constant speed the difference must exceed the head produced by booster. Reference to Figs. 7.1 and 7.2 will make this clear. In all cases a sufficient pause between events must be ensured to allow the conditions in the system (pressure surges, etc.) to settle.

Boosting may be less than successful where there are a number of branches off a main and where the intention is to raise the pressure at the end of that main. Careful hydraulic calculations should be undertaken, as most of the increased head will probably dissipate itself at the various branches, resulting in increased leakage.

Figs. 7.1 and 7.2 show that boosters are frequently best located on the track of a main rather than at pumping stations (or sources): not only may power be saved, but also the maximum pressure imposed on the main will be reduced. Booster pumps for such locations should be designed to work unattended under automatic control. They are almost universally electrically driven, and are frequently located underground in a bypass alongside the main, a reflux valve being installed in the main to carry unboosted flow and to prevent recirculation during boosting periods. Where speed variation is not required, a submersible pumping set or sets installed within casings may afford a convenient layout, motor and pump being immune from the damp conditions liable to occur.

Control may, as already mentioned, be effected by pressure, by time, by rate-of-flow, or by combinations of these. Care must be taken to ensure that low pressures leading to separation do not occur on the incoming side of a booster, especially when starting or accelerating.

In a recent instance, the head on a pumping station delivering into a long rising main was about 398 m (1 305 ft) but it was expected that in the near future the increased friction loss due to the growing demand would cause the head to rise at times to some 418 m (1 370 ft). It was intended, when demand further increased, to reduce the head required of the pumps by the use, when advantageous, of an inlet booster capable of applying about 73 m (240 ft). Thus the main pumps could continue to work near to their best load conditions, their efficiency (and their output) being maintained despite the increase in head-range resulting from growth in demand—and also, in due course, from mains duplication.

The cost of installing booster plant for increasing the capacity of a main is usually a small fraction of the alternative cost of duplicating or renewing the main itself. Moreover, the operating cost of boosting is in general small, especially where the pumps, which are generally unattended, are required to run only during periods of peak flow.

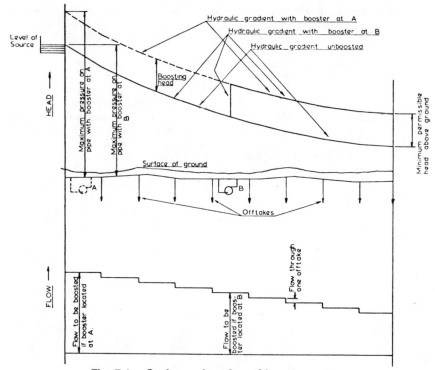

Fig. 7.1.   Optimum location of booster pump

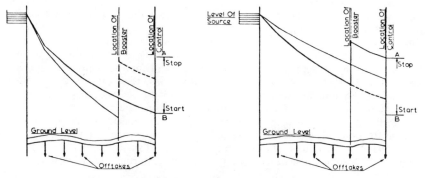

Fig. 7.2.   Stability of control of booster pump

Repumping to Local High Spots

To avoid raising the whole of the water required by an area to a head sufficient to satisfy the highest-lying consumer, repumping to supply local high spots or high buildings is frequently adopted. The plant is almost always electrically driven and automatically controlled. Further discussion of the types of plant applied to such duties will be found under Distribution Boosting in Section 3.

SELECTION OF SITE

The ideal site is rarely available and the final location of pumping plant may be a best compromise of several factors, principally those listed below:

  (i) Availability of electricity supply of adequate capacity.
  (ii) Vulnerability of power supply; is a duplicate mains feed available from an independent source?
  (iii) Hydraulics of suction and delivery lines relative to the ground level at the station and to the desired flow capacity.
  (iv) Access for delivery of plant and fuel if mains power is not to be used.
  (v) Environmental aspects, such as proximity to domestic property in relation to noise, etc.
  (vi) Space for future development.
  (vii) Liability to flooding, particularly in the cases of river intake stations and underground booster chambers; in the case of the latter, can reliable drainage be provided?
  (viii) Availability of telephone lines for data transmission and control.
  (ix) Space for surge protection equipment.
  (x) Value of land.

ACQUISITION OF ELECTRICITY SUPPLY

As noted above, the availability of an adequate supply of mains electricity will be a determining factor in locating pumping plant. As soon, therefore, as a suitable site has been identified the local Electricity Board should be approached with approximate details of the intended load. This will enable them both to provide a budget cost and an estimate of the time required for making a supply available.

The Board may specify power factor and starting current restrictions in their response and it is well worth agreeing to install correction equipment. The importance of this early contact with the Electricity Board cannot be over emphasised, since they may require to carry out extensive reinforcements of their supply network to meet the requirements. Where this entails erection of overhead lines, planning and wayleave difficulties can make this a lengthy process, longer even than constructing the pumping station.

The Board's response may also indicate problems in providing the specified voltage with consequent need for design modifications.

In most areas the range of three-phase supply voltages provided by the Electricity Board is standardised to give supplies at 415, 3300, 6600 and 11000 volts whilst for local 415v three-phase distribution, a neutral connection is also provided to give a 240 v single-phase supply from each phase to the neutral.

The type of electricity supply required will depend upon the size and importance of the plant. In a distribution network, a large pumping installation supplying a reservoir having more than one day's storage capacity may be less vital, in terms of the electricity supply requirement, than a smaller booster installation having no immediate storage. However, because of the need to maintain supplies under all conditions, it is preferred if all medium to large installations are provided with either duplicated electricity supplies or a single mains supply and standby generation. If extremely vital, then all options may be required.

Automatic duplicated electricity supplies may be fed from separate sources or from a ring circuit and offers of such supplies should be carefully considered to determine their ultimate reliability. In the case of supplies fed from separate sources, they may only be separate sources in a local sense and it is essential to establish the location of their common source to assess the risk of complete failure. Supplies fed from a ring circuit may be affected by voltage reduction if the ring is opened, resulting in possible tripping of the plant which would negate the purpose of the duplication.

When supplies are duplicated, availability of a switched alternative supply may be acceptable if an interruption of up to one hour can be tolerated and the cost of providing such supplies may be less.

Diesel or gas turbine driven generators may be installed either for standby or to meet peak loading of the plant. In the former case, synchronisation with the incoming main supply will not be necessary, provided that the generator can be started quickly if the main supply is interrupted, but the area Electricity Board will require assurance that the generator output cannot be connected to the main switchboard whilst the main supply is alive. It will thus be necessary to ensure that the appropriate switches are electrically and mechanically interlocked so that they cannot both be closed at the same time.

The electricity supply for smaller installations of, say, 30 kW or less will probably be provided from a local 415 v, three-phase network and below 6 kW, a 240 v, single-phase supply may be adequate. In urban areas, the cost of providing the supply will not usually be great but in rural areas it may represent a large proportion of the cost of construction of the station. Even so, although the alternative cost of diesel generation or direct drive may be somewhat lower, the saving may quickly be absorbed in operating and maintenance costs.

In some areas, the medium voltage network from which a supply can be provided will operate at 480 v, single-phase, which provides 480 v from a centre-tapped single-phase transformer, the centre connection being earthed and run as a neutral to provide 240 v supplies. Pump motors, including submersibles, are not now obtainable to operate from a 480 v, single-phase supply and the largest 240 v, single-phase motor now available does not exceed 5.5 kW. When the required motor load exceeds this limit, it may be necessary to install a single to three-phase converter, which may be either rotary or static, to convert the 480 v, single-phase supply to an artificial 415 v, three-phase supply.

SURGE

General

Interruption of the movement of water along a conduit by the sudden closing of a valve or the stopping of a pump creates a pressure wave which moves foward and backward along the pipeline until eventually damped out by friction. The pressure wave travels at a velocity which depends on the elasticity of the water and that of the walls of the pipe and is reflected each time it reaches the stopped ends of the pipe.

The magnitude of the wave velocity can be calculated from the formula

$$a = \sqrt{\frac{k/d}{1 + \dfrac{K.D}{E.e}}}$$

where   a =   pressure wave velocity (m/s)
        k =   bulk modulus for the liquid (N/m^2)
        d =   density of liquid (kg/m^3)
        D =   internal diameter of pipe (m)
        E =   elastic modulus of pipe (N/m^2)
        e =   thickness of pipe wall (m)

For water in steel pipes "a" is typically 1 100 m/s whilst in plastic pipes it is 300 m/s but this value must be calculated for each application to ensure accurate results.

The time taken for the pressure wave to travel to the end of the pipe and return is termed the reflection time and is expressed as

$$t_R = 2 . \frac{L}{a}$$

where t_R =   reflection time (sec)
        L   =   pipe length (m)
        a   =   wave velocity (m/s)

If the flow velocity in a pipeline is suddenly reduced or increased within the reflection time, a shock pressure wave is produced such that

$$h = a\,(v_i - v_f)/g$$

where   h   =   change in pressure (m)
        v_i =   initial flow velocity (m/s)
        v_f =   final flow velocity (m/s)
        g   =   acceleration due to gravity (9.81 m/s^2)

From the above it is clear that sudden closing of a valve or the stopping or starting of a pump will result in a pressure change of h = ± a. v_i/g, the final flow velocity being zero. This is known as Joukowsky's Law and, in the case of instantaneous stopping of a pump, the output flow will cease and the check valve will close, causing a reduction in downstream pressure which travels along the pipeline at the appropriate wave velocity. If the reduction in pressure is sufficient to reduce the initial pressure to a sub-atmospheric value below the vapour pressure, separation of the water column will ensue, resulting in water hammer when it re-unites.

When the pressure wave reaches the end of the pipeline it is reflected and returns along the pipeline to the check valve at an increased pressure which, but for the effects of friction, is equal to the initial reduction in pressure.

Further reflections follow which, mainly due to the effects of friction, are progressively reduced to the static head in the pipeline.

In the design of all pump installations, it is important that possible surge effects are investigated at an early stage. Knowing the characteristics and materials of the inlet and outlet pipelines, it is possible to predict these effects either by the graphical methods of Schnyder or Bergeron or by a computer aided method.

The Schnyder Diagram

The effect and behaviour of surge pressure waves resulting from the sudden stopping or starting of a pump, together with the additional effects of measures which may be taken to limit their behaviour, are most easily analysed by graphical solutions provided by the Schnyder diagram.

In this, the velocities of flow are plotted as abscissae and the pressure heads as ordinates. By Joukowsky's Law, the change in pressure head at a point corresponding with the passing of a pressure wave is proportional to the resulting change of velocity such that

$$\Delta h = \frac{a}{g} \cdot \Delta v$$

where Δh = change in head (m)
   a = wave velocity (m/s)
   g = acceleration due to gravity (9.81 m/s^2)
   Δv = change in flow velocity (m/s)

Rearranging the equation $\Delta h / \Delta v = a/g$, it is clear that the effect of a wave is to displace the point on the diagram diagonally at a slope of a/g. If a and v have the same sign, so that the wave is moving forwards, the slope of the diagonal will be positive, whilst if backwards, the slope will be negative.

Knowing the characteristics of the pipeline, by this method simple systems can easily be graphically represented, whereas in systems involving boundary conditions, throttles, changes of diameter, branches, etc., the graphical representation becomes more difficult. However, although the task becomes very laborious, this method provides an accurate prediction of surge effects.

Having examined the conditions likely to be encountered in the proposed system without any means of reducing or absorbing the effects of surge, further results can be obtained to enable the most suitable means of suppression to be determined.

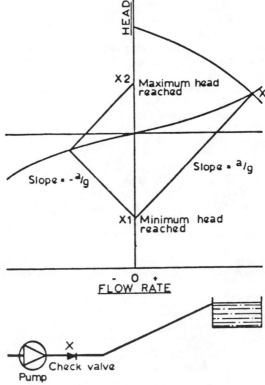

Fig. 7.3. Schnyder diagram

Analysis depends on the most suitable simplification of each application such that the effects of friction are treated as a series of throttles. This is further simplified by the analyst creating travelling observers moving forward and backward at the velocity of the waves. Thus the observers meet only waves moving opposite to their direction whilst the waves moving in their own direction remain at fixed distances ahead or behind them. At boundaries, they must conform to local conditions, otherwise the conditions on each side of the boundary must be mutually consistent. The progress of the observers is determined by their speed along the various parts of the system and the distance to be travelled and, by producing a record of their travels from the start of the disturbance onwards, the sequence of conditions at any point can be analysed. An example of this method is shown in Fig. 7.3 but it must be emphasised that the nature of the system will determine the surge behaviour following the disturbance.

Computer Analysis

Prediction and analysis of surge behaviour in any system can be determined relatively easily and accurately by a computer aided method such the British Hydro Mechanics Research Association Fluid Engineering's *Hypsmop*, based on the characteristic equations of linear momentum and continuity. Following the generation of the pressure wave, its subsequent behaviour depends on boundary conditions in the system and the method allows for non-linear effects such as friction, cavitation and column separation.

Investigations can be undertaken by specialist consultants who, having been given full details of the system, will provide a report indicating the anticipated surge effects and, if necessary, recommendations for the design of preventive measures.

Surge Protection

Because of the possible occurrence of excessive surge pressures which develop when the flow in a pipeline is suddenly stopped, i.e. in a period less than the reflection time of the system, it is clear that these pressures can be avoided by ensuring that the column is brought to rest sufficiently slowly. This can be achieved by the following methods.

(i) Surge Tower

A surge tower (Fig. 7.4) can be used to prevent build-up of excessive surge pressures in the delivery pipeline from a pump by providing a reservoir to feed water into the pumping main downstream of the check valve, after sudden stopping of the pump. This weakens the negative pressure wave and prolongs the retardation

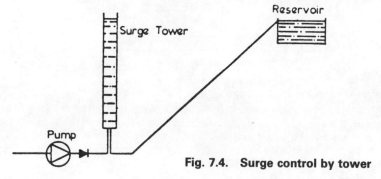

Fig. 7.4. Surge control by tower

process. The inlet to the tower can be throttled to increase the damping of the system.

The main disadvantage of this method is that the tower must be at least as high as the pump delivery head, which is not usually possible, although surge towers have been used on hydro-electric pipelines.

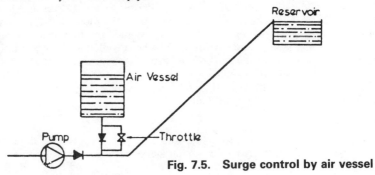

Fig. 7.5.   Surge control by air vessel

(2) Air Vessel

This method requires the installation of an adequately-sized air vessel (Fig. 7.5) which is connected to the pipeline downstream of the pump delivery valve. An air compressor, usually controlled automatically to replace air which is absorbed by the water, maintains a predetermined amount of air in the vessel, the pressure of the air being equal to the pump delivery head.

When the pump stops, water flows from the vessel into the pipeline through a non-return valve and the air pressure reduces. The greater the air volume the smoother the process and when the surge wave is reflected and the pressure rises, water enters the vessel against the cushion of air. The system is damped by returning the water to the vessel through a throttled bypass, the throttle normally being an adjustable butterfly or sluice valve.

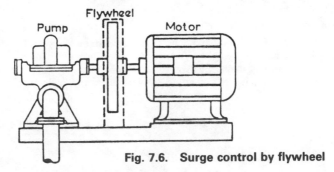

Fig. 7.6.   Surge control by flywheel

(3) Flywheel on Pump

By fitting a flywheel on the shaft between the pump and motor (Fig. 7.6), the inertia of the unit is increased and it is thus possible to prolong the rundown time of the unit beyond the reflection period of the system. The benefit gained by this method in reducing the effects of surge is offset by increased starting difficulties due to the increased inertia of the unit.

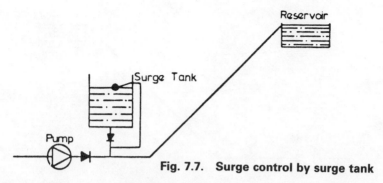

Fig. 7.7.   Surge control by surge tank

(4) Surge Tank

Negative pressure, which results in cavitation at a point in the pipeline, may be counteracted by the connection of a surge tank (FIg. 7.7) at that point.

The outlet from the tank is through a check valve and, if sudden stopping of flow in the pipeline results in a negative pressure, water flows from the tank into the pipeline to fill any void before the return of the reflected wave, which is thus damped. The tank is refilled through a float-valve controlled connection from the pipeline to restore the level after each operation.

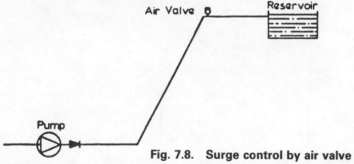

Fig. 7.8.   Surge control by air valve

(5) Air Valve

This method is an alternative to the surge tank described above. By fitting an air valve protected against pollution at any critical point on the pipeline where negative pressures may occur (Fig. 7.8), air is drawn into the pipeline when the pressure becomes sub-atmospheric. However, to cushion the ensuing increase in pressure, the air is allowed to escape only at a slow rate until, following the return to steady state conditions, the pipeline is fully vented.

(6) Controlled Delivery Valve

If the flow rate can be reduced to zero in a period exceeding the reflection period, excessive surge pressures can be avoided. Thus, by this method, the pump check valve is replaced by an actuated valve (Fig. 7.9); automatic stopping of the unit is so arranged that the valve closes slowly before the pump is stopped.

The valve can be electrically actuated but is usually hydraulically actuated and controlled by solenoid valves which are so connected as to ensure that the valve closes in the event of failure of the electricity supply.

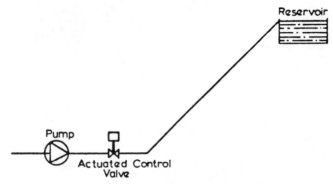

Fig. 7.9. Surge control by actuated delivery valve

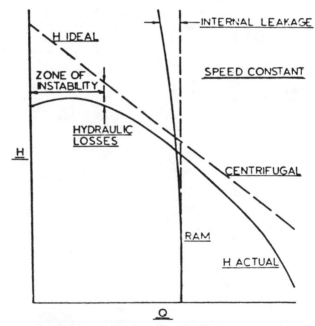

Fig. 7.10. Comparison of ram and centrifugal pump characteristics

3. PUMPING PLANT

GENERAL

The primary need for pumping plant is to raise a fluid from one level to a higher level and various types of machine can be used. Although it is not possible to describe all types of pumps in this chapter the following sections describe the types in use for applications in the water industry. Further details may be obtained from text books[1-4] and from manufacturers' catalogues.

In general use, pump types fall into two classifications, namely displacement or turbine. In the former, pressure energy is added to a given volume of the liquid which is delivered on each stroke or revolution of the pump shaft whilst, in the latter case, kinetic or velocity energy is imparted to the liquid by the rotation of an impeller. In either case, the energy added to the liquid converts at the pump outlet to provide the pressure and velocity energy required to meet the hydraulic conditions in the system. The characteristics of the ram and centrifugal pump are compared in Fig. 7.10

The most common form of the displacment type is the piston or ram pump but this is seldom used now in waterworks practice.

Turbine or impeller pumps generate head by the application of torque to a rotating impeller to provide kinetic energy to the liquid, a proportion of which is converted to pressure energy at the impeller outlet. The pump inlet is designed to guide the liquid to the impeller whilst the outlet design must ensure the best conversion of energy leaving the impeller.

Because of variations in impeller design, the types of pump vary greatly in form and, in order to classify them, it is convenient to adopt the concept of specific speed. This is defined as the rotational speed at which a pump, geometrically similar to that being considered, would deliver at unit flow against unit head. Specific speed is defined by the equation

$$Ns = N. \sqrt{Q/H^3}/4$$

where   Ns = specific speed (rpm)
        N = actual speed (rpm)
        Q = volume flow (m^3/s)
        H = delivery head (m)

In the above units, the specific speed varies from approximately 20 rpm for a radial impeller to 250 rpm for an axial impeller.

When the speed of a pump is changed, the generated head varies as the square of the speed whereas the delivery flow rate is proportional to speed. Accordingly, the power requirement varies as the cube of the speed.

Fig. 7.11 shows the effect of operating pumps in series (tandem) and Fig. 7.12 the effect of operating them in parallel.

The following sections describe the types of pump in general use in distribution systems in the water industry.

BOREHOLE ABSTRACTION

Abstraction from boreholes was originally achieved by reciprocating pumps of the well or bucket type but the impeller pump is now favoured.

Borehole Pump

This type comprises a vertical spindle centrifugal pump (Fig. 7.13) designed for use in narrow boreholes. Due to limitation of the diameter, the head per stage is low, thus requiring a number of stages to achieve the working head.

Because of the length of the delivery column between the pump end and the head of the borehole, it is necessary to guide the shaft at sufficiently short intervals by water lubricated bearings to prevent distortion or whip of the shaft at critical speeds. These bearings are carried on "spider" or wheel shaped supports which are clamped between flanges in the delivery column and their function is to locate the shaft in the centre of the column.

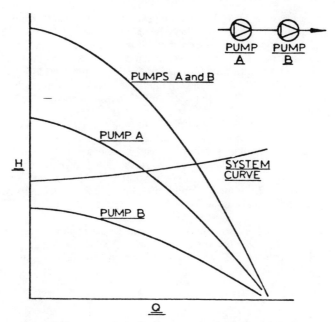

Fig. 7.11. Centrifugal pumps—operation in tandem

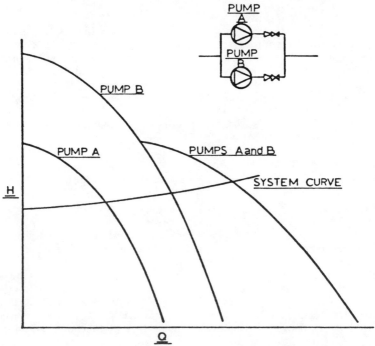

Fig. 7.12. Centrifugal pumps—operation in parallel

The vertical motor is mounted at the head of the borehole on a pedestal which usually accommodates the shaft gland or seal, the thrust bearings, the delivery bend and an air valve to vent the delivery column on starting.

A variation of the design employs a motor having a hollow shaft through which the pump shaft is passed and clamped at the top of the motor. The thrust load of all rotating parts of the unit is thus carried by the motor bearings.

In either case, the vertical position of the shaft can be adjusted to enable the pump impellers to be centralised in the casings. Because of the length of the driving shaft and the need for intermediate bearings, care must be taken when testing to allow for increased internal losses when calculating the efficiency, which is not comparable with pumps having shorter drive shafts.

Submersible Pump

The pump end is similar to that of the borehole pump but the long driving shaft is eliminated by fitting a submersible electric motor under the pump (Fig. 7.14). The motor may be of the wet type, in which the liquid filling the motor surrounds the insulated stator windings, or the dry type having the stator windings in a sealed can, the liquid filling only the space between the rotor and the stator.

The liquid filling the motor is separated from the water being pumped by a shaft seal and the motor is usually fitted with a breather to allow for change of volume of the liquid in the motor with temperature.

The thrust load of the rotating elements of the pump and motor is carried by a bearing in the base of the motor. Because of increase in thrust load with delivery head, it is inadvisable to operate the pump unit against a throttled valve, otherwise rapid wear of the thrust bearing may occur.

The pump end, being centrifugal, comprises impellers having a radial output which is guided to the inlet to the following stage by a diffuser section which is designed to minimise internal losses.

Jet Pump

This unit consists of a multi-stage centrifugal pump (Fig. 7.15) having an intermediate delivery branch in addition to the normal suction and delivery branches. The pump is mounted at the head of the borehole and pipework from the suction and delivery branches is run down the borehole and connected across an ejector which comprises a tube having a narrow throat. Because of the increase in velocity at the throat when water is passing through, a reduction in pressure occurs, by the venturi principle, and water is drawn from the borehole through a third connection, usually fitted with a strainer. The additional water is carried to the pump and discharged into supply from the intermediate branch.

The pump can be driven electrically or by a diesel engine, in the absence of an electricity supply, and although this unit is useful for narrow boreholes, rapid wear of the ejector throat occurs in the presence of sand or grit which results in deterioration in the performance of the unit.

RELIFT PUMPING

In a distribution network, transfer of water from one supply zone to a higher zone is best achieved, in the interests of cost and efficiency, by fixed-rate pumping between service reservoirs along a dedicated pipeline and during hours which ensure minimum electricity supply tariff costs. In practice, this may restrict pumping to a few hours in the day and thus require a plant capacity beyond that which is reasonable. Some compromise must be made, therefore, but additional running costs will be offset by reductions in capital cost.

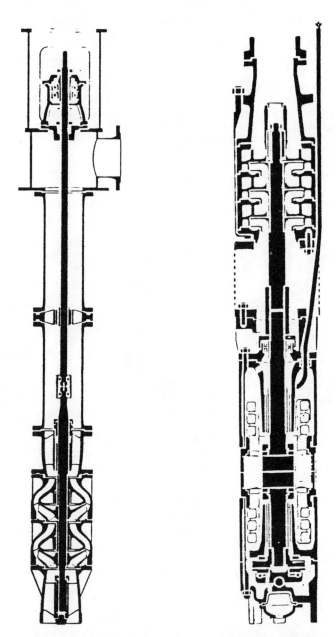

Fig. 7.13.   Deep well turbine pump   Fig. 7.14.   Submersible turbine pump

Source: KSB Manufacturing Company Ltd

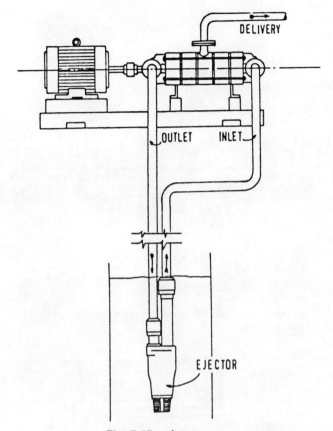

Fig. 7.15. Jet pump

In this type of system, the hydraulic conditions would be constant but for the variation in the water levels in the feeder and receiving reservoirs and energy consumption will vary in accordance with the day-to-day variations in water demand in the zones.

Assuming that the lift from the feeder reservoir to the receiving reservoir is not greater than 80 m, a single-stage pump unit will meet the required duty but, for higher lifts, a multi-stage unit may be required.

The following units can be considered for this application.

Double-Suction, Split-Casing Pump

This type of unit is usually designed for horizontal operation but vertical units are available. The unit (Fig. 7.16) which is usually single-stage, has a double inlet impeller of radial flow design which delivers into a volute casing to direct the flow to a delivery branch. Because of the double inlet, the impeller is hydraulically balanced, thus simplifying design of the bearings which are mounted outside the pump casing. A gland or mechanical seal is fitted on each side of the casing where the shaft emerges.

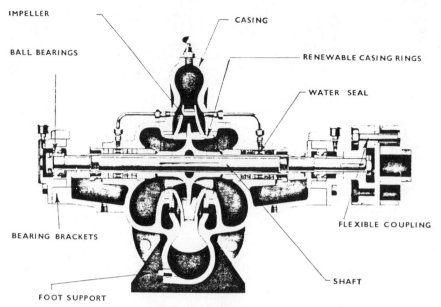

IMPELLER

BALL BEARINGS

CASING

RENEWABLE CASING RINGS

WATER SEAL

FLEXIBLE COUPLING

BEARING BRACKETS

SHAFT

FOOT SUPPORT

Fig. 7.16.   Double-suction split-casing pump
Source: Worthington-Simpson Ltd

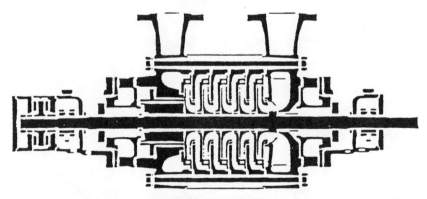

Fig. 7.17.   Multi-stage turbine pump
Source: KSB Manufacturing Company Ltd

The casing, whether the shaft is horizontal or vertical, is usually split on the shaft centre line to enable the interior to be examined without fully dismantling the unit. The suction and delivery branches are incorporated in the fixed portion of the casing to obviate the need to disconnect the pipework.

The design of the suction passages to the double inlet is critical and must ensure that bends are not too sharp nor velocities too great to result in reduction in pressure and possible cavitation at the suction eyes of the impeller. The delivery branch can emerge at any angle relative to the suction but is usually positioned diametrically opposite. The suction and delivery pipework should ideally be free of bends near the pump and, where change of diameter is required, concentric tapers should be used.

Although a two-stage version has been produced, it is normally available as a single-stage unit having a head/quantity curve which is reasonably flat and suitable for delivering large quantities to medium heads.

Multi-stage Turbine Pump

For the delivery of medium quantities to high heads, a multi-stage unit is usually required (Fig. 7.17). The impellers produce a radial outlet flow which is guided to the inlet to the next impeller by a diffuser section and the unit is thus constructed as a number of sections having the suction and delivery branches in the appropriate end section, all being held together by longitudinal bolts. Glands or mechanical seals are fitted where the shaft passes through each end section and the shaft is carried in bearings mounted in brackets attached to the end housings.

Because of the design, a hydraulic thrust is created by the delivery head towards the inlet end and this can be dealt with by fitting a thrust bearing of the ball or roller type. In some units, a thrust disc is fitted inside the inlet end housing and the delivery head is fed to a cavity behind the disc to counteract the hydraulic thrust and keep the impellers centralised.

End Suction Single-Stage Pump

This is usually of the volute type (Fig. 7.18) but may also be of the diffuser pattern.

Although suitable for delivering large quantities to low heads, it is now in general use for delivering medium or small quantities to low heads up to 30 m at speeds of the order of 1 500 rpm, although heads of 90 m can be achieved at twice that speed.

The pump comprises a radial impeller which operates in a volute in spiral form to conduct the water issuing from the impeller to a tangential delivery branch. The inlet branch is positioned on the side of the volute casing in line with the impeller inlet, the drive being from the opposite side of the casing where the shaft is supported on an external twin bearing pedestal. Only one gland or seal is required on the drive side between the casing and bearing housing.

Because the suction and delivery branches are at right angles, the unit can be removed without disturbing the connecting pipework and in some cases the shaft, bearing housing, gland and impeller can be withdrawn for maintenance from the volute casing which remains *in situ*.

Integral units are also available up to 30 kW having a flange mounted motor which fits directly to the pump casing, thus avoiding the need for separate bearings and a coupling, whilst the impeller is fitted to an extension of the motor shaft. In this close-coupled form (Fig. 7.19), the units can be positioned in any way to suit the requirements of the pipework layout.

DISTRIBUTION BOOSTING

In the absence of delivery storage facilities in a distribution network it may be necessary to maintain adequate pressures by boosting. This can be done on a continuous or intermittent basis and good pressure design is vital in the interests of waste reduction and energy conservation. Ideally, the generated pressure should be no more than is adequate for the highest consumer in the area supplied but consideration must be given to the effects of friction in the network and the continuous variation in water demand which may require some degree of compromise.

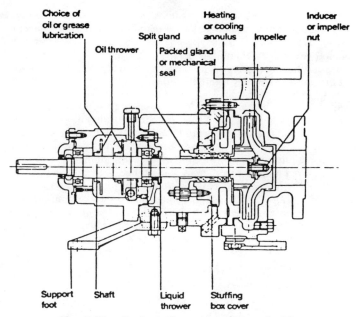

Fig. 7.18.   End-suction pump (bare shaft)

Source: Worthington-Simpson Ltd

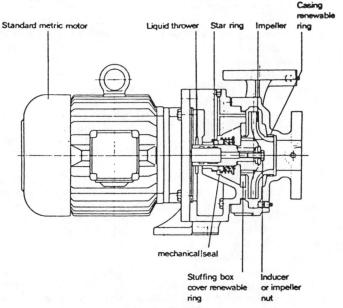

Fig. 7.19.   Close-coupled end-suction pump

Source: Worthington-Simpson Ltd

For continuous boosting, fixed-speed operation can be achieved using either a split casing or end suction pump, as described above, having a flat head/quantity characteristic. In this way, assuming a constant inlet head, the delivery head will vary very little, say no more than 4-5 m, over the designed flow range but the effect at the highest point will also be affected by network frictional losses and the demand rate. Further energy savings may be obtained by varying the pump speed to maintain a constant pressure at the highest point by either transmitting a control signal to the pump from that point or programming the pump speed in relation to delivery flow rate and pressure to achieve the same objective. However, before applying either of these methods, the application should be appraised financially to determine that the "pay back" period for the speed control apparatus is acceptable.

For boosting to higher heads, a multi-stage pump may be required but in this case speed variation will almost certainly be necessary due to the steeper slope of the head/quantity curve. Alternatively, by connecting an air/water vessel to the pump delivery branch, the pump can be run intermittently under the control of high and low delivery pressure gauge contacts. In this way, the pump will operate until the delivery pressure reaches the higher setting when it stops and any further area demand is fed by the air pressure retained in the vessel. When the pressure in the vessel falls to the lower setting the pump starts again to repeat the cycle. Clearly, if the settings are too close, the pump will start and stop frequently and good design requires the lowest frequency of operation coupled with an acceptable pressure operating range in the area supplied. The pneumatic system gives automatic protection against water hammer.

To obtain good stability in the delivery pressure, it is essential to site the pump at a point which will provide the steadiest possible inlet head condition and, in this respect, it is preferable if this type of booster can be installed at a service reservoir site.

Localised boosting may occasionally be required for a small area on the fringe of a distribution network. This application usually requires a low peak flow rate of up to 6-7 l/s to 20-30 m head for which an integral close-coupled end suction unit, having a reasonably flat head/quantity curve and a totally enclosed electric driving motor, may be suitable. This type of unit can be installed in a drained underground chamber and controlled by a time switch to operate continuously during periods when the area pressure is inadequate.

4. PUMP CONSTRUCTION AND SPECIFICATION

GENERAL

The majority of pumps employed in the water industry are of the impeller pattern comprising one or more impellers which rotate in casings designed to conduct the liquid being pumped into the following stage or to the pump outlet branch. The materials of construction depend largely on the application in relation to the hydraulic conditions and the abrasive or corrosive nature of the liquid to be pumped.

The hydraulic conditions, including the quantity and head requirements, will determine the type and size of the pump selected for a particular application, consideration being given to the inlet conditions and the Net Positive Suction Head (NPSH) of the unit. This provides an indication of its cavitational characteristics and represents the difference between the total head available at the pump inlet and the vapour pressure expressed in metres head.

Cavitation results when the inlet head is reduced to a pressure which allows vapour bubbles to form and these later collapse, usually at the inlet to the impeller, causing severe pitting of the blades and, in some cases, noise and vibration.

To prevent leakage from the casing, the pump shafts are fitted with glands (Fig. 7.20), or seals (Fig. 7.21). When fitted with packed glands, the shaft passes through a stuffing box into which are inserted a number of square-sectioned rings of packing material. These usually consist of woven cotton impregnated with tallow or a tallow/graphite mixture to provide lubrication between the material and the shaft. The rings are cut to length to fit around the shaft and inserted into the stuffing box, with the joints staggered to ensure a good seal, then compressed by an external adjustable gland plate which is designed to protrude into the stuffing box.

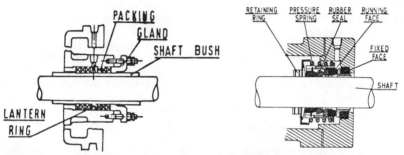

Fig. 7.20. Soft-packed stuffing box   Fig. 7.21. Mechanical seal

On multi-stage pumps, the gland at the inlet end of the shaft may be required to seal against a sub-atmospheric pressure to prevent air from entering the casing. In this case, an intermediate lantern ring is inserted between the rings of packing material in line with a tapping through which liquid is injected from the first or a subsequent stage of the pump to counteract the negative pressure. A lantern ring may also be inserted in the stuffing box at the delivery end of the shaft to improve sealing. The section of pump shaft in the stuffing box is usually fitted with a removable sleeve of bronze or other suitable material which can be renewed as wear occurs and, although the purpose of the gland is to seal, some slight leakage may be desired to provide lubrication and cooling between the packing material and the shaft bush.

To achieve complete sealing of the liquid, it is normal to fit a mechanical shaft seal in place of the packed gland. This comprises a stationary seating having a polished face, which may replace the gland plate, against which runs a polished carbon ring carried internally on the shaft with a rubber sealing sleeve or bellows and a pressure spring to hold the fixed and running faces together. If the liquid being pumped contains any abrasive particles, it may be necessary to fit a stationary seat having a hardened face of ceramic or other materials to extend the running life of the seal.

MATERIALS OF CONSTRUCTION

The components of any type of pump should be made of materials which are suitable to withstand the working environment and conditions.

Impeller pumps handling cold, clean water within the pH range 6 to 9 are usually constructed having cast iron casings and impellers, high tensile steel shafts and cast steel or bronze renewable wearing parts such as wear rings and shaft sleeves. When some degree of corrosive attack may be expected, they should be fitted with bronze impellers and wearing parts, whilst, in the case of submersible pumps, all bronze construction may be required.

When the liquid being pumped contains abrasive particles, as in the case of borehole abstraction, erosion of the internal surfaces of the pump may occur resulting in a rapid decline in performance, so that coating of the internal fixed and moving surfaces by a wear resistant material, such as ceramic, may be required. In this case, attention must also be paid to the gland or seal materials.

As noted earlier, the presence of entrained air will also cause cavitational erosion of internal surfaces due to impingement of minute air bubbles and this should be prevented by suitable design of the inlet arrangements.

Internal corrosion can occur by contact between components made of dissimilar metals as a result of electrolytic action, although with some liquids this can have a self-inhibiting effect. Usually where electrolytic current flow can be foreseen between main components, such as in the case of a submersible pump and its driving motor, insulating joints can be fitted to inhibit current flow and the resulting corrosion. Similarly, where corrosive attack may be induced by dissimilar metals in surrounding pipework and valves, insulating joints can be fitted at the pump branches.

In general practice, the price of the materials of construction increases with their resistance to corrosion and this has an obvious effect on the cost of the pump unit.

PIPEWORK AND VALVES

The configuration of the inlet and delivery pipework and the type of valves used in the installation of a pump unit (Fig. 7.22) have a marked effect on its performance.

The inlet pipework should be amply sized and as free as possible from bends to minimise loss of inlet pressure which may result in cavitation. Similarly, the delivery pipework should be designed to offer the absolute minimum resistance to flow between the pump and the delivery main since most losses are irrecoverable and represent a continuous energy loss when the unit is in operation.

Pipework should include gradual bends rather than elbows and the branches should be swept or angled in the direction of flow rather than right angled. Although this may not be possible within the space available, it may be economically sound to increase the required space to avoid higher energy requirement and operating costs.

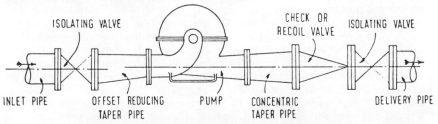

Fig. 7.22.   Pipework and valves around pump

The majority of modern pumping installations are designed to operate automatically and without local attention. The valve arrangements can be simplified to provide no more than isolation of individual pump units for occasional maintenance or repair and, for this purpose, sluice or butterfly valves can be selected to provide the minimum restriction to flow when fully opened. To prevent reversal of flow through the pump, when standing, an adequately designed check valve will normally be suitable but where surge occurs when the pump is stopped, a recoil check valve having surge control facilities should be fitted.

Actuated valves, which are controlled from the pump starter to open slowly after starting and to close before the pump stops, may also be applied in place of the check valve to control surge on starting and stopping of the pump but they should be fitted with some form of hydraulic fail-safe protection to close in the event of failure of the electricity supply when the pump is running.

PRIME MOVERS

In the absence of an electricity supply, pumps may be driven by either petrol or diesel engines or gas turbines. Difficulties with transport and storage of petrol supplies have led to more general use of diesel engines which can be provided with control devices for fully automatic operation. Although they will thus operate without attendance, more frequent surveillance is required than with single electrical drives.

Diesel engines up to 100 kW can be operated at speeds of 1 500 rpm but above this, speeds reduce as loads increase. Gas turbines can produce higher speeds for larger loads but have not yet achieved a high operating efficiency and the fuel consumption rate is high.

Although shunt wound DC motors were once widely used for pump drives, these are now only used for some small dosing pump applications.

The commonest form of AC electrical drive is the squirrel cage induction motor which comprises a wound stator, usually for a three-phase supply, and a rotor having copper or aluminium bars in the core slots brazed at each end to a ring of the same material to form a cage. Ideally the rotor should rotate at the speed of the stator field but, due to resistance in the cage, it loses some revolutions at full load, which is termed "slip". Thus, in a two-pole machine, the field rotates at 3 000 rpm whilst the rotor, on load, rotates at 2 900 to 2 940 rpm and, in a four-pole machine the field rotates at 1 500 rpm whilst the rotor, on load, rotates at 1 440 to 1 480 rpm.

The synchronous motor, having a DC excited rotor, is similar in construction to a three-phase alternator. It is started as an induction motor then operates at synchronous speed, that is, at the speed of the rotating magnetic field in the stator. On load, it can operate at unity power factor or can be over-excited to produce a leading power factor to correct the lagging power factor of other motors in the station and thus reduce the kVA demand.

The earliest form of three-phase AC motor was the slip-ring induction type, which has a three-phase wound rotor, the end of each winding being brought out to slip-rings mounted on the shaft. By connecting a variable three-phase resistance to brushes running on the slip-rings, the speed could be controlled such that it was maximum with zero external resistance and *vice versa*. Although normally used for fixed speed application, it can also be used for variable speed purposes by varying the value of the rotor resistance but the latter application is wasteful of energy since the motor essentially absorbs full load energy under all speed conditions and surplus energy at lower speeds is dissipated as heat in the rotor resistance.

The most efficient systems for achieving sub-synchronous speeds are those which recover the slip ring energy and return it to the supply system. These employ the stator fed AC commutator motor or wound-rotor, slip-ring motor in conjunction with devices such as the induction regulator or static rectifier inverter. The most important development work is related to inverters which produce a variable frequency for the control of the simple squirrel cage motor. These systems are not as efficient as the stator fed motor.

The benefits of solid state electrical technology can now be applied to provide simple and compact variable speed systems. By rectification to DC of a 50 hertz mains supply and inversion to AC at an infinitely adjustable frequency from 0 to 50 hertz, or in some cases higher, the speed of a squirrel cage induction motor can be controlled by varying the speed of the stator field and, thus, the rotor output. Some problems have been encountered with these drives due to the generation of harmonics, which may affect other consumers in the supply network, and heating of the iron stator and rotor cores in the motor due to increased eddy currents. Although both problems are being overcome by improved design, the area Electricity Board will require to know when these devices are being applied, in case of adverse effects on other consumers.

Fig. 7.23 shows the speed/torque characteristics of four types of electric motor and Fig. 7.24 shows the speed/torque characteristics of four types of impeller pump.

SWITCHGEAR AND STARTERS

In large installations provided with duplicated electricity supplies, the switchgear design should ensure that the benefits of duplication are applied throughout the electrical distribution system. All main switchboards should be fed from both supplies across a busbar sectionalising switch so that a fault at any point in the system can be easily isolated and bypassed without affecting the output from the plant. However, it is important that the two incoming switches and the bus-section switch are mechanically interlocked so that only two of the three can be closed at any time to prevent reverse feeding or interconnection of the incoming supplies.

The former practice of employing oil or air circuit breakers for the incoming and bus-section switches incorporated in a switchboard fed from duplicate transformers has now been replaced by the use of manual isolating switches, having a fault/make, load/break rating, provided that full overcurrent and earth fault protection is fitted to each transformer primary circuit breaker. A red pushbutton is also usually fitted in an accessible position on each incoming isolator to enable the appropriate transformer primary switch to be tripped in emergency.

An automatic starter is employed for control of the motor driving each pump unit and, for a number of drives, the starters may be incorporated in a switchboard operating at the required voltage. Each starter comprises one or more triple-pole contactors which are electrically actuated and, if necessary, interlocked to ensure a precise sequence of operation. Protection devices are included to monitor the motor running current, and, in some cases, the electrical insulation resistance, and trip the unit if the current becomes excessive or leaks to earth.

For voltages of 3 300 and above, vacuum contactors, which require less maintenance, are now in common use.

When an AC motor is connected to a supply, a large current is drawn which may reach six times the value of the full load current of the motor. This may result in a momentary voltage drop in the distribution system or supply network which may not be permitted by the area Electricity Board. This method of starting is termed "direct-to-line" and other methods of starting must be considered if the starting current is to be limited to a lower value.

By reducing the voltage initially applied on starting, the current can be controlled

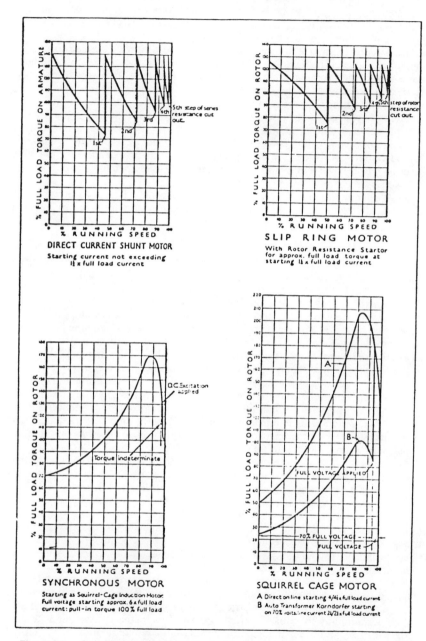

Fig. 7.23. Speed-torque characteristics for four types of electric motor

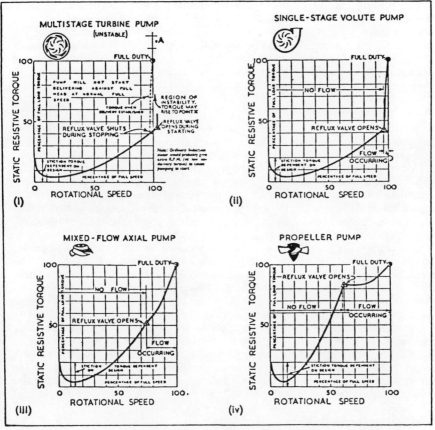

Fig. 7.24.   Speed-torque characteristics for four types of impeller pump

and this method is employed in the star/delta starter and the auto-transformer starter. In the former, the starter coils of the motors are connected in "star" formation until the motor almost reaches running speed. This effectively connects two coils across each phase instead of one to reduce the voltage applied to each coil. The stator coils are then quickly reconnected in "delta" formation by the starter to apply full voltage to each coil for the running period.

The main disadvantage of this method of starting is that high voltage transients can occur, due to the momentary break when changing from the star to delta connections, but these can be overcome by use of the Wauchhope system of starting.

The auto-transformer starter employs an auto-transformer to apply the reduced starting voltage to a delta connected stator and, when the running speed is reached, the auto-transformer is bypassed to apply full voltage to the motor. The benefits of this method are that the starting voltage can be adjusted, if necessary, and Korndorfer connection of the starter ensures smooth starting, in that, once the starting process has begun, there is no break in the supply to the motor.

The starting current of the motor when using either a star/delta or auto-transformer starter is normally limited to three times full load current as compared with six times for a direct-to-line starter. However, if further reduction of the starting current is required, it may be necessary to apply a slip-ring induction motor to enable it to be reduced to 1.25 times the full load current. Solid state starting devices are now available to provide a "soft start" and these may be worth considering, subject to cost and reliability.

PLANT INSTRUMENTATION AND CONTROL

The telemetering of measurements and conditions in the distribution network has been dealt with in Chapter 5 and is considered further in Section 6. Aspects of instrumentation and control affecting control of the plant are considered below.

In spite of the sophistication of telemetry systems or apparatus, which depend on either a hard wire or radio carrier circuit between the control centre and each outstation, risk of failure of contact with pumping plant warrants consideration of control by local automation. Overriding control of the plant from the control centre may also be required but the essential requirement is that, in the event of telemetry failure, the plant will continue to function as normally as possible.

In all pump installations, there is a need to monitor conditions by the continuous observation of voltage, motor current, inlet and delivery water pressures, flow rates, bearing temperatures and vibration and measurements of these parameters may be transmitted to the control centre. However, although flow and pressure measurement values may be required as operational data for recording at the control centre, it may be adequate to monitor the remaining measurements only at the outstation and provide alarm outputs to the control centre, and probably tripping facilities to stop the plant, in the event of deviation of any measurement outside predetermined limits. It may further suffice to transmit a single common alarm to the control centre and provide an annunciator panel at the outstation for each pump unit to indicate the cause of the stoppage to the visiting member of the maintenance staff.

PREPARATION OF SPECIFICATION

In preparing a specification for pumping plant, the following items should be included.

Conditions of Contract

Whilst constructional work for the foundations and building will usually be carried out under the Conditions of Contract prepared by the Institution of Civil Engineers or by the Royal Institute of British Architects, the provision and, if required, the erection of the plant will usually be undertaken under the Conditions of Contract prepared jointly by the Institution of Mechanical Engineers, the Institution of Electrical Engineers and the Association of Consulting Engineers, generally referred to as the I.Mech.E. Conditions, which are revised from time to time. The specification must clearly state the edition of the Conditions under which the contract will be conducted.

Variations of the standard Model Form A conditions were produced in 1978 by the late Mr. Eric Gordon of the South West Water Authority on behalf of the National Water Council, to meet the needs of the water industry and the conditions incorporating these amendments are referred to as Form G.

Specification of Plant

Following a study of the requirements and application, the engineer will have a firm idea of the type of plant required and the duty of each pump unit to be included in the contract. However, the specification should not be too rigid as to the type and design of pump, otherwise the manufacturer may be prevented from offering units of his standard pattern which, if suitable for the application, will lower the cost. Whenever possible, the specification should give full details of the hydraulic conditions under which each unit will operate, including static and friction heads.

If the prime movers are to be included in the contract then details of these too must be included in the specification. For electrical drives, details should include the type of electricity supply available and the type of motor. In the case of direct boosting applications, where the pump delivery quantity will vary according to demand, the motor should be specified as non-overloading.

When the prime mover is to be purchased separately and issued free to the pump manufacturer, usually to save handling charges, the type of drive should be stated, although its details such as load and speed will depend on the pumps offered. For diesel drives, it is important to ensure that the directions of rotation of engine and pump are compatible.

All plant should comply with relevant British or international standards and the health and safety requirements of the country in which it will be used[5,6].

Pump Tests

To ensure that the performance of the pump units meets the requirements of the specification and the offer made in the tender, each unit should be tested to determine either its efficiency or energy consumption, usually at the specified duty point. It is also worth while to extend the tests to cover the full range of the pump from zero to maximum flow.

Test procedures are laid down in BS 599 (Methods of Testing Pumps) which now includes borehole and well pump tests, previously covered by BS 722.

Bonus and Penalty Clauses

In the case of larger plants it is generally advisable to require a guarantee of the performance of each unit. Knowing its application and existing energy costs, a value can be derived for deviation of efficiency by one per cent on the basis of the estimated cost of operating through its useful life. This value is applied as a bonus to the manufacturer for each one per cent by which the efficiency of the unit exceeds the efficiency declared in his tender. Conversely, it is deducted from the tender price for each one per cent by which the efficiency falls short.

Bonus or penalty can also be applied in terms of predicted energy consumption in terms of kWh per unit quantity delivered.

If tests are conducted under BS 599, a tolerance will be required related to the standard of testing. However, it may be preferred to apply the bonus and penalty clause to site tests, on completion of installation, without tolerance whilst tests under BS 599 at the manufacturer's works may be included to ensure that the plant is suitable for delivery to site.

Liquidated Damages

These are applied when the contractor overruns the period of the contract, essentially to compensate the purchaser for loss of income due to delay in completion of the contract. Although there may be acceptable reasons for the delay, after a firm date for completion has been determined by the purchaser, damages are usually deducted at a weekly rate of 0.5 to 1 per cent of the contract price up to a maximum of 10 per cent.

Variation in Costs

Variation in the contract price is permitted if the cost is like to rise, or fall, during the period of the contract. To provide a firm basis for the calculation of the variation, a formula has to be agreed between the purchaser and contractor and, for electrical and mechanical contracts, the BEAMA formula is usually applied. This is produced by the British Electrical and Allied Manufacturers' Association and is calculated on the basis of indices which they publish monthly for the appropriate type of labour and materials.

Comparison of Tenders

After arithmetical checking of the tenders, they should be carefully examined to ensure that all plant offered is comparable in performance, accommodation needs etc.

It is most important then to compare annual capital and estimated operating costs over the expected life of the plant[6,7] to determine the most favourable offer.

5. BUILDINGS

PLANNING REQUIREMENTS

The factors governing site selection from engineering considerations are noted in Section 2. The planning authorities should be consulted at as early a stage as possible, particularly where "green belt" or other special locations are involved, to avoid wasted design effort. Contact should be continued during the evolution of plans to ensure that when final planning drawings are submitted they are likely to prove acceptable.

In England, planning consent is not required for the erection of plant on operational land, provided it is less than 15 m in height. However, as a matter of courtesy it is usual to inform the planning authority of intended work.

TYPES OF STRUCTURE

Buildings for pumping plant are required primarily to accommodate and protect the machinery, at the same time providing the accessibility necessary to operate, maintain and repair it. Developments in remote control and telemetry have virtually removed the need for stations to be manned. Thus with security now a vital consideration, an excellent solution is to construct the station wholly or partly underground. Savings in architectural finishes and external maintenance are likely to at least offset any additional costs entailed in burying the structure, while further benefits in terms both of noise and heat insulation will accrue. It should be noted that Electricity Boards are unwilling to permit service apparatus to be housed in confined underground spaces and therefore meters, etc. may have to be accommodated in surface kiosks.

It is possible to employ outdoor type machinery and to dispense with any enclosure. Temporary shelter will be required for maintenance and major overhaul and careful thought should be given to the problems of noise, sabotage and vandalism.

Design

Accessibility and Layout of Plant

The facilities for installation, servicing, dismantling and removal of plant must receive most careful consideration, whilst keeping the size of the structural envelope to a minimum. Provision of overhead travelling cranes is expensive in terms of the structure, since it must sustain the crane beam loads and afford the necessary clear headroom. The availability of very powerful mobile cranes on hire obviates the need for built-in lifting facilities if hatches or removable panels are provided; this will certainly be a suitable solution for underground stations. Sufficient manoeuvring space must be allowed for the mobile crane.

Careful thought should be given to provision and layout of cable and pipe ducts, bearing in mind the minimum radii to which cables may be bent. Good aesthetics do not demand concealment of the working parts of an industrial installation; well planned, neatly installed pipes and cables are easy on the eye and more practical to maintain than those concealed behind panelling and boxing.

Design of pipework must include both flexibility to accommodate tolerances in assembly and for in-service dismantling of individual pump units without loss of the entire station. Equally, provision of anchorage at bends and junctions must be thought out, bearing in mind the need, perhaps, to extend the installation in the future and the effects of anchoring loads on floors, walls etc.

Foundations and Vibration

Well constructed foundations and solid bolting down are essential to trouble-free operation, particularly where pump and motor are not integral but joined by shafting and couplings. Generous allowance of concrete should be made around holding down bolts to avoid cracking and spalling of foundation plinths. Where reciprocating machinery is involved, consideration must be given to design of the foundation blocks, for if reciprocating frequency approximates to the natural frequency of the foundation, resonance will occur, with consequent excessive vibration of the whole assembly[8]. Similar considerations apply to large rotating machines since perfect balance is never achieved.

In cohesive soils, such as boulder clays, settlement resulting from vibration is extremely unlikely. Vibrators are frequently used to consolidate granular soils, such as sands and gravels, and the best effect is obtained by applying vibrations within the range 500 to 2 500 impulses per minute. This range corresponds with the operating speed of many commonly used machines and the foundation material should be investigated carefully or the advice of a foundation expert sought.

Where vibration is likely, foundation blocks should be isolated with damping material from the rest of the structure.

Isolation of piping from vibrating machinery may be provided in several ways, one of the more satisfactory being a convoluted bellows coupling made of stainless steel.

Drainage

Bearing glands are likely to leak at some stage in the life of the plant and provision should be built in for conducting the leakage water to the building drainage system.

Cable entry points are often difficult to seal and drainage in the cable duct just inside the building will remove this source of trouble.

Wherever possible, drainage from the structure should be by gravity although in underground stations an automatic sump pump may have to be used.

Acoustic Insulation

As few modern stations are intended to be manned, noise is no longer of importance to shift attendants and maintenance staff should wear ear protection whilst in noisy areas. However, noise may carry for considerable distances outside a building and minimising this will be essential where there are nearby dwellings.

The aim must be to contain noise as near to its source as possible for which purpose acoustic shields can be fitted around motors. Careful attention should be given to apertures in the building, to reduce noise emission. Ventilation requires particular care to ensure adequate cooling whilst preserving the acoustic barrier.

The use of submersible pumps avoids the problems associated with containing noise, since they are extremely quiet in operation.

Heating, Ventilation and Lighting

In above-ground stations, some background heating is likely to be required to protect the installation against frost damage and damp penetration. Where a large flow or body of water is available, the application of a water-to-water or water-to-air heat pump should be evaluated[9].

In underground stations there is less likelihood of frost damage but condensation will be a hazard. Recent installations have used dehumidifiers to overcome this and their operating cost is about one quarter of the alternative heating load.

Ventilation requirements depend upon the nature of the machinery; oil engines require greater ventilation than electric motors and manufacturers will assist with heat generation figures. Internal combustion engines should draw their combustion air from outside if possible, to avoid having to heat air unnecessarily within the building.

For unmanned stations, windows should be eliminated if possible; this will assist in reducing vandalism, as well as in improving heat and sound insulation. Roof lighting is preferable in manned stations. Artificial lighting installations should be planned carefully in relation to parts requiring regular maintenance; extra floodlights can be brought in for major breakdown work.

Aesthetics and Finishes

Generally the more simple a structure is, the less offensive will it be. Wherever possible, external materials should be used which are similar to or at least in harmony with other structures in the area. If no architect is to be employed then a study of "The aesthetic aspect of civil engineering design[10]" is thoroughly recommended.

Finishes should be kept as simple and maintenance free as possible; the use of plain concrete and pointed brickwork can be very satisfactory as well as economical if conscientiously executed. If concrete floors are used it is important to seal them to avoid dust problems.

Good workmanship and attractively painted plant will help to ensure that the building is well maintained. Light colours for plant and exposed pipework are best; pipes should be ordered without external bituminous protection which will "bleed" through light coloured paint finishes. Pipes, cables, etc. should be colour coded in accordance with BS 1710: 1975.

Protection against Vandalism

As noted above, the underground pumping station is the most vandal-proof and secure. For above-ground stations where windows cannot be eliminated, they should be glazed with clear acetate sheeting, which is highly resistant to breakage, or protected with an outer window of this material. Doors should be of steel or steel faced timber, outward opening and mounted on steel or steel faced frames. Tiled or slated roofs are easily damaged by bricks and large stones: decorated troughed steel sheeting is much more able to withstand such missiles. Concrete roofs are robust structurally but usually rely on external membranes for waterproofing and these are frequently troublesome—even before attack by vandals! Explosion damage is rendered much more severe by the containing effect of a solid roof.

It is no longer satisfactory to mount transformers externally in gated pens. At the very least they should be fully caged to keep intruders out.

Security

The previous section dealt with the "casual" vandal. There is a need also to try to protect the structure against explosives used by saboteurs. A secure fence will prevent the parking of a booby-trapped vehicle adjacent to the building. Wells or sunken areas adjacent to the building should be avoided, or enclosed with mesh, since blast from explosives dropped into such areas will be more intense.

To prevent incendiary and other devices being thrown into the building, windows should be unbreakable as described above, or mesh protected, and should remain closed as should doors. Ventilators should be securely protected to prevent items being pushed into the building by this means.

For both unmanned and manned stations, an intruder alarm system for doors and windows should be linked to a suitable manned control centre.

Health and Safety

Before building plans are finalised consultation with the undertaking's safety officer and with the fire brigade may improve working convenience and safety as well as obviating the need for later structural alterations.

CORROSION

If cathodic protection is applied to pipelines connected to a pumping station, then it is essential to provide properly insulated flanges which incorporate non-conducting sleeves and washers for the bolts, if possible outside the building. It is advisable to repeat such flanges at the connection to each pump. It is most important to prevent current leakage into the reinforced concrete structure of the station and into the pumps, since corrosion may result.

6. CONTROL, OPERATION AND MAINTENANCE

SYSTEM CONTROL AND OPERATION

General

Pumping plant is generally controlled in relation to the following parameters either singly or in combination:

(a) Level, in reservoirs or tanks, both on inlet and outlet, and in wells or boreholes.

(b) Pressure.

(c) Rate-of-flow.

(d) Time.

In addition, a number of factors may be involved in connection with protection—for example, temperature of bearings, overloads, deficiency of residual chlorine, etc., or a discrepancy between a control and the behaviour of the item controlled—for instance, the failure to deliver of a pump which should have started. Safeguards may instigate an alarm at the control room, or may automatically apply remedial action, or both.

Measuring instruments are covered in Chapter 5 whilst the starting, stopping and speed controlling of the plant have been described in Section 4.

In a few instances measuring devices themselves operate a control mechanism directly (for example, float-operated level gauges which trip switches). However, in the majority of cases the instruments are associated with transducers which convert the quantity measured into a form (say an electric current of a few milliamperes, or a digital number) suitable for actuating a display instrument for effecting control of, for example, valves, pumping plant, etc. for transmission to other sites by cable or by radio (see later) and for combination, where required, with the output from the transducers of other instruments.

The output from a transducer (the signal) may take a number of forms—for example, an electric current, a potential difference, a frequency, the duration of each of a series of impulses (VDI) etc, or a digital number. Where information of a measured quantity is concerned (as opposed to "two-state" information, such as pump on/pump off) the signal will, except in digital transmission, usually be proportional to the quantity concerned. Accuracy will then depend, not only on that of the instrument itself and of the transducer, but also on that of the reinterpreting transducer. Where distant transmission is involved, accuracy will further depend on the absence of mutilation of the signal (for example, by leakage through faulty insulation of cables carrying a signal current) in transmission. With a digital system, once the information is converted into digital form, no error except accidental can occur in transmission, and the information is already in a form suitable for actuating display or control or for computation at any site.

It is true that measurement of a variable quantity cannot, by digital means, be truly continuous, but the speed of electronic addressing, checking, encoding and decoding is so great that intermittency is virtually no disadvantage. For the same reason the serial use of a cable or radio link is permissible, whereby the one channel may transmit a number of "packages" of information. Accuracy depends, of course, on the number of digits used, but can easily be made to exceed greatly the accuracy of the instruments themselves.

Stability

Where control is effected in accordance with a variable quantity which is itself affected by the response, care must be taken to ensure stability. For instance, where the speed of an impeller pump is to be regulated so that a pressure produced by the pump shall not stray outside a pair of limits, the change in pressure resulting from one step in speed-regulation must always be less than the interval between the limits; otherwise, each step would, in most circumstances, give rise to a step in the reverse direction, causing instability. It is also in general necessary that there should be a time interval between control impulses sufficient to allow the system to stabilise after each change, otherwise temporary and local phenomena, such as pressure-surges, may cause unwanted regulation. Where control is not by steps but continuous, similar considerations apply and careful analysis must be made to ensure freedom from hunting.

Where control is in accordance with the time-integral of a quantity which is affected by the response, the steps must not be so small as to give rise to unacceptably short time intervals between control events. For instance, where start and stop are occasioned by low and high level in a delivery tank, the volume contained in the tank between the levels must be such that the pump runs are not objectionally short.

The simple instances mentioned above are introduced to explain the principles involved in ensuring stability and are, of course, applicable to controls of all kinds.

Local Control

Whilst it is possible to operate plant manually in response to the parameters set out above, almost all control is now by local automatic or remote means.

In many cases it is desired that plant shall run so as to achieve a pre-set duty, or programme of duties, unless modified by intervention from, say, a remote control centre. Such set-point control will usually involve a local closed-loop control system, often with proportional and sometimes with integrating and derivative elements. Any "set-point" control system must in general conform with the guidelines for stability given earlier.

The simplest form of local automatic control may be achieved by direct switching from time, level and pressure measuring instruments or a combination thereof, but it is becoming more usual to employ a simple programmable micro-processor. This device is able to store information in relation to off-peak pumping tariffs, minimum acceptable pressures or reservoir levels, likely demand pattern in relation to the day of the week etc. and thus to regulate plant operation to most economic effect. Teletransmission of data to a master station may or may not be incorporated.

Remote Control

The use of digital telemetry for remote control and information gathering is now almost universal. In order to effect control, information is needed at the control centre. This is obtained by sending interrogations, in digital form, serially to each outstation by telephone authority or private line, or by radio link. The last of these is likely to be the cheapest but the use of radio for this purpose requires Department of Trade and Industry permission.

Each data point (instrument, starter, etc.) at each outstation from which information is required has a digital address, and when an interrogation is addressed to it, it recognizes this address and sends back both the address (for checking) and the information (as it might be "12 m" or, in the case of a valve, "closed"). The control room checks the retransmitted address and, if correct, then accepts the information. If not, it repeats, and only when correct will it proceed to send an interrogation to the next point on its list, and so on through the whole sequence. Information is thus available at the control room, up-to-date to an instant within the last cycle of interrogation, to be used for display, record, or processing in combination with other information.

For the transmission of control, a command signal is initiated by the operator (or by the computer) and the address checked as already described. All operative signals, whether consisting of a single command or a multi-step sequence, must be suitably correlated with information as to their effect: for instance, the number of the successive steps of an "inching" adjustment must be limited by a signal intimating the attainment of the desired result.

The process computer dedicated to data logging and control can be programmed in respect of each outstation with parameters similar to those listed under "Local Control" above to enable the most cost-effective operation to be maintained.

No description can here be given of the electronic devices concerned in coding, decoding, processing and storing information, for which reference must be made to a reliable textbook[11,12].

The dependence of operations on a central telemetry system should be carefully evaluated in terms of equipment reliability, power supply, etc. Whilst the cost of a standby process computer may not be justifiable, some means of manually interrogating outstations, such as a simulator or self-contained micro-computer, should be provided. Standby power supply for the control centre and outstations is essential.

Electricity Tariff Considerations

These are generally of the following type:
   (i) a service charge per kVA installed in respect of liability to supply;
  (ii) a maximum demand charge per kVA or per kW of demand incurred during peak demand periods, preferably monthly where no load-relieving plant is concerned; where the demand is charged per kW, there is usually an accompanying minimum power factor requirement.
 (iii) a charge per unit consumer, generally on a sliding scale; and
  (iv) a coal clause, being an increase per unit proportional to changes in the price of coal.

Other forms of tariff are in use, but the above type is fairly standard for pumping stations, naturally with differing local rates of charge. It may be possible to negotiate a special tariff for a particular requirement and it is certainly worth the attempt.

Power factor correction has been noted in Section 2.

Careful attention to tariffs, operating hours and related electricity accounts is most important. All accounts should be checked to ensure that the most advantageous tariff is being used in relation to operating hours and load, both of which may have increased or decreased since the initial selection and which may be altered with beneficial results. Simple micro-computer programmes can and should be devised for this work.

Purchase of Fuel and Diesel Oils

Fuel oils of heavy quality for boilers, and more refined products for internal combustion engines, are usually purchased on a specification of gross calorific value and low sulphur content, the latter of particular importance to the internal combustion engine. Prices are usually governed by international agreement and taxation, and can rarely be modified by negotiation except as regards discount for large quantities.

The use of detergents in fuel should be carefully considered. In winter, anti-waxing additives are usually included by petroleum suppliers; however, if oil has been purchased in summer and stored for winter use, it will not contain those compounds; the additives may be purchased separately.

Where diesel engines are provided for emergency standby and where adjacent buildings are heated by oil, it may prove worth while to operate the heating plant on the lighter, more expensive grades of oil, suitable for the diesel engine. By this means, the heating oil in store may, in emergency, be applied to the diesel engine.

MAINTENANCE

General

Routine preventive maintenance can most satisfactorily be provided by an itinerant team or teams of specialists. If at all possible such work should be divorced from emergency repairs, since the latter will always take precedence and the former suffer.

Planning

A schedule of all points requiring routine attention should be prepared for each works. It is vital that such schedules are set against firm calendar dates; to prepare the schedule without committing it to specific times in the works programme is a waste of effort!

To be most beneficial, the maintenance schedule should include a list of equipment and spares, lubricants etc. likely to be required. Micro-computer based maintenance scheduling systems are now available and these will print out daily work sheets with all relevant information. They can be programmed to include complete parts inventories for each item of plant as well as specification details, such as output, power requirements etc. The low cost of micro-computers and the comparative cheapness of the software programmes makes investment in maintenance scheduling equipment very attractive.

Spares Holding and Restocking

A list of spares should be drawn up for each new item of plant in consultation with the manufacturers. Such lists should be checked against existing spares holdings to ensure that undue quantities of parts common to plant at other stations are not held. It is important to ensure that a spares re-ordering system operates to avoid costly out-of-service time resulting from failure to replace items used from stock.

Obsolescence

Development, particularly in electronic components, is currently very rapid. Equipment, therefore, becomes obsolete in comparatively few years: perhaps 3 to 4 for electronic control components and say 7 to 10 for electric motor control components. Because of the high cost of financing stock, manufacturers do not maintain spares holdings for very long after production ends and it is important to be aware of what parts of one's system are no longer available. This is particularly crucial where long lead times are involved in making replacements, such for example as the change to a "next generation" of telemetry equipment.

Change-over of Plant

In most waterworks installations, standby units are provided and it is common practice to rotate the duty amongst two or more similar items; this system can lead to a situation where all units reach breakdown within days of each other. Whilst it is important to operate standby plant, it is better to ensure that some units are truly designated as such and that their operating hours are kept well down on those of the duty plant.

Health and Safety

Proper training in the correct operation and maintenance of plant is essential to its successful running. Such training should never be regarded as a once and for all event; regular follow-up refresher training should be an integral part of the annual operating plan.

Correct working procedures both for operating and maintaining the plant should be produced and operators should have access to and be familiar with these as part of their training.

Where work on electrical installations is involved, a permit to work system should be drawn up together with appropriate lists of qualified personnel[13].

Water Hygiene

All operational and maintenance personnel should be constantly reminded of the hazards to health entailed in working on apparatus handling treated water[14].

7. REFERENCES

1. Anon, "The British pump market 1981-1982", C. H. W. Roles and Associates.
2. Pollak, F. "Pump Users' Handbook", compiled by the British Pump Manufacturers' Association, Trade and Technical Press.
3. Anon 1968, "Pumping Manual, third edition", Trade and Technical Press.
4. The Institution of Water Engineers 1969 "Manual of British water engineering practice, Vol. II: engineering practice", 4th ed., IWES London.
5. The Institution of Electrical Engineers 1981 "Regulations for electrical installations", 15th ed.
6. Gardiner, J. 1958 *J. IWE*, 12, 13, The waterworks mechanical engineer.
7. Institution of Civil Engineers 1969 "An introduction to engineering economics".
8. Irish, K. and Walker, W. P. 1967 *Concrete*, 327, Foundations for reciprocating machines.
9. Sumner, J. A. 1976 "Domestic heat pumps" Prism Press, Dorchester.
10. Institution of Civil Engineers 1964 (reprint) "The aesthetic aspect of civil engineering design".
11. Emanuel, P. and Leff, E. 1979 "Introduction to feedback control systems", McGraw-Hill, New York and London.
12. Atkinson, P. 1968 "Feedback control theory for engineers", Heinemanns Educational Books, London.
13. Factories Act 1961 "Memorandum on the electricity regulations" (now embodied in the Health and Safety at Work Act 1974), HMSO, London.
14. National Water Council 1979 "Water hygiene: occasional paper No. 2".

Chapter 8

MAINLAYING—PIPES AND ANCILLARY EQUIPMENT

1. TYPES OF PIPE AND SELECTION

INTRODUCTION

PIPES represent a large proportion of the capital invested by water authorities and the selection of the right type of pipe and joint is of great importance.

Pressure pipes (Table 8.I) are made of various materials and fall broadly into three categories; rigid, semi-rigid and flexible. It is an understanding of the properties and capabilities of pipes in these three categories which will enable the designer to select the correct pipes and joints for a main[1].

Since the last war great strides have been made in developing the iron pipe and introducing pipe made of concrete, plastic, steel and composite materials to produce a stronger and lighter weight pipe to meet far more exacting operational requirements of higher internal pressures, greater loadings in highways, tighter control of leakage and to allow easier handling and speeding up of pipelaying work.

In order to make the proper choice it is necessary to examine the properties of the pipe taking into account, where applicable, some of the following considerations:

(1) Hydraulic performance.
(2) Working and test pressures and surges.
(3) Maximum and minimum depth of cover of crown of pipe.
(4) Details of backfill material.
(5) Anticipated superimposed loading on ground surface.
(6) Length and weight for handling and storage.
(7) Resistance to corrosion and chemical action.
(8) Coatings and linings.
(9) Permissible longitudinal and diametral deflection.
(10) Pipe embedment and support conditions.
(11) Ease of making repairs and future connections.
(12) Ring stress to withstand heavy backfill loads at depths in excess of 3 m without deformation of pipe.
(13) In waterlogged ground the weight of pipe in relation to risk of flotation.
(14) Flexibility of joints to enable pipes to be laid on a curve.
(15) Lengths of pipes in relation to number of joints required.
(16) Risk of damage from third parties.
(17) Longitudinal frictional forces and 'beam' action due to ground movement arising from mining subsidence and extremes of temperature.

The use of pipes in the full range of diameters from 100 mm to 1 800 mm where applicable, according to their material of construction, will be considered in three groups: rigid, semi-rigid and flexible.

RIGID PIPES

Grey iron, prestressed concrete and asbestos cement pipes may be classed as rigid conduits that fail by rupture of the pipe walls from relatively small deflections,

---

TABLE 8.I. Types, Sizes and Duties of Pipes

Group	Type	British Standards	International Standards	Maximum available diameter (mm)	Working pressure range (bar)*	Used for distribution systems	Used for trunk mains
Rigid	Grey iron	BS 4622	ISO/R13	600	10-16	Yes	Yes
	Prestressed concrete	BS 4625	—	1400	4-12	No	Yes
	Asbestos cement	BS 486	ISO/R160	900	7.5-12.5	Yes	Occasionally
Semi-rigid	Ductile iron	BS 4772	ISO/R2531	1600	25-40	Yes	Yes
	Steel	BS 534 BS 3601	ISO/R559	2134	To design—only limited to steel and joint strength	No	Yes
Flexible	uPVC	BS 3505	ISO/R1165	600	6-15	Yes	Occasionally
	PE	In course of preparation	—	600	3-10	Yes	Occasionally
	GRP	BS 5480	—	1800	6-16	No	Yes

Note:* 1 bar = 10.2 m (33.455 ft) head of water

although in some areas the majority of failures are due to pitting. The ability of a rigid pipe to carry an external load is directly related to ring strength and the pipe manufacturer's specification for diametral deflections should be observed.

Grey Iron

Grey spun iron[2] was the last of the rigid iron pipes, its production being discontinued in this country in 1981. The oldest rigid cast iron pipes in use today, made by a horizontal casting process, were laid between 1664 and 1668 to convey water from the reservoirs at Picardy to the fountains of Versailles. In 1846 the vertical casting technique became the universal method of casting iron pipes and production did not cease completely until as recently as 1966. The next step foward was the discovery of the centrifugal system of casting and this spun process produced a denser and fine-grained homogeneous metallurgical structure of superior strength to cast pipes. The wall thicknesses of spun pipes were 75 per cent of those of pit cast pipes of the same class and diameter.

Spun pipes, latterly referred to as grey iron, were used in this country from the early 1920s and used extensively in the post war years up to the 1970s. It is important to know the properties of grey spun iron pipes as so many exist in distribution and trunk mains systems throughout the world and for a long time there will be need to carry out repairs and maintenance to pipelines of this material.

Many water undertakings have for a long time specified factory linings of cement mortar, particularly where local water supplies have exhibited corrosive attack.

PRESTRESSED CONCRETE

Prestressed concrete pipes[3] were first introduced in the UK in the early 1950s. Originally two specific types were manufactured, the 'cylinder' and the 'non-cylinder' designs. The 'cylinder' pipe is a welded sheet steel cylinder having steel socket and spigot rings welded to its ends lined with suitably compacted concrete, circumferentially prestressed to withstand internal pressure and external design loads and subsequently coated with cement mortar to protect the steel cylinder and prestressing wire.

The 'non-cylinder' design has no steel cylinder but is prestressed both longitudinally and circumferentially. It is no longer manufactured.

Prestressed concrete cylinder pipes are primarily used for bulk transmission of raw or potable water under pressure but are also suitable for conveying slurries and sludges, sewage and some trade effluents and brine. The steel cylinder of the pipe is the basis of its reliability, providing a continuous water-tight membrane throughout its length. Further advantages are: the pipe can withstand heavy backfill loads at depths up to 4 m cover and normal superimposed loads with no fear of damage or deformation; the weight of the pipe limits risks of flotation before backfilling; its extremely smooth bore has excellent flow characteristics; and its resistance against corrosion substantially maintains its original carrying capacity. About 1 000 km of prestressed concrete cylinder and non-cylinder pipes have to date been laid throughout the world. Failures are few and most are the result of aggressive ions in soil or groundwater attacking the cement mortar and subsequently the prestressing cables.

Reliability can be a matter of concern when used as a major feed to a large area and where no alternative supply is available should a burst occur. Repair time can be a serious matter in such circumstances because repairs take longer than with other conventional materials (see Chapter 10, Section 3).

Asbestos Cement

Asbestos cement pressure pipes came into prominence in the 1930s. They are manufactured from a homogeneous mixture of asbestos fibre and portland cement filtered into a thin layer of fine slurry in which all the asbestos fibres lie flatly and then this film of asbestos cement about 0.25 mm thick is applied to a rotating polished steel mandrel on which it is rolled to the requisite pipe thickness.

Asbestos cement pipes are manufactured in sizes up to 900 mm. Their chief use is for smaller diameter mains in distribution systems although since the 1950s they have been used more extensively in trunk and reinforcing mains. Advantages claimed for them include: freedom from internal corrosion and thereby maintenance of their original carrying capacity; immunity from attack by sulphate-reducing bacteria in corrosive soils, provided that bitumen dipping is applied; and lighter weight than corresponding iron pipes.

Asbestos cement pipes are prone to beam breakage in the smaller sizes and appropriate precautions should be taken in handling, laying and backfilling. Pipes can be drilled and tapped for connections but have not the same strength or suitability for threading as iron and at the points of service connections it is common practice to fix gunmetal or corrosion protected ferrous saddles into which ferrules are screwed.

The factors of safety against bursting under pressure and against failure in longitudinal bending are less than for grey iron pipes and the choice of a route avoiding heavy impact loads in a carriageway, the use of flexible joints and good bedding and well consolidated backfill are essential factors in minimising pipe failure.

In common with many asbestos-based materials, pipes are subject to the requirements of the Asbestos Regulations 1969. Certain cutting operations require safety precautions, including the use of protective clothing and equipment.

SEMI-RIGID PIPES

Ductile iron and steel may be classed as semi-rigid conduits and have the ability to deform under the effects of external loading.

In consequence the pipe better absorbs the load from backfill and has a greater resistance to shock loads such as those arising from traffic loads and pressure surges than a rigid pipe.

Ductile Iron

In 1948 it was discovered that small additions of cerium or magnesium to molten grey cast iron resulted in profound changes to the metallurgical structure. This resulted in a material of greatly enhanced mechanical properties which when made into pipes is known as ductile iron, and when cast into other products is commonly known as spheroidal graphite iron.

A comparison of the minimum modulus of rupture of a ductile iron pipe of 625 MN/m^2 with that of a grey iron pipe of 275 MN/m^2 confirms the superior strength of the ductile iron pipe.

Ductile iron pipes are supplied in sizes up to 1 600 mm diameter and are suitable for all types of water mains laid in almost any ground conditions and locations subject to suitable corrosion protection.

Other advantages compared with grey iron pipes are:

(a) The extra strength and toughness of ductile iron permit the production of pipes with reduced wall thicknesses that are lighter, easier to handle and lay, and less susceptible to damage.

(b) In consequence of having the ability to deform under the effects of external loading, the pipes will not carry as great a vertical load before deforming.

(c) Pipes can operate at higher levels of stress, thereby permitting the pipe to work at higher internal pressures.

When unprotected in aggressive soil conditions, ductile iron may not be able to resist the effect of corrosion. Factory applied bituminous paint represents little more than a cosmetic coating in terms of resisting the effect of corrosion and additional protection should always be used.

Steel

Steel pipes are manufactured by two processes—welded and seamless. The welded steel pipe, available in standard sizes up to 1 800 mm diameter, is made by plates or strips of steel formed into a pipe and welded together at the edges. The seamless steel pipe available in standard sizes up to 400 mm diameter is formed from a steel billet hot pierced by a rotary or thrust process.

The main advantage of the steel pipe compared with pipes of other materials is its greater strength and elasticity which enables a pipeline to be located in difficult ground conditions where movement might take place and where there are significant traffic loading and pressure surges.

The success of a steel pipeline depends largely on the reliability of the internal and external protection and this must be as near perfect as possible for both pipes and joints. In addition it is considered good practice to afford cathodic protection to steel pipelines.

Steel is used mainly for large diameter pipelines, the further advantages for this use being:

(i) Suitable for laying in ground subject to mining subsidence and heavy backfill loadings.

(ii) Less weight than an iron or prestressed concrete pipe of corresponding diameter, resulting in savings in transporting, handling and laying.

(iii) Available in longer lengths than other pipes and, consequently, fewer joints required.

(iv) Reliability for use as a major aqueduct as leakage is usually confined to pin holes and mechanical joints and is rarely catastrophic. It is easily controllable enabling security of supplies to be maintained.

(v) Minor repairs can be carried out by welding, major repairs by use of standard methods with Viking Johnson couplings (see Chapter 10, Section 3).

(vi) Due to the thin wall, greater capacity for the same outside diameter of other materials.

(vii) Suitable for self-supporting spans.

(viii) The ability to incorporate fabricated special pipes and fittings into a pipeline when space is restricted.

(ix) Carrying capacity largely unimpaired as internal concrete or bitumen lining prevents growth of modular incrustation.

Ovality does occur under heavy backfill loads. This can result in leakage from flexible joints and must be taken into account when selecting pipes for use under these conditions. Steel pipelines laid in towns should preferably have welded joints as a safeguard against catastrophic failure and to dispense with thrust blocks which may be difficult to place or, inadvertently, be removed later; the likely presence of electrolytic corrosion or stray currents in urban areas requires cathodic protection.

Care should be taken when using flexible joints, in lieu of welding, due to the relative stiffness of couplings and adjacent pipe, which may produce differential movement in the absence of careful backfilling.

In order to determine pipe thicknesses calculations must be made using all available criteria including range of pressures and flows, surge limit, degree of compaction of backfill specified and factor of safety desired.

FLEXIBLE PIPES

uPVC (Unplasticised Polyvinyl Chloride), PE (Polyethylene) and GRP (Glass Reinforced Plastic) may be classed as flexible conduits[4-7], tending to have low inherent strength and deflecting under loadings. They derive a large part of their load bearing strength from the ability to transfer top loads to the side fill and it is therefore essential that the trench should be carefully prepared and the backfill well consolidated round the pipe.

uPVC (Unplasticised Polyvinyl Chloride)

Plastics [8-10] are becoming more widely used for water pipes throughout the world and one of the most commonly used is unplasticised PVC[11,12]. The properties of this thermo-plastic material enable pipes to be manufactured to close dimensional tolerances, to be light without being weak, rigid without being brittle and to be virtually immune from corrosion. It is widely used for distribution mains and is suitable in circumstances where ground movement and corrosive soils limit the use of pipes of other materials.

There are limitations in the use of uPVC. Impact strength decreases with lowering temperatures and tensile strength decreases with increasing temperatures and, as a result, careful handling, stacking and laying of the pipe in extremes of temperature are essential. To avoid fractures or deformation of the pipe when laying, its support must be as uniform as possible, free from stones or other hard objects, and the fill material must be well compacted. If uPVC pipe is selected for a pumping main account must be taken of its limitations in respect of pressure surges.

Over the last decade there has been a continuous improvement of extrusion processes in the manufacture of plastic pipes and in the techniques of laying, jointing and backfilling. Consequently failures that were rather more frequent than expected have fallen to acceptable proportions and pipe users now express general satisfaction with uPVC pipes. uPVC pipes have mainly been used in smaller diameters for distribution systems but, with improved pipe manufacturing processes, an acknowledgement of the material's limitations and a better understanding of laying techniques, uPVC pipes are satisfactory for larger diameter trunk mains. However, constraint on the use of uPVC pipe for a trunk main arises from the tendency for a fracture to develop into a split along the length of a badly laid pipe, resulting in large losses of water and extended time for carrying out repairs. In spite of this there appears to be limited use made of uPVC above 300 mm diameter, within the industry.

The financial advantages of uPVC pipes lie in reduced installation costs compared with iron, steel and concrete pipes. The savings can be achieved by intelligent use of their light weight, availability in long lengths, ease of jointing and their good flow characteristics with little age reduction due to their immunity from encrustation. Furthermore they are cheaper than polyethylene pipes.

PE (Polyethylene)

Another plastic material used for water pipes is a polymer from which polyethylene (PE) pipes were first manufactured in the mid-1950s. The old generation of PE pipes were first restricted to low density grade for small diameters of up to 50 mm but later larger bore sizes in low and high density grades were introduced.

A new generation of this old material has now been produced, a modified high density polymer, also known as medium density polymer, specially chosen because of its exceptional weld compatibility, its long-term performance at both ambient and elevated temperatures and improved resistance to stress cracking and stress propagation.

PE has been used fairly extensively in the gas industry for some time and manufacturers are now introducing this material to the water industry. Pipes up to 100 mm diameter can be supplied in a coil of 150 m of pipe as well as straight lengths, but pipes between 180 mm diameter and 500 mm diameter are supplied only in straight lengths up to a maximum of 12 m.

Pipe used by the gas industry is coloured yellow and for other applications is coloured black. The water industry and the manufacturers have adopted a colour coding scheme which identifies blue PE as a water industry product[13] and pipes up to 250 mm nominal diameter are supplied in this colour. PE pipe is widely used for service pipes but water undertakings are now laying lengths of small diameter PE pipe in distribution systems and field trials are being carried out to develop specifications for pipes and mainlaying.

Early results show that PE pipe will be satisfactory for use in pressure water mains. It is inert, flexible, lightweight and has the required structural strength without being brittle. It is suitable for use where ground movement is experienced and corrosive soils are present, and where long ducts and flexibility in bending are required. The material itself would appear to withstand surge pressures better than uPVC pipe and to be more resistant to freezing because of the good thermal insulation properties. A special use is the rehabilitation of buried pipelines by the insertion (slip lining) technique (see Chapter 10, Section 4).

There are however a number of, as yet undetermined, factors with blue PE used below ground such as its shelf life, fatigue in weld areas and permeability of the material and when selecting blue PE pipes careful consideration must be given to these factors. It is proposed that black PE will continue to be used above ground. PE is prone to creep properties which require special precautions in the use of conventional mechanical fittings.

GRP (Glass Reinforced Plastic)

GRP pipes[14-15] are composed of three basic constituents: glass fibre, resin and sand. In the design of the pipe the whole of the strength is considered to be derived from the glass fibres which are bonded together by the resin, forming a matrix which also renders the structure impermeable to the fluids being carried. The wall thickness of GRP pipes designed to provide adequate ring strength for low pressure applications (below 10 bar) would be too thin for the pipe to be sufficiently robust to withstand the rigours of handling, transportation and installation. Consequently, graded inert sand is incorporated into the wall of the low pressure pipe to increase the thickness and, by so doing, the stiffness of the pipe.

Over the past few years GRP pipes have begun to be used for large diameter pipelines for the conveyance of raw and potable water and many sewage and industrial trade effluents.

GRP pipes are light in weight compared with steel and concrete pipes of similar size making handling, transporting and laying easier and their smooth bore provides

TABLE 8.II. Types of Joint

Class	Type	Material	Examples of trade names or descriptions	Maximum standard sizes available—nominal bore of pipe (mm)	Maximum working head (bar)	Deflection between adjacent pipes (degrees)
Weld	Butt	Steel	—	2 134	100	None
	External sleeve	Steel	—	2 134	100	2
	Internal sleeve	Steel	—	2 134	100	2
	Butt fusion	Polyethylene	—	630	10	None
	Socket fusion	Polyethylene	—	630	10	None
Mechanical	Flange	Steel	—	2 134	100	None
		Ductile iron	—	1 600	25	None
	Shouldered	Steel	Victaulic	600	15	1
		Malleable cast iron	Victaulic	900	10	1
	Self-anchored socket and spigot	Ductile iron	Anchorable Tyton Tie Bar	400 1 200	10 To specific requirements	3
	Movement	Steel	—	To specific requirements	To specific requirements	None
		PE	Aqua lock			
Filler	Socket and spigot lead, lead wool, asbestos, etc.	Grey Iron Steel	— —	1 200 1 800	24	2
Gland (Rubber or similar ring forced into a sealing position by a rigid peripheral gland)	Single (gland fits into pipe socket)	Grey iron Ductile iron	Bolted gland Stanlock	1 200 600	25-40 25-40	4 4
	Double (sleeve over plain ended pipes with two glands bolted)	Steel Cast iron	Viking Johnson Gibault	1 600 250	10-35 12	2-6 4
Sealing ring (Rubber or similar ring forced into a sealing position by the entry of the pipe end and by water pressure)	Single (ring fits into pipe socket)	Prestressed concrete Ductile iron Ductile iron uPVC GRP	Stanpress Tyton Stantyte Anger Loc-Ring RPM	1 400 600 1 600 500 600 1 800	12 25-40 25 9-15 6-15 16	1.5 3-5 4 2 1 3
	Double (sleeve over plain ended pipes with two rubber rings)	Asbestos cement	Widnes	900	25	1.5-5

good flow characteristics. They can also be laid in chemically unsuitable ground, such as former industrial and chemical sites where intensive corrosive conditions are present which would attack other materials. The joints would, however, require special protection to ensure reliability of the pipeline.

The manufacturers' design charts and tables for pipe embedment should be adopted and backfill round the pipe well consolidated in accordance with the recommendations.

2. TYPES OF PIPE JOINTS AND SELECTION

INTRODUCTION

Pipe joints also fall into three classes: rigid, semi-rigid and flexible. It is necessary to understand their capabilities so that the right joint can be used with a particular pipe to achieve the best design of the pipeline (Table 8.II). A particular type of pipe can be jointed with one or more types of joint to suit the circumstances in which the pipeline is laid and has to operate (Table 8.III). For instance, a rigid asbestos cement pipeline may have flexible Viking Johnson couplings or a flexible polyethylene (PE) pipeline may have a welded or heat-fused rigid joint.

RIGID JOINTS

Welded Joints

Welded joints on steel mains are suitable for sizes of 600 mm diameter and above; in this size range they are the cheapest type of joint for steel pipes and internal welds and fettling can be satisfactorily undertaken. They are suitable for all pressures and can be used on pipelines above and below ground.

The simple butt-welded joint for which pipes are supplied with plain ends is suitable for long aqueducts over all types of ground even with underground movement conditions because the joints will be as strong as the pipes themselves and will therefore not draw apart under the longitudinal tensile strain. Butt joints are particularly suitable for large diameter steel pipes in confined spaces and across difficult obstacles where self-supporting pipework with limited points of anchorage is required, such as spanning gaps, laying in ducts and tunnel and under watercourses. It is necessary to lay pipes with butt-welded joints in a straight line and any change of direction must be made with a bend or in the case of small changes, with a specially chamfered ring.

The socket and spigot welded joint can be either externally or internally welded but it is usual to have the essential jointing weld on the inside when the pipe diameter is large enough to permit internal access, and often with a secondary run around the outside of this pipe to give additional security and to assist with testing. The advantage of this type of joint is that it is self-aligning and adjacent pipes can be deviated up to 2° so that the pipeline can be laid on a curve. On the other hand it is more expensive than the butt-welded joint because an extra joint is required on each pipe and there is the extra cost of forming the socket.

The solvent rigid joint[16] for uPVC mains was used extensively when small diameter plastic pipes were first introduced but has proved unsuccessful for underground use in the water industry. However, this solvent rigid joint is suitable and has given satisfactory service when used for industrial pipework layouts above ground.

The butt or socket welding technique for PE pipe involves heat welding the pipe, either as two butt ends or as a socket fitting using specialist equipment. This rigid

TABLE 8.III.   Suitable Pipe Joints According to Circumstances

Type of pipe	Buried	Above ground	
		Simply supported and held subject to only longitudinal thrust	Subject to side thrusts, shear and bending forces
Grey iron	Socket and spigot, run and caulked lead Bolted gland	Flanged	None
Prestressed concrete	Socket and spigot, 'O' ring, rubber gasket Push in	None	None
Asbestos cement	Asbestos cement sleeve with two 'O' rubber rings Cast iron bolted collar and flanges with rubber rings	Viking Johnson steel coupling	None
Ductile iron	Socket and spigot Rubber gasket Push in Stanlock	Self anchored socket and spigot Steel toothed rubber gasket Push in Tie bar joint Viking Johnson steel coupling	Flanged
Steel	Socket and spigot, run and caulked lead Flanged Viking Johnson steel coupling Welded	Viking Johnson steel coupling Flanged Welded Victaulic	Welded Flanged
uPVC	Socket and spigot rubber gasket push in	Solvent welded	None
PE	Heat fusion welding	Heat fusion welding, Electrofusion	None
GRP	Socket and spigot, 'O' ring, rubber gasket, push in	None	None

joint will not pull apart under loading and enables long lengths of flexible PE pipe to be formed which are particularly suitable in the presence of ground movement, in long ducts and in situations where the pipeline must be laid on a curve. The major advantage of heat welding enables the full potential of PE to be realised. It can be jointed above ground and snaked into the trench, thereby reducing labour and road reinstatement costs to a minimum by the adoption of narrow trench working. Electrofusion jointing is a relatively new method of welding PE pipes together, involving a socketed collar into which is built a wire coil through which an electric current is passed, thereby heating the internal face of the collar and the external faces of the pipe to a temperature suitable for welding the two faces together. An advantage is that it can join two pipes of different grades of PE. The technique is presently under development with a view to producing a system that would minimise on-site risks associated with conventional heat-welding techniques.

Flanged Joints

Rigid flanged joints which are self-anchoring have many specialised uses; for exposed pipework in pumping stations and treatment plants; in cross-connection chambers; in spanning gaps; or where disconnection should be easy and quick but rigid pipework is required. The thickness of the flanges, their diameter, the number and size of bolts are determined by the duty the pipeline has to perform. Flanges on grey iron pipe are screwed or cast on as an integral part of the pipe, whereas flanges on ductile pipe are cast, screwed or welded on the pipe. Steel pipes have the flanges welded, screwed or expanded onto the pipe. Flange joints are available for PE pipelines for some systems.

Joint rings used to be made of natural rubber but now are manufactured from synthetic rubbers such as Ethylene Propylene Diene Monomer (EPDM) to overcome problems of biodegradation of natural rubber.

Semi-rigid Joints

Caulked Lead Spigot and Socket Joint

This is the traditional type of socket and spigot joint with run lead, lead wool or asbestos compounds caulked into place. This joint was extensively used in the past, and consequently a large proportion of existing iron distribution and trunk mains and some large steel trunk mains have lead caulked socket and spigot joints.

The use of this joint is now limited to repair work and then only when old iron mains in poor condition or with non-standard outside diameters have to be jointed (see Chapter 10, Section 3).

Flexible Joints

Gland Joint

These joints are formed by a rubber or similar ring forced into position by a rigid peripheral gland. Gland joints have no significant longitudinal strength but permit deflections of up to $4°$[17].

There are two types of gland joints: firstly, where the pipes are socket and spigot and the ring is forced into the space between the spigot of one pipe and the socket of the next, the gland being drawn up towards the socket; secondly, detachable sleeve couplings fitted on plain ended pipes known as a double collar.

The socket and spigot gland joint developed from the introduction of the spun iron pipe in 1922 and in achieving the means of compressing the sealing gasket a number of designs have been produced:

(1) Cast iron bolts hooked behind the socket and bolted to the pressure flange.
(2) A cast iron pressure ring with three helical lugs engaging and locking on rotation with three similar lugs on the socket thereby sealing the joint.
(3) A threaded cast iron pressure ring which engages with a similar thread on the socket of the pipe and when screwed in position seals the joint.
(4) The bolted gland joint involving the compression of the wedge-shaped gasket ring by a cast iron gland secured to a flange cast integrally with the pipe socket by a series of cast iron T-headed bolts.

These socket and spigot gland joints have been superseded by an improved bolted gland joint for use with ductile iron pipes.

Detachable sleeve coupling gland joints will joint plain ended pipes of any material, or different materials providing the outside diameters are the same. The sleeve is shaped to receive a gasket ring into each end and the rings are forced in by glands drawn together by bolts. When laying pipes continuously the detachable sleeve has an internal central register which enables the sleeve to be located centrally across the two pipe ends to be jointed. However, the sleeve can be provided without the central register where couplings are to be used for closures.

The most widely used detachable sleeve coupling is the Viking Johnson coupling. A maximum angle of up to 6° depending upon diameter between adjacent pipes is possible. Allowing expansion and contraction, this coupling is suitable for pipes liable to be subject to ground movement and thermal expansion and contraction. It is used for large diameter steel pipes where flexibility is required and has many specialised uses such as jointing asbestos cement and ductile iron pipes.

Another detachable sleeve coupling is the cast iron detachable joint which has particular use with asbestos cement pipes but is also useful for jointing grey iron and ductile iron in special situations. This joint will give a deflection of 4°. To avoid problems associated with jointing a relatively flexible steel pipe (thin walled) with relatively 'stiff' joint couplings (VJs), care must be taken to avoid differential movement under external load. Where aggressive soils are present, the gland joint must be protected against corrosion, otherwise the associated nuts and bolts can soon fail.

Sealing Ring Joint

These joints are formed by a synthetic rubber ring (EPDM or similar material) forced into a sealing position by the entry of the spigot end into the socket end of the pipe and by water pressure without other mechanical compression. They are also known as 'push in' or push-fit joints and occur in the form of spigot and socket pipes designed for a particular type of joint; or as a detachable sleeve coupling.

The spigot and socket sealing ring joint is designed to permit angular deflection in any direction and axial movement to compensate for ground movement and thermal expansion and contraction. This joint is used for prestressed concrete, ductile iron, uPVC and GRP pipes.

The joint on the socket and spigot prestressed concrete pipe incorporates an 'O' ring rubber gasket which locates in a groove in the specially formed spigot end ring. A deflection of up to 1.5° can be made at each joint.

Ductile iron pipe has a socket designed to achieve more uniform diametral deflection of the socket and spigot of the joint when subjected to external loading. The joint employs a specially shaped rubber gasket located in the specially formed socket end ring. A deflection of between 3° and 5° can be made at each joint depending on the diameter of the pipe and the type of joint.

The uPVC pipe has a socket thicker than the remainder of the pipe wall to ensure that the socket in which the rubber ring is retained can resist joint stresses. This thickening may be produced as an integral process or as a separate sleeve around the socket. The rubber ring locates in the specially formed socket end ring. Joints and sealing ring profiles and dimensions are not to standard. Consequently there is no guarantee of interchanges between sockets of one manufacturer and sealing rings of another, thereby creating stocking and repair difficulties.

Care should be taken not to pull uPVC pipe beyond the recommended angle of deflection otherwise the resulting stress induces longitudinal splitting failure when the pipe is subsequently tapped for service connections.

Displacement of rubber-rings is common if joints are made casually, so use of a 'feeler-gauge' to ensure proper positioning is essential. However, not all uPVC pipes are designed with loose rings and at least one manufacturer presently produces socket and spigot pipes with integral rubber joint rings.

A deflection of up to 1° can be made at each joint.

A sealing ring joint is now available for PE pipe in limited sizes.

The GRP pipe joint incorporates an 'O' ring rubber gasket which locates in a groove in the specially formed spigot end ring. Depending on the diameter of the pipe a deflection of up to 3° can be made at each joint.

The detachable sleeve coupling sealing ring joint is a sleeve, the internal diameter being slightly greater than the external diameter of the pipes to be jointed. It has two internal grooves in which 'O' type rubber rings are located and the joint made by the entry of the spigot pipe ends. For jointing asbestos cement pipes the sleeve is made of asbestos cement and this joint will give a deflection of between 1.5° and 5°.

SPECIAL JOINTS

Self-Anchored Joint

The Victaulic joint is an example of a self-anchored joint. The steel pipes for this joint have a grooved or shouldered end and the joint is formed by a circular bolted housing made in rolled steel or malleable cast iron in two parts for sizes up to 350 mm diameter and three or four parts for larger diameters which retain a shaped rubber ring sealing the joint. The joint allows a small angular movement between adjacent pipes and a small longitudinal movement but is capable of withstanding heavy longitudinal loads thus transmitting the load across the joint. It has special uses where there is a need for flexibility with end strength where flange joints would not be suitable.

Another form of self-anchoring joint is a modified version of the ductile socket and spigot joint. This is achieved by having a stainless steel toothed insert moulded into the rubber gasket. When the main is pressurised the teeth grip onto the spigot surface preventing joint separation.

Tie Bar Joint

For larger diameter ductile iron pipes self-anchoring joints can be constructed by positioning flanges on each side of the joint and coupling together with tie bars.

Ball and Socket Joint

This is a special unit where deflection of up to 22½° in all directions is required. A spherical cast iron spigot is accommodated in suitable housing where it is secured by a gland. This gland, when bolted in position, also serves to compress the jointing material and so seal the joint. The ball and socket joint gives no provision for longitudinal movement and some form of expansion joint is necessary in the system. This joint is now rarely used.

Movement Joint

Exposed or overground pipes at bridge crossings are liable to appreciable changes in length due to temperature variations and specially designed movement joints are necessary to prevent the forces resulting from the stress induced in the pipeline from being transmitted to a structure or apparatus which is incapable of withstanding such forces safely.

This type of movement joint, constructed in steel, consists essentially of a central sleeve in which the pipe ends are free to move in either direction or a long spigot housed in a deep socket. The space between the pipe and the sleeve or the spigot and the socket is packed with a jointing material compressed by a bolted gland against a stop end inside the sleeve or the socket. The sliding surfaces of the joints are metallized by spraying with zinc.

There are other forms of movement joints, an example being an angular compensator used in pipework over a bridge. The angular compensator consists of tied hot-formed heavy-walled bellows of chromium-molybdenum steel between flanges. Bars attached to the flanges and hinged in the centre of the bellows resist the tendency for the bellows to extend due to internal pressure and compel the bellows to bend about their centres in a vertical plane where there is movement of the pipeline. When designing movement joints, care must be exercised in ensuring that movement takes place within the joint without affecting the overall stability of the body of the joint.

Repair Clamps and Couplers

A repair clamp is used to seal serious leakage from lead-caulked socket and spigot joints on iron and steel pipes and to secure lead joints following recaulking after ground movement. It consists of a cast iron anchor ring built up in sections which is secured to the pipe socket and a split follower ring attached to it by a series of bolts. Tightening of these bolts causes the follower ring to compress a rubber gasket or lead wool against the face of the lead joint.

Another form of joint repair clamp is the split socket clip made in two halves to be bolted together with sealing surfaces fully machined and glanded end rubbers to give a tight water seal.

For sealing leakage from a crack or split in a pipe of any material a split plain clamp in two halves to be bolted together can be used. The water-tight seal is achieved by a neoprene gasket lining in the clip.

A PE electroweld coupler without centre register is suitable for use as a repair coupler providing that the weld can be done under waterfree conditions.

3. TYPES OF PIPE FITTINGS AND SELECTION

INTRODUCTION

Pipe manufacturers produce a wide range of pipe fittings to facilitate change in pipe diameters and joints, change in direction of pipeline and the installation of miscellaneous apparatus.

CHANGE OF PIPE DIAMETERS AND JOINTS

Tapers

Prestressed concrete diameter tapers are fabricated in mild steel and lined and coated with concrete. They may be concentric or flat and are available with socket, spigot and flanged ends.

Tapers up to 600 mm diameter for use with asbestos cement pipes are manufactured in cast iron, being concentric with double spigot joints. For asbestos cement pipes between 600 mm and 900 mm diameter tapers are fabricated in steel.

Ductile iron tapers are available with a concentric or flat profile and have double socket joints or double flanged joints.

Tapers for steel pipes are fabricated from steel plate to suit requirements for length, change of diameter and joint.

uPVC and PE tapers are normally concentric and generally provided with spigot ends for connecting into pipe sockets although flanged ends can be obtained.

GRP tapers are concentric and are available with socket, spigot and flanged ends. These fittings are usually fabricated in steel.

Change Fittings

When it is necessary to join pipes or fittings of the same nominal size, one with an inch sized socket, spigot or flanged end and the other with metric sized ends, fittings are available with one end to imperial dimension and the other end to metric dimension. These fittings, in ductile iron, can be used with grey iron, asbestos cement and ductile iron pipes, and are available as change collars, as socket and spigot pieces with gland or lead caulked joints, as change spigots and as double flanged change pieces and Viking Johnson change couplings.

A change of pipe material can be achieved between grey iron, asbestos cement, ductile iron, and uPVC, using ductile iron, uPVC change pieces and nylon-coated aluminium pressure fittings. Special ductile iron fittings with 'push in' joints in the range of 150-300 mm diameter are made to suit similar nominal diameter uPVC pipe.

A change of pipe diameter can be achieved at a flange joint by a flange, the outside diameter to the table of the nominal size of the larger pipe, the bore to the diameter of the smaller pipe and drilled with two bolt circles. The inner bolt circle is sometimes provided as a stud flange for convenience.

Flange Adaptors

Flange socket and flange spigot pieces are used when incorporating a double flanged sluice valve into a pipeline and when transferring from a flexible to a rigid jointing system. These fittings are available in ductile iron, steel or uPVC for use with asbestos cement pipes, ductile iron, steel, uPVC and PE.

Collars and Closure Units

The collar, a simple fitting for jointing two spigots, is widely used for the insertion of fittings and pipes in existing pipelines and for repair work (see Chapter 10, Section 3). It is available in ductile iron in imperial size for lead caulked and gland joints and in metric size with sealing ring joint.

Split collars, in two halves flanged and bolted, are principally used for the repair of mains which have failed circumferentially. They can be fitted over the break without disturbing the main and the insertion of a new length of pipe becomes unnecessary.

Steel collars with lead caulked joints are seldom used as a Viking Johnson coupling without centre register can be advantageously used instead of collars. Viking Johnson couplings can also be used as closure units for uPVC, AC and ductile iron pipes. uPVC collars utilizing rubber sealing rings are available.

TABLE 8.IV. Types of Standard Bends

Material of bend	Type of joint	Angle of bend—degrees					
		5⅝	11¼	22½	45	90
Prestressed concrete	Sealing ring	—	SO & SP	SO & SP	SO & SP	—
Cast iron for AC pipes	Gland	—	DSP	DSP	DSP	DSP
Asbestos cement	Gland	—	DSP	DSP	DSP	DSP
Ductile iron	Sealing ring Gland Flange	DSO — —	DSO DSO DF	DSO DSO DF	DSO DSO DF	DSO DSO DF
Steel	Weld Flange Gland	— — —	DSP, SO & DP DF DSP	DSP, SO & DP DF DSP	DPS, SO & SP DF DSP	DSP, SO & SP DF DSP
uPVC	Sealing ring	—	SO & SP	SO & SP	SO & SP	SO & SP
PE	Weld	Pipes can be laid on a curve			DSP	DSP
GRP	Sealing ring	DSO	DSO	DSO	DSO	DSO

Note: SO & SP, Socket and spigot; DSP, Double spigot; DSO, Double socket; DF, Double flange.

Closure units are used to close short gaps between adjacent prestressed concrete pipes, which may have been left during laying or which occur whenever it is necessary to remove an existing pipe. Units are supplied with spigot and socket ends, double spigot and double socket ends. Spigot end units may be cut to length on site.

CHANGE OF DIRECTION OF PIPELINE

Bends

Bends, turning through standard angles with various joints, available for pre-stressed concrete, asbestos cement, ductile iron, steel, uPVC and GRP pipes, are listed in Table 8.IV. Prestressed concrete pipes can be deviated 2° or 4° by the use of a bevel pipe or a bevel adaptor and bevelled flanges can be fixed between the flange faces of flanged joints to change direction up to 3° depending on the diameter.

In ductile iron a special 90° duckfoot bend up to 1 400 mm diameter is available and for offsetting a main an 'S' bend is available in diameters up to 300 mm.

Although standard angle steel bends are available a steel bend of any angle can be manufactured by pulling round a straight pipe to even curvature on the smaller bores or by forming a bend by inserting and welding a mitred piece of pipe between two straight lengths of pipe for larger bores.

PE pipe can be deviated through any required angle (CP 312, Part 3) by pulling on a curve the radius of which is a function of the angle required and the cross-section of the pipe. Deviation by curvature of the pipe must be avoided when laying a uPVC main larger than nominal size 150 mm diameter since the additional stresses incurred sometimes lead to failure by longitudinal splits (CP 312, Part 2).

Tees

Prestressed concrete tees are fabricated from a standard pipe with a mild steel branch tube with flange welded into the pipe shell and lined and coated with concrete, the diameter of the branch being less than the nominal diameter of the pipe.

Cast iron tees for use with asbestos cement pipes are manufactured in all diameters up to 600 mm with either spigot end or glange branch. For asbestos cement pipes between 600 mm and 900 mm tees are fabricated in steel.

There is a wide range of ductile iron tees up to diameters of 1 600 mm with sealing ring and gland joints on the barrel of the pipe and sealing ring, gland and flange joints on the branch.

Steel tees are fabricated to any required dimensions from a branch with spigot or flange end welded into the barrel of the main pipe.

Nylon coated aluminium tees are also available.

For uPVC and PE pipes available tees are limited to equal tees of diameters up to 250 mm. For pipe diameters between 250 and 600 mm, grey iron, ductile iron, steel and aluminium alloy tees can be used with suitable change fittings.

A full range of PE fittings are available up to 250 mm at 10 bar and flange adaptors up to 500 mm.

Flanges on double socket tees are available for GRP pipes up to 1 800 mm diameter.

Tees are normally supplied with the centre line of the branch outlet coinciding with the centre line of the main pipe barrel. For special uses, such as washouts, level invert tees are available in cast iron for asbestos cement pipes, ductile iron and steel.

Angle Branches and Crosses

Angle branches, 'Y' pipes, radial tees and crosses are available as special castings in ductile iron and can be fabricated to requirements in steel, but are only normally used in special situations.

MISCELLANEOUS APPARATUS

Underpressure Connections

Mains under pressure can be drilled for branch connections without loss of pressure or interruption of flow by means of a special drilling machine and apparatus. Pipe materials that can be cut by this method include cast and ductile iron with concrete linings, asbestos cement, prestressed concrete, steel and plastic.

The pipe under pressure to be drilled is fitted with a special underpressure branch connection with a split body for bolting onto the pipe and a flanged outlet branch to which a full clear-bore, gate sluice-valve is bolted. The body of the underpressure drilling machine is bolted to the sluice valve and its cutters, operating through the open gate of the sluice-valve and driven by hand or power, cut out of the pipe wall a hole to match the diameter of the branch. Work is completed by withdrawing the cut out piece of pipe wall back into the machine, closing the sluice-valve and removing the machine.

Underpressure branch connections and machines are available for making cuts in pipe walls up to 1 500 mm diameter. Cuts can be made with the drilling machine horizontal, vertical, or at any other angle.

Equipment using electroweld techniques is available with compatible fittings for branch connections in PE which can be carried out under pressure to existing mains up to 250 mm diameter.

Caps and Plugs

Caps with a socket joint are available for prestressed concrete, asbestos cement, ductile iron, steel, uPVC, PE and GRP pipes and with gland, sealing ring or filler joint appropriate to the pipe. Plugs with a spigot joint are available for prestressed concrete, ductile iron, steel and GRP pipes.

Puddle Flanges

Puddle flanges are used to provide a water bar where a pipe passes through a wall. These may be attached to ductile iron pipes by welding, casting the flange integrally with the pipe or by bolting in split form around the pipe. A puddle flange for steel pipe is welded to the pipe. Pipes of other materials are unlikely to be used for this purpose.

Bellmouths

Standard bellmouths with flange connection used for inlets/outlets into reservoirs and tanks are available only in ductile iron. They can be fabricated in steel but require a very high standard of protective coating, such as uPVC.

Hatchboxes

Hatchboxes are used to gain access to a main through a bolted plate. They are available only in ductile iron with flange joints, but can be fabricated in similar form for access to steel pipes.

4. TYPES OF VALVES, APPARATUS AND SELECTION

INTRODUCTION

When in service, valves and apparatus in distribution, secondary or trunk main systems are subjected to one or more of the following loadings:

(a) Internal hydraulic pressure applied to the body, resulting from the valve or apparatus acting as a continuation of the pipeline.

(b) Hydraulic pressure forcing gates, doors and disks onto seatings which have to resist the bearing pressure without distortion in order to maintain water-tightness.

(c) Stresses on spindles, hinges, shafts, bearings and gearing transmitted by pressure on gates, doors and disks.

(d) Longitudinal force from adjacent pipes, bends and other apparatus under pressure imparting a tensile or compressive load through the pipework connections.

Valve and apparatus manufacturers produce a standard range of products to stated specifications and in accordance with the appropriate British Standard. Selection[18-22] can be made to match hydraulic and site conditions from the standard range but, if the valve or apparatus required is non-standard, information must be supplied to the manufacturer so that it can be constructed and tested to enable it to function correctly at site.

The specification should cover:

(i) Type of valve or apparatus, its location and jointing.

(ii) The maximum internal pressure to be sustained by the body, and whether restrained or subjected to longitudinal forces. This defines the body design.

(iii) The maximum pressure to be sustained by the face of a gate, door, disk, plunger or piston in a closed position. This defines the seat design, the deflection of the seat and body and the gearing or actuator requirements.

SLUICE VALVES

In 1839 James Nasmyth introduced a system of flow control consisting of a wedge-shaped gate controlled by a screwed spindle and nut and although considerable development in gate sluice-valves has taken place the fundamental concept remains.

For most purposes sluice valves[23] are for 10 bar and 16 bar rating and are in accordance with BS 5163: 1974 (Double Flanged Cast Iron Wedge Gate Valves for Waterworks Purposes). To meet duties of higher pressures sluice valves for 25 bar ratings are in accordance with BS 5150: 1974 (Cast Iron Wedge and Double Disk Gate Valves for General Purposes). Valves are normally supplied with ends flanged faced and drilled to BS 4504: 1969 although plain ends for asbestos cement pipes with dimensions to BS 486 are available.

The wedge gate of the valve is available in metal face or soft face (sometimes referred to as resilient seated). The metal face wedge gate, which has been universally used for many years, combines a high standard of reliable performance with proven durability of service. The seating consists of gunmetal face rings on each side of the cast iron wedge, forming a seal when moved in position matching up with corresponding rings in the valve body. The most significant innovation in wedge sealing was introduced in the early 1950s when in place of the conventional all metal construction the entire wedge was encased in synthetic rubber to form an axial and butt seal against the valve body. This is known as the soft faced valve which has been widely used on the continent and is popular in the UK. Features are:

(1) Positive tight shut-off due to resilience of rubber seal accommodating flexing of the valve body.
(2) Seal easily renewable by changing the wedge for a new one. It makes its own tight seal without requiring facing-in.
(3) The valve has a clear bore which ensures optimum flow characteristics and is without the conventional seating recess, needed for the metal faced wedge, in which débris can accumulate.

Metal face valves are obtained as a standard up to 600 mm bore (soft face valves up to 300 mm bore) but above this size each valve is produced to a specification requiring the following basic information:

(a) Pipeline details (diameter, connections and jointing required).
(b) Maximum working pressure.
(c) Maximum closed valve head against which the valve will be required to operate. This will define the gearing and headstock required.
(d) If reversal of hydraulic loading is expected from the downstream end.
(e) Maximum flow velocity through the valve in the fully open position.
(f) Direction of closing.
(g) Type of operation required; spur or bevel gears, details of any particular control requirements.

The three usual forms of sluice valve operation are by hand, electric motor and hydraulic or pneumatic cylinder.

Hand Operation

Standard valves up to 600 mm bore are supplied with a horizontal handwheel or tapered stem cap for a valve key and are operated by hand, subject to any unbalanced pressure on the gate being overcome when opening the valve. Hand operating with higher unbalanced pressures or with valves above 600 mm bore can be achieved by relieving the unbalanced pressure through a bypass valve and so reducing the operating force on the main valve. The bypass valve can be connected to tees placed upstream and downstream of the main valve and for valves over 300 mm bypass tees are incorporated in the body of the main valve. Another method is to include a bevel gearbox with a ratio of say 3:1, hand operated by a wheel in the vertical position.

Valve operation can be further improved by incorporating anti-friction features of ball-thrust bearings at the spindle thrust collar and machined gunmetal shoes on the wedge and channels in the body.

Electric Motor

Power operation of large valves avoids arduous and time consuming manual efforts. In the non-critical areas of movements they can be operated faster than by hand and can also be controlled automatically through telemetry, by time, pressure and flow control and by water level using a float switch.

The actuator is an electric motor attached to the top flange of the valve bonnet and operating the valve through reduction gearing.

Hydraulic or Pneumatic Cylinder

This consists of a double-acting piston and cylinder appropriate to the operating medium employed—water, oil or compressed air. The cylinder is mounted on the valve bonnet by means of a distance piece and the piston rod is connected to the valve stem. The control is by means of a multi-way cock on the operating pressure lines to the cylinder which can be manual or solenoid operated.

BUTTERFLY VALVES

The flow control system of the butterfly valve is a disk pivoted on a shaft within the valve body, operating through a vertical or horizontal plane. Valves up to 1 200 mm bore are available for 16 bar rating; between 1 200 mm and 2 000 mm bore, for 10 bar rating; and for larger bore one specially made for 6 bar rating. Valves should comply with BS 3952: 1965 (Cast Iron Butterfly Valves for General Purposes) which is an imperial standard or with BS 5155: 1974 (Cast Iron and Carbon Steel Butterfly Valves for General Purposes) which is a metric standard.

Valves are supplied with ends flanged, faced and drilled to BS 4504: 1969 although the smaller bore valves have a body which fits inside the bolt circle of pipe flanges.

The disk/body seal can be a metal seal comprising a nickel-plated rim on the disk and gunmetal or stainless steel face ring on the body, or a rubber seal comprising a synthetic rubber face ring or 'O' ring in a recess round the edge of the disk. A metal seal disk will give maximum water tightness when the pressure is acting on the shaft side of the seat and the rubber seal disk will give leakproof shut off under flow from either direction.

Butterfly valves are also usually operated by hand, electric motor or hydraulic or pneumatic cylinder.

Hand Operation

Where it is not necessay for valves to be fitted with power actuators a worm and shaft geared actuator operated by a handwheel is required, except for small sized valves for light duty where an operating lever directly moving the disk will suffice.

Electric Motor, Hydraulic and Pneumatic Actuators

Power operation of large valves, or of valves operating under high unbalanced pressures, or by remote control, is achieved by an electric motor mounted on the side of the valve driving the disk shaft through worm gearing, or by double-acting cylinder type hydraulic and pneumatic actuators driving on the disk shaft through rack and pinion.

REFLUX VALVES

Reflux valves, also described as non-return valves, check valves, retaining valves or foot valves, are valves through which flow can proceed in one direction only. A reversal of flow causes the valve to close and remain closed until flow is re-established in the unique direction.

The first consideration in choosing a reflux valve is that in its particular application it shall close without causing shock. The various types of reflux valves are the flap, recoil, tilting disc, and lifting disc.

Flap Reflux Valve

Also described as the swing check valve this has a single door or flap, hinged so that when hanging freely the valve is closed. Flow in the forward direction causes the door to swing open, the amount of opening depending upon the velocity of flow and the disposition of metal in the door. The performance of the valve can be improved and slamming of the door minimised by the use of a lever and weight or the weighting of the door and the angle at which it is set. Valves to BS 5153: 1974 (Cast Iron Check Valves for General Purposes) are available in sizes up to 1 800 mm at 6, 10 and 16 bar ratings with flanged ends. Valves in sizes over 600 mm involve the use of double and multi-door configurations and a bypass incorporated in the body is an option for all valves over 250 mm bore.

Pump Discharge Reflux Valve

This valve has the mechanical and hydraulic characteristics of closing the door in the shortest possible time and is for use in pumped systems in which rapid flow reversal can take place, leading to valve slam if unsuitable valves are used.

A single door valve is available up to 600 mm bore at 10, 12, 16 and 20 bar rating; for sizes from 700 mm to 1 600 mm bore at 6, 10 and 16 bar rating the valve is multi-door. The ends are flanged and valves above 350 mm bore may have a bypass incorporated in the body.

Tilting Disc Reflux Valve

The valve door or disc is of aerofoil section pivoted in such a way that the reaction of the flow stream through the valve at normal velocities supports the disc positively against its stop where it remains at rest, thus reducing hinge wear. In its simplest form its use is not recommended where severe reversal of flow conditions, which could result in surge, is likely to occur but it is suitable for installation in horizontal pipelines where low headloss is a critical factor. Special spring-loaded versions with higher headloss but improved anti-slam performance are available.

The valve is available from 350 mm to 1 400 mm bore at 2.5, 3.5, 6, 7 and 10 bar rating. The ends are flanged and a bypass is incorporated in the body.

Lifting Disc Reflux Valve

This valve is specifically for installation in horizontal or vertical small diameter water mains where water columns are extremely active and likely to induce valve slam, resulting in water hammer, if flap reflux valves are used.

The valve is available from 25 mm to 80 mm bore at 16 bar rating. It has a vertical spring-loaded action seating a horizontal disc onto a waterway in the valve body.

AIR VALVES

There are three types of air valves available for varying duties—small orifice, large orifice and double orifice.

Small Orifice Single Air Valve

This valve can be used for automatically releasing air accumulating in a pipeline under normal working conditions, to prevent accumulations of air interfering with pipeline capacity. The valve consists of a float arrangement, usually a plastic float with an integral lever, contained in a chamber sealing off a small orifice vent. When water is present in the chamber under pressure the orifice is held closed by the upthrust of the float. Air accumulating in the system eventually enters the valve body under working pressure and depresses the water level in the chamber. When the water level is lowered to a point when the relatively heavy weight of the float is sufficient to uncover the orifice, air is expelled at working pressure until the water level again rises, lifting the float to seal off the orifice.

The valve body has a 25 mm diameter screwed inlet to which an isolating cock can be fitted, and the complete assembly then fitted into the main. Valves are obtainable with operating pressures of 6, 10, 16 and 25 bar rating with varying outlet orifice diameters from 3.50 mm to 1.75 mm.

Large Orifice Single Air Valve

This valve is used for automatically exhausting air from a pipeline when it is being filled with water and for automatically ventilating a pipeline when it is being emptied of water. Similar operating principles apply as in the small orifice valve.

This valve body can be provided with a 25 mm screwed inlet but for use with larger mains the outlet is 50, 80, 100 or 150 mm diameter and is flanged. The flanged outlet valves can be isolated with a butterfly or sluice valve or can have an integral screwdown isolating valve. Valves are obtainable with operating pressures of 16 bar or 25 bar with varying outlet orifice diameters from 41 mm to 116 mm diameter.

Double Orifice Air Valve

This valve has one large orifice for release and admission of air when filling and emptying the main and one small orifice for release of air accumulating under normal working conditions, when internal pressure from either air or water would prevent the operation of a large orifice; both chambers are separate but integrated into a single unit assembly and having a single pipeline connection. The outlet is 50, 80, 100 or 150 mm diameter and is flanged. The flanged outlet valves can be isolated with a butterfly or sluice valve or can have an integral screwdown isolating valve. Valves are obtainable with operating pressures of 16 bar and 25 bar rating with varying outlet orifice diameters as in single small and large orifice valves.

REGULATING AND CONTROL VALVES

Valves specifically designed for regulating and control purposes perform these duties in in-line and in terminal conditions. The various types are shown in Fig. 8.1 and their duties are listed in Table 8.V.

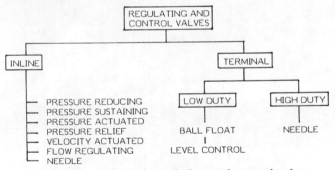

Fig. 8.1.   Types of regulating and control valves

Pressure Reducing Valves

The function of this valve is to get rid of unwanted pressure energy and this involves throttling control through hydraulic and mechanical means. The valve can be a globe valve with horizontal seating or a needle valve if a watertight closure is required or, if there is always a residual flow in the main, a double-beat valve is used.

There are two types of control systems when the main valve element is controlled either by a weighted piston in a side cylinder mechanically through a pivoted lever actuating the valve, or by a spring-loaded diaphragm relay valve hydraulically actuating the valve. The controlled downstream pressure in the main supports the

TABLE 8.V.   **Duties of Regulating and Control Valves**

Type of valve	Duty
Pressure reducing	*Constant downstream pressure* To obtain a constant outlet pressure from a higher constant or variable inlet pressure. *Variable downstream pressure* To obtain a reduced outlet pressure from a higher constant or variable inlet pressure, the reduced outlet pressure to vary in a given manner with the rate of flow through the valve.
Pressure sustaining	*Constant upstream pressure* To limit a variable inlet pressure to a definite minimum value. To keep an inlet pressure constant under varying flow conditions. *Variable upstream pressure* To control an inlet pressure so that this pressure varies in a given manner with the rate of flow through the valve.
Pressure relief	To prevent a rise of line pressure above a predetermined intensity. To reduce a constant or variable inlet pressure by the required amount.
Pressure actuated	To stop flow in a system when a given pressure is reached.
Velocity actuated	To stop flow in a system when a given velocity is reduced.
Flow regulating	To maintain a constant rate of flow. To divide a flow into two definite proportions. To mix two flows in definite proportions. To maintain proportional flows in separate mains. To maintain a constant rate of flow by the introduction of make-up flow.
Ball float	To control rate of flow, shutting and opening a discharge into a free water surface, thereby controlling water level in a tank and replacing water withdrawn from a tank.
Level control (or altitude)	Control of water level in overhead tank, regulating flow in and flow out and sustaining an inlet pressure to a set value.
Needle	Free discharge to atmosphere. Applications to pressure reducing, pressure sustaining, float control, pressure relief, emergency self-closing and altitude.

weighted piston or spring-loaded diaphragm and any variation in pressure operates these mechanical and hydraulic systems which in turn adjust the main valve setting to restore pressure to the preset level.

Adjustment of the outlet pressure on the hydraulically activated valve can be made by an electric motor fitted to the relay valve which can then be operated on site by flow regulation or from a remote point.

Standard valves with specified duties of pressure reductions are available up to 600 mm diameter outlets and inlets which are flanged. If a high standard of smooth operating and fine control is required a needle valve can be used. When a straight ratio of pressure reduction is required, such as for a single supply, a pressure reducing unit actuated by a diaphragm is used for small diameter pipes.

Pressure Sustaining Valve

A pressure sustaining valve sustains a pre-determined pressure immediately upstream of its position in the pipeline. It is a pressure reducing valve modified in a very simple manner by moving the pipe connection from the bottom of the side cylinder to the inlet seat of the valve, the lever fulcrum is changed to form a lever of the second order, and the balance weights adjusted to the pressure intensity which the valve is required to sustain. Modifications are also made to the hydraulically actuated pressure reducing valve to convert it to a pressure sustaining valve. If a high standard of smooth operating is required a needle valve can be used. Hydraulically actuated valves can have the pressure setting adjusted by means of remote sensing by electro/mechanical means from a central control point.

Variable Pressure Reducing Valve

This type of valve lowers its output pressure at times of low flow, thus allowing a substantial reduction in overall system leakage. Such valves may be operated directly by the line fluid, or by telemetry link from a remote pressure sensor or by the use of a microprocessor. Potential energy savings from the use of such valves are very high.

Pressure Relief Valve

A valve arranged as for a pressure sustaining valve with the weighted piston in a side cylinder operating mechanically through a pivoted lever can be applied as a pressure relief valve without any rearrangement, the balance weights in this case determining the blow off pressure. Spring-loaded valves do not fulfil this condition, for they require too great an increase in pressure to provide a reasonable aperture. If a high standard of smooth operating is required a needle valve can be used. Also available is a globe valve operated by a pressure sensing pilot similar to that mentioned in connection with pressure reducing valves.

Pressure Actuated Self-Closing Valve

This valve is used on a trunk or secondary main to minimise loss of water following a burst. The valve is provided with an hydraulic operating cylinder so proportioned that the valve gate is opened and normally held open within limits either side of the operating pressure. Should a burst main occur in the system, giving a marked reduction of pressure in the downstream main, the mechanism operated through the hydraulic cylinder causes the main valve gate to close.

Velocity Actuated Self-Closing Valve

This valve is used on a trunk or secondary main to minimise loss of water following a burst. During normal operation the gate of the valve is balanced by a mechanical system of weights against a transmitted reaction due to the velocity of flow. Should this velocity increase due to a burst main the mechanical system is actuated. This admits pressure to the hydraulic operating cylinder which in turn actuates the piston thereby closing the valve gate.

Flow Regulating Valve

A constant-flow valve maintains a constant set rate of flow in what would otherwise be variable-flow conditions. The controlling factor can be the differential head across a Venturi tube, flow nozzle or similar device, the head on a weir or measuring flume or the pitot head resulting from velocity of flow. A constant-flow valve is operated by a diaphragm which is subjected to the differential head resulting from the passage of the flow of water under control through a flow nozzle incorporated in the valve. Any tendency for the flow to increase or decrease from the set conditions induces a varying of the differential head, which causes the valve to close down or open up returning the flow to its previous set condition.

Other flow control valves work on similar principles to the constant-flow and are specially designed to suit the individual duties specified under flow regulating valves in Table 8.V.

Ball-Float Valve

The float valve is essentially an automatic flow control valve in which the regulating principle is the level of some free water surface. A float valve can be arranged to give any flow from progressive throttling as the water level rises, to continuous full flow from a predetermined minimum level until the required top level is reached.

Low duty ball-float valves have two basic float valve elements available, the single beat and double beat. The latter, with twin internal flow passage, produces a greater change in discharge and allows a reduced imbalance of pressure across the valve thus reducing the closing forces which would otherwise obtain on a single beat valve. Standard valves are available up to 450 mm diameter at a maximum working pressure of 10 bar rating and the float and lever arrangement from the piston of the valve is designed to meet the duty required.

For high pressure and high velocity duties a needle valve with the float gear is necessary to give smooth operation without vibration, erosion and noise to which conventional types are liable.

Level-Control Valve

This valve, also described as an altitude valve, controls the level of water in an overhead tank, itself being controlled by a ballcock in the tank.

When the water level falls from the set position the ballcock opens, reducing pressure on a relay valve diaphragm which allows a spring to open the relay valve. This in turn reduces pressure in the valve cylinder, actuating the opening of the valve and allowing water to pass into the tank. When the water level in the tank reaches a maximum the reverse process takes place to close the main valve.

Needle Valve

The needle valve was introduced to overcome the limitations of a sluice valve when discharging to atmosphere. It achieves smooth flow conditions and minimises erosion, cavitation and vibration during all stage of opening and closing.

A needle valve widely used for many applications is the Larner-Johnson valve, originally developed for use on hydro-electric power plants in the USA. Fig. 8.2 shows a Larner-Johnson valve in open and closed positions.

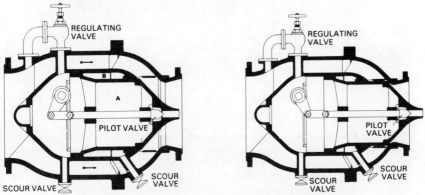

Fig. 8.2.   Sections through Larner-Johnson valve
Open (left) and closed (right)
Source: J. Blakeborough and Sons Ltd.

The operating force is obtained from the line pressure in the valve body and is governed by an internal pilot valve, which opens or closes an orifice in the plunger nose. The plunger is shaped to form two chambers, A and B, which receive a continuous supply of pressure water from the valve body—the first through a regulating valve and the second through clearance round the plunger. The regulating valve is adjusted so that the water entering the plunger is less than the discharge capacity of the fully-open pilot valve.

The throat of the valve is of smaller diameter than the inlet, so that the water velocity is greatest and pressure is lowest in the region of the plunger nose.

The static pressure on the downstream or outer face of the plunger is thus lower than the pressure admitted through the regulating valve to the chamber A, and, if the pilot valve is closed, pressure builds up in the plunger and causes movement in the closing direction. When the pilot valve is opened, the discharge from the orifice exceeds the supply to the chamber A, and the pressure in the latter falls to the downstream value. The pressure in the annular chamber B is not sensibly affected and thus creates an unbalanced force, moving the plunger in the opening direction. When the pilot valve is halted, the plunger stops in a position giving balance between the hydraulic forces on its inner and outer faces.

The Larner-Johnson valve has applications for large discharges to atmosphere, for pipeline stop and regulating valves including pressure reducing, pressure sustaining, float control, pressure relief, emergency self-closing and altitude valves.

Fire Hydrants

Fire hydrants provide the principal means of drawing water from mains for fire fighting but can also be used as washouts and for many other purposes.

There are two patterns used, both conforming with BS 750:1977. The screwdown hydrant has an integral body containing the screwdown valve and an outlet with a detachable copper alloy or nylon round thread outlet piece.

The wedge-gate valve hydrant has an 80 mm wedge-gate valve to which is bolted a flanged outlet bend with a detachable gunmetal or nylon round thread outlet piece.

FLOW MEASUREMENT IN PIPES

It is generally required that apparatus for the measurement of flow in pipes shall allow continuous and steady movement of the fluid and cause little resistance. It is also important that such apparatus shall be made throughout of the most durable and corrosion-resistant materials so that accuracy of measurement will be maintained for long periods.

Flow meters fall into three groups: those relating to pressure differences and shape of flow; those using mechanical means; and those based on the use of magnetic fields and ultrasonic sound waves.

Pressure Difference Meters

At a localized reduction of the cross-section of a pipe there is a change of pressure which may be related to the velocity of flow by the application of Bernoulli's theorem. A Venturi meter using this principle consists essentially of two taper pipes connected by a short cylindrical throat from which pressure tappings are taken from the upstream and downstream ends of the throat and connected to a U-tube manometer which is usually provided with electrical means to transmit the pressure differences to a recording instrument. Not less than 10 diameters of straight pipe should precede the Venturi taper pipes or tube, but several times this length is advisable if there are bends or valves immediately upstream.

A development of the Venturi tube is the Dall tube which contains the throat within a straight pipe. It works on similar principles to the Venturi tube but advantages claimed are lower head loss, about 25 per cent shorter length, less cost and ease of installation.

The orifice meter, simpler but less accurate than the Venturi or Dall meters, consists of a sharp-edged circular hole in a thin steel plate set squarely across the pipe, generally between a pair of flanges. Pressure tappings either side of the orifice plate lead to a manometer and thence to a recording instrument.

An even less accurate flow measuring device is the pitot tube, consisting of two tubes each with a small orifice at the end. They are inserted into the pipe, one facing directly towards the direction of flow and the other close to it and set at right angles to the flow. Both tubes are connected to a manometer from which velocities can be measured.

To measure the flow in a pipe, the pitot tube should be so arranged, by means of stuffing boxes, to be traversed across the pipe in two directions at right angles. From those readings the mean velocity and thence the flow can be calculated.

A more recent development, but using well established hydraulic principles, is the vortex shedding flowmeter.

Vortex shedding is the name given to the natural effect that occurs when a gas or liquid flows around a blunt or non-streamlined object. The flow, unable to follow the shape on its downstream side, separates from the surface of the object, leaving a highly turbulent wake that takes the form of a continuous series of vortices forming and being swept downstream. Each vortex first grows and then becomes detached or shed from the object—hence, the name given to the phenomenon, vortex shedding.

If the vortex-generating object is correctly shaped and placed in a pipeline with the correct relative dimensions, it forms a primary flow element that generates pulse signals over very wide flow ranges at a frequency proportional to the volumetric flow rate approaching it. As the approaching flow separates from the flow element, vortices form and shed alternatively on either side of the triangular shape. Measurement of flow is made by detecting the rate at which vortices are shed from the fixed flow element. As the flow rate increases, the frequency with which the vortex forms and sheds increases at the same rate. As a result, the number of vortices generated is directly proportional to the amount of fluid passing through the device.

Mechanical Flow Meters

There are two main groups of mechanical flow meters—volumetric and inferential.

Volumetric Meters

Volumetric or semi-positive meters can be either of the rotary piston or nutating disc type, the latter being less widely available and in a limited number of sizes. Rotary piston meters are made in the 15 mm-100 mm (½"-4") size range and employ a circular piston driven by the water in an eccentric path around an accurately machined working chamber, each revolution representing the transfer of a known volume of water. The nutating disc meter is similar in principle but uses a disc instead of a piston. The nutating disc is driven by the flow of water through a chamber, each nutation being equivalent to a known volume of water. A spindle mounted axially through the disc transfers the motion through a magnetic drive to a straight reading register.

The advantage of this type of meter is its ability to accurately register very low flow rates, and generally it fulfils Class C requirements of BS 5728. It is widely used in sizes up to 40 mm (1½") diameter and selectively in larger sizes where flow conditions demand its low flow capability.

Its installation requirements are flexible, and the volumetric meter can be fitted horizontally, vertically or in an inclined position.

Inferential Meters

Two types of inferential meters are made in the small size range between 15 mm and 40 mm (½"-1½")—multi-jet and single-jet. Larger meters from 40 mm-500 mm (1½"-20") are of the helical vane or turbine type.

The inferential meter infers the quantity of water passed by the speed of rotation of a rotor or vane, the movement of which is then transferred by appropriate gearing to a counter or register.

The minimum accurate registration of an inferential meter is higher than that of a volumetric meter, and generally the multi-jet fulfils Class B requirements of BS 5728 and the single-jet meets Class A conditions. Both these types of meter have rotors mounted vertically so that they can only be fitted in horizontal pipelines.

The helical vane or turbine type meter is designed for bulk flow requirements with a vane mounted in line with the flow. These meters can meet Class A or Class B conditions of BS 5728, depending on manufacture, and they can also be fitted in horizontal, vertical or inclined pipes. The meters have high capacities combined with low head loss characteristics.

Combination and Compound Meters

For the measurement of a very wide flow range, combination meters are produced. These normally consist of a helical vane main meter with either a small volumetric or inferential meter fitted in parallel on a bypass, the flow being controlled by an automatic valve which operates according to the demand. The valve ensures that the flows are accurately measured throughout the range by the appropriate meter.

The compound meter comprises a turbine mechanism for high flow with an internal bypass to a nutating disc meter for low flow measurement. An automatic hydraulic valve is fitted integral with the main body. This type of meter considerably reduces the chamber size due to its compact construction.

Magnetic Field and Ultrasonic Sound Wave Meters

These flow meters have no moving parts, and do not present any obstruction to the waterway.

The magnetic flow meter creates a DC magnetic field which defines velocity profiles within the pipe by a sensor which emits pulses to a measuring transmitter indicating rate of flow.

The ultrasonic flow meter makes use of ultrasonic sound waves to sample the velocity profile within the pipe. The flowmeter consists of a sensor tube and electronic transmitter indicating rate of flow.

Chart Recorders

Chart recorders are available to record rates of flow directly from flow transmitters having electrical linear or square law analogue outputs and from transmitters having pulse units which will drive remote indicators, chart recorders and automatic reading and billing equipment. A digit totalising counter can also be incorporated.

These instruments can record from most types of flow meters—Venturi tube, Dall tube, orifice plate, vortex shedding, turbine, combination, compound, rotary piston, nutating disc, magnetic and ultrasonic.

When setting up a chart care must be taken to ensure that the stylus or pen is properly zeroed and calibrated to the graduation on the chart.

Data Logging

Data logging equipment which will continuously log pressure and bi-directional flow can be coupled to printers, chart recorders etc. for read back and to computer for permanent storage of information. The pulse units available for all turbine, vortex meters, helical vane, magnetic flow meters, nutating disc and compound meters, are fully compatible with available data logging devices.

5. PROTECTION OF PIPES AND JOINTS AGAINST CORROSION

General

All metallic pipes and fittings are vulnerable to both internal and external attack by corrosion[24-27]. The degree of attack depends upon the nature of external soils, the characteristics of the fluid being transmitted and the type of protection afforded.

Metallic corrosion, in the presence of water, is a chemical reaction accompanied by the passage of an electric current similar to that which takes place in a battery cell except that in the case of a pipe, the metal surface acts as both the anode and cathode, with corrosion holes developing at anodic sites.

In certain anaerobic environments, sulphate-reducing bacteria assist the cathodic reaction and so corrosion can take place in both aerated and anaerobic waters.

The adjacent use of metals of dissimilar electro-potential gives rise to galvanic corrosion, where cathodic reaction takes place on the least reactive metal and anodic reaction on the more reactive metal, causing the latter to be eaten away progressively at a rate depending upon the dissimilarity of the metals, their size and the type of water.

The deposition of sediment and slimes on internal metal pipe surfaces is conducive to microbiological activity which tends to deplete oxygen levels, thus stimulating localised corrosion.

It is therefore necessary to protect pipes and joints, including bolts and associated apparatus, against such attack to avoid growing burst frequency rates as pipes grow older and become weaker with continuous corrosion. Furthermore, internal corrosion débris gives rise to complaints of discolouration and poor pressures due to inferior flow characteristic[28].

IRON PIPES

Internal and External Protection

Vertically cast iron pipes and, to a lesser degree, spun iron pipes have withstood the test of time in terms of durability. Material thickness is a factor affecting durability and performance when withstanding the effects of corrosion.

Although ductile iron[29], which has currently become the most common type of iron pipe, is a stronger material, pipe thickness is 20 per cent less than for pipes made of grey spun iron, which in turn was 25 percent less than for pipes made of cast iron in the 75 and 100 mm diameter range.

Information on comparative corrosion behaviour for grey and ductile iron is still being collected but there is unlikely to be much difference because of the known similar behaviour of these two materials. In the circumstances greater attention must be paid to the effects of corrosion if similar life spans are to be expected. Once laid, there is little that can be done in terms of *in situ* protection against external corrosion and if severe the only remedy rests with complete renewal.

Until recently coal tar has been the most common form of protection applied both internally and externally to the pipe at the manufacturing stage as a paint layer about 100 microns thick. It, however, affords little protection to the pipe in resisting the effect of corrosion. Coal tar has now been replaced with non-toxic bitumens but the process still only serves as a cosmetic coating and additional protection is recommended even if only a slight possibility of corrosion exists. Polyethylene sleeving is suitable for this purpose.

Factory applied, internal cement mortar linings have now been available for nearly 50 years, and although they are known to be durable and capable of affording good protection against corrosion it is doubtful whether more than 5-10 per cent of all distribution mains are so protected. The modern trend, however, appears to be towards the application of such linings at the manufacturing stage as a standard for iron pipes used in the UK. Furthermore, the process is becoming more widespread under *in situ* conditions where existing mains are in need of renovation.

The cement mortar lining provides an alkaline environment adjacent to the pipe bore surface which effectively eliminates corrosive attack, thereby preventing internal tuberculation and minimising any losses in hydraulic capacity and complaints of discoloration. Standard cement mortar lining thicknesses have been revised; amended thicknesses are now available (Table 8.VI).

Should the water be of a type likely to attack cement structures, then an approved bituminous paint complying with BS 3416:1975 for Type II may be applied as a sealing coat.

External protection of factory produced pipes still relies generally upon bitumen paint. Two types of bitumen paint are recommended by BS 4772:1980, a hot

Table 8.VI.   Specified Thicknesses of Cement Mortar Linings

Nominal diameter of pipe (mm)	Thickness of lining (mm)		
	Nominal	Mean value	Individual minimum
80	5	3.5	2.5
100- 600	5	4.5	3.5
700-1 200	6	5.5	4.5
1 400-2 000	9	8	7

Source: British Standard 4772: 1980

applied grade complying with the requirements of BS 4147:1980 for Type I, Grade d material, and a cold applied grade complying with the requirements of BS 3416:1975 for Type II material. Bituminous paint lining thicknesses are typically 75-100 microns and inevitably contain 'holiday' defects and for this reason do not provide complete or permanent protection.

Although some experimental work has been conducted in providing better external protection by the use of epoxy materials and specialised wrappings these have yet to emerge as a commercial proposition due to obvious financial constraints.

The Water Research Centre is presently conducting a national survey on the performance of ductile iron and, based upon the evidence so far obtained, are recommending the use of loose polyethylene (PE) sleeving as standard practice[30,31]

Although not intended to be an air and watertight enclosure, the PE sleeve should prevent contact between pipe and surrounding backfill. There have been very few reported corrosion failures of PE sleeved iron mains, except where incorrect application procedures have been identified.

PE sleeving for the protection of buried iron pipework should conform with the specifications in BS 6076:1981. The nominal PE sleeving thickness currently recommended for all pipe diameters is 225±25 microns. Operational guidelines for the installation of PE sleeving on ductile iron pipelines are shortly to be issued within the water industry by the Water Research Centre.

Zinc External Protection

The application of zinc by zinc-rich paint or sprayed metallic zinc as a coating for external surfaces is available for ductile iron pipes up to 800 mm diameter. The protection of ductile iron pipes by a sprayed metallic zinc coating of 25/30 microns has been used in France for more than 20 years and from these and 9 year long special trials in France, England and Germany the advantages appear to be:

(i) Zinc coating will remove the risk of serious corrosion in aggressive soils when the oxide skin of the pipe has been damaged.

(ii) In all soils zinc coating will increase the life of a pipe.

(iii) Zinc coating will give added security under PE sleeving, a method recommended for pipelaying in urban areas or where there is a risk of local areas of high corrosivity.

(iv) Zinc coating is mechanically strong and the protection it affords is unlikely to be damaged during handling, as is the case with organic coatings, and even areas of bare iron exposed through the zinc coating will be protected.

Alternative External Protection Systems

Other systems used in the past by UK utilities for the external protection of buried iron mains have included factory applied wrappings of bituminous or petrolatum-based tapes and cathodic protection as described in Chapter 9, Section 2. Coating systems other than those described above have been used by certain European Water Authorities for external protection—for example, spirally extruded polyethylene (West Germany).

STEEL PIPES AND SPECIALS

Internal Protection to Pipes

"Hot Dip" bituminous coating alone is not a recommended form of protection for steel water mains.

Bitumen Linings to Pipes

Steel pipes should be prepared by either shot blasting or pickling in dilute sulphuric acid, then washed and phosphate coated. The treated pipe is then primed and subsequently spun while a bituminous lining is applied, complying with BS 534: 1966, to a thickness of between 2 and 7 mm for 300 to 900 mm pipes respectively.

Plastic Linings to Pipes

After descaling, pipes may be protected with an approved epoxy paint, applied in successive spray coats up to thicknesses of 0.15 mm and 0.3 mm, depending upon the viscosity of the transmitted fluid. The lining is visually inspected and 'holiday' tested with a low voltage detector to ensure it is free from discontinuities and pinholes.

Plastic linings are expensive and would only be adopted for some special reason.

There are two principal methods for effecting continuity of bituminous linings when using Viking Johnson joints, namely:

(1) simply coating the pipe ends with a high-build bitumen based paint, or,
(2) filling the gap between the outside of the pipe and the inside of the coupling with molten bitumen, poured from the outside through a hole in the coupling, which is contained by a backing-up ring, until solidified.

In the case of welded joints the gap left in the lining is filled by hand, after welding, with molten lining composition applied by trowel.

For plastic linings the pipe is coated over the ends and for a distance on to the outside when Viking Johnson couplings are used. Where welding is involved the resulting unprotected area at the pipe ends is coated with composition after jointing.

External Protection to Pipes

When laid underground, steel pipes should first be primed with a primer to BS 4147 : 1973 and then hot bitumen enamel applied, into which is embedded a glass tissue. A second spiral wrap of pre-impregnated, longitudinally reinforced, glass tissue is applied and completely bonded to the other surface to a final minimum thickness of 2.5 mm. Where increased resistance to mechanical damage during transit, storage and laying is considered necessary, then the outer wrap mentioned above should contain additional reinforcement in the form of a woven glass cloth.

The surface is finally given a heat reflecting coating of lime wash.

Continuity of External Linings at Joints

Joints are usually covered with light metal moulds and the annular space between mould and pipe joint is filled with molten bitumen.

Alternatively, bitumastic paint or putty may be applied, particularly over bolts and nuts, and wrapped with a plastic tape or bandage comprising woven fabric made from inert synthetic fibres impregnated with a corrosion inhibitive plastic. The latter technique would apply to any exposed metallic joint whether connecting steel, iron, AC, concrete or plastic pipes.

FITTINGS, SPECIALS AND APPARATUS

A variety of protective materials are now available for fittings, specials and general distribution apparatus including nylon, plastic, epoxy, zinc, bitumen and synthetic rubber, depending upon the degree of corrosion likely to be encountered. Two part powder epoxy dip or electrostatically deposited coatings which are fused to metal surfaces under heat appear to be growing in favour due to their apparent superior performance.

Aluminium fittings, protected with the above mentioned coatings, are now being regularly used in the UK water industry after first being introduced some 20 years ago. They are light to handle, have good flow characteristics and, above all, are resistant to corrosion.

Resilient seated sluice valves with rubber coated gates and 'straight through' bores protected with two part powder epoxy are now preferred by many engineers for their corrosion-free properties and afford a more reliable shut-off. They have almost completely replaced conventional metal-seated valves in West Germany, where they have been in use for over 20 years.

Concrete Pipes

Metallic fittings and apparatus incorporated within a concrete pipeline are dealt with in a similar manner to that described.

The 'Stanpress' type joint used for prestressed concrete cylinder pressure pipes is protected either by a cement grout or by a waterproof cord and tape with the cord effectively sealing the area between the mouth of the socket and the shoulder of the spigot end of the adjacent pipe, with the waterproof tape preventing the ingress of water to the joint.

Although prestressed concrete pipes are not generally subject to corrosion, some types of ground water may attack ordinary portland cement. Depending upon the outcome of a soil survey, it may after consultation with the manufacturer be prudent to use a sulphate-resisting cement in the cover coat or some other special protection.

6. STRESSES ON PIPES AND JOINTS

INTERNAL STATIC AND SURGE PRESSURE

Internal static pressure on pipes induces circumferential and longitudinal stresses, the latter developing when the main changes direction through bends, branches and tees, changes size through tapers and flange reductions, or has closed ends or restrictions caused by apparatus[16]. A pipe is chosen to carry the circumferential stress without extra strengthening or support and with rigid flanged, welded or anchor joints the longitudinal stress load can be absorbed in the pipeline. In the case of semi-rigid and flexible joints an external form of anchorage or support is required.

The pipes, joints and fittings in a main must withstand the highest internal pressure to which the main is likely to be subjected. That is usually in excess of the normal working pressure and, consequently, regard must be had to the test pressure to be applied before the main is commissioned and the possibility of surge pressure. Stresses developed by surge pressures can be very high and to provide pipes, joints and fittings strong enough to withstand a pressure surge likely to occur would in nearly all cases be very uneconomical. The method adopted is to restrict the magnitude of any surge[32] (see also Chapter 7).

External Loads

The external loads on a pipeline arise from a number of factors[33-37].
(a) The weight of the pipe, fittings and the contents.
(b) The weight of the trench filling.
(c) Impact from the use of consolidation plant when refilling the trench.
(d) Superimposed loads from heavy vehicles and plant during the construction period.
(e) Traffic loads when the pipeline is situated under roads and railways.
(f) Wind and ice loads in the case of the pipeline laid above ground.
(g) Earth movement due to the effect of temperature changes inducing frictional forces and bending stresses.

Particular care must be given to the embedment of semi-rigid and flexible pipes because of the greater reliance on the backfill to withstand the vertical loads. Design of embedments is recommended and pipe manufacturers have produced calculations, compaction guides and embedment charts which should be consulted when considering a pipe of a particular material for the condition in which it will be laid.

There are two types of installation considered: pipes laid in trenches, where trench width is 0.6 m over outside diameter of pipe, and pipes laid under embankment conditions. The design procedure considering both an empty pipe and a pressurised pipe requires an evaluation of these factors:

(i) The weight of the trench filling.
(ii) All possible superimposed loads.
(iii) Diametral deflections assumed by the pipe under the effects of the total load.
(iv) Ring bending stress induced in the pipe under the effects of the total load.
(v) The extent to which the pipe embedment will consolidate with time and increase the initial stresses and deflections created—described as deflection lag factor.
(vi) The effect of internal pressure which tends to re-round pipes which have assumed a diametral deflection under the effects of a top load.
(vii) To ensure that ring bending stresses and diametral deflections are within specified design limits of the modulus of elasticity of the material of the pipe.

The foregoing factors are evaluated by computer analysis using programmes from which the embedment charts are produced.

For the bedding and consolidation of rigid pipes, details of the bedding factors for different classes of beds are given in the Building Research Establishment publication "Simplified Tables of External Loads on Buried Pipelines" and pipe manufacturers have also produced bedding factors and loading charts for grey iron, ductile iron, steel, asbestos cement, prestressed concrete and uPVC pipes.

EARTH MOVEMENT

Adverse ground conditions can be expected from a number of causes[38,39]:

(1) Deep mining subsidence.
(2) De-watering activities, such as brine pumping.
(3) Waterlogged ground in sandy silt, clays and peat.
(4) Made up ground.
(5) Disused mine shafts.
(6) Shallow mining subsidence.
(7) Ground movement due to the effects of climatic changes.

Mining subsidence has the effect of tilting the surface of the ground, subjecting it to tensile and compressive horizontal strains. A combination of horizontal strain and vertical bending causes ring fractures on rigid pipes and buckling on flexible pipes. One method of combating mining subsidence is to use short pipes with flexible joints, capable of longitudinal movement without leakage[40], and to lay the pipes on a soft bed which will minimise the effect of both the horizontal ground grip of the frictional force and the bending stresses on the pipeline. Another method is to use steel pipes with welded joints because an all welded steel pipeline is able to accommodate normal subsidence strains and, although the steel may yield to the subsidence load, serious failures are unlikely. Polyethylene pipe with heat welded joints is also suitable for these conditions.

Brine pumping operations can result in areas of subsidence and the same recommendations as for mining subsidence apply.

Waterlogged ground can vary considerably in its capability to satisfactorily support a pipeline. If only a small differential settlement is expected a flexible joint would probably take this movement without damage to the pipe and leakage from the joint. Should conditions be less stable it is necessary to stabilize the ground, or have a concrete bedding the width of the trench, or cover a wider area with a concrete raft, or in very serious ground movement conditions support the pipes on piles.

When crossing into and out of made up ground flexible joints should be used when there is any chance of settlement.

Disused mine shafts must be filled and pipework crossing the made up area should be of welded steel pipes.

Shallow mining will impose quite severe local subsidence. It can also take the form of a pot-holing crater of up to 6 m diameter and its depth the thickness of the coal seam. If these conditions are suspected it will be prudent to lay steel pipes with welded joints: flexible joints may eventually be pulled and water leakage could go undetected into the shaft which had caused the movement.

TEMPERATURE STRESSES

Water very rarely freezes in mains laid with normal cover, unless the frost is extremely severe, as compared with service pipes which tend to freeze at the point of entry into a property, then progressively freeze towards the main in the event of low temperature continuing.

Exposed pipelines and pipework subject to wide temperature ranges do however expand and contract to an appreciable extent and when designing such pipework allowance must be made for these temperature stresses, in addition to those stresses resulting from internal static and surge pressures. In the case of crossing bridges and viaducts using steel pipes a number of alternatives present themselves:

(a) Each pipe to be rigidly connected to the structure of the bridge or viaduct and jointed with flexible joints capable of accepting such relative movements as may occur.

(b) Each pipe to be rigidly connected to the structure and jointed with welded rigid joints in which case the longitudinal stress imposed by differential thermal effects will be taken by the steel pipeline.

(c) A steel pipeline with welded or flanged joints supported and attached to the structure at intervals, with sliding bearings permitting longitudinal movement relative to the structure, and incorporating movement joints at each end of the structure and where there is a change of direction of the pipeline.

CHEMICAL ATTACK

The soil and if present the ground-water, in which it is proposed to lay trunk and secondary pipelines, should be examined, samples being taken for chemical examination together with a soil resistivity survey to ascertain whether the soil or ground-water may be considered aggressive to certain pipe materials and external pipe coatings.

The chemical analysis of water being conveyed by the pipe should also be known so that any potential problems of taste or toxicity arising from contact of the water inside the pipe with the pipe material or pipe lining can be identified. There is much to be gained by carrying out a careful study of external and internal chemical attack so that the choice of the pipe coating, pipe material and thickness, and pipe lining will be capable of satisfactorily withstanding the conditions under which it is to be laid and will operate. (See Chapter 10, Section 1).

HANDLING AND STACKING

Damage to pipes, fittings and joint components may be caused during transit, handling and storage by:
    (i) Insecure fixing on lorry or wagon.
   (ii) Improper use of handling equipment.
  (iii) Use of unsuitable handling equipment.
  (iv) Incorrect stacking methods.
   (v) Vandalism.

Pipe manufacturers give specific advice on methods of transporting, handling and stacking their pipe of a particular material and this should be closely followed. Insurance cover for stores stacked in areas prone to vandalism should not be omitted and special surveillance may be considered.

When pipes, fittings and joint components are received from the manufacturers they should be inspected for damage as well as being dimensionally checked. This inspection and checking should include:
   (1) the pipe, fitting and joint;
   (2) external and internal coatings;
   (3) cement mortar linings;
   (4) jointing surfaces.

DRILLING AND TAPPING

Fitting service connections to pipes is carried out using purpose-designed drilling and tapping machines. Various manufacturers produce two basic types of machine, those for making connections to non-pressurised mains and those for making connections to pressurised mains, usually described as an under-pressure drilling and tapping machine. A good working rule is to confine the nominal size of the service to a maximum of one quarter of the nominal diameter of the main. This avoids weakening the pipe by removal of an undue amount of the pipe wall and ensures an adequate screw thread hold of the ferrule despite the curvature of the pipe wall.

Service connections are normally required from distribution mains comprising grey iron, asbestos cement, ductile iron, uPVC and PE pipes.

The ferrule connections in common use on grey iron and ductile pipes are of two basic types, that which depends on the screw thread on the inlet for both sealing and anchorage, and that which incorporates separate sealing components, the screw thread being used primarily for anchorage. Ferrules can be drilled and tapped into grey iron and ductile iron pipes of all diameters.

Asbestos cement pipes up to 100 mm diameter require a gunmetal or corrosion protected ferrous saddle drilled and tapped, permanently clamped to the pipe, through which the threaded ferrule passes before passing through the wall of the pipe. For larger diameter pipes coarse threaded ferrules may be used without a saddle.

A connection is made to uPVC pipe through gunmetal tapping saddles and the ferrule is inserted by the use of the basic drilling and tapping machine or a self-tapping ferrule screwed into the saddle.

Service connections are made to PE pipe using a saddle fusion fitting which takes two forms. First, a simple saddle through which hand tappings may be made on non-pressurised mains or under pressure using a special under pressure tapping tool. Secondly, a self-tapping saddle which incorporates an integral cutter by means of which the tapping may be accomplished on unpressurised mains or pressurised mains without necessitating the use of special "under pressure" equipment. Gunmetal saddles are also available for PE pipes, but are to a special design to overcome the creep properties of PE.

Pipe manufacturers specify standard and special equipment and ferrules for drilling and tapping their pipes and it is recommended that their advice is taken into account.

7. REFERENCES

1. Bromell, R. Y. 1976 "Design criteria and experiences in the cases of various materials", International Water Supply Association, Eleventh Congress, International Standing Committee on Water Distribution, Pipes and Pipelines.
2. Andrews, N. 1965 "Cast iron pipelines, their manufacture and installation", Stanton and Staveley.
3. Ooykaas, G. A. 1952 *J. IWE*, 6, 85, Prestressed concrete pipes.
4. Batchelar, T. G. 1960 *J. IWE*, 14, 383, Polythene water pipes.
5. Water Research Association 1964 "References to practical uses of plastic materials in water main and service laying".
6. Stevens, I. M. and Littlewood, R. G. 1979 *Chemistry and Industry*, Plastic pipes for the transport and distribution of potable water in the UK.
7. National Water Council 1980 "Slimline Pipe" Sub-Committee No. 4, Standing Technical Committee on Sewers and Water Mains.
8. Gill, D. 1960 "Present state of standards for plastic water pipes; a review", Water Research Association.
9. Gill, D. 1960 "Mechanical properties of Gean RA 170 high impact PVC tube for water supply", Water Research Association.
10. Gill, D. 1963 "Impact strength of PVC pipe", Water Research Association.
11. The Uni-bell Plastic Pipe Association "Handbook of PVC pipe", Dallas, Texas 75234.
12. American Water Works Association "PVC pipe design and installation M23".
13. Water Industry Specifications "PE pipes, joints and fittings".
14. Severn-Trent Water Authority/Water Research Centre 1976 "Glass fibre reinforced pipes".
15. National Water Council/Department of the Environment 1979 "Glass fibre reinforced plastics", Standing Technical Committee on Sewers and Water Mains—Materials and Standards.

16. Boulton, P. and Moreau, F. 1965 "Strength tests on solvent welded (cemented) joints for PVC pipes", Water Research Association.
17. Chisholm, R. 1973 "Pipe jointing lubricants—summary of field trials", Water Research Association.
18. Boucher, P. L. 1948 "Choosing valves", Glenfield and Kennedy.
19. Boucher, P. L. 1952 *J. IWE*, 6, 397, Some aspects of valve engineering in water supply.
20. Morgan, H. D. 1957 *J. ICE*, 537, Control of flow by gates and valves.
21. Miller, E. 1968 *J. IWE*, 22, 91, Developments for valve engineering for water supply.
22. British Valve Manufacturers Association "Technical reference book on valves for the control of fluids".
23. Livesey, R. 1972 *J. IWE*, 26, 430, A note on waterworks sluice valves.
24. British Hydromechanics Research Association 1975 "Proceedings of the First International Conference on the Internal and External Protection of Pipes".
25. British Hydromechanics Research Association 1977 "Proceedings of the Second International Conference on the Internal and External Protection of Pipes.
26. Hassan, U., Jewsbury, A. and Yates, A. 1978 "Pipe protection, a review of current practice", British Hydromechanics Research Association.
27. British Hydromechanics Research Association 1979 "Proceedings of the Third International Conference on the Internal and External Protection of Pipes.
28. Lamont, P. 1973 "Effect of time on the carrying capacity of pipes and pipelines" 4th Symposium on Pipeline Engineering in Waterworks Practice, University of Salford.
29. Collins, H. 1974 "Corrosion characteristics and protection of buried ductile iron pipe", British Cast Iron Research Association, Report X26.
30. Hayton, J. G. 1964 *J. IWE*, 18, 465, The use of loose polyethylene sleeving as a form of protection to spun iron water mains against external corrosion.
31. Oliphant, R. 1976 "Corrosion protection of iron pipes by polythene wrapping", Water Research Centre, Report 38E.
32. Lupton, H. R. 1965 *J. IWE*, 19, 81, Surge control in pipelines.
33. Clarke, N. 1966 "Loading charts for the design of buried rigid pipes", National Building Studies Report 37.
34. Kowalewski, P. 1976 *G.w.f. Wasser und Abwasser*, 117, Investigations into pipe fractures.
35. Brennan, G. and Young, O. 1976 "Some case histories of recent failures of buried pipelines", Transport and Road Research Laboratory.
36. Compston, D. 1978 "Design and construction of buried thin wall pipes", CIRIA Report No. 78.
37. Nath, P. 1981 "Pressure on buried pipes due to revised HB loading", Transport and Road Research Laboratory.
38. Summerton, J. D. and Findlay, G. E. 1972 *J. IWE*, 26, 359, The design of a trunk main with particular reference to the long term effects of ground settlement.
39. Transport and Road Research Laboratory 1978 "Ground movements and their influence on buried pipes".
40. Blackburn, A. B. 1948 *J. IWE*, 2, 382, The jointing of a large steel trunk main subject to mining subsidence.

Repair of Derwent Valley aqueduct
(left) **replacement of section**
(above) **preparing lead seal**
(Severn-Trent Water Authority)

Chapter 9

MAINLAYING—PLANNING AND CONSTRUCTION

1. MAINLAYING—PLANNING

INTRODUCTION

WATER mains fall naturally into three groups: distribution, secondary and trunk[1]. Distribution mains are used to supply premises in the streets in which they are laid and as their capacity need only be large enough to meet local peak demands they are generally of small diameter. Distribution mains supply domestic, non-domestic and small industrial consumers through communication pipes connected to the mains (see Chapter 11).

Trunk mains convey water from one point, a pumping station or a service reservoir, to another point or to a district where the water will be used and are usually of large diameter, their size being related to the rate of flow required, the acceptable head loss and the distance between the points[2]. Secondary mains form the links between distribution and trunk mains and often fulfil the functions of both. They are also used for supplying consumers direct—generally the larger industrial consumers whose individual demands are too heavy to be met by the distribution mains—and for reinforcing distribution mains.

SELECTION OF ROUTES FOR DISTRIBUTION MAIN LAYOUTS

The route of a distribution main will normally be located in the footpath or verge of a public highway or private street. This can be in housing estate developments; in general improvement areas and infill developments in urban areas; in industrial and commercial developments; and in housing in rural areas.

In housing estate developments the distribution mains layout should follow these guidelines:

(1) Mains adjacent to carriageways and parking areas should normally be located under paved footways or otherwise be protected when there would be risks of damage from vehicles parked on soft ground.

(2) A single main along the road—but located on the side serving the most houses—thus maximising the use of short side connections; dual mains may be justified in trunk roads on the grounds of cost or safety.

(3) Avoid dead-ends wherever possible by completing a loop; this may reduce the need for periodical washing out.

(4) Provide for a larger diameter main as a feeder ring main.

(5) Distribution mains should not be oversized as long retention of water at low flow can produce quality problems.

(6) Allow for fire hydrants and any improvement to the distribution system for fire purposes as requested from and financed by the fire authority.

(7) Mains should be located in accordance with the recommendations made by the Joint Committee of the Civil and Municipal Engineering Institutions "Report of Joint Committee on Location of Underground Services" and supplemented by the DoE/DoT "Design Bulletin 32—Residential Roads and Footpaths: Layout Considerations", unless there is a clearly agreed variation made in consultation with other statutory undertakers, local authorities and the developer, or other conditions preclude their use.

Some modern housing developments have unusual layouts and, consequently, mains might have to be laid across open spaces, around banks and mounds in landscaped areas, service strips and car parking areas. This might mean that, in order to achieve the most economical mains layout, the developer should install longer supply pipes than usual.

For all housing estate developments there is a need for early consultation with the developer to agree:

(a) width and location of footways for the location of services;

(b) any special decorative paving to be avoided;

(c) easements or laying under the terms of PUSWA;

(d) access for maintenance of mains, communication pipes and associated apparatus across private land;

(e) whether the highway is to be adopted as public or remain under private control.

Distribution main routes in general improvement areas and infill developments in urban areas have to be carefully selected to avoid existing underground mains, sewers and cables and the layout adapted to fit existing carriageways and footpaths. General improvement areas (which usually involve the demolition of old property and sometimes a revised street layout) may need the provision of new mains to replace existing mains that have passed their useful life or mains that have to be abandoned because the new layout may place gardens, walls or even buildings over them.

Industrial and commercial developments may require large amounts of water, sometimes at a high instantaneous rate of flow, with additional requirement for fire fighting based on the advice of the fire authority. Provision must be made for additional mains capacity to meet these demands by incorporating larger diameter mains into the distribution main system and in some cases linked to a trunk main by a secondary main.

In rural areas distribution mains have to serve small numbers of properties scattered over large distances and consequently the route of the main is very often along a narrow country road. Laying in the carriageway should be avoided and if there is not a suitable verge an alternative route in private land should be selected and an easement or terms of PUSWA negotiated well in advance of the date of mainlaying.

At an early stage layout plans for new housing estates and general improvement areas must be obtained from the developers and when the routes have been selected these plans, indicating the mains layouts supplemented by larger scale details of pipework connections, should form the working drawings for forwarding to other public utilities and local authorities and ultimately for the construction drawings for laying the mains.

References to relevant legislation[3] are contained in Chapter 2.

Location and Protection of Public Utilities and Local Authority Apparatus

As soon as the routes for the mains have been selected all other public utilities—telecommunications, electricity and gas, and local authorities in respect of highways and bridges and as water authority agents for sewerage—who may have apparatus and structures within the route through which the mains are to be laid —should be approached requesting details of their apparatus and structures[4]. This will enable the final line and level of the mains to be fixed and drawings prepared in readiness for serving of notice under PUSWA. This Act has three main purposes. First, it contains a uniform code for the protection of highways and bridges. Secondly, it contains a code of protection for statutory undertakers where road or bridge alterations or transport works are likely to affect apparatus of the undertakers in a street or controlled land. Thirdly, it contains provisions for the mutual protection of undertakers having apparatus in the same street or controlled land. References to this legislation are contained in Chapter 2.

DISPOSITION OF MAINS AND SERVICES ON RESIDENTIAL ESTATES AND DEVELOPMENTS

From the beginning of the housing programme in the late 1940s statutory undertakers have been conscious of the need to site their mains and cables in agreed allocated positions in footpaths and verges of housing estate roads. Prior to water reorganization the former water undertakings made local arrangements, mostly based on the ICE/I.Mun.E Report, with the Post Office, Electricity and Gas Regional Offices to secure a space for the water main in the footways and verges. In the 1970s, liaison groups of statutory undertakers and local authorities were being set up in various regions throughout the UK to deal with housing estate development and the new water authorities were then able to participate in these liaison groups on equal terms with the nationalized statutory undertakers and the new metropolitan local authorities. However, the most significant step forward has been the formation in 1977 of the National Joint Utilities Group, NJUG.

This group was established by British Gas, the Water Industry, British Telecom and the Electricity Supply Industry. Its aim was to promote co-operation between the utilities with the prime object of improving safety among operatives, and protection of the public when work was being carried out. Equally important, however, were the potential savings in time and money from a co-operative approach to long-term development and in short-term maintenance and repair work.

NJUG has produced a number of publications and those relevant to housing estate development are "No. 2—Provision of Mains and Services by Public Utilities on Residential Estates" and "Model Guidelines for the Planning and Installation of Utilities Supplies to New Building Developments".

CONSULTATION WITH FIRE SERVICE

In accordance with the Third Schedule of the Water Act 1945 all undertakers are under an obligation, at the request of the Fire Authority concerned, to fix fire hydrants on their mains (other than trunk mains) at such places as may be most convenient for affording a supply of water for extinguishing any fire. Further reference to legislation is made in IWES Water Practice Manual No. 1[5].

Accordingly it is necessary in the mains layout planning stage to consult with the Fire Service to determine where fire hydrants are required and perhaps to consider a contribution towards the enlargement of mains for fire purposes.

SELECTION OF ROUTES FOR TRUNK MAINS

The choice of a route for a trunk main is governed by the key points through which the line must pass and the most direct route between these points.

Key points are determined by the reservoirs, pumping stations, treatment works, service reservoirs and supply points into the distribution mains network which need to be connected and the hydraulic conditions required in relation to ground levels.

Between key points the most direct route is influenced by considerations of the geological structure of the ground, particularly in respect of stability, any corrosive soil conditions, such special works as river, railway and motorway crossings, means of access, need to avoid interfering with high grade agricultural land, urban infrastructure and industrial complexes.

POWERS TO LAY TRUNK MAINS

Section 19, Third Schedule of the Water Act 1945 gives power to lay mains but it is considered that it does not give the same protection as a properly negotiated easement, a Water Order or an Act of Parliament.

In laying through private lands therefore it is normal to acquire easements, the terms of which, besides providing for the laying of the main, prevent the carrying out of certain types of development which might interfere with the repairing or renewing of the pipeline or restrict its use. Some suggested heads of terms for a pipeline easement are listed in Appendix A. When a trunk main is part of a water supply scheme it is sometimes appropriate to apply for powers under Water Order procedure or even seek an Act of Parliament. It is then possible to define precisely the land required for access, construction and maintenance of the trunk main and all the ancillary work, such as improvement of water courses at washouts, and obtain if necessary compulsory purchase powers.

It is, however, recommended that land for pipelines is best acquired by negotiation with the landowner and in this respect it is also wise to take note of guidelines issued by the National Farmers' Union and the Country Landowners' Association.

Some water authorities have produced codes of practices for laying pipelines across agricultural land and these form a useful reference in dealing with these matters[6,7].

INVESTIGATION OF ROUTES FOR TRUNK MAINS

It is essential to investigate carefully all conditions of the proposed route for a trunk main in the early design stages. The first step is to produce preliminary drawings from ordnance sheets but preferably from aerial photographs, on which contours at say metre intervals within a strip of land 500 m wide are shown.

This will aid a visual inspection to identify urban and industrial areas, roads, railways, watercourses, canals, land drainage structures, coal mining areas, gravel workings, tips, industrial waste land, geological faults and areas of subsidence. With this information entered on the preliminary contoured drawing it should be possible to plot fairly accurately the best line for the route of the trunk main in readiness for the detailed site investigation.

In built-up areas this investigation will be particularly concerned with the location of other services in addition to determining the ground conditions, and this might for example require numerous pilot holes the full width of a carriageway to reveal and establish the actual positions of buried pipes and cables.

Site investigations for ground conditions are best carried out by site investigation consultants and contractors, who normally carry out the whole operation from siting and sinking trial boreholes, testing the samples, interpreting the results and producing a report with recommendations.

MOTORWAYS, DUAL CARRIAGEWAYS AND ROAD IMPROVEMENT SCHEMES

Following notification of proposed motorway, dual carriageway[8] and road improvement schemes, a thorough investigation must be made to identify all distribution and trunk water mains which may be affected by these proposals.

It is necessary to ensure that the roadworks will not affect the condition and stability of an existing water main, increase or reduce its depth of cover or in any way reduce the capabilities of maintaining and repairing it. If this cannot be guaranteed the water main must be replaced on another route which is satisfactory for operating and repairing purposes. It is usual to recharge the cost of this work, subject to any allowances for deferment of renewal or betterment, to the Ministry of Transport or the County Council responsible for the road improvement work. On planning the water main diversions, consultation and agreement at an early stage with the road authorities, their consulting engineers and contractors is essential.

FINANCIAL PROVISIONS

The cost of trunk water mains is normally budgetted for and provided from the water authorities' and water companies' capital funds, or in special circumstances is rechargeable, whereas distribution mains and secondary mains are financed from a number of alternative sources:

   (i) Provisions of Section 37, Water Act 1945
   (ii) Provisions of Section 36, Water Act 1945
  (iii) Lump sum payment under Section 27, Water Act 1945
  (iv) Rechargeable cost
   (v) Capital fund
  (vi) Main in lieu of supply pipe

The method by which they are financed depends upon the circumstances in which the distribution and secondary mains are laid.

Section 37—Water Act 1945

An owner of land, local authority or private developer, who proposes to erect thereon buildings for which a supply of water for domestic purposes will be needed, can require the water undertakers to lay the necessary water mains to such points as will enable the buildings to be connected thereto at a reasonable cost.

Before complying with this requisition the undertakers may require the owner to undertake to pay in respect of each year a sum amounting to one-eighth of the cost of the water mains, less any amounts received in charges for the supply of water from those mains, until the aggregate amount of these charges exceeds the prescribed sum or until the expiration of a period of 12 years, whichever occurs first. When the owner is a private developer the water undertakers may also require him to deposit with them a sum as security not exceeding the total cost of the mains. The annual sums due under the guarantee are usually taken from the deposit and interest is payable on the balance by the water undertakers at a rate prescribed from time to time by regulations made by the Secretary of State. Alternatively a bond may be arranged through a bank to guarantee deficit payments to the water undertaker.

Section 36—Water Act 1945

Where owners or occupiers of existing premises in any area are prevented from making a valid requisition because of an insufficiency of the aggregate amount of the charges for the supply of water which would be payable annually in respect of the premises, Section 36 enables a local authority to guarantee the relevant deficit for a period not exceeding 12 years and requires the water undertakers concerned to accept such guarantee. Thereupon the undertakers must lay the necessary mains to bring water to the area.

In the appropriate circumstances a grant under the Rural Water Supplies and Sewerage Act 1944 may be obtained by the water undertaker for the benefit of the local authority guaranteeing the scheme.

Section 27—Water Act 1945

This section enables the water undertakers to finance a water main which may be needed to provide a bulk supply of water to industrial or commercial premises. The water undertaker is obliged to give this supply of water on reasonable terms and it is normal for the consumer to pay a non-returnable lump sum to meet the whole cost of providing a water main from the existing distribution system to the boundary of the property and, if necessary, providing other water mains to reinforce the distribution system should this be deemed necessary. An agreement for the supply may take into account an agreed rate of consumption and corresponding installation of water storage capacity.

Rechargeable Cost

This normally occurs when a water undertaker is requested by a highway authority to divert and relay water mains during new motorway and road improvement schemes or if a water main needs to be diverted because of opencast coal mining or gravel working activities. The total cost of this work incurred by the water undertaker is recharged to a highway authority, usually in instalments as the work proceeds, or as a lump sum payment from the National Coal Board, or the private gravel company. The water undertaker may choose to lay larger diameter pipes than those they are replacing and consequently the difference in cost between the larger main and the size of the main it replaces is defined as betterment and is borne by the water undertaker. When replacing an old water main with a new one the water undertaker enjoys a deferment of renewal benefit and consequently the highway authority must be reimbursed to the value of this benefit. This is calculated from the Bacon Woodrow Formula issued by the DoE under provisions of Section 23(4) of PUSWA.

Capital Fund

Should the water undertaker lay new distribution or secondary mains to renew deteriorated mains or link and reinforce parts of the distribution system for its own purpose their cost is financed, as in the case of trunk mains, from a capital fund.

Main in Lieu of Supply Pipe

When a distribution main is laid in lieu of a supply pipe the cost of providing and laying that supply pipe is used as a contribution towards the cost of that distribution main.

2. MAINLAYING—LAYOUT AND ADVANCE PREPARATION

DISTRIBUTION AND SECONDARY MAIN LAYOUTS

The design of the distribution system[9,10] in respect of consumer demand and future requirements is dealt with in Chapter 5. The location of the pipes and apparatus needs to take into account:

(1) The division of the system into zones of adequate and uniform pressure including 'pressure reduction' and 'flow measuring' equipment.

(2) The employment of as low and uniform a pressure as possible, consistent with an adequate supply and fulfilment of statutory obligations.

(3) The provision of alternative means of supply by introducing ring mains and cross connections.
(4) The use of the most suitable pipe, fittings and valve materials to meet local ground conditions in respect of: rock strata, corrosive soil, sloping site, ground movement and subsidence; superimposed and impact traffic loads; quality of water to be transmitted through main; varying pressure conditions due to surge.
(5) The layout and construction of pipe joints, valves, chambers etc., so as to minimise the risk of ingress of polluted material into the system.
(6) The reduction to the minimum of 'dead ends'.
(7) The subdivision of the system for waste detection.
(8) Future maintenance of the reticulation, for example by air scour, flushing, repairing burst mains and maintaining apparatus.

APPARATUS AND CONTROL FITTINGS FOR DISTRIBUTION MAINS

Distribution and secondary mains require the provision of the following apparatus and fittings for the operation, control, repair, measurement and efficient functioning of the system:

line control valves, reflux valves, air valves, hydrants, washouts, pressure reducing valves, pressure sustaining valves, flow control valves, float valves, bulk supply measuring meters, waste measuring meters, pressure recorders and booster pumps.

Line Control Valves

On distribution and secondary mains the type of line control valve used is almost universally the sluice valve. Valves should always be provided as near as possible to the point of connection of one main to another and if that main can be fed in either direction a valve should be provided each side of the branch. Distribution mains should be fitted with a valve at each end of a street and intermediately in a long street. In general valves should be placed at as short intervals as economically viable to minimise dislocation of the supply if a portion of the main has to be taken out of use for any reason. Adequate valving is also essential because much of the average distribution and secondary mains system is located adjacent to or near buildings, so that water escaping from a broken main may cause serious damage or injury.

Reflux Valves

Reflux valves are fitted in the distribution system where it is necessary to prevent backflow. They will be located at booster pumping stations, at bottom inlet mains to service reservoirs where there is a separate outlet, and for zoning off districts in the distribution system.

Air Valves

Air valves are not required for distribution mains where there are service connections to consumers through which any air in the mains will dissipate Secondary mains without service connections will need air valves to fulfil the same functions as they do on trunk mains.

Hydrants

Hydrants are fitted primarily for fire fighting and the valve controlling the outlet can be either metal face or soft face (see Section 4, Chapter 8).

Hydrants can also be used for flushing, swabbing, air scouring, as injection points for disinfection, for pressure testing and location of pressure recorders, and for mains relining activities (Chapter 10, Section 2) or waste metering (Chapter 12). Fixed jumper hydrants are necessary for air-injection when used for air scouring.

Washouts

Washouts are required at low points and dead ends to enable the distribution and secondary mains to be drained for maintenance or repair. On the distribution and secondary main systems the duckfoot bend fire hydrant or the screwdown fire hydrant will serve as a washout.

Pressure Reducing Valves

PRVs are located in distribution networks where it is necessary to limit the downstream pressure to a pre-set maximum independent of the upstream pressure.

For maintaining pressure within a specified range in a distribution zone a self-contained variable flow PRV operating in relation to flow is available as a unit made up of a plug valve and actuator.

Pressure Sustaining Valves

PSVs are located in distribution networks where it is necessary to protect the upstream pressure from falling below a pre-set minimum.

Flow Control Valves

Constant rate of flow valves or automatic self-closing valves are rarely required on a distribution mains system. However, in some circumstances they are needed on mains at the point where they are fed from a trunk main or a service reservoir. Flow control valves are sometimes used on large diameter services supplying industrial premises to protect other consumers where the distribution system is delicately balanced.

Float Valves

The float valve is essentially an automatic flow control valve in which the regulating principle is the level of some free water surface; consequently, it is used on the inlet pipe to service reservoirs, suction tanks and water towers.

Bulk Supply Measuring Meter

Flow measuring meters should be installed on secondary mains feeding each distribution zone and these can be inferential 'fan' or 'vane' type, 'positive' or 'displacement' piston type, the turbine blade type with recorders, Dall tube, magnetic flow or ultrasonic. Orifice plate meters for permanent installations are not recommended due to their lack of accuracy.

Waste Measuring Meter

When laying the distribution mains system the opportunity should be taken to include a waste water meter installation (Chapter 12).

Pressure Recorders

Pressure recorders should be located at key points in the distribution system and the pressure recorded should be transmitted to a central monitoring location.

Booster Pumps

Booster pumps may be required to improve supplies to consumers whose situation, due to level, distance or insufficient mains capacity, prohibits the provision of an adequate water supply (Chapter 7).

TRUNK MAIN LAYOUTS

Following the planning stage when site investigations have been completed, outline drawings prepared and the route of the trunk main, the material of the pipe and the type of joints have been selected in accordance with the criteria previously outlined, the detailed layout in line and level must be finalised[9-28].

The line should be carefully checked on site to ensure that:

(a) when the trunk main is in operation, access for repair and maintenance is satisfactory;

(b) any road, railway and watercourse crossings are located in the best place;

(c) where the route crosses ground subject to movement or waterlogged, measures necessary to ensure stability of the trunk main are not prohibitive in cost;

(d) there are no underground structures existing or planned on the line of the trunk main;

(e) laying pipes in corrosive soil using protective measures is not prohibitively expensive;

(f) easements with provision for duplication if required are obtainable at reasonable cost, particularly where mineral rights might be exercised in the future.

Wherever possible trunk mains should be laid to falls between washouts at the low points and air valves at the high points. A minimum gradient of 1 in 500 is desirable because on slacker gradients it is more difficult to get rid of air and some water may be retained in occasional dips in the pipeline.

A gravity trunk main conveying water over long distances can be constructed using non-pressure pipes laid to gradients and discharging like an open channel. Where the gradient of the pipeline reverses by dipping down or rising to follow a changing profile of the ground, pressure pipes must be used in the layout of an inverted syphon when going under a valley or a syphon when going over a hill.

The minimum depth of cover to a trunk main is 1 m and this is normally possible in rough open land, hilly or rocky country. In agricultural land modern farming practice usually has well maintained drainage which must remain undisturbed and consequently it is normally necessary to lay pipes below land drains and ditches. Increased cover, as much as 3 to 4 m, is sometimes needed in urban areas where it is necessary in some cases to get below public utilities' apparatus and sewers. In urban areas it is essential during the layout and advance preparation stage to fix the line and level of a trunk main in relation to the position of existing public utilities' apparatus, sewers and drains and it is essential to maintain close consultation with the public utilities and local authorities. Road closures and traffic diversions are often necessary and at this stage meetings with the police and highway authority are essential to discuss arrangements.

All the foregoing conditions need to be investigated and decisions made on the final line and level at this stage, from which accurate working drawings for the construction of the trunk main can be produced.

APPARATUS AND CONTROL FITTINGS FOR TRUNK MAINS

Trunk mains require the provision of the following apparatus and fittings (as described in Chapter 8, Section 4) for operation, control, repair, measurement, inspection and functioning:

line control valves, reflux valves, air valves, washouts, flow control valves, flow measuring meters and access manholes.

Line Control Valves

Sluice valves are generally used for line control on a trunk main and, depending on operating circumstances, are placed at intervals of 1 to 5 km to enable sections of the main to be isolated for repair and maintenance. For ease of charging they are best located at the high points, with air valves on either side, or at the low points with bypasses to wash-outs, using the bypass for charging purposes. Unless the pressure is low, valves larger than 300 mm diameter require gearing and, where power is available, operation by an electric motor. If required, motorised sluice valves can be operated by remote control through telemetry (Chapters 5 and 7). They should be provided with expansion or flexible joints each side of the valve and should be fitted with bypasses for ease of valve operation or charging the main. Sluice valves on trunk mains exceeding 300 mm diameter can, with economy, be made smaller than the main, the extra loss of head being very small if the valve has an area equal to half that of the pipe and is largely recovered in a long taper. Ease of access to a line control valve is important because the time taken to shut a valve in an emergency is largely spent on reaching it. Butterfly or disc valves are also used as line control valves but from a purely hydraulic point of view there is little to choose between the butterfly and the gate sluice valve. The butterfly valve has advantages in its lighter weight, greater ease of operation and less installation space, but the gate sluice valves are more robust, reliable, and easier to maintain. Butterfly valves may prohibit swabbing of trunk mains and restrict man access. There is also a risk of too rapid a closure, particularly when the valve is almost closed, causing surge problems.

Reflux Valves

Where a trunk main is a pumping main reflux valves are fitted at the pumping end, to prevent backflow in the event of a burst, and at the delivery end if it is a bottom inlet into a service reservoir with a standpipe or separate outlet main.

Air Valves

Air valves are required to discharge air when a trunk main is being filled, to admit air when it is being emptied, and to discharge air accumulating at any time (which can often occur on a pumping main). They must be fixed at all high points on the pipeline relative to the hydraulic gradient and it is often desirable to locate them where the gradient of the main changes and where the gradient of the main is parallel to or less than the hydraulic gradient. Measures must be taken to ensure that the chamber housing an air valve does not become flooded, otherwise back-siphonage of polluted water into a pipeline could occur following drain down resulting from a burst.

Washouts

Washouts are located at low points in the trunk main, preferably where there is a point to discharge into a watercourse or a ditch. In urban areas, in the absence of a suitable watercourse, it will be necessary to construct a discharge chamber from which water may be pumped to the surface water drainage system.

The washout consists of a tee, preferably with a level invert, a line valve each side of the branch and a control valve on the branch discharging to waste. The distance between line valves should take account of the time required to empty the pipeline during emergency conditions and should relate to the allowable time needed to repair or maintain the pipeline.

Providing the washout branch is less than 9″ (225 mm) diameter, Section 34 of the Water Act 1945 allows the water undertaker to discharge into any watercourse without restrictions or the need to notify the appropriate authorities when works are being constructed, repaired or cleaned or if they have to be emptied or examined. It is, however, suggested that it would be prudent to consult the quality and pollution control section of a water authority before finalising the location and size of a washout discharging into a watercourse and likewise a local authority when requiring to discharge into the surface water drainage system. In some cases it may be necessary to construct a lagoon to settle out main debris prior to allowing discharge to watercourse.

Flow Control Valves

Sluice valves are sometimes used as a cheap but very inefficient way of controlling flow by partially closing the gate. This method of dissipating energy leads to cavitation damage around the gate and is not recommended for general use. There are a number of special valves for trunk main flow control of which the Larner-Johnson type is widely used for stop and flow regulation duty. Free discharge control and self-acting versions such as emergency self-closing valves, pressure reducing valves and float controlled valves are available.

Another valve suitable for flow control at a pipeline intake, or at any other point along the pipeline, is one in which the water is divided into jets which produce an essentially turbulent downstream flow in such a way that the excess energy representing the surplus head in the main is dissipated harmlessly. Flow control valves on trunk mains should be installed adjacent to a geared sluice valve which acts as a guard valve, both valves being bypassed with a small diameter valved connection.

When a flow control valve is to be shut down immediately following a burst trunk main fed from a service reservoir, it should be operated by electric motor actuated by a high flow meter reading activating the motor, thereby closing the valve. On a closed pumping system other arrangements are necessary (Chapter 7).

Flow Measuring Meters

Meters with recorders should be installed at the trunk main intake and its discharge point. Venturi tubes and Dall tubes have been widely used in the past but now the magnetic flow meter and the ultrasonic flow meter are being developed for this purpose.

Access Manholes

Access to large diameter trunk mains for internal inspection and repairs to pipes and joints must be provided at regular intervals no greater than 1 km apart. It can be by a standard hatch box or a tee with a flanged outlet sealed with blank flanges which, if required, can serve a dual purpose as part of an air valve connection.

Access manholes can also be designed for swab launching or retrieval to facilitate periodic cleaning of the main thereby minimising water quality problems, ensuring prevalence of good flow characteristics and reducing energy costs where pumping is involved. The water quality aspect becomes increasingly important as undertakings take the opportunity of linking demand centres together via large diameter mains to optimise regional storage. This policy leads to different waters using the same main, the reaction of which can produce problems of discolouration unless care is taken to keep mains deposits under control.

PIPEWORK CONNECTIONS

Pipework connections are made to enable the transfer of water between parallel trunk mains, from trunk mains to secondary mains, service reservoirs, distribution systems and washouts, and from pump and gravitational deliveries into trunk mains. The advantages and economical results obtained from cross-over connections situated at every 2 to 3 km between parallel trunk mains are:

(i) The discharge of the aqueduct can be increased by instalments to meet demand by progressively laying successive sections of new pipeline between cross-connections. This is achieved by establishing the cross-over connections when the first trunk main is laid.

(ii) The sub-sections of the trunk main can be laid between established cross-over connections with minimum disruption to those trunk mains in operation.

(iii) In the event of the need to shut down one main for repair or maintenance it is only necessary to isolate a sub-section between cross-over connections, thereby maintaining about 75 per cent of the total capacity of the trunk main system.

Three alternative cross-connection layouts providing similar control facilities are shown in Fig. 9.1.

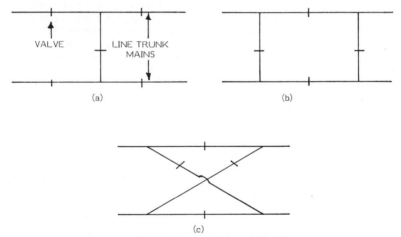

Fig. 9.1. Alternative cross-connection layouts

Most pipework layouts are designed to meet the special needs and requirements of any particular function but in preparing the detailed layout of the pipes, specials, fittings and apparatus basic guidelines should be observed:

(1) Ensure that the pipework layout and valve arrangements will, when operated, perform the functions required by the designer and user.

(2) Duplicate or provide alternative connections and supply facilities so that the overall function of the system can continue, albeit in limited manner, when a fitting or valve is removed.

(3) Allow adequate space between fittings and valves for on-site maintenance.
(4) Provide sufficient detachable fittings to facilitate disconnection and removal of any fitting or valve.
(5) Ensure that the chambers in which pipework layouts are housed are of sufficient size to allow on-site working, have removable covers to allow access to lifting tackle and plant, have a drainage sump and if possible a permanent dewatering pump. The chamber should be constructed in reinforced concrete, incorporating in the base the requisite pipe supports and anchorages. Access points should be made as vandal-proof as possible and the whole chamber designed as a water retaining structure to minimise ingress of ground water.
(6) Provision should be made for plant and equipment in the chamber and pipework connections to be accessible for maintenance and repair.

ANCHORAGES AND SUPPORTS

Except when using welded, flanged or self-anchored joints which can be designed to take the loads caused by internal pressure in the pipe, ground movement and temperature change, the unbalanced loads must be taken by external resistances.

In the cases of change of direction fittings, a bend or tee in plan requires a thrust block to dissipate the thrust from the fitting to the soil and is usually formed by placing concrete between the outside of the bend or barrel of the tee and the side of the trench[13]. At a bend looking up in the vertical plane it is necessary to transmit the downward thrust to a foundation of concrete, while a bend looking down in the vertical plane needs to be surrounded by a block of concrete whose weight is sufficient to counter-balance the upward thrust. This block of concrete must not encase the joints of the bend but if this limitation poses a problem an alternative would be the appropriate size block situated under the bend held in place with corrosion protected steel straps restrained by foundation bolts. A dead end also requires a thrust block to transmit the thrust exerted on the end cap to the end wall of the trench.

Pipework connections which normally comprise a layout of rigid jointed pipes, fittings and valves but with some flexible joints to facilitate removal of any pipe, fitting or valve for repair or replacement, need to be supported on a reinforced concrete raft. As an integral part of this raft support system, individual reinforced concrete supports are incorporated to provide thrust blocks for horizontal and vertical bends and tees, or as pipe supports on which pipes can be held in place with corrosion protected steel straps restrained by foundation bolts.

Each concrete anchorage and support system must be individually designed, taking into account the maximum thrust exerted on the pipe or fitting by the maximum internal pressure anticipated or (1.5 × maximum working pressure of the pipes), whichever is the greater, together with an allowance for surge pressure if anticipated and thrusts exerted by temperature changes in cases where pipework is exposed. This thrust must be satisfactorily transmitted through the concrete anchorage and support system to ground whose load bearing capabilities are adequate.

Chambers are constructed around all types of valves, meters and access manholes and in many cases part of the reinforced concrete support raft can form the base of the chambers. Often a chamber constructed around a single valve which has flexible joints can be designed so that the base and the part of the wall through which the pipe passes, act together as a thrust block to transmit pipeline thrusts to the surrounding ground.

ROAD, RAILWAY AND WATERCOURSE CROSSINGS

Crossing a road, railway or watercourse always requires special work, the extent of which depends on the size of the pipe and the magnitude of the obstacle to be crossed.

Road Crossings

Distribution and secondary mains crossing minor roads and major roads, including dual carriageways, can usually be laid in trench half the width of the road at a time. Ductile iron pipes are best suited for this purpose and for a wide or dual carriageway a line control sluice valve each side of the crossing is recommended.

A trunk main crossing an existing major road or motorway on the level or under an embankment can be inserted inside a thrust bored steel pipe with welded joints or inside a pipe jacked concrete pipe tunnel. The trunk main, ductile iron or steel with rigid or self-anchoring joints, can then be threaded through on rollers or skids.

Crossing a major road or motorway in cutting requires a pipe bridge. When distribution, secondary or trunk mains have to be diverted on new lines because of major road improvements and new motorways, it is the practice for box culverts, and bridges to accommodate the re-routed mains, to be constructed at the same time as the major road and motorway structures. A line control sluice valve each side of the crossing, a washout on the low side and an air valve on the high side are recommended.

Railway Crossings

Distribution, secondary or trunk mains can be laid across railway tracks on the level or under an embankment by means of thrust boring or placed in a driven tunnel or culvert. Crossing railway tracks in cutting is usually carried out by bridging. Wherever possible an existing road bridge should be used, laying the pipes under the road or footpath or attaching them to the bridge structure. Work under or over the railway tracks has to be carried out in accordance with British Rail conditions which often impose constraints upon the design.

Watercourse Crossings

Pipelines may have to cross streams, canals or large rivers. Other obstacles adjacent to watercourses which may have to be taken into account are floodbanks and defences which must not be breached and, in some cases, a floodplain which must not be obstructed by a pipeline above ground.

The methods normally employed for watercourse crossing are bridging, tunnelling, cofferdam trenching, underwater trenching, temporary watercourse diversions or thrust boring.

It has been common practice to use bridging for many years and this continues to be a preferred method, subject to favourable cost comparison with other methods, planning requirements and land drainage and flood alleviation requirements.

Wherever possible an existing road bridge should be used but if a new crossing point is needed a special bridge is required on which the pipes are supported[29] or, alternatively, self-supporting pipes are used or a pipe arch formed by the pipes themselves.

Examples of existing pipe crossings are:

(a) 24″ (600 mm) diameter steel main attached by sliding bearings, permitting longitudinal movement to a 1 100 m long motorway viaduct crossing a river and a railway[30].

(b) 24" (600 mm) diameter steel mains located in pipe ducts fixed by sliding supports to a box girder road bridge 1 400 m long[31].

(c) Purpose built three arch profile bridge 70 m span, of precast concrete sections prestressed on site, carrying four 48" (1 200 mm) diameter steel pipelines[16].

(d) Purpose built prestressed concrete bridge 80 m span, of bowstring design with a single boom, a bottom tie member of parapet girders with a deck between on which two 21" (525 mm) diameter steel pipes are carried[32].

(e) Purpose built prestressed concrete bridge 70 m span, of arch design from which are suspended two 33" (825 mm) horizontal steel pipes[33].

(f) A horizontal self-supporting 60" (1 500 mm) diameter welded steel pipeline spanning 30 m[34].

(g) A flat-arch self-supporting pipe bridge formed by 33" (825 mm) diameter flanged steel pipes carried on abutments spanning 70 m[33].

(h) Purpose built bowstring design, the arch members being two 60" (1 500 mm) diameter steel pipelines supporting a single lane road carriageway 50 m long.

Tunnelling will depend for its success on the material of the river bed and in general some form of compressed air is necessary for driving tunnels under water. If the watercourse is wide, navigable and more than one large diameter trunk main is needed, the driven tunnel is probably the most satisfactory method[35-38].

The method of laying within cofferdams is still frequently used and could be a more economical method if navigation is not interrupted too seriously with the partially blocked waterway[39].

Underwater trenching is an alternative to cofferdam excavation[40,41]. A trench is scooped out by a dredger across the river bed and a pipeline, preformed on the banks to the profile of the trench, is launched into the river. It is floated into position over the trench and is then ballasted and allowed to sink into the trench. Checking final location is carried out by divers followed by a certain amount of backfill and anchoring by sandbags, but for the most part the trench is left to silt itself.

When a dry watercouse bed is needed to lay the pipeline, a cofferdam the full width of the watercourse can be placed upstream with a pipe or channel built through and continued beyond the line of the proposed pipeline to convey the flow of the watercourse downstream of the workings[42].

CATHODIC PROTECTION OF BURIED FERROUS METAL PIPELINES

External corrosion of buried ferrous metal pipelines can be minimised by applying cathodic protection techniques[43-46]. Their successful application depends on understanding their advantages and limitations and determining in the planning stage the type of application appropriate to the circumstances.

If steel or ductile iron pipes are selected for a pipeline, and it is suspected that the soil conditions through which it is to be laid are corrosive, the first step is to commission a specialist consultant to carry out a soil resistivity and groundwater survey. The results of this field survey work taken together with the pipeline system, existing or proposed, will enable the consultant to make recommendations (see Chapter 10, Section 2).

In the case of existing pipelines electrical current surveys are conducted to:
(i) assess the quality of the protective coatings;
(ii) check their electrical continuity;
(iii) trace leakage current to other structures to prevent possible damage to them;

(iv) ascertain the voltage and amount of current required to effect cathodic protection.

For the design of cathodic protection installations for new pipelines:

(1) detailed knowledge of site conditions is required;
(2) the proposed pipe coatings to be used must be specified;
(3) electrical continuity of the pipeline to be protected must be achieved;
(4) that part of the installation, such as pumps and apparatus, which must not be affected by electrical currents, should be insulated from the pipeline system at a flange.
(5) the availability of power supplies must be established;
(6) adjacent structures and installations which may be adversely affected by improperly applied cathodic protection must be identified;
(7) all public utilities who may be affected should be consulted.

There are two methods of cathodic protection, the sacrificial anode system which consists of groups of two to five magnesium anodes installed adjacent to and wired to the pipeline to be protected, and the power impressed system which consists of permanent high silicon iron or graphite anode ground beds installed adjacent to the pipeline and into which a current of up to 10 amps is continuously fed at a low voltage through a transformer from the public electricity supply or other electrical energy source.

The choice of a method depends on circumstances. For smaller systems in a low-resistivity soil, particularly in congested areas where there are large numbers of other buried metallic structures, sacrificial anodes, despite their maintenance needs, are preferable. For larger projects, particularly pipelines across country, the power impressed system is more economic in operation and maintenance. In general this sytem is cheaper on a long-term basis than the use of sacrificial anodes.

When considering the economics of cathodic protection, the cost of its provision (between 1 and 2 per cent of the cost of the pipeline) should be weighed against:

(a) the future cost of repairing leaks;
(b) the value of the reliability and security of the pipeline;
(c) the cost of reconditioning or relaying the pipeline in the event of severe corrosion;
(d) the cost of providing a high standard of protective coating to the outside of the pipeline;
(e) the cost of backfilling round a pipeline with inert material in corrosive sub-soil conditions.

REMOTE MONITORING AND SENSING

To make the best use of instrumentation, control and automation (ICA) equipment in the water supply system, particular attention must be given to the siting and installation of flow meters, pressure gauges and flow control apparatus which need to be recorded and monitored at a control centre. The instruments and sensor cells must be housed in properly constructed buildings and chambers which provide a suitable environment for their best operating performance, with a layout favouring easy maintenance.

The field of ICA is continuously under review by the Water Research Centre and improving sensor cells with microchip control is just one development. A move into sophisticated instrumentation equipment highlights the need to ensure that the basic flow and pressure equipment on the pipelines is properly installed and appropriate technical resources are available for maintenance work.

WORK IN THE PUBLIC HIGHWAY AND EASEMENTS

Following consultations with the highway authority and other street managers notices under the Public Utilities Street Works Act 1950 should be issued when the details of distribution, secondary and trunk mains routes in the public highway have been finalised. At the same time any proposed working in the carriageway, which could result in traffic restrictions and road closures and the need to use traffic signals, should be planned as far in advance as possible with the Highway Authority and the police.

The easement rights which may be needed for construction of all sizes of pipelines through all types of private land include:

(i) A strip of land within which a pipeline or pipelines may be laid and this should include adequate working area, space to store spoil from the excavation space to line out pipes in readiness of laying, and space to move pipes and plant and equipment.alongside the trench. This working strip is required only for construction purposes.

(ii) Any areas of land for storing pipes and materials, for spoil tips and temporary offices, or for access, are required for the duration of the construction work.

(iii) The right to tip spoil in low places where the pipeline would otherwise be laid with insuffient cover.

(iv) The right to improve watercourses where a washout from the pipeline discharges immediately into a watercourse which is too small for the expected flow.

Easement rights and land acquisition required in perpetuity for the inspection, repair and maintenance of the pipeline and apparatus and possible future duplication of the pipeline include:

(1) A strip of land, within which the pipeline is located, where the undertakers will have rights of working at all times without notice.

(2) A right of way at all times without notice on foot or with vehicles along existing roads, tracks or delineated land to gain access to the easement strip.

(3) Land which has been sterilized by groups of valves, fittings and chambers to be purchased outright.

(4) Provision of vehicle accesses to key points on the route.

Payments for easement rights are usually negotiated through land and estate agents based on normally accepted compensation rates for loss of crops, use of land, and so on, and a generous single payment is preferable to lifetime annual compensation agistments. It may also be necessary to make *ad hoc* payments or provide a water supply to the landowner for special temporary or permanent facilities required but not covered by the easement agreement, such as compensation for cattle movements[6,7].

For negotiating easements some suggested heads of terms are listed in Appendix A.

3. MAINLAYING—ENGINEERING CONSTRUCTION

PREPARATORY SITE WORK

Distribution mainlaying on new housing sites should not normally commence until the route is clear from builders' and other utilities' materials and equipment, the kerb races laid so that precise line and levels of the footpath and carriageway are known, and a space for the distribution main in relation to other utilities' apparatus has been allocated.

Mainlaying in the public highway must be preceded by detailed planning with the highway authority and any other street managers and public utilities to define working areas, lengths of the highway available for work, highway restrictions and closures, siting of barriers, signs and traffic signals, storage areas for pipes and fittings, disposal of spoil, access at selected points over open trench and any restrictions on plant and equipment working.

Preparatory work for trunk mains across country requires the limits of easements to be defined and fenced, working and storage areas to be fenced, with stockproof fence if necessary, the route set out in line and level with pegs and site rails, pipes and fittings delivered onto storage areas and, where appropriate, strung out along the pipe trench.

EXCAVATION

Distribution and Secondary Mains

Trench dimensions for distribution and secondary mains up to 300 mm diameter are set out in the National Water Council productivity manual—module eleven which, apart from setting standard excavation and trench dimensions, builds elemental time standards contained in the National Joint Data Bank to a level essential for the detailed scheduling of work to pre-determined levels of performance[47]. Excavation in carriageways, footpaths and verges free from other obstructions and in open land is normally carried out by mechanical excavators but in carriageway and footpath localities where there are obstructions from pipes, cables and apparatus, breaking open the surface by pneumatic hammers and excavation by hand is required. A new technique for the excavation of trenches in the public highway for pipes up to 250 mm diameter makes use of the vacuum cleaner principle to remove the spoil. This vacuum excavation method is used to dig trenches from 110 to 325 mm wide up to a depth of about 1 m. After the road surface is broken in the conventional manner the sub-soil is fragmented with lightweight long-handled pneumatic digging tools and the soil is removed by the vacuum unit through a 100 mm diameter flexible hose. Pipes are laid on a bed of sand and gravel and trenches are backfilled using special tamping tools.

Trunk Mains in Urban Areas

A plan of the route is prepared showing existing roads, railways, watercourses, buildings and structures and from the best known information the location of underground service and apparatus. The best route for the main is then selected and set out on site[28,48,49].

Following the breaking open and stripping out of hard road and paved surfaces, excavation for trunk mains in the public highway in urban areas can be carried out by mechanical excavator, provided that pilot holes are excavated ahead of the work to pin-point every pipe, cable and piece of apparatus so that the most favourable position of the pipeline can be precisely set out in advance. Where services appear in the trench it is necessary to excavate by hand until safe to continue with the mechanical excavator. The minimum depth of trench for a trunk main is likely to be 1.5 m and with superimposed traffic loads in the vicinity, trenches normally require timbering with "hit and miss" poling boards and walings, close boarded timbering or sheet piling supported with adjustable tubular struts. Temporary underpinning and supportive measures for buildings, structures, apparatus and services close to or crossing the trench may also be necessary.

All services crossing the trench must be supported from above and sewers and surface water drains which are exposed should be relaid and supported, preferably with new uPVC pipes, to avoid sewage and storm water entering the excavation. There should be adequate measures taken to keep the workings as dry as possible; sufficient drainage pipes and, if necessary, dewatering equipment must be available.

Procedures applying to brittle gas and water mains which might be affected by deep excavation have been agreed at national level between the National Water Council and the British Gas Corporation. Brittle mains will be grey iron and asbestos cement; 'deep' is classified as all excavation carried out at a depth greater than 1.5 m below ground surface. Gas mains, water mains, water mains relining, sewers and river engineering schemes come within the ambit of these model procedures.

Trunk Mains in Rural Areas

In agricultural land it is usual to strip the top soil by scrapers and stack it for use in final reinstatment.

Trench excavation carried out by back-acting or continuous bucket type excavators will have vertical sides which usually require timbering or sheet pile supporting. In open country the vertical sided trench can be dug quickly and cheaply with a continuous bucket excavator and, providing the ground stands up well, needing only the minimum trench support, and sufficient speed of working can be maintained, this is a satisfactory method. In restricted locations and urban areas there is no alternative to the vertically sided trench.

A battered-sided trench can be used when the working area is not restricted. The batter required for the wall of the trench depends upon the material of the trench sides and on its degree of saturation but normally 45° is suitable. Excavation is often carried out by a dragline excavator which can easily be adapted as a crane for laying pipes. Although the latter saves an item of plant it can slow down the rate of working and also means more material has to be excavated than with a vertical sided trench. However, backfill can be spread laterally ensuring that little, if any, surplus spoil has to be removed to tip. This method is at least as economic as the vertical sided trench.

Where land drainage systems are encountered the position of all land drains cut or disturbed should be prominently marked and after pipelaying should be re-laid and reinstated to ensure satisfactory operation of the drainage system.

Drains which foul the pipe must be taken up as far back as necessary to provide an adequate fall over the main and relaid to a flatter gradient. Where this is impracticable the drain across the pipe must be replaced by an inverted syphon arrangement.

General

Trench excavation should not proceed at a greater rate than laying the pipes. Generally it is better to limit the length of trench by reference to the time taken to lay the pipes and backfill between the joints, a common rule being that trenching should be about two days ahead of pipelaying.

The working space requirements dictate the width of trench required for any given size of pipes. With a battered-sided trench 0.3 m of extra width on either side of the bottom is normally adequate, but if the trench is vertically sided and deep, additional space should be provided as well as space for timbering the sides. A minimum of 0.5 m clear space laterally is required for jointing.

Where rock is encountered it is excavated with pneumatic rock drills but, if this slows down progress, explosives may be used subject to conditions being suitable—that is, not in a built up area or close to roads, railways and structures.

TRENCH DEWATERING

In clays, rock and similar sub-soil the normal method of removing ground and drainage water as it enters the excavation is by pumping from a sump. Should sand and silt be present the fines will be carried into the excavations and if this is continued over a period there is a danger of subsidence of the adjacent ground. In this case the removal of ground water is achieved by the use of wellpoint dewatering equipment.

The wellpoint system of dewatering consists of putting down into the ground below the lowest excavation level perforated suction pipes, which are joined together at the surface by a header pipeline laid along the ground. The header pipe collects the discharge from all suction pipes and carries it to a wellpoint pump which, by creating a vacuum in the system, removes the water from the ground. This method of dewatering has proved extremely successful and has enabled very steep sandy faces to be worked where, in natural conditions, they would have slumped.

A different problem is met when the sub-soil is impervious yet very wet, which can often be the case with silts and silty clays. The problem is the unstable nature of the ground with the bottom of the excavation becoming unsound; dewatering by sump pumping or wellpointing will not work because water will not flow through the silts to the abstraction points. In this case the method of electro-osmosis, which consists of forcing water (by a passage of electrical current) to a dewatering point similar to that of the wellpoint dewatering system, may prove successful in maintaining the vertical sides of an excavation taken out in a wet unstable silt.

THRUST BORING AND TUNNELLING

When passing under obstructions such as roads, railways and watercourses some form of tunnelling will be used.

One method is thrust boring in which a steel shield pipe sleeve is jacked forward from a thrust pit constructed at one side of the crossing and the material is excavated by a rotating auger which moves the material back to the thrust pit where it is bucketed out. New lengths of steel or concrete pipes are welded or jointed together and are jacked forward as the tunnelling proceeds, finally appearing in the reception pit at the other side of the crossing[50-52]. For the larger size pipe sleeves the method of thrust boring is similar except that men enter and excavate the material manually at the working face and the auger is dispensed with. When the material to be excavated is rock, the use of explosives is sometimes necessary.

When the steel or concrete sleeve is in position the water-carrying pipes of ductile iron with self-anchored joints or steel with welded joints are jointed and threaded through on skids or rollers attached to the pipe. The annular space between the two pipes is usually grouted solid. This method can be used for 100 mm distribution mains and up to 1 800 mm trunk mains. Subject to working pressures being within the strength limits of large concrete pipes, those with flush socket and spigot joint with rubber ring (after jacking into position and having the inside space of the joint sealed with epoxy mortar) can serve as a pressure or gravity pipeline.

The thrust boring technique is successful for short drives of up to 100 m and for pipes up to 2.5 m diameter but for pipelines of longer lengths and larger diameter the tunnel should be constructed by traditional methods. As well as accommodating a number of pipelines which require to be handled, placed on plinths and jointed, tunnels are also required to carry large quantities of water from major source and treatment works. In rock, the tunnel section can be a vertical wall lined with concrete and an arch roof of precast concrete segments and, in other material, circular sections formed by pre-cast reinforced concrete segments bolted together. A particular lining for tunnels driven through stiff clays ("Wedge Block" tunnel lining) has been developed[31]. When the tunnel is shallow it can be constructed by the cut-and-cover method and in this respect a reinforced concrete box culvert would be more suitable for accommodating pipes.

PIPE LAYING AND JOINTING

Most pipes are still laid singly in the trench but with increasing use of polyethylene pipes in a coil, and the use of butt fusion welded joints, the technique of laying long lengths for distribution and some secondary mains is becoming more common.

Pipes[53-54] should be laid on an even bed throughout which has been trimmed by hand to the correct gradient and not allowed to bear on any hard points or rest upon underground structures. Where the excavation is in rock the trench bottom beneath the pipe should be excavated to an extra depth of 150 mm and the pipe laid on dry weak concrete. If the ground is too soft to permit the pipes to be laid directly upon it, an additional 150 mm depth of trench should be excavated into which a concrete foundation 125 mm thick is placed over the full width of the trench. The pipe is then bedded on 25 mm dry concrete on the concrete foundation. However, this method should be avoided for plastic pipes and where rock is encountered the bed should be 150 mm thick of imported granular fill.

When it is necessary to lay on less stable ground in marshy or peaty areas pipes should be supported on piers founded on stable material, if this is to be found at no greater depth than 1.5 m. Care should be taken to avoid point loads being transmitted to the pipe, particularly in the case of plastic pipes.

When encountering waterlogged sand and silt, support to the pipes can be provided by piles subject to ground conditions being suitable[17,55]. Bored as opposed to driven piles are generally preferred, as the plant required for this installation is considerably lighter, an important factor when working on unstable ground. Should piling prove unsatisfactory, an alternative method may be to lower the water table by laying an earthenware drain surrounded by hardcore alongside the main trench and at a depth of 0.5 m below pipe invert. If this dries out the ground sufficiently a 150 mm thick reinforced concrete raft can be placed across the bottom of the trench, its width depending on the bearing capacity of the sub-soil. The pipes are then laid on the raft and haunched up with concrete. A plastic pipeline full of water has approximately the same specific gravity as waterlogged peat and should therefore remain in a stable position in these conditions.

The operation of lowering the pipe on to the prepared bed of the trench, and controlling it while being offered to the preceding pipe already in position prior to jointing requires skill and expertise and the use of the appropriate plant and equipment. Pipe cutting to produce required lengths for make-up pieces will be carried out on site, using an appropriate pipe cutter for the material. Flame cutters should never be used on material other than steel. The precise technique of laying will depend on the pipe material being used and the advice of pipe manufacturers should be taken into account.

Empty pipes after laying will have a tendency to float in a flooded trench and the danger of heavy rain suddenly inundating a previously dry trench should be anticipated. It is good practice to ensure that a pipe when laid is secured against floating by backfilling part of the pipe between joints. In order to prevent flotation there could be a temptation to allow the ingress of the flood water into the pipeline through the open end of the pipe or through washouts, etc, but this is highly undesirable on water hygiene grounds and should be avoided. Pipe stoppers should be used to prevent the entry of ground water, mud or vermin whenever mainlaying is suspended.

The full range of pipe joints used for distribution, secondary and trunk mains is described in Table 8.II. Each particular joint and the material of the pipes it joins together has its own method of forming and the pipe manufacturers provide detailed jointing instructions for their products.

Anchorage and Support Structures

As soon as the pipework has been laid and jointed the concrete anchorage and support structures must be cast before backfilling has commenced.

Where concrete bedding and haunching to pipes is required this work should be carried out with care being taken to keep joints clear of the concrete. The concrete anchorage and support structures referred to in Section 2 will have been designed in advance and during construction it is essential that the sides of the trench are trim and vertical; that properly formed shuttering to correct dimensions is secured; that steelwork is fixed; and that concrete is placed and consolidated against undisturbed ground and around the pipe or fitting to achieve a good bond. Before casting the concrete structures it is essential to check that all joints have been properly made and in particular that bolts on flange joints are tightened to the correct tension.

Chambers housing valves, connection layouts, and meters on trunk mains will in some conditions have to be constructed as water-retaining structures to prevent ingress of ground water and if pipes are cast into the wall they may also have to act as an anchorage structure.

Support structures for pipe bridges are of either reinforced concrete or mass concrete blocks, forming abutments each side of the crossing into which the pipe to be supported is cast. These concrete abutments must be founded on stable material and bonding between the pipe and the abutment must ensure that the forces induced by the dead loads, temperature, water pressure and other line loads are transmitted to the supporting abutment.

Testing

Testing[56] of pipes and fittings usually begins in the factory by the manufacturer and in order that these components are satisfactory when received on the site it is good policy to visit the manufacturers to encourage high quality standards and adherence to delivery dates. In some cases it might be necessary to employ a pipe inspection consultant to carry out more thorough checks. After mainlaying, a strength test by applying water pressure is carried out to check:

(a) the mechanical soundness and leak tightness of pipes and fittings;
(b) the leak tightness of the joints;
(c) the strength of the anchorage and support structures;
(d) the quality of workmanship of the pipelayers and jointers.

Before a distribution, secondary or trunk main is subjected to hydraulic testing, all change of direction and change of diameter fittings and valves should be permanently anchored, end caps at each end of the test length temporarily but securely anchored, and sufficient backfilling placed round the top of the pipes to prevent movement under test. Testing against a closed valve is not recommended unless there is no alternative.

As far as possible, joints should be left exposed until testing has been satisfactorily completed, unless the joints have been tested as pipelaying proceeds.

Water mains may be tested in lengths varying from a few hundred metres up to about a kilometre depending on whether they are situated in streets or in open country, on the availability of test water, and on many other factors. The test pressure applied should be 1.5 × maximum working pressure to which the main is likely to be subjected, plus a suitable allowance for surge.

When hydraulically testing a main the first essential is to ensure that all air is expelled from the main by charging slowly. After filling, with chlorinated water if possible, the main should be left under moderate pressure for a period in order to achieve conditions as stable as possible for testing. The length of this period will depend on the stabilisation of the main under pressure, the quantity of air trapped and absorption of the pipe material. Testing absorbent pipes, pre-stressed concrete, asbestos cement and concrete lined ductile iron is complex due to the need to ensure that the pipe material is fully saturated; this can take many days before the pipeline is ready for testing.

The pressure is then brought up to the test value by a hand-operated, plunger pump and all exposed joints and fittings are examined for watertightness. When all obvious leaks have been rectified the test pressure should be maintained for a period during which the drop in pressure is noted and the amount of water pumped in to restore the test pressure is measured. A pressure drop during the specified period of test may be caused by such factors as changes in temperature, absorption of water, movement of pipe under pressure and air going into solution. Accordingly it is normal to specify an allowable limit of leakage and the most commonly used permissible leakage loss is stated in BSCP 2010 as 0.1 litre/mm pipe diameter/km/24 hours/30 m head.

In cases where apparent leakage rate exceeds the acceptable limit, a systematic search for leaks must be made. Following a visual inspection on exposed sections of the pipeline normal methods of sounding are tried. If these are not successful it is usually necessary to cut and cap to isolate and test sections of the pipeline to identify the approximate position of a leak for more intensive investigation, if necessary by excavation. Another method is to inject nitrous oxide which can be detected at leaks by an instrument probing down to the pipeline at selected points.

Special procedures should be used for the testing of polyethylene systems to overcome their ductility.

The use of air pressure for testing water mains is not advocated. However, low pressure air testing can be useful for locating defective joints in waterlogged conditions.

BACKFILLING AND REINSTATEMENT

Selected soft fine material should be used for the initial backfill round the pipes and should be carried out in layers of about 150 mm consolidated thickness, each layer being well rammed and consolidated, with particular care being given to compacting the material under and round the pipe[57]. No stones, rocks or any sharp materials are to be allowed close to the pipe and no large boulders should be included in any part of the backfill. If the excavated sub-soil is not suitable for returning as backfill, imported granular material should be used. Pneumatic or other powered rammers can be used on the initial consolidation providing that their size, weight and method of operation preclude the possibility of any damage to the pipe or its protective coat or sheathing. Consolidation should be carried to a depth of about 300 mm above the top of the pipe and, in the case of pipelines across agricultural and open land, the remaining volume of the trench can be filled and consolidated by mechanical plant.

For pipelines in the public highway it is necessary to complete the backfilling of trenches according to the specifications laid down by the highway authority and this will involve graded stone and concrete backfill topped by a temporary 'tarmac' reinstatement using a cut-back bitumen binder.

Where pipes are laid at a cover exceeding 2 m, subject to the stability of the ground it may be necessary to haunch the pipe with concrete to half way up for the full width of the trench.

Surface reinstatement on agricultural and open land should as far as possible restore the surface to its former condition. This includes replacing drains, arable top soil, turf or grass seeding, restoring banks of ditches and watercourses, reinstatement of hedges, fences and walls and planting trees and shrubs, and where necessary restoring private gardens.

Pipe trenches in the public highway will have to be finally reinstated to the highway authority's specification but in most cases the highway authority prefer to carry out this work themselves on a rechargeable basis.

HYGIENE AND DISINFECTION

As distribution mainlaying proceeds, care must be taken by the pipelayers to avoid the ingress of pollutant matter into the pipe and when there is an interruption in pipelaying the open end should be temporarily sealed, preferably with a drain plug. Large trunk mains which normally have to be entered for joint making must be cleaned out and washed down with a chlorine solution as the work proceeds and as each section is cleaned and sealed off by some suitable barrier[58].

After hydraulic testing has been carried out and the final connections made, the pipeline should be flushed out and the use of plastic foam swabs to assist the removal of any debris left in the pipeline may be necessary. The pipeline is then disinfected by injecting chlorine at a dose sufficient to maintain a free chlorine residual between 20 to 30 mg/l and leaving standing for at least 16 hours. Chlorinated water must not be washed out into watercourses and the discharge from the washouts should be de-chlorinated when washing out is taking place. Water authority pollution and quality control departments should be informed when discharge into watercourses is taking place.

When washing out has taken place the pipeline is charged with supply water and following satisfactory bacteriological tests the pipeline can be put into service.

SAFE WORKING PRACTICES

The Health and Safety at Work etc Act 1974 and other health, safety and welfare regulations provide the legislative framework to promote, stimulate and encourage high standards of health and safety at work. The aim is to develop a comprehensive and intgrated system of regulations to deal with the health and safety of people at work and the protection of the public where they may be affected by the activities of people at work.

This will apply to all mainlaying activities under the following headings:

(i) The supply to, and the wearing and using by, persons working in the highway, dangerous locations and confined spaces, of appropriate protective clothing and equipment.

(ii) Provision of messing, welfare and first-aid facilities for operatives on site.

(iii) Plant, equipment and transport must be maintained in good condition and operated in a correct and safe manner.

(iv) Steps must be taken to prevent danger to persons working in trenches or excavations.

(v) Materials and spoil should be properly stacked and kept away from sides of trenches and excavations.

(vi) Measures must be taken to prevent vehicles and machines from falling into trenches and excavations or causing damage to trenches and excavations.

(vii) Traffic safety measures for roadworks must be complied with.

(viii) To prevent people from falling in trenches and excavations a pedestrian right of way must be provided, clearly fenced and protected by barriers. Highway authorities, contractors and statutory undertakers have a civil law liability to warn road users of obstructions on the highway caused by their works.

(ix) Care must be taken when excavating close to existing walls and buildings, with the necessary temporary support work being erected before excavation commences.

(x) Exact locations of existing services must be established to avoid the risk of striking gas mains, electricity and telephone cables. Reference should be made to the NJUG Publication No. 1—Recommendations on the Avoidance of Danger from Underground Electricity Cables and Publication No. 2—Cable Locating Devices. Extreme care must be taken when working close to overhead electric powerlines.

(xi) Safe procedures must be carried out when handling, stacking and laying pipes, fittings and valves, etc.

(xii) Safe procedures and the use of protective equipment must be applied when cutting pipes, and using hot lead and bitumen.

(xiii) Utmost care must be taken whilst mains are being hydraulically tested.

(xiv) The use of compressed air and explosives must be properly controlled.

(xv) Chemicals for disinfection must be handled with great care, wearing the appropriate protective clothing.

Safety equipment should be properly stored to be readily available, regularly inspected to ensure its efficiency, and operatives properly trained to observe safety regulations.

The National Joint Health and Safety Committee for the water service have issued safety advisory broadsheets relating to various activities which apply to mainlaying.

Records

Before entering onto and commencing mainlaying work in private land and highway where potential problems are apparent because of existing obstructions, or unsatisfactory structures, or surfaces, it is prudent to make records by photographing and taking appropriate measurements so that any dispute arising after the completion of mainlaying work can be dealt with on the basis of factual evidence.

Accurate and detailed records must be made during mainlaying activities so that at the completion of the work records plans can be produced and issued to operational staff.

4. PLANT AND EQUIPMENT

INTRODUCTION

There is a wide range of plant and equipment available for laying distribution, secondary and trunk pipelines. The type of plant and equipment required will depend upon the size, weight and material of pipes to be handled and laid; the route, whether through urban or rural areas; the type of surface and sub-soil; and obstructions such as rivers, railways, roads and buildings.

EXCAVATION EQUIPMENT

For distribution mains in congested urban areas, where there are known to be obstructions such as underground public utilities and local authorities' apparatus, hand excavation is undertaken, using compressor hammers to break the surface and hand tools to complete excavation of the trench. In urban areas where there is less surface and underground congestion, rotating multi-bucket trenchers can be used. This type of excavator discharges the excavated material behind the machine by a conveyor belt, which is advantageous when working in a restricted width.

For distribution and secondary mains up to 300 mm diameter laid in rural areas and in housing and industrial development in the advanced preparation stage, where there are few obstructions either above or below ground, an offset or centre post wheeled hydraulic excavator/loader is the most suitable excavator.

For the laying of pipelines across open country 'Trenchers', which consist of a wheel with a number of excavator buckets, can be used. This type of plant has the advantage of excavating a trench with a curved bottom which can reduce the need for manual 'bottoming up' of the trench bed. The machine will also, with the use of a conveyor, deposit excavated material away from the side of the trench, thus removing any overburden from the side of the trench, and the excavated material is broken up by the method of operation of the machine thus providing good backfill for the pipe surround.

Where large diameter pipelines are to be laid or deep excavation is required and a machine can be used, a large hydraulically operated excavator on tracks or a rope operated excavator (dragline) on tracks are suitable machines.

Dozers

Tracked dozers with hydraulically operated blades are mainly used on pipelines across open country, stripping and stacking top soil prior to trench excavation, backfilling the trench after initial backfill has been consolidated around pipes, and finally regrading the working area.

Dumpers

Dumpers from small to large dumptruck size are used to remove spoil from site, to import backfill material and to move pipes, fitting and materials around the site.

CRANES

The choice of crane will depend on the weight of load to be lifted, the shortest distance possible of the load from the base of the jib, or boom, and the vertical distance of the lift. Other factors are the safe bearing capacity of the ground on which the crane is sited when performing the lift, and the accessibility of the site from which the crane will be operating.

Cranes can be hydraulically or rope operated, mounted on a powered wheeled chassis for use on roads or ground which is well consolidated and reasonably level, or on tracks when ground conditions are unsuitable for wheels.

Smaller diameter pipes used for distribution and secondary mains can be handled by a hydraulic back-acting excavator with the necessary lifting tackle attached to the bucket.

COMPRESSORS

The compressor is widely used as a power unit for road breakers, consolidation tools, pipe cutters and saws, pumps, and for air-scouring pipelines. They can be mounted on a trailer unit for towing or incorporated in the chassis of a vehicle.

COMPACTION EQUIPMENT

Backfill around and immediately above pipes of all materials should be consolidated with great care using hand tampers and when appropriate air driven tampers. For consolidation of the refilled trench and when required the temporary hardcore or tarmac reinstatement, vibrating plates, heavy rollers or vibrating rollers are used.

PUMPS

The most reliable and widely used pump for dewatering trenches is the diaphragm type driven by petrol or diesel engine. An air lift pump driven by a compressor can also be used but this method is more applicable to the wellpoint de-watering system. The centrifugal pump can move much greater quantities of water than a correspondingly sized diaphragm pump but it can only be satisfactorily used when the water to be pumped is free from large suspended matter.

PIPE CUTTING EQUIPMENT

Hand operated wheel cutters and compressor or petrol engine power-operated wheel cutters, abrasive wheel saws and rotary blade cutters can be used to cut grey iron, ductile iron and steel pipe. Grey iron pipe can also be cut with hydraulic pipe cutters, using the 'squeeze and pop' principle, and steel pipe by means of burning equipment.

Asbestos cement pipe can be cut with a special rotary cutter or a power saw with an abrasive wheel. To turn down the ends of the pipe to the correct size for jointing, a pipe trimming machine or field lathe is used. Care must be taken to ensure that protective clothing and equipment is worn by operators when cutting or trimming asbestos cement pipes.

Smaller diameter uPVC and PE pipes can be cut with a hand saw but for larger diameter pipes a power-operated saw or a special rotary wheel cutter is suitable. To prepare bevelled and chamfered cut ends for making a satisfactory joint, a universal plastic bevelling tool is used.

PIPE JOINTING EQUIPMENT

Pipe jointing equipment is normally required for jointing gland and sealing ring joints on all sizes and materials of pipes.

The equipment consists of wires anchored with clamps on one pipe and a winch on the adjacent pipe which when operated will pull the pipes together, making the joint. This is specialist equipment for each particular joint and is supplied by the appropriate pipe manufacturers.

UNDER PRESSURE CONNECTIONS EQUIPMENT

This equipment is normally available for purchase or hire from the under pressure collar manufacturers and consists of a power or hand operated cutting head. The method of operation is described in Chapter 8, Section 3.

TEMPORARY SUPPORT EQUIPMENT

Timber boards, struts and wedges, steel trench sheeting, tubular scaffolding, scaffold planks, formwork and adjustable tubular struts should be used to give greater security for temporary support to trenches, excavations and poured concrete.

MAINLAYING AND SERVICELAYING VEHICLES

For mainlaying and servicelaying gangs a vehicle equipped to provide the necessary facilities for efficient mainlaying and service laying activities, including the means of carrying out the statutory regulations in respect of backfilling, reinstatement, traffic signing, welfare and safety requirements is essential.

The body of a vehicle designed for this purpose[59] must incorporate accommodation for tools, equipment and materials, facilities for heating, cooking, washing and drying. The chassis must be robust and capable of supporting this load together with accommodating a built-in-power tool source or towing a mobile power tool source.

ROAD SIGNS

Whenever mainlaying work is carried out in the highway, road signs should be used. In all cases the signing of roadworks should conform with the specifications set out in 'The Traffic Signs Manual' which is published by HMSO. There is also a legal requirement to "erect such traffic signs and barriers as may be necessary to guide and warn traffic and to prevent danger thereto" as stated in the Highways Act 1959, Highways Act 1971 and Road (Scotland) Act 1970.

PROTECTIVE CLOTHING

Protective clothing and helmets must be worn for safety reasons and for protection against adverse working conditions and inclement weather.

Care must be taken when selecting clothing and equipment so that the most appropriate and comfortable items are chosen, having in mind the type of job being carried out. Reference must be made to the Health and Safety at Work Act and the Health and Safety Executive Guidelines for use of protective clothing when carrying out any work in hazardous conditions.

5. MAINLAYING—CONTRACT

INTRODUCTION

A mainlaying contractor is usually employed for large diameter trunk and secondary mains although in some circumstances where there is a large amount of work, such as housing site development, a contractor is sometimes used for small diameter distribution mains.

Contracts need to be obtained for the supply of pipes, particularly for fabricated steel, and other ancillary activities such as permanent reinstatement and cathodic protection. The reconditioning of existing water mains (Chapter 10) normally requires a contract based upon the format used for a distribution mainlaying contract[28].

PREPARATION OF CONTRACT DOCUMENTS

The mainlaying contract documents will comprise:

(1) Instructions for Contractors Tendering;
(2) Conditions of Contract;
(3) Specification[60];
(4) Bill of Quantities;
(5) Drawings;
(6) Schedule of Rates and Prices;
(7) Form of Tender[61].

Before preparing the contract documents it is necessary to plan and survey on the ground the best possible route for the distribution, secondary or trunk main from which plans, and where necessary, sections are produced and the proposed line and level of the pipelines are established. At the same time obstructions such as railways, rivers and classified roads are detailed on the plan and wayleaves, easements, rights of access, and material storage areas identified, together with any other features likely to involve the contractor in carrying out the work. For trunk and secondary mains additional drawings detailing pipework connections, supporting structures, washouts and sluice valves are required.

The plans, design data and drawings provide the scope, size and details of the distribution mains, secondary or trunk main schemes on which to prepare the Specification, Bills of Quantities and Schedule of Rates and Prices. The basis of the Specification is contained in the National Water Council's publication "Civil Engineering Specification for the Water Industry", the basis for the Bills of Quantities can be obtained from the Institution of Civil Engineers' publication "Civil Engineering Standard Method of Measurement" and Schedules of Rates and Prices are set out in the "Federation of Civil Engineering Contractors' Schedules of Dayworks Carried out Incidental to Contact Work".

TENDERING AND CONTRACT LETTING PROCEDURE

The contract documents are normally accompanied by Instructions to Tenderers, which state inter alia:

(a) Tenders must remain open for acceptance for a specified period.
(b) Tenders must be signed together with completed Bills of Quantities and Schedules based upon the design and specification in the tender documents.
(c) The employing organization does not bind itself to accept the lowest tender or pay any expenses incurred by the tenderer.
(d) The tenderer will not disclose any information appertaining to his tender to any other party.
(e) The last date and time for the receipt of tenders.

The conditions appertaining to a contract are the ICE Conditions of Contract (Fifth Edition) 1973 (Revised January 1979).

It is usual to invite tenders from at least six contractors and these can be chosen from a standing list of suitable contractors who have been chosen for their particular expertise and competence or from a select list of contractors who have replied to an advertisement. Tenders returned by the return date should be opened by no less than two persons and the amount of the tender and other relevant information entered into a register and witnessed.

Opened tenders must be checked arithmetically and examined for sufficiency of rates and compliance with the Instructions to Tenderers. They must then be subject to a detailed appraisal to ensure that the tender recommended for acceptance is the most favourable in all circumstances.

The documents for the accepted tender are bound into a contract which is signed and sealed by the contractor and the employer and at this time a date is fixed to commence the works.

CONTRACTOR'S PROGRAMME

It is important to ensure that the contractor thoroughly understands the employer's requirements and has planned the mainlaying work to achieve construction to the specification and by a required completion date. Distribution mains projects can generally be programmed on a bar chart but for larger mains, particularly through urban areas where timing of the operations is essential to maintain access, routes, traffic control and maintenance of public utilities, a comprehensive network programme which takes into account these inter-related factors is needed.

The employer is usually responsible for:

(i) Obtaining easements, wayleaves, access routes and land for storage of pipes and materials.

(ii) Arrangements with public utilities when working in proximity, crossing or needing to divert their apparatus.

(iii) Arrangements with highway authorities for work in the public highway, British Rail for railway crossings and water authorities for watercourse crossings.

(iv) Ordering and arranging for delivery of pipes, specials and apparatus needed for the mainlaying.

These activities must be pre-planned and carried out by the employer in advance of acceptance of a tender ready to feed into the successful contractor's programme.

ORGANIZATION OF WORK

At the commencement of the contract the contractor's first task is to ensure that access routes, working areas, pipe and materials storage areas, and areas for site offices are negotiated and acquired well ahead of the mainlaying work, and are well defined and where necessary fenced. Setting out the work is normally the responsibility of the contractor but it is absolutely vital that the employer's representative on site, who is normally designated the Resident Engineer, ensures that it is correct by personally checking it.

Before commencing excavation and mainlaying the contractor must plan the disposition of the pipes and specials. For distribution mains the small diameter and, in the case of uPVC and PE, lightweight pipes do not present a great problem as they can be stored in small areas and can be handled without the use of lifting plant.

However, careful planning is required with the much larger diameter pipes used for trunk mains. When laying across open country a fenced working width is defined which accommodates the pipe trench itself, a running track for the excavation and lifting plant to operate, two widths for storing topsoil and subsoil from the trench and a space to "string out" the pipes along the route. Trunk mains in urban areas require very special organization for the stacking and handling of pipes as there is rarely space along the route of the main to "string out" the pipes and every pipe and special almost always has to be brought to the trench for laying from the nearest possible storage area which may be some distance away.

SUPERVISING WORK

While overall supervision of the contract by the employer is necessary during the stage when the contractor is taking possession of the site, setting up his organization and laying out the pipes and materials, continuous and detailed supervision is necessary when work commences on pipelaying.

The employer's Resident Engineer must first ensure that the working arrangements, practices and procedures used by the contractor are of the best and are in accordance with the Health and Safety at Work etc Act 1974.

The work carried out must comply with the contract drawings and any other drawings subsequently issued, must be strictly in accordance with the specification and must be of the highest possible quality standard. The burden of ensuring that the standard is maintained falls upon the Resident Engineer, who must apply rigid procedures to achieve this objective. In this respect the maintenance of comprehensive records of events in a diary form and the need to issue in writing and drawings all instructions and variations to the work are essential functions of the Resident Engineer's role.

The Resident Engineer must perform the role of a co-ordinator between the contractor and landowners and tenants affected by the mainlaying operations; he must liaise with public utilities, local authorities, British Rail and water authorities whose apparatus and installations are affected, and with the water undertaking who will probably be making the connections between the existing water mains system and the new water mains.

MEASUREMENTS AND CERTIFICATES

It is usual for arrangements to be included in the contract for payments on account and these normally take the form of interim certificates payable monthly. The Resident Engineer is responsible for agreeing with the contractor the measurement of work carried out and, before issuing a certificate for payment, will have to be satisfied that the work has all been done in accordance with the contract and any variations that may have been ordered. Where nominated sub-contractors and suppliers of materials and plant are involved the Resident Engineer must also be satisfied at the same time that all such sub-contractors and suppliers have been paid.

At all appropriate stages of the work the Resident Engineer must ensure that accurate measurements in line and level are made and recorded so that at the completion of the work records and plans can be produced.

CLAIMS AND DISPUTES

Where extras or variations have been ordered by the Resident Engineer, the contractor can recover payment only if he can show that the Resident Engineer was authorized by the employer to give the orders or that the employers held him out as having such authority. Therefore it is important to both parties that any extras and variations are identified, agreed, and authorized at the time of taking place.

However, it often happens that the contractor must carry out work necessary for the furtherance of the contract which is not part of the contract or suffers delays which he believes are not his fault and these incidents usually result in a claim. It is important that the Resident Engineer anticipates any possible claim of this nature and ensures that his records of incidents are comprehensive and accurate so that he has the factual evidence to discuss the nature and validity of any claim.

Should agreement on claims not be reached the matter is declared a dispute and contracts usually have a clause to the effect that a dispute shall be referred to arbitration. This is a course to be avoided if at all possible and when drafting a contract it is well to keep in mind that disputes in mainlaying work mostly arise from workmanship and materials, access to site and easements, delays caused by unidentified underground obstructions, by constraints when working in urban areas and by conditions of maintaining water supplies and hygiene imposed by the water undertaking when connecting into the existing distribution system.

All parties to a contract should therefore look to it that the contract is properly prepared and understood and that every effort is made to obtain mutual understanding in its execution.

6. MAINLAYING—DIRECT LABOUR

INTRODUCTION

Distribution mains are usually laid by a direct labour force employed by a water undertaking although in some circumstances, when a direct labour mainlaying team experienced in laying large diameter pipes and making special connections is available, they will lay trunk and secondary mains.

Parts of Section 5 are applicable but require the employer's engineer to carry out the activities of programming and organization in place of the contractor.

ORGANIZATION OF DIRECT LABOUR

The Third Schedule of the Water Act 1945 provides the power under which a water undertaking may lay mains, including the breaking open of streets, which is also governed by PUSWA. Responsibility for sufficiency and purity of supply is also covered by the Third Schedule and, whilst satisfying consumers in these matters, a water undertaking must ensure that its direct labour force performs in the most diligent and economical manner. Efforts in achieving these two objectives can sometimes lead to conflict, in so far as the most economical approach to mainlaying and associated maintenance may not always provide an equally satisfactory service. Such conflicts are among the major problems in controlling a direct labour force.

Organization of labour will depend upon the size of area covered and the magnitude of the associated workload. It may prove necessary to sectionalise a labour force and operate from a number of area depots to minimise unproductive travel time. Supervisory staffing levels will need to be adequate, ensuring sufficient time is available for pre-requisitioning of materials, equipment and plant, negotiating wayleaves, easement and accommodation, co-ordinating arrangements with public utilities, local authorities, British Rail and water authorities, and for pre-works site inspections, site supervision administrative duties, cost control and preparation of records.

The number of operatives employed in a mainlaying gang will relate to the size and type of pipe being laid, but for the majority of work involving small diameter distribution mains, a gang comprising a jointer, banksman and excavator driver with machine would normally suffice, supplemented by a lorry and driver who would be shared by a number of gangs when required. In certain cases the gang size could be reduced to two men, comprising the jointer and excavator driver with machine.

In contrast to the mode of operation prior to the early 1970s, when large housing sites were being developed, distribution mainlaying work now follows a pattern of many smaller jobs of up to about 100 m length. This calls for a greater emphasis on gang mobility rather than fixed site accommodation; consequently, detailed in-works planning is crucial to an efficient and economic job.

Large diameter trunk and secondary mains require much larger gangs and works planning must be based upon 'fixed site accommodation'.

Direct labour used for distribution, secondary and trunk mainlaying must always be in competition with contract labour. Therefore, not only should the quality of direct labour work be at the highest standard, but it must be carried out at a cost which will be comparable with a contract price.

ORGANIZATION OF VEHICLES, PLANT, EQUIPMENT AND MATERIALS

To obtain maximum flexibility some water undertakings aim for multi-functional gang units capable of carrying out distribution mainlaying, servicelaying and associated maintenance studies. This requires the provision of mobile workshops capable of accommodating all small tools, plant, equipment and fittings relevant to mainlaying and service laying, with pipes and other heavy materials still delivered by lorry (see Section 4). The type of materials carried on vehicles must take account of the range of gang duties carried out and the stock level should in turn reflect the economic balance between frequency of stores visits, vehicle capacity and the size of lorry fleet generally supporting gang activities.

The range of light plant and tools carried on gang vehicles tends to be similar for mainlaying and servicelaying activities with roadbreaking, ramming and pumping plant forming the base and being either petrol or compressed-air driven, with many undertakings preferring the use of integral rather than mobile compressors. Vehicles with demountable bodies are preferred by some; an arrangement under which vehicle bodies are transferred to fleet-spare chassis when servicing is due, thereby eliminating the need for transferring kit and materials to spare vehicles.

It is important to adopt accountability systems for items of plant and equipment and transport to identify quickly 'rogue' performing items and mistreatment by operatives so as to ensure that lost time due to plant and transport breakdown is kept to a minimum. In view of the frequent introduction of new equipment on to the market, it is important to identify a particular officer with the responsibility for development and associated training with the object of undertaking trials on newly marketed kit and, if successful, then to ensure operatives are trained in its proper use.

Costs of operating the water undertaking's vehicles and plant should be regularly monitored to ensure that they remain competitive with the cost of hired vehicles and plant.

METHODS AND PROCEDURES IN CARRYING OUT WORK

The adoption of standing orders for mainlaying methods and procedures is important when employing a relatively large direct labour force, to ensure that the best workmanship and the most economical and safe approach prevails when carrying out work. A high standard of excavation and temporary support, pipelaying and bedding, selective backfilling, compaction, temporary reinstatements, and roadsigning, is required. Particular attention to pipe testing and disinfection are also important aspects relating to mainlaying.

It is equally important that safe systems of work are clearly laid down for particular and potentially hazardous operations in an effort to keep accidents to a minimum and ensure compliance with safety legislation.

PRODUCTIVITY PAYMENT SCHEMES

Water undertakings have now adopted the Water Industry Productivity Payment Schemes (WIPPS) to evaluate the performance and working methods of operatives and to apply their productivity payment to an identified workload. A productivity scheme specification usually consists of two parts, the first part being general conditions, setting out the principles of applying standard times, allowances, recording and checking work, proportion of incentive bonus payments, calculation of bonus and frequency of payment, and the requirements for equality of work, safety and care of equipment and tools.

The second part of the specification deals with the activity and, in the case of a productivity payment scheme relating to mainlaying operatives, defines the operatives involved, describes the range of work, determines the method of work and the equipment involved, and the duties of the operatives covered by the specification. A scheme for mainlaying operatives is usually a direct type with the productivity payment based on the individual performance of each operative arrived at by applying the allowances for jobs (which standard times are already timed and calculated by Work Study Assistants) to the time sheets completed by the operatives which show the details of work done, travel time, lost time and attendance hours. The specification also sets out an appropriate range of levels of performance in relation to productivity payments as a percentage of the basic rate of pay and all the data acquired through the procedures in this specification enable amounts of productivity payments for both unmeasured and measured work to be calculated[62].

MONITORING QUALITY AND COST CONTROL

Quality of work relies largely on the degree of supervision and in this respect it is vital to ensure that the supervisors responsible for a job plan, direct and monitor every aspect of the operatives' tasks.

Budgetary control and financial monitoring form part of the accountability data, which is also the responsibility of operational supervision. Site diaries for each individual scheme must be maintained with a view to accounting for job content and subsequent unit cost. Such data are then assessed with that from other jobs as a basis for compiling estimates for future work.

WORKFORCE NEGOTIATIONS

Close consultation between the water undertaking's management and the trade union officials and shop stewards is essential at both local and regional level.

Problems at local level usually concern working practices, productivity payment schemes, welfare conditions, interpretation of nationally agreed rules on wages and conditions of service, and on occasions individuals' personal problems. It is always prudent to get all parties in a dispute together quickly and resolve it at local level as soon as possible.

When agreement on a dispute at local level fails it is essential to activate the procedures for a Regional Joint Industrial Council hearing immediately because any delays at this stage or at local level will be to the detriment of the smooth operation of a mainlaying job.

7. REFERENCES

1. University of Salford 1969 "Proceedings, 2nd Symposium on Pipeline Engineering in Waterworks Practice".
2. Davies, G. 1968 *J. IWE*, 22, 281, Trunk pipeline selection—what size and when?
3. Pipe Lines Act 1962, HMSO, London.
4. Water Research Association 1964 "Location of buried non-metallic water pipes and mains".
5. The Institution of Water Engineers and Scientists 1979 Water Practice Manuals, Book 1, "The structure and management of the British water industry".
6. North West Water Authority 1977 "Code of Practice to be employed in the construction of pipelines in agricultural land".
7. Severn-Trent Water Authority/National Farmers' Union/Country Landowners' Association 1981 "Code of Practice for burying pipelines".
8. Trott, J. J. and Gaunt, J. 1976 "Experimental pipelines under a major road: performance during and after road construction", Department of the Environment, Transport and Road Research Laboratory, Report 692.
9. Stephenson, D. 1976 "Pipeline design for water engineers", Elsevier, Amsterdam.
10. Stephenson, D. 1981 "Pipeline design for water engineers, 2nd edition", Elsevier, Amsterdam.
11. Serpell, C. A. 1949 *J. IWE*, 3, 17, The laying of a steel pipeline.
12. Ramsey, H. G. 1949 *J. IWE*, 3, 285, The laying of a large steel main.
13. White, W. F. 1950; *J. IWE*, 4, 13, Vyrnwy aqueduct: fourth instalment pipeline.
14. Fraser, D. D. 1952 *J. IWE*, 6, 210, The construction of the Butterbridge diversion aqueducts, Loch Sloy hydroelectric project.
15. Atkinson, A. 1955 *J. IWE*, 9, 385, Thirlmere aqueduct.
16. Atkinson, A. 1955 *J. IWE*, 9, 392, Haweswater aqueduct.
17. Reynolds, K. J. and Wilson, A. C. 1959 *J. IWE*, 13, 405, The design and construction of a 36 in. diameter aqueduct with particular reference to adverse ground conditions.
18. Willis, J. S. M. 1962 *J. IWE*, 16, 85, Design of the Yorkshire Derwent aqueduct.
19. Ash, R. V. 1966 *J. IWE*, 20, 435, The Great Eau scheme: North-East Lincolnshire Water Board.
20. Hammond, T. H. and Winder, A. J. 1967 *J. IWE*, 21, 15, Problems affecting the design and construction of the Great Ouse water supply scheme.
21. Roberts, K. F. and Thomas, E. H. 1967 *J. IWE*, 21, 155, Laying and maintaining prestressed concrete pipelines.
22. Saxton, K. J. H. 1970 *J. IWE*, 24, 397, Operation of the Grafham Water scheme (Great Ouse Water Authority).
23. Carlyle, W. J. and Owen, R. C. 1973 *J. IWE*, 27, 287, The river Towy scheme for the West Glamorgan Water Board.
24. Titford, A. R. and Reader, R. A. 1974 *J. IWE*, 28, 309, The design and construction of the river Ancholme scheme for the North Lindsay Water Board.
25. Greeves, J. A. de M. and Dunlop, D. S. 1974 *J. IWE*, 28, 343, The Lough Fingrean water scheme.
26. Medley, P. R. and Eccles, P. G. 1976 *J. IWES*, 30, 412, The Ambergate intake and pumping station.
27. Scivier, J. B. and Riley, R. W. 1977 *J. IWES*, 31, 389, Water supply scheme in Iran with 1 100 m pumping head.
28. Pipelines Industry Guild 1983 "Pipelines, design, construction and operation".
29. Ashton, R. P. and Randall, K. V. 1960 *J. IWE*, 14, 194, Pipe-bridge crossing of the river Teme at Graham's Cot.
30. Godden, H. C. 1970 *J. IWE*, 24, 209, The design and construction of the twin 24 in. water main crossings of Tinsley Viaduct (Sheffield Water Undertaking).
31. Stevenson, G. 1978 *J. IWES*, 32, 141, The laying of 24 in. trunk mains over the Erskine Bridge.
32. Anon 1955 *J. IWE*, 9, 424, The Gunthorpe pipe bridge.
33. Winter, T. S. R. 1960 *J. IWE*, 14, 327, Problems in the design and construction of a large scheme of capital works.
34. Whitehead, R. C. 1958 *J. IWE*, 12, 247, Birmingham waterworks—some recent developments.
35. Anon 1957 *J. IWE*, 11, 492, Wedge-block tunnel lining (Metropolitan Water Board).
36. Cuthbert, E. W. and Wood, F. 1962 *Proc. ICE*, 257, The Thames-Lee tunnel water main.
37. Cooley, P. 1982 *J. IWES*, 36, 9, Wedge-block tunnels in water supply.
38. Baty, R. J. 1982 *J. IWES*, 36, 97, Redevelopment of aqueduct crossing of Manchester Ship Canal and river Mersey.
39. Knill, M. W. 1965 *J. IWE*, 19, 489, 60 in. pipe crossings under the river Weaver and the Weaver Navigation.
40. Seddon, H. 1948 *J. IWE*, 2, 187, The laying of a dual pipeline across the river Dee.
41. Ruffle, N. J. and Stoddart, R. C. 1963 *J. IWE*, 17, 315, A 24 in. diameter pipe crossing of the river Wear at Hylton.

42. Dore, S. M. 1952 *J. IWE*, 6, 331, An inverted syphon for the Assabet river crossing of the Wachusett aqueduct.
43. Spencer, K. A. 1956 *J. IWE*, 10, 51, The water engineer and cathodic protection.
44. Spencer, P. G. 1960 *J. IWE*, 14, 137, Maintenance of steel mains and some applications of cathodic protection.
45. Institution of Water Engineers 1973 *J. IWE*, 27, 125, Experience with cathodic protection of mains: report of Research Panel No. 13.
46. British Gas 1979 "Code of Practice for cathodic protection of buried steel pipework".
47. Water Industry Productivity Manual 1982 "Standard excavation and trench sizes for water supply and distribution activities".
48. Trott, J. J. and Gaunt, J. 1972 "Experimental work on large steel pipeline at Kirtling", Department of the Environment, Transport and Road Research Laboratory, Report LP.472.
49. Burgess, D. E. 1973 *J. IWE*, 27, 365, The design, planning and construction of a 45 in. diameter water main across a congested area of West Bromwich.
50. Concrete Pipe Association 1975 "Jacking concrete pipes", Technical Bulletin No. 5.
51. Pipe Jacking Association 1981 "Guide to pipejacking design".
52. Shurlock, S. H. 1982 *J. IWES*, 36, 151, Problems in tunnelling by pipe jacking at Tilehurst.
53. Davies, D. G. 1959 *J. IWE*, 13, 391, PVC pipelines in Cheshire.
54. The Institution of Water Engineers 1967 *J. IWE*, 21, 586, Main-laying techniques for mains approximately 18″ diameter and over, final report of Research Panel No. 3.
55. Salter, R. J. 1958 *J. IWE*, 12, 485, Pipelines through waterlogged ground.
56. Green, B. M. 1974 *J. IWE*, 28, 136, Testing of pipelines.
57. National Water Council/Department of the Environment, Standing Committee on Sewers and Water Mains 1980 "Granular bedding materials for buried pipelines".
58. Taylor, E. W. and Whiskin, L. C. 1951 *J. IWE*, 5, 219, The disinfection of water mains after laying and carrying out repairs.
59. McAllister, T. J. 1983 *J. IWES*, 37, 133, The development of a mainlaying and servicelaying vehicle.
60. National Water Council 1978 "Civil engineering specification for the water industry".
61. Institution of Civil Engineers 1983 "Guidance on the preparation, submission and consideration of tenders for civil engineering contracts recommended for use in the United Kingdom".
62. Close, W. G. 1957 *J. IWE*, 11, 403, Aspects of work study in relation to main laying.

APPENDIX A: SUGGESTED HEADS OF TERMS FOR PIPELINE EASEMENTS

The following items are those normally sought in an easement agreement for a pipeline:

Easement rights required:

(1) A right to construct, maintain, use, inspect, and operate aqueducts, pipes, valves, meters, hydrants, telemetry outstations, automatic control equipment, etc, and to have and enjoy a flow or passage of water.

(2) A right to reconstruct, renew, repair, relay, and cleanse the same.

(3) A right to enter and use additional land for working space. (It is normal to acquire a full width working area and this right is only required in particular circumstances).

(4) A right of way over access routes to the easement, fittings, etc.

(5) A right of way so far as the grantor may grant them over occupation roads.

(6) A right to enter and be upon the easement lands for the purpose of exercising the various rights.

(7) A right to erect temporary fences.

(8) A right to erect and maintain gates, stiles, and markers.

(9) A right to widen, deepen, and re-align watercourses (as required for washouts).

(10) A right to tip on land (to bring the level up to that of the surrounding land to provide adequate cover in particular cases).

(11) A right to appropriate or carry away spoil.

(12) A right to improve access routes to key points which require regular visits.

The grantor to covenant:

(a) Not to use the easement land for any purpose which would endanger the pipes, etc, or interfere with the flow of water.

(b) Not to plant any tree or cause or permit any development on or across the easement.

(c) Not to place on or in the easement any fences, cables, drains, etc. at an angle of 45° or less with centre line.

(d) Not to alter the level of the easement more than 150 mm downwards or 450 mm upwards or in any way so as to endanger the pipes, etc.

(e) Not to withdraw support from the pipes, etc.

The undertakers to covenant:

(i) To exercise the rights so as to cause as little damage as reasonably possible.

(ii) To maintain communications, accesses, etc.

(iii) To pay compensation to the grantor or tenants for all damage done in the exercise of the rights.

(iv) To restore surfaces as far as possible to the original levels and conditions.

(v) To restore all topsoil as far as possible in the position from which it was removed.

(vi) To make good all fences, roads, and drainage.

(vii) Not to fell trees unless reasonably necessary.

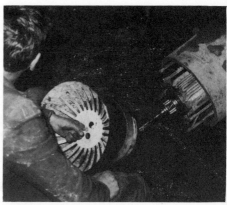
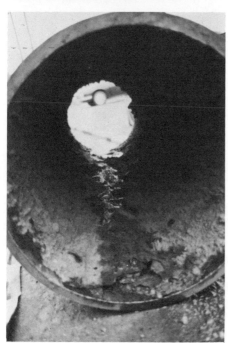

Relining of water mains

(*top left*) **Mains scraping device**
(*top right*) **Relining head and trowel**
(*Severn-Trent Water Authority*)

(*bottom left*) **Main before scraping**
(*bottom right*) **Main after relining with concrete**
(*South Staffordshire Waterworks Company*)

Chapter 10

MAINTENANCE OF WATER MAINS

1. THE PROBLEMS

INTRODUCTION

THIS chapter covers the maintenance problems associated with a deteriorating system. In the UK the distribution system is made predominantly from cast iron mains of small diameter[1], as shown in Tables 10.I and 10.II.

TABLE 10.I. Proportion by Length of Mains by Diameter

Diameter (mm)	Per cent
50–150	81.9
151–300	11.3
301–600	5.3
601 and above	1.5

TABLE 10.II. Proportion by Length of Mains by Material

Material	Per cent
Cast iron	85
Steel, AC, Concrete	10
uPVC	5

Most of these iron water mains received only a thin coating of coal tar or bituminous material immediately after manufacture. Taking the tables together, about 70 per cent of the UK distribution system is 150 mm or smaller in diameter and made from cast iron with a thin lining of less than 0.1 mm. The deterioration of this predominantly cast iron system leads to a range of problems including:

(1) Reduction in water quality.
(2) Reduction in carrying capacity leading to low flows and pressure.
(3) An increase in bursts.
(4) An increased leakage level.

WATER QUALITY

The water quality within a distribution system can deteriorate markedly as the water progresses from the treatment works to the consumer. Deterioration is usually revealed by changes in the aesthetic water quality but the hygienic quality of the water may also suffer.

Dirty or discoloured water can occur for several reasons, a number of which are interrelated. These include the corrosion of iron mains, poor or insufficient water treatment, biological growth within the main or disturbance of existing deposits by the replacement of a traditional supply with one of very different composition.

Similarly a taste or odour problem may originate from the raw water source, the treatment works, the pipe network or the domestic plumbing. If the water leaving the treatment works has a high chlorine demand or the mains within the distribution system are corroded, then residual disinfectant concentrations at the extremities of the system may be low or non-existent. The reduced disinfectant level means that the water and the distribution system are unprotected against any bacterial contamination that occurs, for example from bursts or repairs, unless further careful disinfection precautions are taken.

Aquatic animals enter a distribution system primarily through the treatment works. They can then establish breeding populations within the distribution system. When the visible species occur at a consumer's tap they lead to consumer complaints.

Pressure

If an unprotected iron main carries a corrosive water then corrosion products may build up within that main. This will increase the hydraulic roughness and reduce the cross sectional area which will reduce the carrying capacity of that main.

Other deposits such as microbial slimes also can cause a drastic reduction in the carrying capacity of the main, far greater than that expected from a reduction in diameter alone[2].

A reduction in carrying capacity leads to a subsequent reduction in pressure during periods of high demand. This loss in pressure can lead to consumer complaints.

Bursts and Leakage

Mechanical failure of pipes occurs when there is insufficient strength to withstand the internal or external forces applied to them. A loss of strength can be caused by corrosion of iron or steel, by leaching of cement from an asbestos cement pipe, or by crack growth in uPVC resulting from stress concentrations or cyclic stress. Failure may also be caused by an increase in the load applied to the pipe resulting from changes in traffic patterns, ground movement or pressure surges.

The deterioration of joints can lead to increased leakage. The corrosion of metals other than cast iron can also lead to leakage from, for example, ferrules and communication pipes.

Deterioration of Fittings

The fittings on a distribution system are also prone to deterioration. Many valves and hydrants are left unoperated for a number of years, become unserviceable and also may become "lost" due to road resurfacing.

Debris within the distribution system may have an adverse effect on the various fittings used. Hydrants, particularly those on branches off the main, can become heavily encrusted leading to a major reduction in flow from them.

Service Reservoirs

The structural deterioration of service reservoirs may cause several problems. Leakage may occur because of cracks in the walls and floors. Water and air-borne contamination can gain access via cracks in the roof, wall and floors and by broken covers or vents. Corrosion can make iron work such as steps and gantries hazardous or affect the performance of valves and level indicators.

2. THE DELETERIOUS PROCESSES

CORROSION

Introduction

Metallic corrosion in water is a chemical reaction accompanied by the passage of an electric current. This is illustrated for iron in Fig. 10.1. A metal ion leaves the site on the metal surface (known as the anodic site) and enters the water, leaving behind excess electrons which migrate to nearby cathodic sites where they are used by a balancing reaction, which in natural waters is usually the reduction of oxygen (reaction 2). Below pH 6 or when oxygen is absent an alternative cathodic reaction is the reduction of hydrogen ions to hydrogen. In anaerobic environments, such as beneath deposits and in soils, sulphate reducing bacteria can help drive the cathodic reaction by reducing sulphate to sulphide (reaction 3).

When dissimilar metals are coupled together the cathodic reaction tends to become localised on the less reactive metal, the anodic on the more reactive. Preferential attack of the latter occurs and this is termed galvanic corrosion. The extent to which galvanic corrosion becomes a problem depends on the magnitude of the difference in potentials between the metals, their relative surface areas and the composition of the water in contact with the metals.

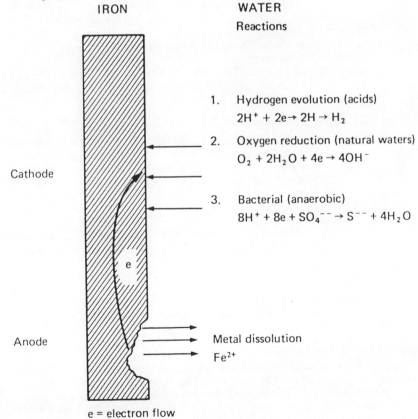

IRON   WATER

Reactions

1. Hydrogen evolution (acids)
$$2H^+ + 2e \rightarrow 2H \rightarrow H_2$$

2. Oxygen reduction (natural waters)
$$O_2 + 2H_2O + 4e \rightarrow 4OH^-$$

3. Bacterial (anaerobic)
$$8H^+ + 8e + SO_4^{--} \rightarrow S^{--} + 4H_2O$$

Cathode

Anode — Metal dissolution Fe^{2+}

e = electron flow

Fig. 10.1. Reactions on the metal surface in a simple corrosion cell

Internal Corrosion of Iron Mains

Internal corrosion occurs when a water aggressive to the metal is in direct contact with the metal. Several factors affect the rate at which the metal corrodes[3a]:

(a) *Internal pipe surface*

The casting skin of iron oxides, silicates and alumino-silicates will form a barrier against corrosion of the underlying metal. However, this skin is brittle and cracked and is usually abraded prior to the application of a lining material. These cracks and abraded areas are susceptible to corrosion.

(b) *The lining material*

Coal tar is the most common lining found in iron mains and is generally very thin (about 0.1 mm) giving only temporary protection in an aggressive water supply. In contrast, cement mortar linings are very durable and prevent internal corrosion over many years.

(c) *Water composition*

The corrosivity of a water supply towards cast iron largely depends on its chemical composition. The details of this relationship are not well understood and the following generalisations are based on the few studies of iron corrosion performed in water of potable quality:

(i) Increasing the alkalinity or hardness of the water decreases its corrosivity towards cast iron. This is true irrespective of the value of the Langelier Index.

(ii) Increasing the concentration of chloride or sulphate generally increases the corrosivity of supplies.

(iii) Microbial activity will occur within sediments and slimes in the pipe. This activity reduces the oxygen level and this stimulates localised corrosion under deposits.

External Corrosion of Iron Mains

External corrosion of iron mains also occurs by an aqueous electrochemical mechanism as described earlier. Variations in soil water content and soil type at different points on the main will lead to the formation of anodic and cathodic sites along the length of the main and localised corrosion will take place.

External microbiological attack of iron mains can take place under anaerobic conditions, for example in permanently waterlogged soils. This is due to the action of sulphate reducing bacteria.

The soil resistivity is generally acknowledged to be the most reliable indicator of the corrosivity of soils towards iron mains. Soils with resistivities less than 30 ohm.m are potentially corrosive towards cast iron.

Moisture content and soil resistivity are inevitably interrelated, so the resistivity (and hence the corrosivity) of the soil may exhibit seasonal variations due to changes in water table level. Thus, soil resistivity determinations carried out on a single occasion may not necessarily identify all of the potentially corrosive areas along the line of a main.

Corrosion of Non-ferrous Metals

Each of the non-ferrous metals/alloys used in distribution systems can suffer deterioration under certain circumstances. Hot-stamped brass will dezincify in waters with a high chloride-carbonate hardness ratio and fittings may become blocked with the corrosion product[4,5] at high pH. Copper can suffer from a general form of corrosion, cuprosolvency, which leads to blue or green stains on sinks and baths. It also suffers from at least two types of pitting corrosion. Type 1, which occurs in cold water systems, is associated with the presence of carbon film in the tubes[6]. Type 2 is much less common and occurs in hot water systems supplied with soft acidic waters high in manganese[7].

General corrosion of galvanised iron surfaces can occur in low pH waters even where they have significant hardness levels[8]. In the presence of dissolved copper the attack takes the form of severe pitting[7]. Corrosion at soldered joints rarely causes sufficient deterioration to cause leakage. However, significant contamination by lead can arise if solder is exposed in the bore of the tube[8].

DETERIORATION OF NON-METALLIC MATERIALS

About 85 per cent of distribution pipework in the UK is cast iron; asbestos cement and uPVC make up a large proportion of the remaining 15 per cent. uPVC and asbestos cement deteriorate in different ways to cast iron.

uPVC pipes can fail from fatigue caused by rapid pressure oscillations or under normal gravity head conditions. The presence of scratches on the inside surface, deep notches on the outer surface of the pipe or foreign bodies within the pipe wall can cause high stress areas within the pipe. These may be accentuated by external point loads. The pipe may subsequently fail at these high stress points[9,10].

Asbestos cement pipe is fabricated from asbestos fibres and ordinary Portland cement. If these pipes are used for conveying waters of a negative Langelier Index the lime may be leached from the cement matrix leading to a weakened pipe.

Asbestos cement pipework is also at risk from external attack in aggressive soils, particularly those with a low pH and/or high sulphate contents.

MECHANICAL FAILURE OF CAST IRON PIPES

The failures commonly found in cast iron pipes are of three main types:

(1) circumferential fractures;
(2) longitudinal fractures; and
(3) holes.

Circumferential fractures are a common form of failure in small diameter pipes (100 mm and less) and are generally attributed to beam loading. A study[11] of pipe failures has shown that as the diameter decreases the circumferential failure rate increases. This reflects the lower bending strength of small diameter pipes.

The pipe wall stresses that cause circumferential fractures generally arise as a result of two main processes. These are deformation of the pipe, causing bending moments and longitudinal forces, and corrosion of the pipe causing loss of strength.

Ground movements and uneven loading are the chief factors causing pipe deformation. They arise from:

(a) consolidation and settlement of the trench backfill and bedding;
(b) temperature and moisture changes in the soil;
(c) subsidence due to the collapse of old mine workings or unstable geological conditions;
(d) adjacent excavations;
(e) traffic loading;
(f) ground shock waves due to blasting, pile driving, etc; and
(g) direct impact by diggers, etc.

These factors are discussed in detail elsewhere[12].

Unprotected cast iron pipes in aggressive environments lose strength with time due to corrosion. This may take the form of external attack in aggressive soils or internal attack in aggressive waters. Both forms weaken a pipe and this can lead to failure when the imposed load is greater than the remaining strength of the pipe.

Holes occur where local corrosion attack has completely penetrated the pipe wall. External forces weaken the remaining plug of graphitised material until it is finally dislodged by the internal water pressure, leaving a hole.

Longitudinal fractures in small diameter pipes are generally associated with preferential corrosion damage along a longitudinal section of the pipe. With larger diameter pipes, ground loading may produce tensile hoop stresses that contribute to longitudinal fractures.

FORMATION OF DEPOSITS

Deposits in distribution systems may be formed by precipitation, microbiological activity and corrosion[3b]. Progressive water sampling through the distribution system has revealed decreases in residual coagulant, algae, manganese, dissolved organic matter and silica[13,14]. Similar materials have been found in sediments and the easily disturbed surface layers in pipes and tubercle surfaces. This is due to the precipitation of corrosion products and the carry-over from inefficient treatment works. Corrosion products in iron mains are usually in the form of tubercles. These generally have the same structure and similar composition to that illustrated in Fig. 10.2.

MICROBIOLOGICAL AFTERGROWTHS

Treated water will undergo some changes in its microbiological properties[13,14,3c] on passing through a distribution system; these changes can be associated with the following effects:

(i) Formation of slime resulting in increased frictional losses[2].
(ii) Changes in the chemical quality of the conveyed water[14].
(iii) Corrosion of cast iron pipes[14,3a].
(iv) Formation of tastes and odours[3d].
(v) Alteration of the form of particulate matter[15].
(vi) Destabilisation of adhesive deposits and dissolution of iron corrosion products under anaerobic conditions.
(vii) Acting as a food source for animals[33].
(viii) Deterioration of materials of construction[16].

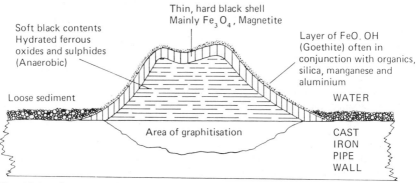

Fig. 10.2.   Cross-section of a typical corrosion tubercle and loose sediment in a cast iron pipe

Microbial activity can be a major factor in the deterioration of water quality in distribution in supplies derived from lowland sources. Such supplies usually exhibit the following characteristics[3c].

(1) The plate count (22°C/7 day, YEA) exceeds 10^3 CFU/ml.
(2) The TOC after treatment is 2.0 mg/l or above and falls in distribution by 0.5 mg/l or more.
(3) The mean depletion of dissolved oxygen in distribution exceeds 15 per cent.
(4) Disinfectant residuals cannot be maintained throughout the distribution system.

In such sources the problems are likely to involve persistent discoloured water complaints and taste and odour problems.

The major site of microbial activity is probably not the water itself, except in a small number of supplies with a high level of nutrients. Activity is believed to be concentrated in surface deposits and loose sediments[13]. However, microbial growth is not restricted to slimes and deposits in water mains or service reservoirs. It may be associated with other sources of organic nutrients, such as natural rubber sealing rings[16].

The first evidence of serious deterioration of rubber sealing rings using natural rubber was noticed in the Netherlands in 1949, and was subsequently shown to be caused by bacterial activity. Subsequently, biodeterioration of rubber sealing rings was reported from other countries[17]. In 1960 the Dutch specification for sealing rings was amended to exclude the use of natural rubber in favour of styrene butadiene synthetic rubber.

In the UK, experiments were set up at three sewage works in 1966 to compare the behaviour of natural and synthetic rubber rings for sewer pipe joints. In the 1970s the WRC investigated examples of deteriorating rings both in sewers and water mains[16,18]. The cause of deterioration was found to be *Nocardia asteroides*. Natural rubbers should therefore no longer be used for sealing rings.

CONTAMINATION

A water supply system can become contaminated for several reasons. The most common reasons are back siphonage, direct contamination at burst/repair sites and at service reservoirs.

When a section of the distribution system is depressurised due to a normal shutdown, failure of the main or of a pump, there is a danger of back siphonage. An example of this is shown in Fig. 10.3, where continuing consumption or leakage in an isolated section of main can pull contaminated water into the main.

Any point where the distribution system is open to atmosphere is a potential site for contamination. This is particularly true for service reservoirs, laying new mains, burst repairs and renovation sites. During the course of any repair, ground water should be kept below the invert level of the main and any open ends of the cut sections sealed by pipe stoppers. Chlorination should follow when a main has been opened (see Section 13).

3. INVESTIGATION OF WATER QUALITY PROBLEMS

DIAGNOSING WATER QUALITY PROBLEMS

The problem of poor water quality within a distribution system has many potential causes. The selection of the most cost-effective remedy usually requires an investigation which should be designed to identify the true cause(s)[3f].

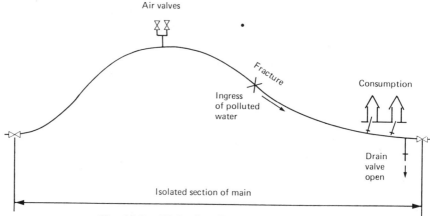

Fig. 10.3.   Risk of polluted water ingress

Poor water quality is often associated with particulate matter which arrives at a consumer's tap and causes consumer complaints. This may arise from corrosion, poor or insufficient water treatment, microbiological activity and changes of water supply type. Changes in flow within the distribution system caused by bursts, hydrant testing and valve operation also can lead to the disturbance of loose deposits and cause consumer complaints.

Therefore, to determine the true cause of such problems requires a clear and logical approach[3g]. A comprehensive scheme for doing this is described in another publication[3f] and is summarised in this Section, which concentrates on discoloured water although approaches for dealing with other problems such as tastes, odours and animals are described in the above publication.

INITIAL ASSESSMENT

Water quality problems are often revealed by consumer complaints which may be used to evaluate the nature and extent of a problem as a first step towards solving it.

To define the extent of the problem, details of *all* consumer complaints should be recorded and locations identified, possibly by plotting on a map. By relating the position of the complaints and the appropriate supply zone, it should be possible from this information to indicate which source or area(s) of the distribution system is giving rise to the majority of the complaints. The details of the complaints should also indicate any seasonal variation and the most common type of complaint.

Given the background information and the distribution of complaints it may be possible to determine the reason for the problem. Examples of problems which can be solved at this stage are those related to the domestic plumbing and those caused by abnormal operation of the distribution system.

In many cases, especially where complaints are frequent and widespread, the cause is not as obvious and further investigations will be necessary. The next logical step is to investigate the source and treatment of that source.

WATER TREATMENT ASSESSMENT

When assessing whether the water treatment works is an important factor in causing water quality problems, the first step is to assess the historical water quality data. It is then possible to compare this data with appropriate guidelines and make a judgement as to whether the works is, or has been, at fault.

A suggested guideline[3h] is given below and compared with the appropriate European Community (EC) standard[19].

Obviously such guidelines are subjective and are a compromise between the need to limit the amount of deposit-forming substances entering distribution and the cost of treatment. If the works has regularly kept to such guidelines in the past and is producing water of this quality at present, it is unlikely to be contributing to a water quality problem.

However, if the historical data suggest that the guidelines values have been exceeded for any length of time then, even if the treatment works is now satisfactory, deposits may well still lie within the distribution system. These deposits can then be disturbed by flow changes, act as a food source for animals and micro-organisms, and cause stagnant conditions.

If the treatment works is not satisfactory then the performance of each stage should be monitored[3h]. A typical sampling scheme in a conventional sedimentation/filtration plant is shown in Fig. 10.4. It should be noted that frequently a fault in one stage of the treatment process produces problems in a later stage. Once the treatment fault is diagnosed and rectified it is important to monitor the improvement by routine sampling and to clean any accumulated debris from the distribution system (see Section 7).

If the treatment works is shown to be satisfactory then investigation of the distribution system is required.

TABLE 10.III.　Guidelines for Treated Water Quality[+]

Parameter	Suggested value to avoid discoloured water	EC Directive[19]	
		GL*	MAC**
Turbidity (JTU)	<0.5	0.4	4
Colour (°H)	<10	1	20
Iron (mg/l)	<0.05	0.05	0.2
Aluminium (mg/l)	<0.1	0.05	0.2
Manganese (mg/l)	<0.05	0.02	0.05
Dissolved oxygen (per cent saturation)	>85	A note in the comment column states 75 per cent of saturation value unless a groundwater.	
pH (pH units at 25°C)	6.5 <pH <9.0	6.5 <pH <8.5	

Notes: [+] In addition to statutory health regulations
　　　　* Guide level
　　　　**Maximum admissible concentration

DISTRIBUTION SYSTEM INVESTIGATION

The quality of a supply may deteriorate during distribution because of corrosion, an unstable water, or because of mechanical, chemical or microbial interactions with existing deposits. It is important therefore to distinguish between these various factors. This is done by a combination of water sampling through distribution, an assessment of the water corrosivity, an examination of pipe samples and deposits and simple bottle tests.

Water Sampling in Distribution

Routine random daytime sampling, used for checking the overall quality of water

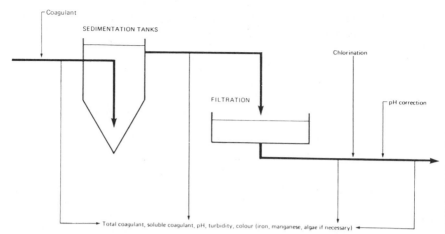

Fig. 10.4.   Typical sampling scheme for sedimentation-filtration plant

supplied to the consumer, is not an efficient means of establishing the cause of discoloration problems.

A more appropriate method is to divide the network into areas according to supply type, nature and concentration of complaints, average pipe age and rough estimates of the time the water takes to reach the area. The water can then be sampled from locations close to the extremities of the pipework within each area. These locations are likely to experience the most obvious deteriorations in water quality. Samples should then be analysed for parameters which may indicate the nature and extent of deterioration. The relevant parameters are colour, turbidity, iron, manganese, aluminium, disinfectant residual, dissolved oxygen and microbiological parameters. The results will identify those areas where consumers are receiving unsatisfactory water, whether it is confined to certain types of area and what is unsatisfactory about the quality.

How any deterioration arises can be gleaned by sequential sampling. This involves monitoring a body of water as it passes from the treatment works to the consumer's tap and determining the chemical and microbiological changes which occur. It is obviously important to ensure that observed changes are not a function of a variable supply leaving the treatment works. Thus the approximate times for water to reach different areas should be estimated and arrangements made to closely monitor the final water at the treatment plant for the appropriate length of time prior to sampling in distribution.

The parameters given in Table 10.IV have been observed to change in distribution and may indicate any deleterious processes. Selection of relevant parameters will depend on the type of supply and distribution system.

An example of a sequential sampling exercise is shown in Fig. 10.5, where aluminium is quite clearly being precipitated through the distribution system.

The points chosen for sampling must reflect the quality of water received by the consumer and exclude the effects of domestic plumbing unless specifically required. Samples taken from hydrants, however carefully taken, can show large inconsistencies and are not recommended.

Samples of the water in the main adjacent to the premises can be taken, if the

TABLE 10.IV.   Changes in Parameters Related to the Incidence of Water Quality Problems

Parameter	Process
Decreases in: Algae, Aluminium, Manganese, Iron, Silica	Precipitation
Decreases in: Dissolved oxygen, Disinfectant residual; Increases in: Plate count	Microbial activity
Decreases in: Total organic carbon	Microbial activity and/or precipitation
Increases in: Iron, Turbidity	Microbial activity and/or precipitation and/or corrosion

TABLE 10.V.   Times (minutes) Required to Flush Five Pipe Volumes from a Service Pipe at 5 litres/minute Flow Rate

Pipe diameter (mm)	15	22
Pipe length (m)		
10	1.8	3.8
20	3.5	7.6
40	7.1	15.2

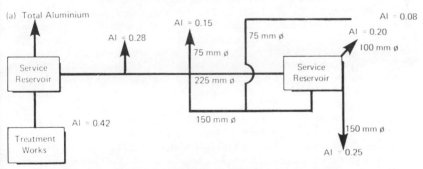

Fig. 10.5.   An example of sequential sampling

taps are flushed to remove any effect of the service pipe. The necessary flushing times, based on replacement of five service pipe volumes, are given in Table 10.V. If a particular house has to be visited frequently an outside tap can be used.

ANALYSIS OF DEPOSITS

Various types of deposits found in mains include sediments lying on the pipe invert, soft layers of slime on pipe surfaces and adhesive corrosion products ranging from small blisters to large tubercles.

Loose deposits can usually be flushed from the mains in problem areas, using fire hydrants. A hydrant should be cleaned before being used for this purpose and also disinfected if a bacteriological analysis of the deposit is to be performed. The detailed recommended procedure for obtaining deposits from mains is given elswhere[14,3f], but involves sterilising and cleaning the hydrant bowl and then collecting the deposits in a hydrant bag. Those deposits passing through the bag are settled out in a small settling tank.

The deposits should be examined by noting the general appearance and colour of samples and a small representative portion should be examined under the microscope. Occasionally, well defined entities can be recognised and if they represent a large proportion of the deposit their presence may be a significant factor in any problem. This may include animals and their remains, algae and their remains (in particular diatom frustules) and iron bacteria. Frequently, however, a large proportion of a deposit appears amorphous under the microscope. A chemical analysis of such deposits normally provides the most useful information. This analysis would generally include iron, aluminium, calcium, silicate and loss on ignition. This chemical analysis will reveal the extent of the precipitation process. The organic carbon content is another useful parameter but its determination requires special apparatus and can be time consuming.

Corrosion Rate Measurement

Distribution system sampling can be used to determine the extent of a discoloured water problem and distinguish between some of the deleterious processes which are occurring. However, difficulty is often experienced in trying to differentiate unambiguously between active iron corrosion, deposits of iron coagulants, microbiologically enhanced corrosion and movement of iron deposits from one part of the distribution system into another. A method[20] is available for measuring cast iron corrosion rates in potable water and this can be used to show if corrosion is likely to be an important factor.

However, in many circumstances the corrosivity of a supply is apparent from its composition or its historical effect on the amount of tuberculation inside mains. Soft moorland supplies are generally recognised to be corrosive towards iron, irrespective of their pH values. The internal condition of mains as observed at cut-outs and repairs is another very useful indication. The corrosion rate technique is likely to be out of most benefit in lowland surface and underground supplies.

Bottle Tests

In some cases the quality of a water may deteriorate because it is initially unstable as it goes into distribution. An example is an anaerobic groundwater containing dissolved iron which gradually oxidises after chlorination and partial aeration to give a visible precipitate. Keeping samples of the final water in clean bottles and monitoring quality over a reasonable time period will identify such problems.

4. DIAGNOSING PRESSURE PROBLEMS

BACKGROUND INFORMATION

There are a large number of potential causes of poor pressure problems. These include corrosion, closed or partially closed valves, jammed swabs, poor booster output and incorrect pipe size. The correct remedial action for each of these problems is clearly different. It is important therefore to determine the specific cause of the poor pressure before any remedial action is undertaken. The first stage in an investigation is to collect and organize whatever data are already available, such as past pressure surveys and complaints of poor pressure. Complaints should be plotted on a map, omitting those which are due to operating failures such as bursts and power failures. This technique, along with any recorded pressure measurements taken within the distribution system, should indicate areas where pressure and flow are inadequate. A detailed flow and pressure survey can then be used to diagnose the causes.

FLOW AND PRESSURE SURVEYS

The aim of these surveys is to see whether the hydraulic gradient within a system is smooth (due to corrosion or large slime build up) or changes abruptly (due to partially closed valves, jammed swabs, etc.) and whether a booster station is up to specification. There are basically two types of exercise, measurements on a single pipeline and network analysis of the whole system.

Single Pipeline Measurements

In single pipeline measurements a flow is induced from, for example, a hydrant or washout and carefully measured. The pressure drop along the length of the main is measured using accurate pressure recording devices. By looking at the hydraulic gradient, or the C or k values for each section of the main between pressure measuring points, it is possible to determine whether the pressure drop is even or changes abruptly. If there is a sharp change in hydraulic gradient then a partial blockage is the likely cause. It should be possible to determine the general location of the blockage by taking further pressure measurements in the section where the pressure drop is greatest. The exact location of the blockage can then be determined by rodding from access holes. With a smooth but steep hydraulic gradient the problem is one of corrosion or slime build up. Pipe sampling will indicate the difference between these two problems.

Network Analysis

Network analysis[21] (see Chapter 6) can be considered as an extension of this simple exercise. A model is developed of the distribution system flow which is then verified by pressure measurements. Poor flow and pressure areas will be highlighted. Once the model is developed and verified it can be used to predict whether any remedial action proposed for the areas of poor flow and pressure will enable the system to meet future demand.

5. REMEDIAL ACTION

Based on the previous sections the problems of poor quality and poor pressure can be investigated in a logical way and their cause determined. Clearly once the specific cause of the problem has been identified the appropriate remedial action can be implemented. If several potential solutions present themselves then a more detailed study of these options will have to be undertaken considering both long and short term factors. Details of the appropriate remedial action are given in Sections 6 to 16.

6. PLANNED REHABILITATION OF WATER MAINS

INTRODUCTION

Sections 3 and 4 have described logical approaches for solving both water quality and pressure problems as they arise. These approaches are reactive and essentially deal with certain problems when they become obvious to the consumer or cause operating difficulties. The problems, however, are symptoms of processes which could have been prevented with foresight and which will increase future operating costs. This is particularly worrying in those systems suffering from corrosion, where pipework may become unserviceable and relatively low cost solutions such as renovation may not be applicable because of insufficient residual strength. The costs of extensive pipe renewal could become a burden.

A more satisfactory strategy for managing supply systems would be on the basis of cost-benefit analyses of their long-term maintenance requirements. The aim should be to provide the manager with a mechanism by which he can quantify existing and future operating costs and problems; this will enable all necessary work to be planned and scheduled economically.

Work on the existing distribution system would therefore be justified if one or more of the following criteria were met:

(a) The work is the most economic way of correcting a current shortfall in the level of service.

(b) The work is the most economic way of correcting a predicted future shortfall in the level of service.

(c) The work achieves a saving in projected costs.

DEVELOPING A STRATEGY

Any strategy for the planned rehabilitation of water mains must be capable of identifying capital work on mains which fall into one or more of the above categories and must also quantify the long term benefits and costs.

The problems caused by the deterioration of water mains have properties which determine the form of the strategy. One is the large difference in the condition and performance of pipework, not only between distribution networks, but also between pipelines within one network. These differences place an emphasis on the local assessment of system condition and performance rather than the use of national "rules".

Another factor to be considered is the scale of the operating costs for troublesome systems; generally speaking the annual costs of repairs, responding to complaints, cleaning operations and leakage are individually small compared with the annuitised cost of mains rehabilitation or replacement. Therefore, to make an economic decision all these costs must be gathered together in a manner which allows them to be related to specific lengths or groups of pipes of uniform condition and environment. It is important to note that a good information system is very helpful, especially when dealing with the larger and more complex networks.

Finally, any strategy must be practicable and sufficiently flexible to allow the easy incorporation of improvements in technology or understandings of the problem. For example, the long-term future costs of owning and operating a main are likely to be no more than an educated guess in many cases—but as local information is collected over a period it is likely that trends in operating costs (for example, leakage, repairs, etc.) will become discernible. With the right approach future alterations should improve implementation of the strategy in terms of its reliability and convenience but not affect the strategy itself.

Summarising the above points leads to the following requirements for a strategy for rehabilitation:

(i) Standards of service to the consumer should be set at the outset and regarded as objectives to be met whatever remedial work is undertaken.

(ii) Within the constraints set by standards of service, decisions should be made on economic grounds. A clear statement of benefits, capital costs and revenue costs is necessary.

(iii) As a consequence of (ii) the best available predictions of future system condition, performance and associated costs are required. It is not enough just to tackle current problems at minimum expenditure for the current year.

(iv) The local assessment of system performance and condition will need to be emphasised. Reliable information and a good system for handling it are prerequisites.

(v) The strategy should contain all the steps necessary for proper economic decisions. Local factors, information and an understanding of pipe deterioration processes will determine the manner in which it is implemented.

Fig. 10.6 lists the major steps of a strategy which has been proposed to meet the above requirements[22]. At the time of writing many of these ideas are in their formulative stages within the water industry but are likely to be implemented in the near future.

7. CLEANING METHODS—REMOVING LOOSE DEPOSITS

Loose deposits in a main can be disturbed by a change in flow in the main and discolour the water. In some cases the removal of the deposits will lead to a sustained reduction of this discoloration. In other cases only a temporary reduction will be achieved as deposits may be swept in from other areas or active corrosion may be occurring in the system being cleaned. There are three techniques for cleaning loose deposits from mains; these are flushing, swabbing and air scouring.

FLUSHING

Flushing involves the opening of a hydrant or washout on the main and generating an increased flow to remove loose deposits. The velocity required to pick up and transport particulate matter is known[23] and is shown in Table 10.VI for a material with a specific gravity of 2.7 (a typical value for deposits). Achieving these velocities may not be feasible in low pressure areas and in larger diameter mains.

Flushing in one area may lead to disturbance elsewhere as increasing the velocity in the length of main being cleaned may cause increases in velocity in other lengths

TABLE 10.VI. Velocity and Flow Required to Suspend and Transport Solids of Specific Gravity 2.7 and 0.2 mm diameter in a Water Main[23]

Pipe diameter (mm)	Velocity required (m/s)	Flow required (l/s)
50	1.3	2.7
75	1.6	7.2
100	1.8	15
150	2.2	41
200	2.6	83

of main upstream of the cleaned section. Generally, flushing consumes large volumes of water and is ineffective in low pressure areas but is a simple technique to use.

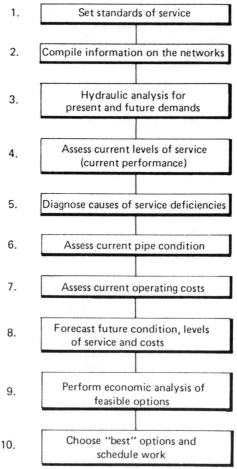

1. | Set standards of service

2. | Compile information on the networks

3. | Hydraulic analysis for present and future demands

4. | Assess current levels of service (current performance)

5. | Diagnose causes of service deficiencies

6. | Assess current pipe condition

7. | Assess current operating costs

8. | Forecast future condition, levels of service and costs

9. | Perform economic analysis of feasible options

10. | Choose "best" options and schedule work

Fig. 10.6.   A strategy for rehabilitating water mains

SWABBING

Cylindrical polyurethane foam swabs have been widely used since the mid '60s when the technique was introduced by the WRC[24,25,26]. The swab is inserted into the main and driven along by water pressure pushing the soft deposits before it. The swabs are porous and allow about 10 per cent of the water flow to pass, which aids the transport of the deposits ahead of the swabs.

Swab Selection

Soft, hard and scouring grades of swab are available. The soft grade is very compressible and has low tensile strength. If it meets an obstruction in the main it is likely to either squeeze through or be torn into small pieces which will not block the main. This grade should be used for all exploratory work when the general condition is unknown or where reductions in cross sectional area are serious. The soft swab should cope with a 50 per cent reduction in nominal pipe diameter. However, if tuberculation is the cause of large reductions in the pipe diameter, swabbing should not be used.

The hard grade, which is less compressible and stronger, is best used where encrustation and fittings do not significantly reduce the pipe diameter. However the swab should pass a 30 per cent reduction in diameter.

Generally the swab diameter is 25 per cent oversized for pipe sizes up to and including 300 mm, and by 75 mm in larger pipes. The length/diameter ratio should be 2 for small sizes (less than 100 mm) and 1.5 for larger sizes.

Swabbing Small Diameter Pipes (less than 150 mm)

Fire hydrants are usually the most convenient entry and exit points. The swab is forced into the main through a hydrant by removing the valve and spindle. The hydrant is then closed. Water flow is induced from the exit hydrant and the swab begins to move. The swab follows the flow of water and will leave the main via the exit hydrant. If there is a connection off the main that is taking more water than the hydrant, the swab will turn into that connection and could be lost in the distribution system. To prevent this, all flows in side connections should be stopped. Swabs should travel at 0.3-1.2 m/s.

It is possible to inject a swab into a main via a fixed jumper hydrant by loading the swab into the stand pipe and applying water pressure from either a pump or mains supply whilst opening the hydrant. Unfortunately in some hydrants the bowl is large and the swab will be bypassed by the water and remain in the bowl.

It is usual to limit the first run with a soft swab to approximately 400 m. This is often the shortest distance between hydrants and the swab may be torn into small pieces before arrival at the exit hydrant. If this is the case other cleaning techniques should be considered or subsequent swabs used until a swab emerges in reasonable condition, thus ensuring that the length of pipe has been cleaned. If a swab jams it is often possible to reverse the flow and retrieve it through the entry hydrant.

AIR SCOURING

It is possible to generate water velocities in a main in excess of those suggested in Table 10.VI by using air scouring[27,28]. The technique involves the continuous injection of filtered compressed air into the main, along with a continuous but smaller flow of water. Under certain conditions the water will form into discrete slugs and these are forced along the main at high velocities. There is no need to regularly switch the water or air on and off to achieve this. The correct technique is illustrated in Figs. 10.7 and 10.8.

Equipment

The equipment needed for air scouring is not elaborate. It consists of an appropriately size compressor (38 l/s for 75–100 mm diameter mains, 59 l/s for 100–150 mm diameter mains and 118 l/s for 150–200 mm diameter mains) matched air cooling, filtering and control equipment (Fig. 10.9) and appropriate air hoses and stand pipes.

Oil-free air is provided from a roadside compressor by first cooling the air using an air cooler and then filtering this cooled air. Using the correct cooler and filters breathing air standard can be achieved.

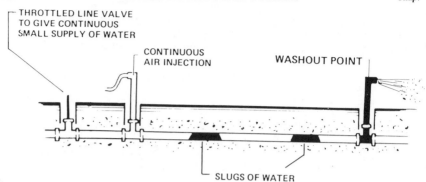

Fig. 10.7. Slug flow technique

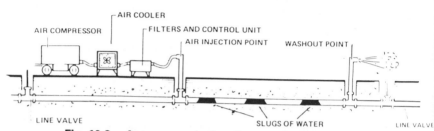

Fig. 10.8. Arrangement of equipment for air scouring

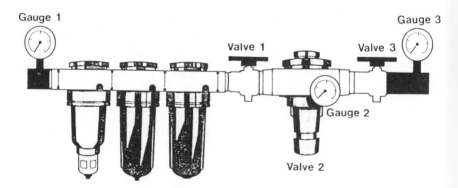

Planning an Air Scouring Exercise

Air scouring should be carefully planned to ensure the minimum of disruption and the maximum efficiency. The length which can be effectively cleaned by air scouring depends upon the available static pressure (the higher the pressure the longer the length), pipe friction (the higher the friction, the lower the C value, the shorter the length which can be cleaned), compressor size (the larger the compressor, the higher the slug velocity, but the shorter the length cleaned) and pipe gradient (longer lengths can be cleaned running uphill rather than downhill). The detailed determination of the length which can be cleaned at any one time is given elsewhere[27]. The aim in planning any air scouring exercise is to arrange for each single length to be as long as practicable. The maximum practical length is about 1000 m.

When air scouring an urban area advantage can be taken of the complexity of the system and the number of equipment moves can be reduced. This is illustrated in Fig. 10.10.

Performing an Air Scouring Exercise

The detailed operation of an air scouring exercise is given elsewhere[27,29]; a summary of the technique follows. The compressor and air scouring equipment are set up at the injection site and the injection hydrant sterilised. The discharge hydrant standpipe is then firmly wedged as the discharge of the water can be quite violent. The mains static pressure is then measured and the pressure regulator on the air scouring equipment is set to 0.5 bars below that static pressure. With the main isolated and the two hydrants (injection and discharge) opened the air injection is started and the water driven out. When the main is empty the upstream line valve is cracked open to allow a small amount of water into the main. After several minutes slug flow should be seen at the discharge hydrant. The discharge hydrant will run full for a few seconds till the slug arrives and then splutter for 20–40 seconds before the next slug arrives. Once the main is cleaned and the water runs clear the air injection is stopped and the mains can be refilled.

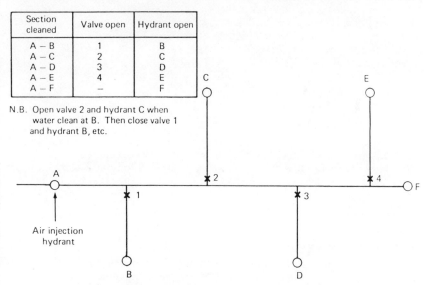

Section cleaned	Valve open	Hydrant open
A – B	1	B
A – C	2	C
A – D	3	D
A – E	4	E
A – F	–	F

N.B. Open valve 2 and hydrant C when water clean at B. Then close valve 1 and hydrant B, etc.

Fig. 10.10. Air scouring a 'complex' system

8. ANIMAL DISINFESTATION

EXTENT OF THE PROBLEM

About 150 different kinds of animal have been found in British water mains, and few distribution systems are without any animals. The density and composition of animal populations vary widely, from heavy infestations including large species which cause consumer complaints to sparse occurrences of microscopic species.

Symptoms of Animal Infestation

The presence of excessive numbers of animals in a distribution system is often revealed by consumer complaints. The problem is an aesthetic one, as none of the animals found in British mains is known to cause or carry diseases. It is therefore a matter of maintaining animal numbers at such a level that the consumer is unaware of their presence, either directly or indirectly. Consumer complaints can be a measure of success or failure in achieving this end, but are not a reliable guide to the extent of animal infestations. It is therefore advisable to sample the system routinely to assess the level of animal populations. This allows preventative measures to be taken before infestations are severe, and may allow action to be taken at a time which is more convenient to water undertakings.

Diagnosing the Cause

The first step towards diagnosing the cause of frequent complaints of organisms in the water supply is the identification of the offending animals using identification keys[30,31]. The animals would normally be obtained from hydrant samples but may also come from consumers who complain.

If the offending animals are aquatic, the next diagnostic step is to assess their population. The only practicable way of doing this is to flush a number of mains and collect the animals dislodged by the flushing procedure. Details are given elsewhere[30,32] but the aim is to determine the number of animals in a standard volume of water or in a particular length of main.

Estimates of the abundance of each species are made using the following logarithmic scale:

$$
\begin{array}{ll}
+ & 1-\ 9 \\
++ & 10-\ 99 \\
+++ & 100-999 \\
++++ & 1000 \text{ or more}
\end{array}
$$

The numbers of animals to be expected and which may be tolerated obviously vary with the species. Most 2.5 m³ samples will contain smaller species such as mites and Cyclops in the first one or two categories without producing consumer complaints. Water fleas such as Chydorus may be present in the fourth category without ill effect—hundreds of thousands may give dirty water complaints. On the other hand, Asellus or Gammarus in the first or second category would be regarded with concern.

Control of Animals

The available control measures are described here and further details about practical applications are given elsewhere[3i,33]. Methods of reducing the numbers of animals in water mains fall into two categories:

1. Disinfestation procedures to overcome particular infestations.
2. Long term control measures to restrict the potential increase of animals in the mains.

There is some overlap between the two categories.

DISINFESTATION PROCEDURES

Two principal types of disinfestation procedure are available: the use of mains cleaning techniques and chemical treatment.

For control purposes, the animals may be divided into three groups:

(a) Those which swim freely in the water or on the surface of the pipe or deposits (for example, Gammarus, Cyclops).

(b) Those which burrow in the deposits (for example, nematodes, chironomid larvae).

(c) those which cling to the pipe surface (for example, Asellus) or are permanently attached to if (for example, Dreissena, Plumatella).

The measures adopted to control an infestation depend on the group to which the offending animals belong, their potential for causing complaints and the numbers present.

In general the free-swimming animals are relatively easily removed by flushing, the burrowing animals require somewhat more stringent action, whilst animals attached to the pipe wall require dislodging before they can be flushed from the pipe.

The Use of Mains Cleaning Techniques

Flushing removes most free-swimming animals, providing that adequate flows are available and that flushing is done systematically from the treatment works towards the extremities of the system. The flushing should be from a treated section to an untreated section and be performed in a methodical manner. The water should approach the hydrant from one direction only.

Where normal water pressure is too low for effective flushing of pipe deposits and burrowing animals, air scouring or swabbing may be a more effective remedy. The advantages and disadvantages of the techniques for removing loose deposits are discussed in Section 7 and the same arguments should be applied to the removal of burrowing animals. Swabbing and air scouring may also be effective in removing lightly attached organisms and can achieve good removal of Asellus. However where Asellus are a major problem, better removal is likely to be achieved at a lower cost by chemical treatment and systematic flushing.

Chemical Methods

Two chemicals are usually employed for animal control in mains, chlorine and pyrethrins. A third, permethrin, has been introduced as a substitute for pyrethrins[34].

Chlorine

The normal concentrations of chlorine or chloramines in water leaving treatment works are not very effective against most of the animals found in distribution systems. The higher concentrations applied during pre-chlorination may be effective in reducing animal penetration through treatment works. Chlorine is used to control oligochaete worms such as Nais. An infestation can be controlled by maintaining 0.5 to 1 mg/l total residual chlorine throughout the distribution system for a week or two.

Recurrence can be prevented by maintaining 0.2 mg/l to the ends of the system. These concentrations are higher than normal but in some cases this is the only effective treatment method. To minimise chlorine consumption it is important to maintain as clean a distribution system as possible.

Chlorine (1–2 mg/l residual chlorine) may be used to prevent infestation of raw water mains by the free swimming larvae of *Dreissena polymorpha* (the zebra mussel). The sedentary adults are resistant to extremely high concentrations.

Pyrethrins and Permethrin

Pyrethrins have been used effectively to control Asellus in water mains and have also been used against other crustaceans (such as Gammarus) and also insect larvae (namely chironomid larvae). Natural pyrethrins are now in short supply and a synthetic analogue, permethrin[34], is being introduced as a substitute. While permethrin is chemically distinct from pyrethrins, it shares a number of properties which are important to its use in water mains.

The recommended dose for both is 10 µg/l which should present no hazard to a consumer who drinks water which contains these concentrations. However it is prudent to consult Environmental Health Authorities and to inform the Regional Health Authorities with regard to renal dialysis patients. Both substances are very toxic to fish, so appropriate warnings of their use should be given and dosed water should be disposed of carefully.

Details of the techniques involved with pyrethrin/permethrin dosing are given elsewhere[33,3i].

LONG-TERM CONTROL MEASURES

Long-term measures can be employed to prevent animal populations reaching nuisance proportions or, following disinfestation, to prevent recurrence of problems. The principal object is to deny the animal a food supply and this may be achieved by the following methods:

(i) Improvement in the performance of treatment works with respect to suspended solids removal and animal penetration. This will reduce the entry of nutrients (particularly algae) into the system and thus reduce the recolonisation of the mains by animals.

(ii) Periodic cleaning of service reservoirs and routine systematic flushing, swabbing or air scouring of distiibution systems. This will remove particulate organic matter which has settled out, and will also remove many animals.

(iii) Maintenance of a chlorine residual throughout the distribution system. This will inhibit micro-organisms which may convert dissolved organic nutrients into particulate matter, and also inhibit some animals.

(iv) Attention to ventilators and manhole covers on service reservoirs, etc. This will prevent animals entering treated water.

(v) Elimination of unused dead ends in the distribution system and, where practicable, the use of mains of such a size that the velocities are kept relatively high. This will reduce the volume of stagnant or slow flowing water, which is conducive to precipitation of solids and animal growth.

9. CHEMICAL TREATMENT MEASURES

INTRODUCTION

Corrosion inhibition is a very common practice in the water industry. The majority of surface waters for example are "pH corrected" to give a positive Langelier Index primarily to produce a water that is believed to be non-corrosive. Other measures adopted are the regular dosing of polyphosphates (e.g. *Calgon* and *Kalipol*) or sodium silicates.

Although there are several reports concerning the beneficial effects of chemical treatment, it is prudent to treat the conclusions with caution; often the evidence is ambiguous. Conversely, applications of chemical treatment have been reported as ineffective in cases where corrosion is unlikely to have been the cause of discoloration.

The principal uses of corrosion inhibitors are for reducing consumer complaints. When effective they may work by reducing the corrosion rate itself, stabilising deposits existing within the mains or by complexing with deposits and corrosion products and rendering them less visible.

SUITABLE CHEMICAL TREATMENTS

It is essential that any chemical used to treat a supply of drinking water should not cause a health hazard, either in the short or long term. It should also be easily handled, easily dosed and inexpensive. These criteria lead to the following choices:

(1) Sodium silicates.
(2) Sodium polyphosphates.
(3) pH correction to a positive Langelier index.
(4) Increasing the calcium and bicarbonate ion concentration.

The health aspects of adding phosphates and silicates to drinking water have been reviewed[35]. It was concluded that there were no health risks when used at normal concentrations. Methods (3) and (4) above employ chemicals such as lime and carbon dioxide which have a long history of safe application to water supplies. More details of these treatments are given elsewhere[3].

TESTING CORROSION INHIBITORS

Before corrosion inhibitors are used on the full scale it is essential that their efficacy is tested. The following procedure is recommended:

(a) check that the cause of complaints is corrosion (see Section 3);
(b) determine the extent of the problem (see Section 3);
(c) check that the proposed inhibitor reduces the corrosion rate using a method for measuring corrosion rates (see Section 3);
(d) investigate the costs and benefits of alternative remedies such as relining (see Section 10); and
(e) if the use of a corrosion inhibitor is indicated, test it in a confined area of the distribution system .

PRECAUTIONS

Chemical treatment for corrosion control is most effective when the corroding surface is not screened by sediments and slimes. It follows that these treatments are most likely to succeed in pipe networks which are precleaned by flushing, swabbing or air scouring.

Both silicates and polyphosphates have been known to disperse deposits containing iron oxide and manganese oxides. Therefore, in the short term, discoloration could be made worse and pipe cleaning operations may have to be increased. This risk is sufficient reason for testing silicates and polyphosphate inhibitors in small watertight zones, after having tested their efficacy as corrosion inhibitors using the corrosion rig and prior to bulk dosing. Any disturbance can then be easily contained and assessed.

The test should be performed in a small zone, and a similar zone chosen as a control to reveal any effects which are a function of temperature or basic water composition rather than chemical treatment. Water samples should be collected from the problem areas both before and after chemical treatment is introduced. They should be analysed for turbidity, colour, corrosion inhibitor, iron, manganese and aluminium. Consumer complaints in the two areas should also be monitored. It is also necessary to design the experiment in consultation with a statistician to ensure that enough samples are collected to reveal changes in water quality which are thought to be significant.

It should be noted that the colorimetric determination of iron[36] is affected by polyphosphate. Acid hydrolysis removes the interference but neglecting this will produce misleading results.

10. PIPE RELINING TECHNIQUES

INTRODUCTION

The cleaning of an iron main to remove all the tuberculation, followed by relining with a durable corrosion resistant material, is an effective method of overcoming discoloration problems caused by corrosion. It will also improve the hydraulic capacity of a badly tuberculated main. This section concentrates on non-structural relining methods because these are the most widely used. However, a structural system, sliplining, is summarised at the end of the section.

Renewing the main will also achieve the same objective but is likely to be a more expensive solution. Both approaches are expensive and the decision as to which option to take will depend on many factors.

Cost of Scheme

Typical capital costs of relining and renewal are shown in Fig. 10.11. In general, cement mortar relining is cheaper than renewal except for small diameter mains in rural areas. However, it is also necessary to consider the future operating costs of the options. For example, it may be cheaper to renew a pipe suffering high repair costs when the long-term operating costs are also taken into consideration (see Section 6).

Residual Pipe Strength

The cast iron main being relined should have sufficient residual strength to cope with the trauma of the cleaning process. At present there is insufficient information to specify this minimum residual strength but some evidence indicates that pipes containing sections with about 2 mm of remaining sound iron can withstand the cleaning process.

Corrosion Rates

Internal corrosion of a cast iron main will be arrested by relining but clearly relining will have no effect on external corrosion. The rate of external corrosion will be a major factor governing the life of the relined pipe.

Future Use

The proposed future use of the main will also govern whether the main should be relined or renewed. Planned redevelopment may limit the useful life of the relined main as a larger diameter main may be required.

The development of a carefully planned and executed strategy along the lines discussed in Section 6 will be required before a logical decision can be made as to whether to reline or renew.

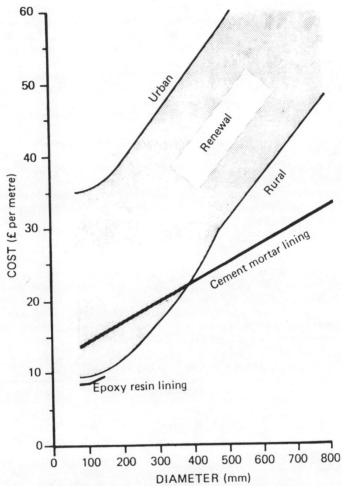

Fig. 10.11. A comparison between renovation and renewal

A relining exercise requires careful planning to ensure that good consumer relations are maintained and that there is minimal disturbance to the environment. These and other operational aspects are described in a report by WRC[37].

CHOICE OF LINING MATERIAL

Until recently the choice of material was either bitumen or cement mortar. At first sight bitumen has three advantages when compared with cement mortar:

(i) The cost is less than half of that of cement mortar.
(ii) A main can be relined and returned to service within a working day compared with a period of 24–36 hours when cement mortar is used.
(iii) The thin bitumen linings (less than 1 mm) have less effect on hydraulic capacity than do the thicker cement mortar linings (greater than 4 mm).

An investigation[38] has shown that *in situ* applied bitumen linings are not very durable and that a general breakdown of the lining after 5 to 10 years is common. Similar investigations[39,40] of *in situ* applied cement mortar linings have shown the material to be durable and that it will remain intact for at least 50 years. This material has other advantages: it produces an alkaline environment adjacent to the wall of the main which protects the iron from further corrosion, and the high pH also helps to heal any cracks that may develop in the lining by precipitating calcium carbonate within them[41].

Problems do exist however in waters of low alkalinity. Increases in pH, normal immediately after lining, have persisted for long periods of time. The only technique available at the moment to overcome this is prolonged flushing or controlled leakage by leaving a washout partly open.

New materials for relining water mains are being developed; the most promising are epoxy resins[42,43] and fast setting cement. Both materials should give a same day return to service, with epoxy resin giving a smoother thinner lining. However, both materials are in the development stage, and at the time of writing questions still need to be answered concerning ease of application, durability and suitability for contact with potable water.

CEMENT MORTAR RELINING

At the moment this is the only available non-structural renovation method of proven reliability and durability. Consequently it is described briefly here and in more detail elsewhere[37].

The first stage of any cement mortar lining operation is to remove existing deposits and the cleaning technique used depends on the diameter of the main being cleaned as indicated in Table 10.VII.

TABLE 10.VII. Cleaning Methods

Method	Diameter range (mm)	Access hole frequency
Drag scraping	75–1050	≤250 m
Power boring	75– 300	≤150 m
Pressure scraping	>375	≤3 km

Power Boring

A series of flexible steel rods (5 m long) are used both to drive and rotate a cutting device comprising one or two pairs of short length steel rods bent in the form of a flail. The drive rods are mechanically rotated and further rods are added as the cutter is driven through the main. The maximum length that can be cleaned from one access, in one direction, is about 150 m although the usual length is about 100 m. During the operation it is important to avoid ferrule blockage and a counter flow of water is maintained to wash out the resultant debris. The advantage of this technique is that it can be used in pipes which are almost completely blocked with tuberculation and the method has a considerably lower incidence of ferrule blockages compared with drag scraping. The technique also leaves a cleaner, smoother finish compared with drag scraping.

Drag Scraping

A drag scraper consists of a series of sprung steel serrated blades mounted in 3 or 4 rows on a cylindrical chassis in a manner that gives complete coverage of the pipe bore. There are eye bolts at each end for the attachment of winch cables. First a rod is pushed through the main to enable the winch cable to be drawn back through. This cable is attached to the scraper and a second winch cable attached to the other end. The cables are fixed to the drums of heavy duty winches (usually mounted on tractors) and the scraper repeatedly drawn through the main until all tuberculation is removed. The debris is removed from the main by the scraper itself or by plungers which are attached to the same cables after the scraper pass. The length between the two access holes is usually a maximum of 150 m but normally about 100 m.

Whenever possible this technique should be used against a counterflow of water. This may however prove difficult as both ends of the main are open for cable access.

Pressure Scraping

A pressure scraper is in many ways similar to a drag scraper. A series of spring steel serrated blades are mounted in rows around a central cylindrical barrel. Each blade in each row is offset to the blade in the previous row. The scraper is loaded into a makeup piece above ground which is then lowered and connected up to the pipe being cleaned. The main is recharged and water pressure drives the scraper along. A certain amount of water will pass through the scraper, keeping the scraped deposit in suspension in front of the scraper. The scraper is caught in a catch box downstream.

Application of Cement Mortar Lining

The mortar is produced in a paddle mixer, using a sand/cement ratio of 1:1. It is then fed into a suitable pump which pumps the material through a hose feeding the lining machine. This machine consists of a spinning head, driven by compressed air. The head is slotted and sprays the mortar centrifugally onto the bore of the pipe. By controlling the winch withdrawal rate, the lining machine is drawn through the main at the speed necessary to produce the required lining thickness. Lengths of 85–120 m are usually lined in one operation, but up to 150 m can be lined in some cases. The initial finish to the mortar is a characteristic orange peel finish. In large diameter pipes the lining can be smoothed by either cone shaped drag trowels or rotating trowels attached to the lining machine. These are not used in small diameter mains as the trowelling tends to block service connections.

Sliplining

Sliplining is the only technique available at present for structural renovation. The technique is to clean the pipe using drag scraping, thus returning the bore of the pipe to its original dimensions. Several lengths of polyethylene pipe are then fused together above ground. A nose cone is attached to the front of the string of pipes. This cone is in turn attached to a winch. The string of polyethelene pipes is then winched through the pipe to be lined. A reduction in the insertion force can sometimes be achieved by "floating" the polyethylene pipe through whilst it is being winched. The annulus between the polyethylene pipe and the original pipe should be grouted.

11. RENEWAL OPTIONS

INTRODUCTION

Any material considered for the renewal option should ideally:

(1) have a minimum service lifetime of 50 years;
(2) not impair water quality;
(3) have adequate structural strength for the service requirements;
(4) be resistant to corrosion;
(5) not support biological growths;
(6) be impermeable to external concentrations of chemicals, especially oils and gases;
(7) have smooth internal walls to minimise hydraulic resistance; and
(8) be simple to joint.

There are currently several materials which meet these requirements and are used for renewal; these include uPVC, ductile iron and asbestos cement.

A recent survey[1] suggests that the proportion of pipe material used for renewal is as indicated in Table 10.VIII.

TABLE 10.VIII. Proportion by Pipe Material of Total Length Renewed

Material	Per cent
uPVC	54
Ductile iron	34
Asbestos cement	9
Others	3

Table 10.IX indicates the proportion of each size range that is used:

TABLE 10.IX. Proportion by Diameter of Total Length Renewed

Diameter	Per cent
50–150	77
151–275	13
175 and above	10

DUCTILE IRON

Spun ductile iron pipe[44] was first manufactuered in the UK on a commercial scale in 1961. Ductile iron is produced by treating a low phosphorus, low sulphur, grey iron melt with magnesium just before casting. This treatment causes the carbon present in the melt to precipitate predominantly in the form of graphite nodules rather than as flake graphite as is normally the case for grey cast irons. The ductile iron pipes are subsequently heat treated. The finished pipe has a combination of tensile strength and ductility which is markedly superior to that which can be achieved in grey iron pipes. The greater strength of ductile iron permits the manufacture of pipes and fittings with thinner walls than those of similar diameter or grey iron castings. Thus, spun ductile iron pipes are typically 30 per cent lighter than equivalent grey iron pipes. Where a pipeline is subject to external stress the superior mechanical properties of ductile iron pipes and fittings render them considerably more resistant to fracture under beam loading conditions than equivalent grey iron castings. Naturally, the ductile iron pipe is susceptible to both external and internal corrosion and should be suitably protected.

Internal corrosion of unlined iron pipes usually leads to tuberculation and a consequent loss of hydraulic capacity and dirty water problems. It is essential therefore that all ductile iron pipes and fittings should be internally protected with a suitable lining. The most common lining is cement mortar which has been shown to provide satisfactory long-term protection in potable waters in the UK. Fittings should also be internally lined with cement mortar by a method which produces a lining comparable to that obtained on pipes.

It is clearly advisable that all ductile iron pipes and fittings should be adequately protected against external corrosion. Factory applied bitumen coatings are thin (75-100 μm) and are primarily intended to prevent atmospheric corrosion of iron pipes and fittings in the stockyard.

Wrapping with loose polyethylene (PE) sleeving is a simple and inexpensive technique for significantly reducing the risk of external corrosion of ductile iron mains, and is strongly recommended for all new iron pipes, irrespective of environmental conditions. Although not intended to be an airtight and watertight enclosure, the PE sleeving prevents contact between the pipe and surrounding backfill. The nominal PE sleeving thickness currently recommended for all pipe diameters is 225 ± 25 μm.

Details of the sleeving techniques are given elsewhere[45].

Loose PE sleeving is not suitable for insulating pipelines in conjunction with cathodic protection systems.

uPVC

uPVC pressure pipe[46] has been available to the water industry for over 20 years. In its early use the material suffered from an apparently high failure rate giving it a poor reputation in some quarters. Over the last 10 years performance has been improved in the following areas:

(a) Manufacturing process, particularly dispersion, leading to a tougher, more consistent product.
(b) Understanding of the role of surge pressures and fatigue failures.
(c) Understanding of the need for careful handling and correct laying procedures.

A study of the failure records of uPVC and ductile iron mains in similar conditions has been carried out by WRC[47]. This indicated that the recent failure record of uPVC is as good as, or better than, ductile iron and this is shown in Fig. 10.12.

uPVC pipes are light and easily handled. Consequently there is a tendency for them to be mishandled more than pipes of other materials. This should be discouraged and reasonable care should be taken in handling and storage to prevent damage to the pipe. uPVC pipes are notch sensitive, such that damage received in handling or laying may cause a subsequent failure. uPVC pipes are flexible and attention should be paid to providing a proper bed and adequate lateral suppport for the pipe. Good, but not over consolidation of the sidefill is required to adequately support the pipe[48]. As a result of an investigation into surge pressure problems[49], an amendment to CP.312 Part 2 has been issued[50]. Users are advised to note the extent of the surge amplitude which each class of pipe is capable of withstanding and to select the appropriate pipe for the application.

ASBESTOS CEMENT

Asbestos cement pipes have been used for over 50 years in the UK[51]. Used correctly, they can provide sound and durable pipelines for the conveyance of water and sewage. They are likely to compete in economic terms with pipes of other materials when used in the right environment.

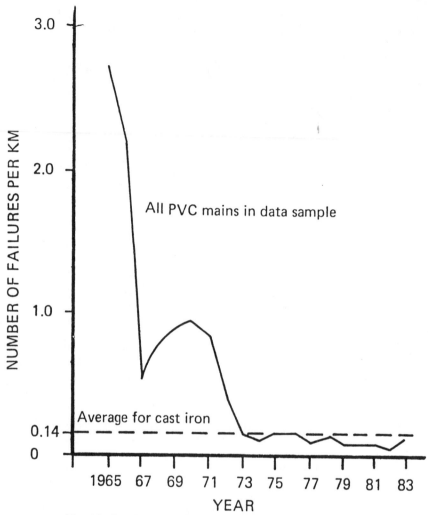

Fig. 10.12. Annual failure rates of uPVC water mains

A negative Langelier Index water will leach lime from the asbestos cement matrix and weaken the pipe. This may lead to a release of asbestos fibres into the water. There is considerable debate as to whether this release causes any health related problems. The available evidence suggests that it is doubtful whether there is a risk from ingestion of fibres as a result of drinking water conveyed by asbestos cement pipes.

To minimise the possibility of fibre release, internal coating is recommended for all pipes carrying water which has a negative Langelier Index and is intended for human consumption.

Asbestos cement pipework is also at risk from external attack in aggressive soils, particularly those with a low pH and a high sulphate content. In these cases the pipes should be externally coated.

Asbestos cement pipes are generally robust, but are susceptible to hair cracks if struck on, or close to, the spigot end. A careful and close visual inspection of pipe ends after unloading, and just before laying, should be carried out. Whilst the presence of hair cracks can usually be detected, their full extent may not be apparent. If it is necessary to reclaim a pipe known to be cracked it should be cut back at least 50 mm beyond the apparent extremity of the longest crack. The position in the pipeline of any reclaimed pipe should be noted.

The low beam strength of asbestos cement pipes compared with iron and steel makes it important to ensure that a firm and uniform bed is provided. For pipes over 150 mm diameter, UK manufacturers recommend laying in a well-prepared trench on a bed of selected backfill.

MEDIUM DENSITY POLYETHYLENE

This is a material new to the water industry but has been used by British Gas for many years. However it must be realised that gas mains operate at very much lower pressure than water mains and that the water industry has different operational requirements to the gas industry. Any limitations of use are likely to emerge as the material is researched for water industry use and the material introduced. The material is specified elsewhere[52,53] and can be mechanically jointed or fixed by socket, butt or electrofusion techniques[54]. MDPE should not be used in contaminated ground.

12. CATHODIC PROTECTION

INTRODUCTION

Cathodic protection (CP) prevents the electrochemical corrosion reaction (see Fig. 10.1) from occurring by making the pipeline cathodic with respect to the soil. This is achieved by connecting the pipeline to a base metal electrode buried in the soil or by impressing a current upon the pipe.

Cathodic protection is frequently used for the external protection of buried steel pipelines, particularly in aggressive soils and other vulnerable areas. It has only been used on a limited scale for the protection of underground iron mains in water distribution systems. In 1973, only some 0.3 per cent of the total length of iron and steel water mains in the UK was cathodically protected[55]. For economic protection, CP is usually applied to pipelines protected externally with a high performance coating system containing a low density of through-thickness defects—for example, thick bituminous sheathing, fusion-bonded epoxy or polyethylene.

DESIGN OF CATHODIC PROTECTION SYSTEMS

To design a cathodic protection system, details of the soil resistivity and pipe/soil potential along the length of the pipeline are required. The Wenner 4-pin technique is most commonly used to measure soil resistivity along the line of a proposed or existing pipeline. The ranges of soil resistivities for different soil types are given in Fig. 10.13.

The general effects of various soil resistivities are given in Table 10.X; however, these figures should be treated with caution and their interpretation should involve specialist advice.

The soil resistivity may vary considerably along the length of the pipe leading to different protection requirements along its length.

Rock type	Resistivity (ohm-metres)

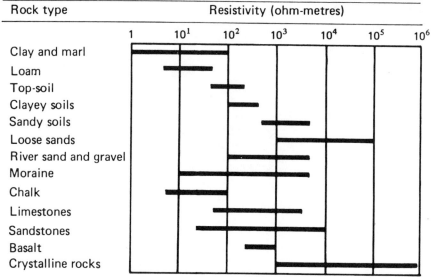

Fig. 10.13. Approximate ranges for the electrical resistivity of rocks and soils

TABLE 10.X.   Soil Resistivity and Effect on Iron Pipes

Resistivity ohm/m	Effect on iron pipe
0– 20	very corrosive
20– 40	corrosive
40–100	mildly corrosive
>100	not generally corrosive

Metals have a natural electrochemical potential with respect to a soil. The potential of a buried metal structure may be measured against a copper/copper sulphate or silver/silver chloride reference electrode using either a potentiometer or high resistance voltmeter. Natural pipe/soil potentials with respect to a copper/copper sulphate electrode can vary from -0.4 to -0.7 V. To achieve protection the potential should be depressed to at least -0.85 V with respect to copper/copper sulphate for normal soils and -0.95 V in anaerobic clays containing sulphate reducing bacteria.

For design purposes it can be assumed that 1 per cent of a sheathed pipeline eventually becomes exposed and that a current of 20 mA/m^2 is required for protection. Sacrificial anodes may produce 10 to 500 mA, giving an effective 800 to 1200 amp.hours/kg over a 10 year life. For impressed current systems a current drain test should be conducted. This involves connecting a portable generator to a temporary ground bed and to the pipeline and adjusting the current output to provide a minimum of -0.85 V protection to the pipeline. The transformer/rectifier rating may then be specified.

SACRIFICIAL ANODES

Anodes are available in varying shapes weighing 2.3 to 27.3 kg (5–60 lb). The larger sizes are used for low resistance soils and high current requirements. Magnesium/zinc/aluminium alloy anodes are usually encased in a 75 per cent gypsum/20 per cent bentonite/5 per cent sodium sulphate mixture and buried in slurry, or below the water table, for good conductivity. The anodes are spaced according to current demand and soil resistivity to obtain uniform protection. Anodes are connected to the pipeline by a thermite bonded copper cable approximately 2.5 mm^2 in area, plastic sheathed and encased in a duct for protection against accidental damage. The cable may be wired to a connection/disconnection plate at a surface post or box in order to measure pipe/soil potential and current with the anode connected or disconnected as required. When exhausted, the anode is abandoned and replaced.

IMPRESSED CURRENT

The positive terminal of a DC power supply is connected to a ground bed and the negative to the pipeline, enabling the potential to be depressed by the necessary amount. A single ground bed may serve many kilometres of line but interference with other structures and excessive hydrogen evolution may occur near the ground bed. Pipe/soil potentials should not therefore be reduced below -2 V with respect to a copper/copper sulphate reference electrode to avoid breakdown of the pipeline coating.

INTERFERENCE WITH OTHER BURIED STRUCTURES

Buried metallic structures adjacent to a main protected with CP may suffer stray current attack (interference). An adjacent metallic structure can pick up the protection current and then discharge that current back to the protected main at a point of minimum resistance. This will accelerate the rate of corrosion of the unprotected structure at the point of current egress. Once discovered, the remedy may be a low resistance metallic bond between the protected and affected structures or a buried electrode to serve as "earth" return. In the latter case the electrode will eventually need replacement. The Joint Committee for Coordination of the Cathodic Protection of Buried Structures has agreed that the operation of CP equipment should not alter the natural soil potential of adjacent buried structures by more than $+20$ mV.

COSTS

The principal objection against the use of CP for iron mains in the water industry is its cost. The initial cost of the CP hardware and installation must be considered in conjunction with the expense of providing a suitable, high quality external coating for the pipe, which is essential in order to minimise current (or sacrificial anode) requirements and hence operating costs.

A report published in 1973[55] indicated that CP systems typically added only about 1 per cent to the overall capital cost of an underground iron or steel water pipeline, although this percentage was considerably greater where CP was applied to relatively short lengths of main. At that time, the annual charge for electricity used in impressed current schemes on water mains in the UK ranged from 62p to £23 per km. In addition to these items, the costs of periodic maintenance and inspection, plus replacement anodes for sacrificed systems, must also be taken into account. Furthermore, CP systems can only be adequately installed and maintained by trained personnel, who may not be readily available to all water utilities.

If incorrectly maintained or neglected, CP systems may become uneconomical (due to excessive current demand or too high a rate of consumption of sacrificial anodes) or the protection system may fail (due to insufficient current capacity or sacrificial anodes of inadequate size).

13. REPAIRS

PIPES

Circumferential Failures and Small Holes

If the pipe is in a satisfactory condition, circumferential failures and small holes (such as a hole caused by corrosion) can be repaired using an external split collar. The most common form of collar is made from two cast iron semi-circumferential shells sealed by a rubber gasket. Varying lengths with 4 or 6 bolt fastenings are normally available for each diameter. The bolts and nuts should be protected from corrosion before backfilling.

A proprietary preformed stainless steel flexible collar is available in 1 or 2 wrap-around sections. The edges of this collar are held in ductile iron brackets pressing a full face nitrile or neoprene rubber gasket against the pipe. There may be interlocking "fingers" in the gasket which mate as tightened, or a tapered and overlapping leading edge. This type of collar is cheaper than cast iron in the larger diameters, say greater than 200 mm. However, circumferential failures are less likely in larger diameters.

Longitudinal Splits and Blowouts

Failures which damage a length of the pipe are usually repaired by replacing part or the whole of that pipe. They occur in all sizes of pipe but more frequently in large diameter. The pipe must be exposed until a sound section is reached and a cut made across a diameter. Very often a complete pipe section is removed.

A socket and spigot length of pipe of the same class and outside diameter is then cut to fit. A collar, complete with jointing rings, is slid onto one open end of the parent main, the repair pipe lowered in and its socket mated to the other open end. The collar is then slid along to close the gap. Where non-standard size pipe is to be repaired, special sizes have to be retained or step couplings used by inserting a plain (double spigot end) pipe and coupling each end, using a change collar or stepped Viking-Johnson coupling. If migration of the collar along the pipe is felt to be a problem, then a change piece consisting of a socket and spigot may be used. This method requires several more fittings than a plain pipe and collar join. Alternative methods of anchoring collars are to insert studs between the spigot ends (as in a Viking-Johnson collar) or to restrain them externally by tie bars and/or concrete.

JOINTS

Joints are remade or reworked for a variety of reasons. These include remaking when new sections of pipe are fitted following a repair or when modifications are made to the existing main. Some joints will be remade or reworked if they are found to be leaking.

Remaking Joints

Run Lead

This is the traditional pipe joint used before the advent of the rubber ring. A spigot is inserted into a socket allowing a 6 mm gap for thermal movement. The annular space is then "yarned" using sterilised hemp or man-made fibres to prevent the molten lead entering the pipe. A circlip and clay seal are fashioned in which to pour the molten lead into the joint cavity. Once the lead cools the circlip is removed and the lead joint is driven home using a club hammer and shaped setts until recessed 1–2 mm in the face of the socket. Weeping lead joints may be "tooled up" and a special cast iron muff clamped over the joint for additional protection. More details of the run lead jointing technique are given elsewhere[56].

Rubber Rings

Perished and failed flange and rubber ring joints invariably require that a section of a pipe be cut out unless a flexible bolted coupling has been used. Techniques discussed earlier should then be used.

Reworking Joints

Leaking run lead joints can often be controlled by reworking the existing lead or by adding finely shredded lead to the external joint cavity and working that. A clamp is then placed around the joint to retain the lead. A muff could also be clamped over an existing socket and spigot joint to stem a leak.

FITTINGS

Sluice Valves

Sluice valves are robust and durable but require high operating forces. Street valves are turned by key and bar on the spindle through a surface box. Some large valves have worm and bevel gears with cranking handles. Several aspects of the valve require attention from time to time.

Spindle Packing

The packing prevents water escaping from the body of the valve through the annular space around the operating spindle. This packing may become worn or damaged in use and water will eventually appear at the surface box. To replace the packing, the stuffing box at the top of the valve has to be exposed and, after closing the valve and removing the stuffing box bolts, the packing rings are removed with the aid of probes. United Kingdom Water Fittings Byelaws Scheme Listing (UKWFBS) replacement packing of the correct width is cut to length to fill the annular gap within the stuffing box. After ensuring that the stuffing box and materials are perfectly clean, the packing rings are inserted with the butt joints staggered. The stuffing box ring is replaced and the nuts are gently tightened onto the new packing. Before backfilling the valve should be operated to test for tightness and the stuffing box bolts further tightened if necessary. The bolts should be protected with tape and the stuffing box by a grommet to prevent intrusion of grit.

Sluice Valve Gates

These may become corroded and encrusted on their sealing surfaces. If this is the case, operating the gate up and down may improve the sealing efficiency. If not the gates should be withdrawn. Mild encrustation can be treated on the spot by scraping and rubbing down but more severe corrosion will require refacing in a workshop. The valve is then reassembled using new gaskets, bolts and nuts as required and if necessary wrapped with approved impregnated tape to reduce further corrosion.

Other Valves and Fittings

Other valves and fittings used on a water distribution system may require repair.

Butterfly Valves

Small valves are removed and replaced prior to renovation in a workshop. With adequate access, larger valves can be serviced *in situ* from inside the pipe. The metal surfaces are scraped, ground and recoated and resilient rings are replaced.

Altitude Valves

Apart from the removal of encrustation and maintenance for wear and tear, the valve may require adjustment for its range of movement and to avoid "hunting".

Larner-Johnson Valves

As for other types of specialist valve, a skilled fitter from the undertaking or the manufacturer should carry out repairs.

Reflux Valves

The paddles and hinges on this valve are liable to become encrusted and have a tendency to stick. Small diameter valves will require removal for repair. Large diameter valves could be repaired *in situ*.

Tees

Tees may fail by corrosion of flange bolts or fracture of the flange or casting. Although bolts may be replaced individually, any leakage may have damaged the gasket and its replacement may require the removal of a pipe section.

Ferrules

A defective ferrule hole may be drilled oversize to re-establish sound metal contact and a larger ferrule substituted. Alternatively a drilled split collar could be used.

Ancillary Equipment

Some valves have electrical or gas operated actuators. Minor faults can be rectified on site but major faults will require replacement of the actuator and its repair in the workshop. Provision should be made for manual operation of the valve during the repair of the actuator.

DISINFECTION FOLLOWING REPAIR

The disinfection procedures for new water mains and for mains that have been repaired are given in an NWC document[57]. The procedure entails charging the main with chlorinated water, allowing a contact time, and then flushing out the chlorinated water followed by bacteriological examination.

For new mains the recommended disinfectant level is at least 20 mg/l of free available chlorine (FAC) with a contact time of 24 hours.

However, for mains that have been repaired, a contact time of this duration is impractical. To facilitate a more rapid return to service the period of contact can be reduced to 2 hours (30 minutes in an emergency) provided a higher dose of chlorine is used.

Although not specifically mentioned in the NWC document, the relining of a section of water mains irrespective of the materials used should be regarded as a repair, and will require chlorination before returning to service. A generally accepted protocol for disinfection after relining is a chlorine dose of 25–50 mg/l FAC with a contact time of 30 minutes. Retrospective bacteriological analysis should be conducted following flushing when the main is returned to service.

14. THAWING FROZEN WATER MAINS AND SERVICES

INTRODUCTION

Water mains and service pipes are normally buried at depths below the frost line but occasionally severe, prolonged cold spells will cause pipes to freeze, especially in still water conditions. Persistent problems in a similar area suggest that the pipes should be buried deeper, or a method of heating them should be incorporated. A less costly alternative method is to arrange for the supply to be kept running.

If a water main or service pipe freezes during a prolonged cold spell there is little point in attempting to thaw it unless additional measures are taken to prevent the main refreezing. The benefits of thawing are normally achieved after the cold spell has ended by assisting engineers to restore supplies more quickly.

METHODS

Several methods have been used to remove ice from pipes and these are electrical, low pressure steam, hot and cold high pressure jetting.

Electrical

The principle is to increase the temperature in a pipe by connecting a low voltage, high current DC electrical supply to it. This is achieved using a welding type transformer operating at several hundred amperes. Although this method is effective, great care must be exercised to ensure that the pipe is electrically isolated from all other services. As it is quite usual for the water main to be used to earth the house supply the use of this method can be hazardous.

The Use of Low Pressure Steam

Small vehicle-mounted boilers have been used to produce low pressure steam which is then injected into frozen pipes. It has been shown to work, albeit at a very slow rate. The use of steam is **not recommended** as leakage into possible voids around the pipe could create a pressure vessel and a potential explosion. If steam is used, then the operator must be protected by a water spray barrier across the opening where the injection pipe is inserted. This will condense any possible blow back of steam.

Hot and Cold High Pressure Water Jetting

WRC carried out some experimental work in 1982[58] using both hot and cold high pressure water jetting to remove ice from frozen pipes. Standard commercially available jetting machines were used, together with standard nozzles. The nozzles incorporated both retrojets, to provide forward motion, and a forward facing jet to remove the ice. The experiments carried out proved the principle of using both hot and cold water jetting but no attempt was made to optimise the parameters (jet size, water temperature and pressure). However, it was shown[58] that a jetting pump capable of as little as 54 bar was suitable although a minimum of 80 bar is recommended.

SAFETY

In both steam and pressure jetting, it is necessary to cut a section from the main or service pipe to obtain access to the main. The use of very high pressures is not recommended as deposits may be removed from inside the pipes, possibly causing discoloration or taste and odour problems.

Usually the authority's jetting equipment belongs to the sewerage division and **on no account** should this be used because of the dangers of contamination. Care must be taken to sterilise apparatus before use and the pipes before returning them to service.

15. MAINTENANCE OF SERVICE RESERVOIRS

INTRODUCTION

The Reservoirs (Safety Provisions) Act 1930 requires that no man-made storage or service reservoir with a capacity of 5 000 000 gallons (22 730 Ml) or more of water stored above natural ground level should be constructed except under the direction of a qualified engineer who has been appointed to the appropriate panel of the Institution of Civil Engineers. The reservoir should not be filled or operated except in accordance with his preliminary certificate. Thereafter, notice must be published and the reservoir inspected by a qualified engineer at intervals not exceeding 10 years, or more frequently as stipulated by that engineer. The owners must record the structural description and capacity, daily water levels related to the overflow sill, and all leakages, settlements and works conducted on the reservoir affecting these matters.

The Reservoirs Act 1975 transfers responsibility for large service reservoirs (25 000 Ml or more above natural ground level) to the Greater London Council, the English or Welsh county councils or the Scottish regional or Islands councils in which the reservoirs are situated. The authorities appoint the inspecting engineers, who must be independent of the constructors and owners. In addition, a supervising engineer, who may be an employee, is appointed to oversee day-to-day safety matters and enforce the requirements of the inspecting engineer's certificate and report. The supervising engineer must keep records, inspect the reservoir twice yearly, submit a report to the inspecting engineer annually and draw his attention to any matters affecting the safety of the structure. Inspections must be carried out within 2 years of the final construction certificate, at intervals not exceeding 10 years, when called for by the supervising engineer or after any alteration which might affect safety. The supervising engineer provides the inspecting engineer with a statutory record, copies of certificates and annexes, inspection reports and other relevant data. Reservoirs not subject to statutory control should be inspected and supervised in a similar if less formalised manner.

THE EXTERNAL INSPECTION

Routine inspections are conducted with a reservoir in service to monitor structural stability. There should be no significant slip or crack in retaining walls or earth banks, nor any water leakage. Grass should be trimmed and lines and levels of banks checked by eye. Any suspicion of movement should be drawn to the attention of the inspecting engineer who may institute a more detailed inspection or survey. Drain valves should be operated to ensure serviceability. Covers should be well fitting and securely locked against ingress of dirt, animals, humans, vegetation or other pollution. Vents should be screened and baffled clear of the ground.

THE INTERNAL INSPECTION

The reservoir, or possibly one cell only, should be drawn down by consumption then emptied via the scour pipes and the valve left open. Isolating valves should be locked shut and marked with a seal. Covers should then be opened to thoroughly vent and the atmosphere checked for oxygen. The responsible engineer should satisfy himself that all is in order and issue a permit to enter the confined space. Appropriate plant, lamps, lifting gear, breathing apparatus and first aid equipment should be to hand. It is advantageous for a microbiologist, bacteriologist and/or chemist to enter the reservoir when first emptied in order to assess its state of water hygiene and recommend any special remedial work. Samples may be required of any deposits or animals found.

The roof should be thoroughly flooded and checked for leaks. Intrusions may appear through the roof, walls or even the floor. All internal surfaces should be thoroughly inspected, using a high power electric lamp, and details plotted on a copy of the record drawing. Sketches and photographs of general views and particularly any cracking surfaces will help illustrate the inspecting engineer's records and any consequent report.

INTERNAL REPAIRS

Roof, Walls and Floor

Suspected leaks should be confirmed by flood test and all intrusion points identified for sealing. Any sealing materials used should be approved for potable water contact unless securely overcloaked. Isolated leaks may be plugged using cement mortar with an approved hardener accelerator/water proofer added.

Cracks should generally be cut out and filled. A non-shrink additive helps avoid mortar repairs reopening. Alternatively, fine cracks may be filled using a penetrating epoxy resin. Hairline or sealed cracks may be overcloaked using an epoxy resin. Epoxy resins have good adhesion, strength and flexibility characteristics.

Generally porous areas of concrete or cement rendering can be sealed using a slurry coat of proprietary cement proofing compound.

If it is necessary to recast the floor, underdrains should be laid or renovated. These prevent back pressures and possible water intrusion. The floor should slope at a gentle fall (1:100) to a drainage channel and sump sited below a materials access manhole for easy removal of silt. The floor may be divided by 50–100 mm high upstands to provide manageable washdown lanes.

Ironwork

Ironwork may be badly corroded following submersion in water. New pipes, access ladders, guard rails, support straps, etc., should be sheathed in a suitable plastic or nylon coating or constructed of corrosion resistant aluminium or stainless steel alloy. Corroded iron is difficult to protect. The surface must first be thoroughly brushed, if possible to bright metal, cleaned and dried, then painted with bitumen or epoxy resin paint. Condensation and water build up during internal repairs is a continuing problem and should be reduced by thorough venting and the use of electric rather than gas lamps and heaters.

Control Pits

Valves, sampling pipes and instruments can be conveniently located in a central chamber to be accessible for operation and maintenance. Electric and telemetry apparatus should be sealed against moisture and maintained at a satisfactory temperature. A full depth visual level tube will avoid the need to enter the water chamber to confirm levels. The only apparatus inside the actual chamber might be a sealed float switch connected to the emergency alarm or an automatic entry valve pilot float.

Sterilisation

An existing service reservoir after entry for inspection, cleaning or maintenance of any type must be sterilised by washing the walls and floors with clean water or chlorinated water (at 20 mg/l FAC) and introducing a minimum depth of 300 mm to the floor. Furthermore, the floor, walls and pillars could be sprayed with permethrin prior to chlorination. However, sufficient time should be allowed between permethrin spraying and chlorination as permethrin is deactivated by chlorine. Adequate safety precautions should be taken during this procedure.

EXTERNAL REPAIRS

Roofs

A badly leaking roof needs to be exposed, scarified, rendered and covered with a suitable membrane. Asphalt, bitumen, rubberised/polythene membranes are stuck to the surface or alternatively buried in the soil thus reducing excavation costs. Secure seals must be made at access points such as covers and vents. The opportunity might also be taken to renew or improve surface water drainage from the roof. A structurally unsound roof might be strengthened by pouring a new reinforced concrete slab over the existing surface.

Walls

Unsound walls may require strengthening by cladding with reinforced gunite, casting a bonded wall or other structural diaphragm. To prevent water instrusion this would best be on the upstream (outer) face of the wall. A less expensive alternative is to ensure free drainage on the outer face by drilled drain and/or syphon tubes to below reservoir level. Any seepage is then always outwards.

Entry Points

Reservoirs should be secure against intruders with all covers and doors of steel, airtight and properly locked. Where possible, little used access covers should be buried or otherwise made inconspicuous. Renovation works might provide the opportunity to improve the security of the venting arrangements.

16. HEALTH AND SAFETY

Men employed in maintenance gangs should be medically fit and free from intestinal disorders. No carriers of disease should be employed on treated water work. All employees should be medically screened by blood tests (e.g. the Widal test for typhoid) and laid off work in the event of any subsequent enteric infection until medically cleared. All employees must be scrupulously clean in their habits and warned that any misconduct could result in dismissal.

Their health and safety should be safeguarded as required under the Health and Safety at Work Act 1974 by providing training and subsequent practical experience for each man. Trained and competent supervisors should approve each working site to ensure a safe working environment. The following points should be included:

(i) Transport should be Ministry of Transport approved for roadworthiness and function and weight limits defined and understood.

(ii) Street works should be adequately signed and protected[59,60].

(iii) Hazardous obstructions such as high pressure gas lines and buried or overhead electric cables should be located prior to commencement of works by reference to plans, liaison with owners, inspection and tracing by instruments as appropriate. Operatives must be clearly instructed of dangers and made responsible for their own safety.

(iv) Excavations should be adequately supported with safe access to deep trenches and guardrails to protect both workers and the public.

(v) Confined spaces must not be entered without approval and the issue of a signed certificate of entry by the responsible officer. Safety apparatus includes gas detectors, lifting gear, personal harness, masks, breathing apparatus and first aid kits which should be readily available for use by trained personnel.

(vi) Lighting, heating and power in confined spaces should be 110 V centrally earthed.

(vii) Personal clothing should include cotton or wool one-piece overalls (for protection against electricity flash), steel-toed safety boots, British Standard helmet and protective gloves as appropriate. In the highway, fluorescent jerkins should be worn or an illuminated bandolier for short duration work which does not merit road signing, such as valve operations.

(viii) Cutting, grinding, welding and lead jointing operations should be performed by qualified personnel only, who should wear a full-face visor. The work should be adequately screened and nearby operators and supervisors similarly protected.

(ix) Lifting should be with approved hoists, ropes, slings hooks and shackles. Selection of apparatus, testing and re-testing should be in accordance with the directives of the Safe Lifting Manual[61]. Men should not attempt to lift weights greater than their capacity. Approved guidelines should be issued and practical exercises held for all manual and supervisory staff.

(x) Accidents of any form should be immediately reported to the supervisor who will record full details and, where not already done, arrange for appropriate medical treatment.

17. REFERENCES

1. Lackington, D. W. 1983 "Survey of the renovation of water mains", Proceedings of the IWES symposium on deterioration of underground assets.
2. Nicholson, R. F. and Buchanan, J. 1981 *Aqua*, 23, 22, Swabbing the Eppalock-Bendigo pipeline.
3. Water Research Centre 1981 "A guide to solving water quality problems in distribution systems", Technical Report TR 167.
   Note: Lettered suffixes 3a to 3j indicate sections of Ref. 3 with initial page numbers as follows, respectively: 92, 30, 79, 108, 69, 26, 13, 51, 133 and 150.
4. British Non-Ferrous Metals Technology Centre 1982 "Dezincification in supply waters", MP 491, 3rd edition.
5. Oliphant, R. J. 1978 "Dezincification by potable water of domestic plumbing fittings", Water Research Centre, Technical Report TR 88.
6. Cornwall, F. J., Wildsmith, G. and Gilbert, P. T. 1973. *Br. Corros. J.*, 8, 8, Pitting corrosion in copper tubes in cold water.
7. Campbell, H. S. 1971, *Wat. Treat. Exam.*, 20, 11, Corrosion, water composition and water treatment.
8. Oliphant, R. J. 1982 "Contamination of potable water by lead from the corrosion of soldered joints" Water Research Centre, External Report 57E.
9. Stephens, J. W. and Gill, B. W. 1982 "Service failure experience of uPVC pressure pipes in the water industry", Plastic Pipes—5th International Conference, University of York.
10. Kirby, P. C. 1981 "PVC pipe performance in water mains and sewers", International Conference on Underground Plastic Pipes, New Orleans.

11. Roberts, N. P. and Regan, T. 1974 "Causes of fractures in grey cast iron water mains", The City University.
12. Needham, D. and Howe, M. 1979 "Why pipes fail", Institution of Gas Engineers, Communication 1103.
13. Ridgeway, J., Ainsworth, R. G. and Gwilliam, R. D. 1979 "Water quality changes", Proceedings of WRC Conference on Water Distribution Systems, Oxford 1978.
14. Ainsworth, R. G., Ridgeway, J. and Gwilliam, R. D. "Corrosion products and deposits in iron mains", Ibid, Oxford 1978.
15. Victoreen, H. T. 1979 "Water quality changes in distribution", Ibid, Oxford 1978.
16. Water Research Centre 1978 "Biodeterioration of rubber sealing rings in water and sewage pipelines", Notes on Water Research No. 18.
17. Blow, C. M. 1975 "Rubber technology and manufacture", Newnes-Butterworth, London.
18. Water Authority Association Advisory Committee 1982 "Rubber sealing rings", Information and Guidance Note, 4-40-01.
19. Council of the European Communities 1980 Official Journal of the European Communities, No. L229, 23, 11, Council Directive relating to the quality of water intended for human consumption.
20. Williams, S. M., Ainsworth, R. G. and Elvidge, A. F. 1984 "Investigating the effect of water composition on iron pipe corrosion; a short term test", Water Research Centre, Technical Report (in press).
21. Crabbe, R. et al 1982 "A guide to water network analysis and the WRC computer program Watnet, Parts I, II and III", Water Research Centre, Technical Report TR 177.
22. Ainsworth, R. G. 1982 "A strategy for water mains rehabilitation", Proceedings of the IWES symposium on deterioration of underground assets.
23. Durand, R. and Condolois, E. 1952 "The hydraulic transport of coal in pipes", Proceedings of the colloquium on the hydraulic transport of coal, National Coal Board Scientific Department.
24. Jenkins, C. A. 1968 J. AWWA, 60, 899, foam swabs for water main cleaning.
25. Irbing, S. and Taylor, B. 1977 "The hydraulic characteristics of foam swabs", Contract report by BHRA for WRC.
26. Jordan, A. C. 1979 "Cleaning water mains with foam swabs", Proceedings of WRC/SWWA seminar: Water distribution systems—problems of water quality and pipeline maintenance.
27. Elvidge, A. F. 1982 "Air scouring of water mains—a method of operation", Water Research Centre, Technical Report TR 179.
28. Elvidge, A. F. 1982 "Air scouring of water mains—WRC experimental work and some theoretical aspects", Water Research Centre, External Report ER 83E.
29. Water Research Centre 1984 "A training video for air scouring operators".
30. Macan, T. T. 1959 "A guide to freshwater invertebrate animals", Longmans, London.
31. Freshwater Biological Association (various dates) "Scientific Publications Series", The Association, Ambleside.
32. Smalls, I. C. and Greaves, G. F. 1968 Wat. Treat. Exam., 17, 150, A survey of animals in distribution systems.
33. Sands, J. R. 1969 "The control of animals in water mains", Water Research Association, Technical Paper TP 63.
34. Abram, F. S. H., Evins, C. and Hobson, J. A. 1980 "Permethrin for the control of animals in water mains", Water Research Centre, Technical Report TR 145.
35. Lingelbach, H. 1970 Neue Hutte, 12, 736, Health aspects of addition of phosophate/silicate inhibitors to drinking water (in German).
36. Dougan, W. K. and Wilson, A. L. 1972 "The determination of iron in water", Water Research Association, Technical Paper TP 83.
37. Parkinson, R. W. 1984 "The operational guideline manual to cement mortar in situ renovation", Water Research Centre, Technical Report TR 200.
38. Parkinson, R. W. 1980 "Durability of in situ bitumen lining in cast iron water mains", Water Research Centre, Laboratory Report LR 1114.
39. Parkinson, R. W. 1979 "Tradition and new relining processes", Proceedings of WRC conference on water distribution systems, Oxford 1978.
40. Holtschulte, N. 1979 "Practical experiences with cement mortar lining of water pipelines", Ibid, Oxford 1978.
41. Wagner, E. F. 1974 J. AWWA, 66, 358, Autogenous healing of cracks in cement mortar linings for grey iron and ductile iron water mains.
42. Parkinson, R. W. 1982 "Renovation and renewal of water mains", Proceedings of Plastic and Rubber Institute conference on the use of plastic and rubber in water and effluents.
43. Parkinson, R. W., Warren, I. C. and North, K. J. 1983 "Recent experiences with epoxy resin lining of water mains", Water Research Centre, Report 106E.
44. Water Authority Association Advisory Committee 1983 "Ductile iron pipes and fittings, Information and Guidance Note, 4-21-01.

45. *Ibid* 1983 "Operational guidelines for the loose polyethylene screening of underground iron mains", Information and Guidance Note, 4-50-01.
46. *Ibid* 1982 "Unplasticised PVC pipes and fittings", Information and Guidance Note, 4-31-01.
47. Critchley, R. and Habershon, J. J. 1981 "An investigation into the influence of pipe characteristics on the failure rate of uPVC and cast iron water mains", Water Research Centre, Report 7E.
48 British Standards Institution 1983 "CP 312: Part 1. Code of Practice for thermoplastic pipe. General principles and choice of materials".
49. Kirby, P. C. 1980 *Plastic and Rubber Materials and Applications*, 5, 78, Surge and fatigue in uPVC sewer rising mains.
50. British Standards Institution 1983 "CP 312: Part 2. Code of Practice for thermoplastic pipe. Unplasticised PVC pipework for the conveyance of liquids under pressure".
51. Water Authority Association Advisory Committee 1982 "Asbestos cement pipe and fittings", Information and Guidance Note, 4-12-03.
52. *Ibid* 1983 "Specification for polyethylene pipe for cold potable water (underground use)", Information and Guidance Note, 4-32-02.
53. *Ibid* 1983 "Specification for polyethylene pipe for cold potable water (for nominal sizes greater than 63 mm)", Information and Guidance Note, 4-32-03.
54. *Ibid* 1983 "Specification for polyethylene fusion joints and fittings for use with cold potable water pressure pipes", Information and Guidance Note, 4-32-04.
55. Institution of Water Engineers 1973 *J. IWE*, 27, 125, Experience with cathodic protection of mains: final report of Research Panel No. 13.
56. Water Industry Training Association 1984 "Run lead jointing", Course D 13.
57. National Water Council 1979 "Water supply hygiene", Occasional Technical Paper No. 2.
58. Strickland, L. 1982 "Thawing frozen water pipes using high pressure jetting", Water Research Centre, Report 87E.
59. Department of Transport 1974 "Traffic Signs Manual" (chapter 8).
60. Department of Transport 1979 "Traffic warning signs for roadworks".
61. Home Office "The use of chains and other lifting gear", Safety Pamphlet No. 3, 7th edition.

Gilroes pipe depot (*Severn-Trent Water Authority*)

(*left*) **Slip-lining of main**
(*above*) **Sounding for leaks**
(*Bristol Waterworks Company*)

Chapter 11

WATER USERS' SYSTEMS

1. INTRODUCTION

THIS Chapter describes how water is supplied to the consumer, how it is metered, how supplies are given for industry and for fire fighting, and how the needs of tall buildings are met. The legislation relating to water supply in Britain is detailed in Chapter 2, including variations applicable to Scotland and to Northern Ireland, and is only briefly mentioned in this Chapter.

2. SERVICE CONNECTIONS

The mains distribution system—281 700 km in England and Wales and about 39 300 km in Scotland—has been described in Chapter 5, but it serves no useful function until consumer connections are provided.

DOMESTIC SUPPLIES

A domestic consumer requiring a supply of water is entitled to demand one under the Water Acts, but this does not include the right of connection to a trunk main. In Scotland, there is a duty on undertakers to provide domestic supplies where this can be done at reasonable cost.

The supply so provided must be wholesome and sufficient for the domestic purposes of all owners and occupiers of the premises.

In other words, once a supply has been given there is a continuing obligation on the undertaker to maintain it, subject to penalties, except in the case of frost, drought, unavoidable accident or other unavoidable cause, or the carrying out of necessary works—for example, a main shut down following a burst to allow repairs to be made.

NON-DOMESTIC SUPPLIES

The right to a supply for non-domestic purposes provides that a supply for other than domestic purposes shall be given on reasonable terms and conditions. This is qualified by a proviso that such a supply need not be given if the supply to domestic consumers is thereby prejudiced, any dispute on this question being subject to appeal to the Minister.

This substantial priority of supply for domestic consumers was, however, challenged in England and Wales during the 1975-76 drought when the maintenance of employment was given priority by the Drought Minister and restrictions imposed on domestic consumers to keep industry at work.

The supply of water for public purposes includes a supply for fire fighting, referred to later in Section 6.

It is important to understand the definitions of supply pipe, service pipe and communication pipe, as these have legal status under the Water Acts. Fig. 11.1 illustrates the standard definitions, but there are many complicated variations, especially in old property with combined supply pipes (Fig. 11.2).

A consumer requiring a supply for domestic purposes must give 14 days' notice of his intentions to lay the supply pipe at his own expense, may be required to pay the

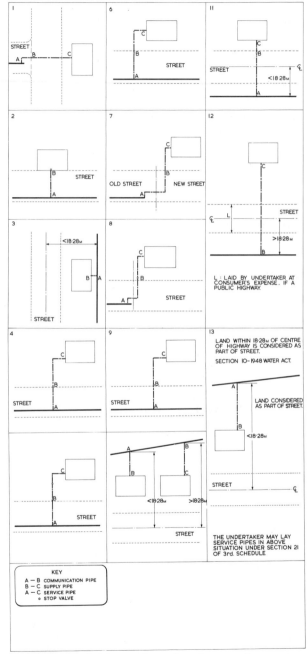

Fig. 11.2.   Illustrating definitions of service pipe etc. in more complicated situations

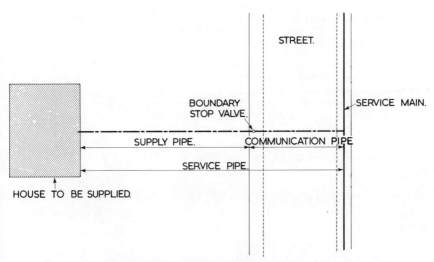

Fig. 11.1.   Illustrating standard definitions of service pipe etc.

estimated cost of the communication pipe and, following this, the undertaking must lay the communication pipe and connect it to the supply pipe within 14 days.

The undertaking will normally adopt a similar procedure for non-domestic supplies, but in this case the connection will usually require a meter (see Section 7). A typical domestic service connection is shown in Fig. 11.3. Most undertakers will lay the communication pipe themselves, either by direct labour or by contract. Legislation in Scotland requires the undertaking to lay the communication pipe and also as much of the supply pipe as is to be laid in a street.

METHOD OF CONNECTION

The connection to the water main in the smaller sizes is nearly always made with an underpressure ferrule for two reasons:

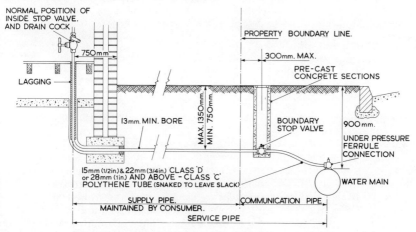

Fig. 11.3.   Typical domestic service connection

(1) tapping the main under pressure avoids the need for the supply to consumers to be turned off while the connection is made;
(2) by keeping the main under pressure pollution is avoided.

The underpressure tapping gear takes various forms, according to the type of material of the main, and self-tapping ferrules are now available which only need a key to operate them.

Typical gear consists of a watertight box strapped to the main in which a drill and tap and ferrule are fitted so that, after the main has been drilled and tapped and the drill withdrawn, the top of the box can be rotated to present the ferrule to the drilled hole for insertion and tightening. Other machines are available which enable a ferrule to be inserted under pressure without the need to rotate the watertight box.

SIZE OF CONNECTIONS

The vast majority of service connections are 13 mm, the relative numbers for one water undertaker being as follows:

Size (mm)	13	19	25	25-50	50
Percentage of total	58	26	10	2	4

For sizes over 50 mm pipeline mainlaying materials are used. Although underpressure connections are available in many cases a standard tee will be inserted after other consumers have been warned of a shut down.

After the ferrule has been inserted and flushed to remove swarf or debris, it is temporarily shut down with a ferrule key while the communication pipe is laid and connected to the supply pipe (Fig. 11.4). The sequence of operations may be altered to suit site conditions.

MATERIALS FOR SERVICES

The original material used for pressurised services was lead but its use within the UK has recently been prohibited by the DoE due to its adverse health effects. It was later supplemented but not superseded by various forms of iron, but this, although cheap and strong initially, is subject to both internal and external corrosion and needs substantial protection. It has now virtually been replaced by one of the following:

(a) Underground copper to BS 2871 Part 1.
(b) Underground copper coated with a uPVC protective coating.
(c) Low density polyethylene to BS 1972 (Type 32).
(d) High density polyethylene to BS 3284 (Type 50).
(e) uPVC to BS 3505.

Copper pipe is expensive and if uncoated subject to external corrosion, especially when laid in ashes.

Coated copper pipe is satisfactory in service but still more expensive, but cost differences in pipe are less vital when total service laying costs are considered. Plastic pipes are much cheaper than metallic pipes. They are highly resistant to corrosion, obtainable in long lengths (thus reducing jointing problems) and flexible but easily damaged by excavators. Being black they can also be confused with electricity cables, and some earlier types are permeable to natural gas and petrol. As a safety measure NJUG (the National Joint Utilities Group) have agreed to colour code small underground pipes as follows:

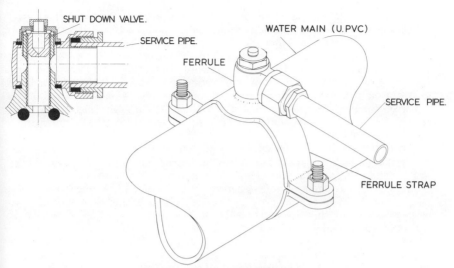

Fig. 11.4. Ferrule connection

(i)	Gas	—		Yellow
(ii)	Water	—		Blue
(iii)	Electricity	—		Black
(iv)	British Telecom	—		Grey

It is intended, when the coloured pipe is introduced, to replace low and high density polyethylene pipe by medium density pipe, and this will be the standard for future use.

HYDRAULIC SIZING

For the hydraulic sizing of services, the reader is referred to the current edition of BS CP 310, "Water Services in Buildings", which is being revised and will be issued later as a BS document with a new number.

For domestic purpose a service pipe of 13 mm diameter is normally quite adequate unless it is very long.

However, consideration should be given to the provision of 19 mm communication pipes and fittings to enable lower pressures to be adopted in the interests of energy conservation and waste reduction. A large proportion of the friction loss in a service takes place in the ferrule and, in some cases, may prevent otherwise satisfactory low pressure operation.

FLOW AND PRESSURE CONTROL

If water flows are high, a restricting orifice can be inserted with the boundary stop valve which can be removed later when flow and pressure control is initiated.

METHODS OF INSTALLATION

The pipeline should be "snaked" (Fig. 11.3) horizontally after connection to the ferrule, to allow for settlement and to prevent lateral tension on the ferrule. It should be at a minimum cover of 0.75 m for frost protection and selected granular backfill carefully consolidated around the pipe, free of sharp stones or known deleterious materials such as ashes. Ideally, cover should not exceed 1.35 m.

Wherever possible, the communication pipe should be laid at 90° to the street line and in a straight line to the stop-valve to aid tracing later.

Plastic pipes are difficult to trace and a dimensional sketch relating to fixed street features should be made of every communication pipe and filed, with a good index, so that if the stop-valve box is covered the communication pipe can be traced.

The communication pipe terminates at a boundary stop-valve paid for by the consumer but with both thereafter the property of, and maintained free of charge by, the water undertaker.

The stop-valve is fitted, usually in a precast concrete chamber, as near as practicable to the boundary of the street abutting the consumer's premises, either just in the street or just in the consumer's premises.

Although by custom most undertakers fit the stop-valve just in the street, high maintenance and reinstatement costs, as well as the now general open plan of front gardens, do suggest that a position just in the front garden is preferable, provided that future accessibility is assured. At least one British water company has always adopted this practice.

In view of the depth of the stop-valve it is difficult to operate a crutch head by hand and a square head—key operated—is preferable. The consumer has the right to operate this stop-valve e.g., to repair an inside stop-valve, provided he has the consent of other consumers where supply might be affected. An undertaker should sell stop-valve keys at a reasonable price to consumers if square head stop-valves are fitted. Square head stop-valves are also a deterrent to a consumer turning on the supply after shut-off for non-payment of water charges.

Where communication pipes are laid to new developments across existing paved streets, reinstatement costs are very expensive and traffic is disrupted. This can be overcome by thrust-boring the pipe under the street, but it is essential that a careful check on the position and depth of other utilities, services and mains is made first to avoid expensive and dangerous damage to them.

Another expedient when more than one supply is required and thrust-boring is not practicable, is to lay two communication pipes in one trench and then branch to two stop-valves at the boundary. Again these should be symmetrically arranged, if possible, to facilitate later tracing.

On new housing estates, service entries to houses should be co-ordinated with the developer and the other utilities, and it may be possible to arrange joint trenching to reduce costs, provided that any gas leakage is not allowed to pollute the water supply. The developer should be asked to provide ducts for the communication pipes to each house before the roads are constructed. These must be clearly and robustly marked at their terminations otherwise much time will be spent in searching for the end of the ducts.

The communication pipe should not be laid until the consumer's supply pipe is completed and left open for inspection to ensure that it is properly laid and at the correct depth. Ideally, domestic plumbing should also be complete and inspected for compliance with the water undertaking's byelaws.

If these points are not insisted upon and communication pipes laid first, it is possible to find the house occupied before inspections have been carried out, and the remedying of defects is then difficult, if not impossible.

The only exception to this is the practice of laying one future communication pipe as a metered building water supply to the site. This saves the expense of an extra connection to the main. Building water supplies are a fruitful source of waste and should be metered. Another method of affording a building water supply is to provide a metered hydrant standpipe.

Such standpipes are frequently damaged or disappear, and a deposit at least equal to their value should be insisted upon in advance of delivery. The communication pipe, the supply pipe and the domestic plumbing should be sterilised before being used, although this is often not carried out. The undertaker should offer this service to the developer on a pre-payment basis.

Providing the communication pipe is laid properly, future maintenance should be minimal. Highway works may require the stop-valve box level to be adjusted so sectional precast surface boxes are desirable to facilitate this.

The stop-valve is likely to become filled with consolidated street debris, and to remove this a long-handled "spoon key" may be used.

The opening of the box should be large enough to enable the stop-valve to be re-washered.

SHARED SERVICE PIPES

It is not always understood that, in former times, particularly in low income areas, it was established practice to install one stand-pipe which fed several properties and, at best, one tap was provided in each cottage kitchen.

One of the problems which inevitably arise when considering alternative supplies is that of shared service pipes, that is, one communication pipe supplying several properties.

Within the distribution system, shared supplies produce difficult and time-consuming problems. Difficulties usually arise only when the existing system becomes inadequate for the purpose, which usually happens, for example, after a row of agricultural or industrial cottages has been modernised or a large building split up into flats.

Since the end of the last war many of these properties have been sold off, particularly with the dispersal of large estates and redevelopment. Each property is then modernised to a high standard and the original service, irrespective of what the statutes say and administrative systems provide for, sometimes ends up trying to meet a demand for water which is grossly in excess of that for which it was originally designed. It is in these cases, when often after a costly renovation has taken place, that the consumer finds there is no water flowing into the new bath which has been installed, and the engineer will need to exercise tact and discretion when advising on remedial measures.

SEPARATION OF SUPPLIES

The Water Acts 1945/1981 provide the legal requirements for separation of service pipes. Attention is drawn to the definition of communication pipe and supply pipe, the positions of which are laid down, and a study of the 1981 Act will show where responsibilities lie. The practical application of the Acts calls for the exercise of tact and, sometimes, persuasion.

Joint supply pipes will be in service for many years, and new problems have been experienced recently where local authority housing has been sold off to sitting tenants. Often these properties were built when the local authority was the responsible undertaking for the water supply and, in these cases, joint supplies were often normal practice.

Each case needs to be considered on its merits, whilst always trying to achieve the ultimate of an independent service for each property.

Scottish legislation provides powers to water authorities to require separate service pipes, subject to certain conditions and procedures.

3. SUPPLIES TO HIGH RISE BUILDINGS

Irrespective of the height of a building the needs of the consumer are the same—that water shall be available at a suitable pressure at all times. Generally this requirement is met without difficulty by water undertakings where buildings are connected to street mains in which the pressure meets statutory requirements and the highest point of draw off in the building is at a level within those statutory limits, allowing for a margin of pressure to overcome loss of head in the pipes and at the draw-off point. In most cases this point will be the float valve controlling the supply to the cold water storage cistern or a feed cistern to a hot water system.

It is recommended that a designer or installer should consult the relevant water undertaking to obtain information as to the statutory requirements concerning pressure and the actual available pressures to the site concerned. This should be asked for to cover a 24 hour cycle. Although the undertaker may be meeting the statutory height of supply there may be some reticence in quoting precise figures as these may vary daily, weekly or even on a seasonal basis, where there is a changing population, as occurs in seaside resorts.

In the past there were several ways in which adequate pressure could be made available at all draw-off points. Probably the simplest was to insert a booster pump in the supply pipe near the point of entry, usually in parallel with a standby unit, and appropriately placed non-return valves to prevent circulation to the street mains.

Whilst this would have had to be with the agreement of the water authority, attitudes to such an arrangement varied according to local conditions. Some undertakers would agree to direct boosting where it was considered that statutory requirements were being met with plenty of mains capacity in support. At least one undertaking permitted in-line boosting where the added pressure would not exceed, for example, 15 m (50 ft) head or where controls were put on pump capacity in relation to the size of main to which a supply was connected. If these limits could not be met, then boosting would be permitted only from a low-level storage cistern.

The reason for such restrictions derived from the problems found to occur when pumps coming in and out of operation caused surges or shock-waves in the undertaker's mains and supplies therefrom. Apart from the environmental effect of water hammer, such surges were found to be contributory to pipe failure. With the present increasing concern that all possible measures should be taken to prevent and reduce waste of water, control of any arrangements likely to cause leakage clearly is important. This has been reflected in byelaws made by water authorities since the DoE revised guidelines were made available in 1978.

Whilst water undertakers have no powers to waive byelaws, in exceptional circumstances application can be made to the Secretary of State for the Environment to relax a byelaw. Therefore, agreement to direct in-line boosting is likely to be rare and the alternative method of pumping only from storage cisterns to other cisterns at a higher level has to be used.

Consideration has to be given to the height, location and quantity of such storage. From the building design aspect, accommodation of the major storage at ground level is preferable but there is still a need to store enough water at high level to carry over a power failure period. Although it is not obligatory to provide storage where cisterns are installed in dwellings, water undertakers' byelaws require a minimum of 115 litres for cold fittings or 230 litres where the storage cistern is to feed both cold fittings and hot water apparatus. Generally, this would be increased *pro rata* where a number of flats receive water from common storage.

A complication arises with the supply of drinking water. When direct boosting was permitted it was common practice to insert a length of large pipe in the booster supply to high level cisterns, with automatic switches arranged so that after the cistern was full the pump did not cut in every time a drinking tap was opened. Only after the water level in the enlarged pipe had dropped to a pre-determined point would the pump be activated. This avoided the need for specially designed drinking water cisterns.

With the present limitation by water byelaws, the enlarged pipe arrangement is no longer possible direct off the mains. It might still be used on the pump delivery pipe from a low level to a high level cistern, in conjunction with a pressure vessel to prevent the low level pump operating unnecessarily when the high level storage is full.

Because of the likely future effect of the EC quality requirements for drinking water, a method of storing such water has assumed greater significance than previously. Although the requirement for "in-house" storage applies to only certain parts of the UK wherever boosting supplies are necessary, water will have to be stored. Currently the view is taken that any tap in a dwelling is liable to be used to supply water that may be drunk. With this in mind and the EC background, consideration is being given to a review of the design of cisterns for storing potable water.

There are existing British standards for cold water cisterns manufactured from steel, cast iron, asbestos, cement and polythene. In addition there are a number of proprietary brands available in uPVC and resin-bonded glass fibre. Different materials call for variation in thickness, method of construction and profile but generally, with the exception of some polythene cisterns, they are of rectangular shape designed to work with a free water surface but with a loose fitting lid.

Comparatively recent revisions have paid more attention to the need for the material not to produce any undesirable effects on the water. Also, more emphasis has been placed on the design of lids to ensure rigidity and prevention of ingress of dirt. Whilst this may well meet present byelaw requirements for general domestic use, it cannot guarantee that the nature of the water after storage will meet the drinking requirements for water supplied to taps which are to be the only source (as would be the case in dwellings set above the height to which street mains can deliver).

Until such time as a new British Standard is produced which deals with all drinking water cisterns, irrespective of material, plumbing designers concerned with high rise buildings and similar supplies should rely on existing water byelaws wherein the proviso to the byelaw requiring a tap under the mains pressure for drinking states that provided where, by reason of the height at which the water is required to be delivered or of some other circumstance, it is not reasonably accessible, the tap may be provided on a pump delivery pipe or distributing pipe drawing water exclusively from a storage system which:

(1) is a closed vessel having a tight fitting access cover bolted or screwed in position;
(2) is properly maintained and, when necessary, suitably lined or coated to preserve the potability of the water;

(3) has an air inlet and an overflow pipe or pipes all suitably screened;

(4) is, where necessary, insulated against heat; and

(5) is supplied exclusively from a service pipe, or from a pump delivery pipe drawing water either from a service pipe or from a storage cistern which is a closed vessel equipped, maintained and supplied as aforesaid.

It will be seen that the hardening of attitudes to in-line boosting has created a need for more attention to the storage of water in a strictly potable condition. At the same time the designer will not have to design his pumping system to cope with varying mains pressure. Once the siting of the low level storage has been decided the suction and delivery head required of the booster pumps can be determined.

An aspect which has become of significance in recent times is the need to be prepared for the effects of industrial action.

The cutting of electrical power would remove the availability of boosting within a building but not necessarily affect the delivery of water to a storage cistern within normal pressure limits. This highlights the need to provide as much storage as possible within the design and structural limitations for a particular building. The advantages of plenty of roof-level storage feeding individual cisterns in each flat become obvious. In this situation the problem of wide variation of pressure on fittings is avoided and the restriction provided by individual float valves will reduce the risk of unequal and heavy demand on the high level cistern in time of emergency.

In the introduction to this Section it was mentioned that reference could be made to other publications which set out detailed descriptions of boosted installations and some of these are listed at the end of the chapter. It is important however, to read these in conjunction with current byelaws (Chapter 3).

MHLG Design Bulletin No 3 shows systems of direct boosting. This would be relevant now only where a byelaw relaxation has been granted by the Secretary of State for the Environment.

The use of delayed action float valves also requires careful thought to ensure that when the water level is lowered to the lower setting sufficient reserve capacity is available.

Since the publication of Design Bulletin No 3, BS 1212, Parts 2 and 3 have been produced which cover the "Garston" type diaphragm float valve, modified to deliver "up and over" discharge to overcome backsiphonage.

4. INDUSTRIAL SUPPLIES—GENERAL

Water use is divided between the following categories:

(a) Domestic use in dwellings and commercial premises.

(b) Agriculture.

(c) Fire and public purposes, for example, street cleaning.

(d) Industry, divided between hygiene needs of employees, incorporation in the product, e.g., food and beverages, and process steam raising, washing, cooling etc.

About half of the metered supply or 17 per cent of the total supply, is used for industrial purposes and discharged as trade effluent.

In recent years, and especially since the 1974 reorganization when the industry became responsible in one authority for both the supply of clean water, the treatment of effluent and the maintenance of river quality, the control of, and standard of, trade effluent discharges has been considerably improved. Charges for trade effluent have also increased and water economy has been brought home to the industrial consumer more through these charges than the metered charge for clean water supplied.

Even now, not all firms endeavour to cut water costs and the economies introduced by the 1975-6 drought are now, in many cases, forgotten.

That is not to say that progress is not being made. New equipment is being designed to be economical in water use and, with the advent of the micro-chip, control systems are now much more accurate and re-cycling of water is increasing.

This is, however, to a large extent being offset by the higher product standards now being demanded. Vegetables are washed and sold pre-packed instead of loose and dirty; meat and poultry carcasses are spray washed and vehicles are steam cleaned; these are all recent developments.

Changes in industrial use match the pace of new development and can be rapid. It is difficult for a water undertaker to get details of expected water demand from developers of new factories as, in some cases, by the time the factory is built the intended product has been changed. The pattern of industrial demand is changing; in the short term it is static or even declining, but within this overall picture there are large fluctuations.

As well as meeting demand and dealing with effluents, the undertaker has to ensure that industrial processes do not contaminate the public supply by back-siphonage or cross-connections between incoming supplies and contaminated process water.

5. ASSESSING AND MEETING INDUSTRIAL DEMAND

QUALITY

Industrial demand can be met in many ways. It can be supplied by direct abstraction from the undertaker's mains, perhaps combined with abstraction from the consumer's own boreholes, or with river abstractions or with the re-use of water inside the factory, or, even, with the use of sewage effluent.

For example, a large rubber works uses the public supply for domestic use and boiler feed, and a large river abstraction for process purposes, mould cooling etc.

A cement works uses the public supply to transport chalk slurry from the quarry to the works and for domestic purposes, sewage effluent to mix slurry and clay, and domestic house refuse to heat the kiln.

DEMAND FOR WATER

Aggregated domestic demand, except in periods of high garden watering, does not vary by more than a factor of three from the average, but industrial demand can vary almost infinitely. Demand may be steady for 24 hours a day, 365 days a year in continuous process works; at the other extreme, water use in large quantities, with difficult effluents, may peak over a few weeks of the year only with almost no demand in between: for example, cider pressing, beet sugar manufacture, processing of frozen peas, etc.

PROVISION OF STORAGE

In spite of the vital nature of an assured water supply to industry, whether it be the small high street hairdresser or the giant multi-national, all users exhibit a similar reluctance to invest in water storage to help to meet peak demands and to provide a reserve in case of mains failure. To some extent this must be blamed on the architects' lack of planning and the unenterprising nature of industrial water tariffs which neither penalize peak demand nor offer financial incentives to those holding storage. Peak demand water meters have been designed and could be used to provide these incentives.

CROSS-CONTAMINATION

Where factories use and re-use water from more than one source, for example, public mains, private abstraction, well or river, great care needs to be taken to ensure that cross-contamination does not occur, with polluted water siphoning back into the public mains.

INDUSTRIAL SUPPLY PROBLEMS

Recent cases noted include:

(i) A consumer complaint of salty taste in water supplied to the quay at a port led to the discovery that seawater had been pumped inadvertently into a private main on the quayside by firefighting pumps on a ferry boat. The crew had connected the firefighting system to the potable water hydrant to provide a freshwater supply for washing down the ship, but the seawater pumps used to pressurise the fire fighting system when at sea were still operating. Seawater was forced into the quayside main which was, in turn, connected to the public supply system.

The quayside main was isolated, and then flushed and disinfected. Modifications to hose connections for the firefighting system have been made to prevent future improper connections. The quayside hydrants will be fed via a break-pressure tank and the hydrants will be fitted with a non-return valve.

(ii) At a pressure filtration works of a water authority, about 500 kg of caustic soda drained into a main as a slug during a period of shutdown following a chlorination alarm. The caustic soda was dosed by a reciprocating pump fed by a stock tank elevated above the pump and the main. The outlet valve of the pump was normally kept closed by pressure in the main, but as consumers continued to draw water the pressure fell, allowing the valve to open and caustic soda to drain through. One consumer suffered skin burns due to showering in water of pH 11.0 or over. Warnings were issued to the public and the system was flushed to remove the caustic soda. Precautions to prevent a recurrence included a flow-controlled isolating valve on the delivery side of the caustic pump and a smaller day tank for caustic soda.

(iii) On a large factory where the plant staff carried out routine tests for chromium in plating waste using tapwater as the "blank" solution, the blank was found to contain chromium. A warning was issued throughout the factory for the staff not to drink tapwater because of chromium contamination.

Investigation showed that backsiphonage had occurred in the plating waste treatment plant and the supply pipes within that building were contaminated, although the waste did not go beyond the building. A water inspector had previously warned of risks but remedial work had not been completed. This has now been done. The undertaker heard of the incident only indirectly but many of the factory employees appeared to have warned relatives and many enquiries from the public were received.

Rules to prevent contamination are set out in the Backsiphonage Report[1] which classifies degrees of risk. However, the price of security is eternal vigilance and an adequate and well trained industrial inspectorate is needed to familiarise factories with these risks.

Industrial quality requests are almost as varied as those for quantity. It is normal for an undertaker to offer drinking water quality and industries needing water of a higher quality are expected to carry out the additional treatment themselves.

Soft water is required for boiler feed, hard water is preferred for brewing. There may be some scope in indicating which sources with surplus capacity are the best in these respects.

For low grade process work, it may be possible to offer partially treated water or sewage effluent, but, again, care must be taken to minimise pollution risks or mistaken use for potable purposes.

It is important to be aware of the water quality requirements for industry and these are referred to in more detail in Chapter 4.

6. HYDRANT AND SPRINKLER SYSTEMS

Fire authorities or county councils are responsible for ensuring that adequate supplies of water, at suitable pressure, are available for fire fighting and to meet special needs. In addition, undertakers give private fire supplies to factories, docks, theatres etc (for relevant legislation see Chapter 2).

Water used for extinguishing fires is taken without payment, but if combined supplies are required—for fire fighting and other uses—it is usual to provide a meter on a bypass (Fig. 11.5).

The Secretary of State intends, upon powers conferred by s.2(2), Water Act 1981, to make an Order as to the method of calculation of charges where the supply is combined, that is, fire plus trade or domestic use, but at the time of writing no such Order has been made.

It is customary for an undertaker to fix a wash-out hydrant at the end of the main and sometimes the fire authority contributes 50 per cent of its initial cost to enable it to be used and plated as a fire hydrant.

In order that these rights can be exercised, an undertaker is required, under s.16(1), Fire Services Act 1947, to give the fire authority written notice and a plan within six weeks of the laying of new mains. The undertaker is not required to fix hydrants to trunk mains.

Having provided fire hydrants, the fire authority will require adequate flow and pressure to be maintained in the water mains. It is difficult to give accurate figures as so much depends on the buildings involved in the fire, the surrounding hazards and the grip of the flames. However, as a guide, Bowman[2] gives the requirements shown in Table 11.I.

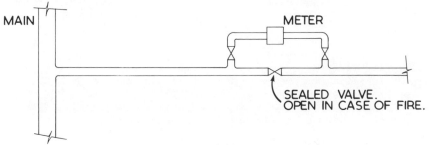

Fig. 11.5.   Provision of meter on fire supply

TABLE 11.1. Water Flow Required for Fire Fighting

Type of fire	Water flow required	
	litres/second	gallons/minute
Simplest	7.5	100
Small house	15-19	200-250
Four houses well alight	30-76	400-1 000
Tenement of six houses	45-114	600-1 500
Warehouse	60-150	800-2 000

The recommendations for hospital protection[3] are shown in Table 11.II.

TABLE 11.II. Water Pressure and Flow Requirements for
Protection of Hospitals

Pressure	Bar	lb/in^2
Running, minimum	4.1	60
Running, maximum	5.2	75
Static, maximum	6.9	100
Flow	litres/second	gallons/minute
Minimum in any riser	22.7	300
Minimum at one hydrant	7.4	100
Minimum at two hydrants	15.2	200
Minimum at three hydrants	22.7	300

It should be borne in mind that after laying fire hydrants, there will be friction losses in canvas hose and at the fire nozzle.

For example[4] at a flow of 7.4 l/sec at the nozzle, 15 m of hose will have a head loss of 0.34 bar (5 lb/in^2).

Where a hydrant is being used at the end of a long length of small diameter main, the delivery of the fire pump may exceed the carrying capacity of the main and care is needed to avoid a partial vacuum. In these cases fire authorities state that collapsible hose should be used on the suction side of the pump.

FIRE HYDRANTS

Earlier forms of fire hydrant have now been wholly replaced by the wedge gate or screwdown type of hydrant to BS 780: 1977 (Fig. 11.6). Wedge gate hydrants are now usually confined to wash-out hydrants at the ends of mains and screwdown types used for fire fighting purposes.

Both types are required to deliver 2000 litres/minute (440 gpm) at a water pressure of 1.7 bar (25 lb/in^2) at the outlet. Hydrant outlets are to a standard of 65 mm bore with round thread (originally London Fire Brigade pattern), to which is screwed a single or double outlet standpipe with, sometimes, its own isolating valve to which single or double hoses may be attached (Fig. 11.7).

British practice favours hydrants in underground chambers to avoid frost and traffic damage but this does mean that hydrants may have vehicles parked over them when required for use.

Hydrant chambers are usually of precast concrete sections terminating in cast iron surface boxes with the following minimum clear openings:

        Wedge Gate type   215 × 495 mm
        Screw down type   230 × 380 mm

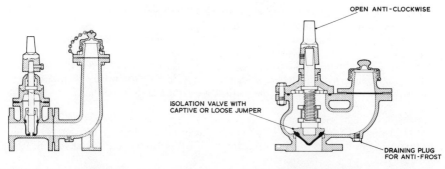

WEDGE GATE VALVE HYDRANT   SCREW DOWN HYDRANT

Fig. 11.6.   Wedge gate and screw down hydrants

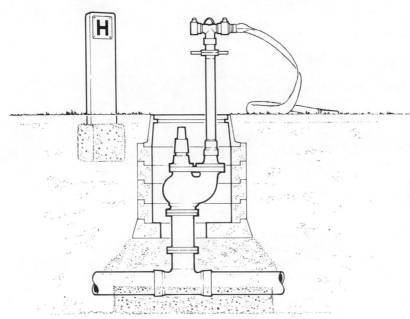

Fig. 11.7.   Typical fire hydrant installation

The isolating valve inside the hydrant can be captive or loose and opens anticlockwise. A loose valve will close automatically if there is a back flow, thus preventing pollution entering the main.

Where hydrants are installed on either side of a sluice valve for emergency boosting, captive valve hydrants will be required, but care should be taken to avoid back flow into the hydrant.

Pillar hydrants are sometimes used on consumer's premises and in areas of high fire risk double hydrants are employed, usually on mains of 300 mm and upwards, either with two outlets controlled by one valve or preferably two outlets separately controlled.

Hydrants are identified by the words FIRE HYDRANT on the lid of the surface box and by a standard indicator plate with a black 'H' on a yellow ground with the size of the main indicated in mm and the distance from the plate to the hydrant in metres.

All hydrants should drain automatically after use to prevent the water freezing and rendering the hydrant inoperable. For this a suitable drain boss is provided at the lowest practicable point on the outlet side with a self-operating frost valve or drilled drip plug.

Except in high risk areas or in rural areas, hydrants are normally spaced at intervals of 90-180 m, normally in the highway but preferably on the verge or footpath where there is one near to the kerb. This location is a matter for the fire authority.

Fire supplies to consumers' premises should ideally be separate non-metered supplies but, as previously mentioned, where a combined supply is laid on, the meter should be on a bypass round a sealed isolating valve.

Where other, non-potable, supplies may be used in a premises for fire fighting, great care must be taken to see that contamination of the mains supply cannot take place by failure to observe the byelaws.

PRIVATE FIRE SYSTEMS

Private fire systems utilizing water as the extinguishing medium or as one of its constituents, usually comprise one or a combination of the following:

(1) Hose reels.
(2) Fire hydrants.
(3) Wet and dry risers.
(4) Brigade inlets.
(5) Automatic sprinkler systems.
(6) Automatic fixed water spraying deluge systems.

NB. Special provision is necessary in the case of high rise blocks—those over 60 m in height.

Hose Reels

These are a hand-held means of fighting fire, consisting of a length of flexible tubing fitted with a shut-off nozzle with permanent connection to a water supply.

The flexible tubing is normally stored on a reel and may be quickly deployed in the event of a fire. The installation, water supply and equipment requirements for hose reels are specified in BS 5306, Part 1 and BS 5274. The nozzle sizes for hose reels are limited to between 4.5 mm and 6.5 mm bore diameter. Hose reels should, whenever possible, be fed from exclusive fire mains; where this is not possible, a check valve should be provided as well as an isolating valve.

Wet and Dry Risers

A dry riser system consists of one or more vertical pipes with outlets at different floor levels (Fig. 11.8). These pipes are normally empty and not permanently connected with any water system, but their lower ends are provided with suitable adaptors for the connection of standard fire hose. The advantage of a dry riser is that the outlets are in preselected positions and much time can be saved in avoiding the running out of long lengths of fire hose from floor to floor. Although the lower end of a dry riser can be connected by means of a fire hose directly with a fire hydrant on a main in a street, it is more usual for water to be pumped into it by

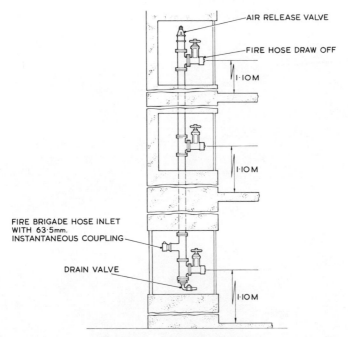

Fig. 11.8. Dry riser system

means of a fire pump. Indeed, a fire pump is essential in many cases if the fire is in the upper floors of a high building and it is at least desirable at other times. Thus, the effectiveness of such a system of fire protection is dependent upon the early arrival of a fire brigade.

A wet riser is a pipe kept permanently charged with water which is then immediately available for use on any floor in a building at which a hydrant (or a landing valve) is provided (Fig. 11.9). The riser is connected to a town main of suitable capacity with a shut-off valve installed. If the building height is such that the pressure in the main is insufficient to supply water to meet the fire brigade's requirements, booster pumps are necessary at suitable levels to ensure the maintenance of the required pressure and flow. Where these pumps are employed the landing valve must be fitted with a pressure regulator.

A similar function to that of a wet riser is performed by what is known as a 'down-comer'. This is constructed of vertical piping, which is supplied with water from a tank in the roof or at intermediate levels.

For such installations as described above, BS 3980, BS 5306 Part 1 and BS 5041, are relevant.

Brigade Inlets

Some sprinkler and hydrant installations are provided with brigade inlets, usually situated in convenient positions near the public street and about 0.6 m (2 ft) above ground level. They are fitted with reflux valves and their purpose is to allow additional water to be pumped into an installation by a fire pump. As there is no certainty about the source from which a fire pump would draw its water (brigades

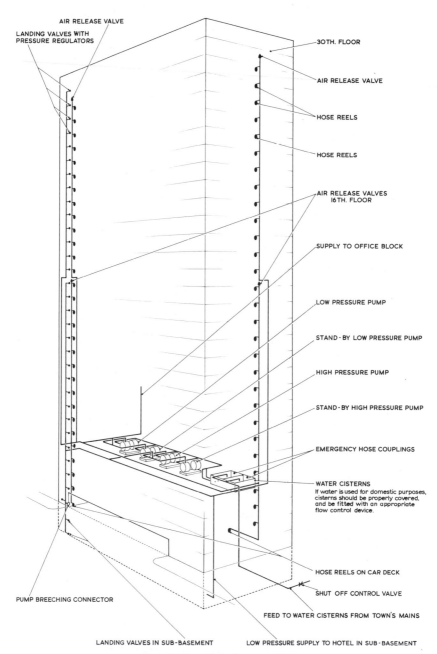

Fig. 11.9. Wet riser system

have been known to pump water from sewers), brigade inlets should only be permitted on wet installations if they cannot be brought into use unless the mains supply has been previously disconnected—not merely shut off.

Similarly, once a brigade inlet has been used, it should be impossible to re-connect the mains supply to the installation without the knowledge of the water undertakers, who will then be in a position to assure themselves that contamination of the distribution system cannot occur.

Automatic Sprinkler Systems

Automatic sprinkler installations provide a means of automatically detecting and discharging water at the appropriate location to control or extinguish fires in the early stages of development.

Systems consist of a water supply connected usually to an overhead piping array onto which sprinklers are fitted. A stop-valve and alarm valve are located in the pipework upstream of any sprinkler heads (Fig. 11.10).

Specialised component parts of the system are constructed to Fire Offices' Committee performance requirements[5] and must be approved to be eligible for recognition for insurance purposes. Each sprinkler head is a thermosensitive device designed to operate individually in case of fire at a predetermined temperature by automatically releasing a stream of water and distributing it in a specified pattern and quantity over a designated area. Fig. 11.11 shows a sprinkler head at point of rupture. In fifty per cent of all sprinkler protected fires, control or extinction has been achieved by the operation of three or less sprinkler heads. Alarm valves are of the check type, designed to allow flow of water in a single direction to the sprinkler system and provide an alarm under predetermined flow conditions.

Where sprinkler installations may be subjected to freezing or temperatures above 70°C, dry pipe alarm valves are used and the sprinkler system pipework is charged with pressurized air. Installations are normally installed to BS 5306 Part 2 and the rules of the Fire Offices' Committee[5].

Sprinkler systems have now been in common usage for almost a century and have proved a reliable and efficient form of fire protection.

For insurance purposes, automatic sprinkler installations are classified according to the nature of the occupancy of risk which determines the water demand requirements. A grading system is applied to water supplies which categorizes them in terms of type and number, determining their suitability in relationship to the nature of the risk. Two independent supplies are often required, such as public supply mains, private reservoirs, gravity tanks, pressure tanks and automatic pumped supplies drawing from a storage cistern or natural source. Each independent supply must be capable of satisfying stated pressure flow requirements for the installation.

Proposals are often made for installations which involve cross-connections between an undertaker's mains and supplies from some other independent source. There are many such installations working quite satisfactorily and without risk to the undertakers but, if they are to be permitted, it is essential that adequate precautions should be taken to prevent contamination of the undertaker's mains distribution system. The most common precaution against contamination is a water-lock which consists of a reflux valve, placed overground in a conspicuous position, closing against the secondary or foreign supply, and an automatic valve which is normally kept closed by water pressure on the installation side of the water lock, closing against the public supply. Between these two valves is a small chamber with a permanently open drain so that any leakage which passes either of the valves

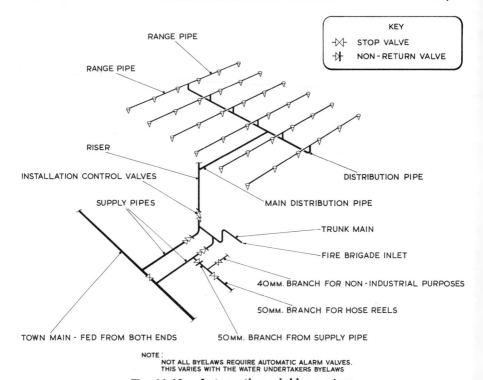

KEY

⊢⋈⊣   STOP VALVE

⊣⋈⊢   NON - RETURN VALVE

RANGE PIPE

RANGE PIPE

RISER

INSTALLATION CONTROL VALVES

DISTRIBUTION PIPE

SUPPLY PIPES

MAIN DISTRIBUTION PIPE

TRUNK MAIN

FIRE BRIGADE INLET

40MM. BRANCH FOR NON - INDUSTRIAL PURPOSES

50MM. BRANCH FOR HOSE REELS

TOWN MAIN - FED FROM BOTH ENDS   50MM. BRANCH FROM SUPPLY PIPE

NOTE :
NOT ALL BYELAWS REQUIRE AUTOMATIC ALARM VALVES.
THIS VARIES WITH THE WATER UNDERTAKERS BYELAWS

Fig. 11.10.   Automatic sprinkler system

Fig. 11.11.   Sprinkler head at point of rupture

in the water lock is apparent at once. Provided the pressure on the installation side of the lock is maintained at a higher level than the pressure on the mains supply and so long as no leakage takes place through the drain of the central chamber, there can be no mixing of the two waters. Regular inspections of the water-lock are necessary to ensure that such conditions are maintained. If a fire occurs and sprinkler heads come into operation, the pressure in the installations will be diminished, opening the automatic valve of the water-lock to admit water from the undertaker's mains.

Automatic Fixed Water Spray Deluge Systems

There are various forms of automatic fixed water spray deluge systems in terms of design and purpose, although in most cases the principles are basically the same (Fig. 11.12). These systems are usually installed for fire control, fire extinguishment or cooling, or combinations of these functions in locations which are beyond the scope of automatic sprinkler installations. Their most common applications are the protection of flammable gas and liquid storage vessels, tanker loading areas, oil-fired boiler houses, electricity generation sets, transformers and process machinery. The distribution pipework of spray systems is normally kept free of water downstream of a deluge alarm valve.

Open spray heads are fitted to the pipework array encompassing the area or object to be protected. A separate fire detection system is located within the protected zone and automatically opens the deluge alarm valve in the event of fire, releasing water into the spray system pipework. Water discharge will occur from all open sprayers in a predetermined pattern and quantity over a designated area or object. Water supply requirements for automatic spray deluge systems are similar to those for automatic sprinkler systems.

7. METERING

Introduction

The earliest commercial water meter in the UK was invented by Thomas Kennedy and patented on 8 December 1852. Although cumbersome, this meter gave long and distinguished service and 100 years later examples were still to be found in service and listed in the current catalogues of the day.

The first semi-rotary meter was patented in 1885 by Frank Waller and it is interesting to note that when some of the earlier models were removed from service in the late 1950s they were found on checking to be accurate within the original specification.

Charging Aspects

Although metering of industrial supplies has been an established practice for many years, the metering of domestic supplies has made little progress. This was probably due to the fact that water charges remain a relatively small percentage of the family budget and, coupled with the lack of cheap small diameter meters, led to the development and retention of a charge based on rateable value for longer than might have been expected, although other methods were considered, particularly towards the end of the 19th century. There has always been a very strong lobby insisting that if water supplies were metered the less well-to-do would not wash or use their WCs frequently enough. Although this lobby is very much weaker now, it is a factor still advanced against metering.

Matters changed, however, with the passing of the Water Act 1973 which

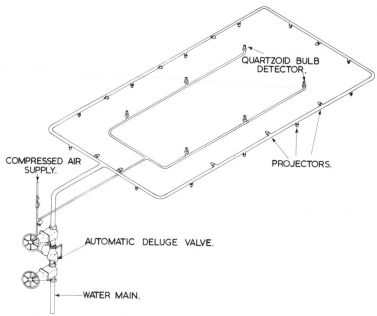

Fig. 11.12.   Automatic fixed water spray deluge system

required water undertakings to pay their way by making changes for services provided. In providing these services undertakers must have regard to costs and, from 1 April 1981, must avoid undue preference and other discrimination against any class of user. An NWC report[6] gives a useful background to household metering and is recommended to those who wish to make a further study of the subject. The DoE response to The House of Lords Select Committee Report[7] stressed the need to ensure a satisfactory balance between the quality of services water authorities provide and the costs borne by their consumers as a result. The DoE also stressed that domestic supplies should be sufficient and wholesome and pointed out the Government does not favour universal metering because of the costs involved and in its absence the price mechanism cannot be used as an effective means of demand management. Charging provisions in Scotland and in Northern Ireland are covered in Sections 17 and 18, respectively, of Chapter 2.

There is a wealth of experience from overseas in metering domestic consumers where it has been common practice for many years, but to date its influence on British practice has not been significant.

TYPES OF METERS

Many types of meters are available to the engineer (Chapter 8, Section 4). The Helix and rotary piston types are shown in Figs 11.13 and 11.14. Special meters are available for waste detection, together with various recording and transmission devices (Chapter 12).

Inevitably, metered systems pose the question of accuracy, particularly at low flows and, in respect of measured supplies to consumers, s.59(3), Third Schedule, WA 1945 lays down limits of plus or minus 5 per cent of consumption registered between which volumetric meters must comply.

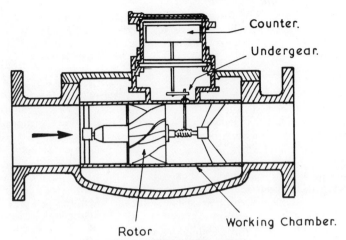

Fig. 11.13. Helix type meter

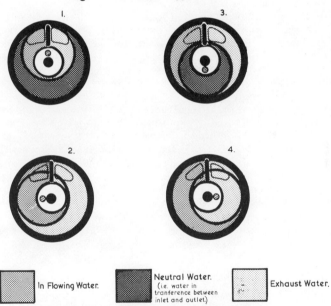

Fig. 11.14. Rotary piston type meter

Considerable work is being undertaken on meter development and testing by the National Engineering Laboratory, the Water Research Centre and by individual manufacturers. Recently, nutating disc meters have been introduced from the United States, together with improved combination meters.

REGULATIONS FOR METERS

With the entry of Great Britain into the EEC, the Community Directive on water meters must be complied with. The UK water industry is represented on a wide range of committees responsible for drafting European and International standards. Not surprisingly, there has been a marked increase in the numbers of overseas meter manufacturers' products in this country and a useful library of information on this subject is being built up by the Water Research Centre.

METERING OPTION

In England and Wales, one effect of the Water Act 1973 on domestic consumers, has been the offering of meter options. Wide publicity has been given to domestic consumers which has included guidelines on meter installation together with advice on how to calculate possible benefits. The experiences of one authority, which offered the option from 1 April 1981 to all domestic consumers, are worth quoting.

Following a significant initial response to the option, the number of consumers requesting the option to meter reduced. From 1 April 1981 to the end of December 1983, over 2 600 domestic properties had meters fitted but this was only 7 per cent of properties where it had been considered the metering option would give a financial advantage to the consumer. Although the takeup has not been large it does remove any question of discrimination in the case of medium or large under-occupied premises.

One authority encouraged metered domestic consumers to save water by issuing, free of charge, two variable-flush, water-saving devices but, even with this incentive, domestic consumers were still slow to take up the option and even more reluctant to fit the devices. In offering the option, consumers were given the benefit of having the meter installed in their premises by an approved contractor. This involved the authority in an extensive training programme and over 500 plumbers across the region were trained.

Training has been one of the successes, but the question of where meters should be sited is still being debated. Options vary from more conventional siting at the boundary of the street in which the main is laid (Fig. 11.15) to inside the consumer's property (Fig. 11.16). In the end, costs will no doubt prove the deciding factor and without doubt it is generally cheaper for the meter to be installed inside the consumer's property.

Whatever method is chosen, there are bound to be some problems and certainly, with meters sited inside buildings, there are difficulties in obtaining access for reading. These can be overcome in many instances by setting up a system of pre-paid meter reading cards or by the installation of remote reading devices fixed on an external wall of the premises.

METER INSTALLATION

In January 1982 the NWC published guidelines for the installation of household water meters. The water undertaker will usually provide the meter, which should comply with BS 5728 Part 1 1979, complete with suitable connectors, to facilitate future meter changes without the use of heat or major disturbances of the consumer's pipework. The connections for 15 mm (nominal size) meters should terminate with, alternatively:

   (a) plain 15 mm (outside diameter) pipework;
   (b) G3/4B or male BSP thread (with perforated nuts for sealing); or
   (c) a Water Authorities Association listed BS mechanical joint e.g., 15 mm compression fitting.

Connectors may be straight or elbow. To aid meter removal straight connections

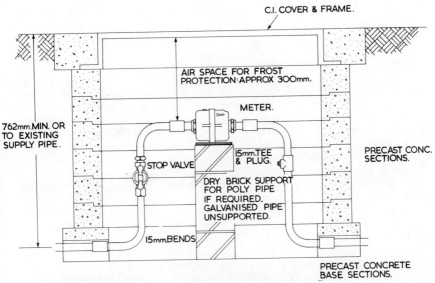

C.I. COVER & FRAME.

AIR SPACE FOR FROST PROTECTION: APPROX 300mm.

METER.

762mm.MIN. OR TO EXISTING SUPPLY PIPE.

STOP VALVE

15mm.TEE & PLUG.

PRECAST CONC. SECTIONS.

DRY BRICK SUPPORT FOR POLY PIPE IF REQUIRED. GALVANISED PIPE UNSUPPORTED.

15mm.BENDS

PRECAST CONCRETE BASE SECTIONS.

Fig. 11.15. Typical external meter installation

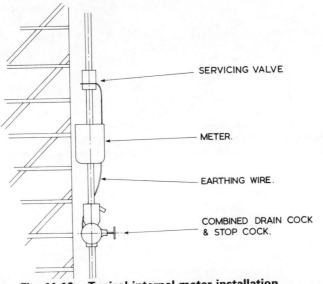

SERVICING VALVE

METER.

EARTHING WIRE.

COMBINED DRAIN COCK & STOP COCK.

Fig. 11.16. Typical internal meter installation

should have flat seats and be complete with 1.5 mm (approx) thick washers to allow for the tolerance in meter lengths. These connections should be installed without modification.

Where consumers are required, or permitted, to carry out the installation, it is essential that they consult the water undertaker with regard to their requirements concerning the installation, before commencing work, and the completed installation should be inspected. Earthing continuity must be maintained by suitable earthing cables permanently fixed prior to cutting pipes for the insertion of meters.

Traditionally, meters have been installed in brick or concrete section chambers with a cast-iron cover of suitable weight, depending on the degree of protection required. Meters have been located at the bottom of the chamber so the inlet and outlet connections were approximately 750 mm below ground level.

This level was chosen since it was considered adequate to protect the meter from freezing (although in the exceptional winter conditions of 1963 some pipes at this depth froze). A meter chamber should provide adequate protection for the meter against frost and accidental damage, be as waterproof as possible and yet give reasonable access facilities for the meter reader.

The development of new materials, particularly plastics, has enabled engineers to take a further look at meter chambers and the whole concept of meter fixing. Existing meter chambers are relatively expensive and involve storing large numbers of concrete sections, separate cast iron frames and covers. It is also physically difficult for meter readers to gain access to the meter and results in much time wasting. The way forward is to improve metering techniques and recently attention has been directed to plastic meter boxes, either with the meter separate or as an integral component. Further development has led to an integral meter and stop-tap box in plastic, with a significant reduction in overall dimensions. This can be supplied either with or without a meter and by the use of a simple blanking off plate in the chamber the integral unit can either be used as a conventional stop-tap chamber or stop-tap and meter chamber. This unit is robust, compact, and has much to recommend it but is only just coming into production.

Meter Maintenance and Repair

In the modern world, with its emphasis on "throwaway" components, it is important to consider to what extent a water undertaking should involve itself with meter maintenance, repairs and testing for accuracy. Various options are available. Meter manufacturers will, for example, often give very keen prices for returning defective meters and supplying exchange units in their place. This could be an attractive proposition since it is costly to develop "in-house" systems complete with meter testing facilities and equipment. Although it is essential to have tight control over meter repairs, it is necessary to examine the cost effectiveness of each method before a firm commitment is made. Regrettably, reliability is questionable since an examination of the stores usually reveals a significant number of meters which have stopped after only a very small quantity of water has passed through them.

To some extent, this is perhaps inevitable since meters, although fixed often on new services, are then frequently connected to an old distribution system where deposits and accumulated sediments find their way through any filter element to clog the meter. In such cases removal of the meter will often allow the debris to be flushed away with clean water. Nevertheless, there is clearly a case for an improved meter which will function on old systems awaiting improvement and yet maintain its accuracy and, even more importantly, maintain accuracy at low flows.

Charging by Meter

Meters play an important role in the determination of charging policies and once a property is metered, be it industrial, commercial or domestic, it gives the supplying authority a better idea of how the water it is supplying is used. For example, it is still difficult to quantify with any degree of certainty just how much water is taken by domestic consumers, although informed estimates can be given. Similarly, the calculation for unaccounted for water, which is an extremely important factor in any supply system, is basically unreliable in the absence of a definitive figure for household use. With the bringing together of the various functions within the water cycle following reorganization in England and Wales in 1974, metering enables a rather more detailed assessment to be made of what is discharged to the sewer by individual properties which, in turn, is reflected in improving charging policies.

The meter options currently being offered to domestic consumers in England and Wales have been brought about by alleged discriminations of the rateable value charges to high rated, medium or large under-occupied houses.

When meters have been installed apparatus exists for improved information on usage and for tariff modification for demand management. The tariff charge should reflect the notional cost of engineering works necessary to fully meet the demand during high peak domestic demand periods.

NEW DEVELOPMENTS

Recently there have been significant developments in the presentation of meter data. It is possible to obtain remote readout devices which can be simply plugged into a meter, whereby the meter reading can be transmitted to a chosen location for easy access. These have not yet been installed on an extensive basis but the results from them are most promising. Digital flow meters are now available but perhaps the most significant development is in the linking of new technology into the labour intensive field of meter reading (see Chapter 13. Section 5).

Transmission of data over considerable distances presents no difficulty and the development of small computerised systems for data storage gives an indication of how meter readings and processing of data could develop over the next few years. It is a far cry from the meters of 100 years ago to the present facility of being able to read, store, then produce an account on site, although due regard has to be paid to the cost effectiveness of these new methods.

Much development is under way to make these procedures available at a reasonable cost, and it is not too far in the future to consider the reading of all utilities' meters by one group of meter readers rather than the existing labour intensive methods and then, at some future stage, to reading utilities' meters over telephone lines or cables back to central computerised systems.

8. PRIVATE SUPPLIES

Where water supplies are not provided by a statutory undertaker, they are usually from private estates, an industry with supplies to owned houses, or farm and other local supplies from factories on a single spring, well or borehole.

While quantity is often adequate except in extreme drought, quality, especially bacteriological quality, can present a problem.

Such supplies are often not sterilized nor regularly sampled, although this is now a requirement under the EC drinking water directive.

Whilst 99 per cent of the population receive a piped supply, there will always be isolated properties too remote to be supplied by a statutory undertaking.

When faced with the cost of adequate treatment and monitoring, private suppliers often opt for the statutory undertaker to take over, and the undertaking may be faced with the cost of expensive rectification to bring the supply up to current requirements.

9. DUAL WATER SUPPLY SYSTEMS

Dual systems—that is, a system with water for drinking and washing supplied from a pure source and a second system say for sewer flushing and fire fighting from some less pure and more cheaply treated source—have not gained acceptance in the UK, largely due to the risk imposed on the community by possible cross-connections, and backsiphonage between systems. In some areas, many years ago, sea-water mains were used for street flushing, but these have now fallen into disuse and are only mentioned from an historical standpoint.

10. REFERENCES

1. Department of the Environment 1974 "Report of the Committee on Backsiphonage in Water Installations", HMSO, London.
2. Bowman, J. 1939 "Water for extinguishing fires", Glenfield Gazette.
3. Department of Health and Social Security 1978 "Cold water supply storage and mains distribution", Memorandum No. 27, HMSO, London.
4. Blair, J. S. 1960 *J. ICE,* 16, 354, Characteristics for fire jets.
5. Fire Offices' Committee 1980 "Rules of the Fire Offices' Committee for automatic sprinkler installations" 29th edition (with amendments).
6. National Water Council 1980 "Charging households for water".
7. House of Lords Select Committee 1982 "Report on the water industry".

Other sources consulted

1. Ministry of Housing and Local Government 1965 "Design Bulletin No. 3, Part 6—Service cores in high flats; cold water services", HMSO, London.
2. Department of Health and Social Security 1978 "Cold water supplies—storage and mains distribution", Technical Memorandum, Document No. 97, HMSO, London.
3. *J.IWE,* 1961, 15, 483, Water supplies to tall buildings, Report of Research Group J.
4. Department of the Environment 1970 "Water services for houses", Report of Housing Development Directorate, Housing Development (v), Parts 1-4.
5. Water byelaws published by water authorities and companies, 1978-1983.

Chapter 12

LEAKAGE DETECTION AND WASTE PREVENTION

1. INTRODUCTION

LEAKAGE detection and waste prevention have exercised the minds and energies of water engineers to a greater or lesser degree over the past one hundred and forty years. The mid-nineteenth century (1844) saw the Report of the Commission of Inquiry into the Health of Large Towns; within a few years there stemmed from this report legislation which led to the establishment of many waterworks systems and, perhaps inevitably, leakage developed.

From that time until recently, leakage detection and waste prevention were not always given the priority of attention which, thankfully, has become the pattern of the past decade, since the formation of the water authorities in 1974.

Often in the past waste detection and prevention were 'Cinderella' functions except during conditions of frost and drought. The early reports of municipal and company activities reveal much thinking on the subject and in some cases indicated that our predecessors were at least conscious of the problem.

It will not be amiss to quote directly from some of these gems from the past. The first[1] states:

"In 1879, as a result of an accident, a waste inspector was employed for the first time. The engine driver at Goldthorn Hill Works suffered an injury while at work, and had to have an arm amputated. As he could not continue at his old duties he was set to work to find waste of water".

In 1880 Feeney[2] wrote:

"It should be borne in mind, that there is no waterworks in the kingdom, constructed on such a scale, as to maintain the supply in the event of a continuous and simultaneous draw off from all the taps. Yet this is very nearly the state of things which arises in winter, when householders turn on their taps day and night to guard against frost and pipes, for want of the simplest protection, are bursting on all sides. In the heat of the summer, the abuse of the water supply, for gardening purposes, and for the relief of the needs of non-paying neighbours who are accustomed to relying at other seasons on their wells, often imposes a severe and unjust strain upon the Company's resources and by augmenting the working expenses, contributes indirectly to increase the cost to regular water consumers. It is therefore in the interest of the community generally that consumers should be advised to exercise prudence and economy in the use of water, not in restriction of legitimate wants, but for the simple avoidance of waste".

In 1888 Hawksley[3] wrote:

"In conclusion, I am pleased to be able to remark that the undertaking appears to me to have been very well managed in every department. I think, however, it is advisable to employ one or two additional inspectors to be solely occupied with the prevention of waste by improper fittings and fittings out of repair".

There are many similar comments from various reports preserved by local undertakings from that time. Young engineering students must of necessity concentrate on gaining their academic qualifications and practical experience, but an occasional delving into the old records can be fascinating and will give some idea of the rich heritage of which we are heirs.

In the years from 1875 to 1957, many technical advances were made[4-9] while, more recently, an IWE symposium[10], a WRA Technical Paper[11] and Report 26[12] have done much to assist water undertakings to standardise the methods and procedures necessary to deal with leakage detection and the prevention of waste on a systematic and economically viable basis.

The report of the House of Lords Select Committee[13], particularly Section 3 on water distribution and leakage control, should be read by all concerned with leakage detection and the prevention of waste. The report advocates a more active leakage control policy on the principles expounded in Report 26[12], which has generally superseded WRA TP 109[11].

The young engineer is therefore now able to draw on a distillation of the ideas of many of his eminently experienced predecessors, while a number of papers[14-21] published from 1972 are in whole or in part relevant to the topic.

Report 26 contains as an appendix a glossary of terms relating to leakage detection and waste prevention which should be consulted by anyone not familiar with the terms used.

2. EFFECTS OF WASTE

PHYSICAL DAMAGE TO HIGHWAYS, SEWERS, STRUCTURES AND TO OTHER UTILITIES

With increasing attention being paid to detection of leakage, the incidence of serious damage to highways and properties should be reduced, provided that repairs are carried out very quickly after leakage has been detected.

The catastrophic bursts which occur from time to time and, which in the case of larger diameter mains, can cause considerable damage to highways, sewers and other utilities and properties, are not likely to be reduced significantly in number by leakage detection programmes.

However, leaking joints and defective mains and pipes which have not completely failed can cause, over a period of time, similar damage. Such leakage, particularly when combined with defective sewers allowing ingress of ground water, can continue undetected for considerable periods before finally causing collapse of a highway or footpath or other consequential damage. Leakage detection on a systematic basis could well reduce considerably the amount of damage caused in this way, provided that repair of any leakage detected is carried out promptly. The cost of such damage to water authorities is not insignificant in financial terms.

ADVERSE EFFECTS ON CONSUMERS

Most engineers will have had experience of the consumer sited at or near the extremity of a distribution system or at some high point in the system, whose call to say the supply has failed or that pressure is extremely low is the first indication of leakage in the system. (Pump failures tend to result in more widespread calls).

This is leakage detection at its most simple but, in urban areas particularly, pressure can be depressed or may be lost completely in parts of demand zones because of increased leakage. WC and storage cisterns do not fill as rapidly as the consumer requires and electrically heated showers fed directly from the cold water supply become inoperable. Increased flow in the local network due to leakage may also result in discoloration of the supply in systems where iron deposition is a problem.

The housewife is not happy if her washing machine ceases to function efficiently, either because of lack of supply or its discoloration. Hot water supplies and central heating systems may be affected if the supply becomes intermittent or is lost completely. Admittedly, these problems are more likely to occur in districts where available mains pressure and capacity are barely sufficient to meet demand at peak periods.

The flooding, or partial flooding, of cellars, gardens and indeed of habitations, though generally caused by the catastrophic or sudden burst, may on occasion be attributed to leakage undetected, but which may have been taking place for some time. As the Water Act 1981 places responsibility for consequential damage on the water authorities, it could be that an authority able to show that it operates a systematic leakage detection and prevention of waste programme would escape penalty or be penalised to a lesser extent than if no such programme were in being.

The repair of leakage during periods of frost should always be a priority. Waste water from leakage running or collecting on road and footpath surfaces and subsequently freezing, if not dealt with promptly, can result in serious accidents.

Fatal accidents caused by such conditions can result in very large compensatory payments. Broken limbs, sprains and bruises may also result in substantial payments, quite apart from the personal mental and physical impact to the people involved.

FINANCIAL LOSSES

The additional costs of treatment and pumping from supply works can be considerable if leakage in the distribution system is not kept under control. Where water is pumped to service reservoirs for onward distribution and excessive wastage is taking place, pumping will be necessary at a higher rate or for additional periods and extra pumps may need to be used. This pattern will be even more obvious where little if any storage is available in the system supplied.

Electricity costs can rise sharply when the operation of additional pumps becomes necessary, even for short periods. Also, it may be that where treatment capacity is limited at treatment works, water quality may be affected if additional loading, due to waste, is placed on the works.

With waste by leakage down to a minimum, abstraction from relevant surface and underground sources will be reduced.

Again, where pressure and flows in a distribution system indicate that some reinforcement or renewal of mains is necessary, it is essential to ensure that the existing system is reasonably leakage free before embarking on costly capital works at that particular time.

Abstraction charges, electricity and chemical costs could well be reduced significantly, probably by some 15 to 25 per cent, and loan repayments for new works deferred would be a further significant cost benefit. These savings cannot be stressed too strongly—it is the duty of all concerned to ensure that the benefits in financial terms are not squandered because of insufficient resources being made available to reduce waste and to keep it at an economic minimum.

INCIDENCE OF CONSUMER COMPLAINTS

Where leakage detection is not carried out systematically and waste prevention not pursued efficiently, complaints of poor supply, loss of supply and discoloration will be made much more frequently than when leakage is under control.

It follows that the additional administrative and operational costs generated by such complaints are a further financial loss for the undertaking, whilst its public image is also adversely affected.

This last factor should not be ignored. Consumers and the media are showing increasing interest in the activities of water undertakings, particularly where new reservoirs or expensive capital works projects are planned or under construction.

3. CAUSES OF WASTE

LEAKAGE FROM SERVICE RESERVOIRS AND TRUNK MAINS

Construction joints in service reservoirs can be sources of leakage and an underdrainage system may indicate such leakage. In the case of older reservoirs with no such facilities detection can be more difficult. Defective ball-valves leading to overflow from reservoirs and faulty outlet and emptying pipework are other causes of waste.

Trunk mains feeding and discharging from service reservoirs are also possible sources of waste, particularly from pipe joints, and such mains should be checked periodically for leakage.

Generally, low levels of leakage are encountered in both service reservoirs and trunk mains.

DEFECTIVE MAINS AND PIPES

By far the largest source of leakage however is from the underground distribution system with its mains and pipes of varying age and material and the multiplicity of joints and fittings, all potential sources of leakage.

Almost all undertakings still have some vertically cast iron mains in service which are between fifty and one hundred years or more old. Most of these were lead jointed and, though reducing in number because of renewal, still make up a significant part of distribution systems. With at least 250 joints per kilometre and numerous connections to property it is obvious that leakage from joints and fittings is a significant factor in the cause of waste.

Most modern mains of spun iron, ductile iron, asbestos cement and uPVC, to mention the more widely used materials, are still susceptible to leakage from joints and fittings to a greater or lesser degree.

Leakage from the glands of sluice valves and from valve body joints are common occurrences and air valves and air taps are further sources of leakages, particularly from worn rings and faulty washers.

Ferrule connections and communication pipes, again of various types and materials, can be additional sources of waste.

UNSUITABLE MATERIALS, AGEING AND CORROSION

Today, with most materials conforming to British Standards, it is unlikely that unsuitable materials will be used in distribution systems. The use of stone pipes in Manchester from 1811 to 1814 as described by Bateman[22] was a disaster not likely to be repeated in modern times.

However, there are some legacies from the past where unsuitable materials were used for mains, pipes and particularly fittings which are still contributory causes of waste. Metal fatigue of cast iron mains in particular, allied in some instances with internal and/or external corrosion of the metal has led to failure. As discussed in Chapter 10, Section 10, some mains of similar age have shown less sign of deterioration and have been satisfactorily scraped and concrete lined. For example two 18″ (460 mm) diameter vertically cast iron mains laid respectively in 1848 and 1875 and reconditioned in 1965 are at the time of writing still giving untroubled service.

More attention is now being paid to the investigation of the corrosion of cast iron mains to ensure that any reconditioning will not proceed unless pipe samples show clearly that the pipe metal is not likely to fail for a considerable period.

Steel mains, if the exterior protection and/or the internal lining have been damaged prior to or during laying, are prone to corrosion at the points of damage. Leakage from such mains is usually local and not catastrophic but can go undetected for considerable periods if leakage detection control is lax.

Asbestos cement and uPVC mains are corrosion free but their ultimate length of service cannot be accurately forecast at this time as they have only been in use for some forty to fifty years, not a long period on the length of service scale!

Communication pipes of lead, lead alloy, copper and polythene have been most used by undertakings over the years though lead has generally been phased out because of cost and the possibility of plumbo-solvency. Apart from the usual causes of failure, metal fatigue, corrosion, chemical attack and faulty laying, such pipes can be damaged during work by other utilities and their contractors and also may give trouble after backfilling due to differential ground settlement.

SOIL CONDITIONS ETC.

The external corrosion of metallic pipes can eventually lead to leakage. Aggressive soils may cause damage because of differing levels of oxygen, moisture, pH and bacterial activity leading to corrosion currents in the pipe metal. Unevenly compacted fill or uneven depth of burial can lead to differential aeration and this and seasonal water level changes in the vicinity of the pipe are each possible sources of future corrosion failure. Organic soils, particularly those contaminated by organic refuse, can result in sulphate reduction corrosion.

Stray electrical currents and, in some cases, dissimilar metals used at connections, are further sources of future waste from leakage.

Most engineers are familiar with the damage which can be caused by soil shrinkage, particularly of clay, and transverse failure of cast iron mains is not uncommon in such circumstances.

Mining subsidence leading to tension, and in some instances to compression failure of mains and joints, though localised, can cause considerable leakage.

Faulty bedding of pipework and inadequate anchoring of bends and valves are further causes of waste in the short or long term.

All the foregoing causes of waste can be eliminated or their incidence considerably reduced when new mains and service pipes are laid. (See Chapter 9).

DEFECTS IN CONSUMERS' INSTALLATIONS

Leakage in domestic and industrial installations, though the consumer's responsibility for repair, is still a factor in causing waste. Faulty tap washers, leaking glands and defective ball-valves are some of the most common causes of waste in the home.

In the factory similar defects and, additionally, incorrectly adjusted automatic flushing cisterns are examples of wastage in the working environment.

NON-STANDARD FITTINGS AND DELAYED REPAIRS

Though byelaw requirements and British Standard specifications give some protection, the increasing use of fittings and materials not meeting byelaw or British Standard requirements by the home handyman and the unqualified plumber can be sources of future leakage which will inevitably result in a higher incidence of waste.

The difficulty of arranging the repair of leakage from consumers' installations, particularly where joint supply pipes are involved, results in greater waste from the affected pipework than would be the case if repairs were effected quickly. The serving of notices on consumers and their efficient follow-up, coupled with the speedy repair of leakage, are essential ingredients in reducing losses from the system.

INEFFICIENT HOT WATER SYSTEMS

The loss from a system because of excessive run off to obtain water of an acceptable temperature is to be deplored. Not only is this wasteful of water but also of energy and the remedy for this wastage is primarily the use of correct design criteria. Stringent byelaw application and efficient inspection of all new installations by the water industry inspectorate is essential if this problem is to be resolved satisfactorily.

EXCESSIVE PRESSURE

Increase in pressure causes increase in flow in piped systems, so that increased

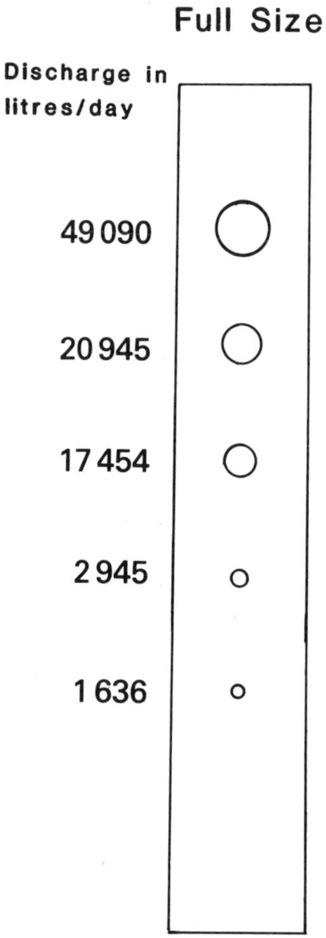

Full Size

Discharge in litres/day

Experiments were carried out by Liverpool Corporation to determine the rate of loss through various sized holes in 0.5 inch diameter lead pipe under a pressure of 31.6 m head. The results are shown in this diagram.

31.6 m head. The results are shown in this diagram.

Fig. 12.1.   Discharges through circular holes in 0.5 inch diameter lead pipe

pressure leads to increased leakage and a consequent increase in waste. Flow from an orifice is usually taken to be proportional to the water velocity and to the square root of the mains pressure at the point of leakage. It follows that the reduction of pressure in a distribution system will have an effect on the rate of leakage and, therefore, on the amount of waste. In some circumstances, there is evidence to suggest that comparatively small reductions in pressure result in significantly greater reductions in leakage than theoretically could be expected and this seems to be an area for further investigation and research.

Reid[23] has stated that: "In the year prior to pressure reduction in a pilot zone, bursts on Corporation mains and services totalled 119. After pressure reduction, for a three year period the aggregate of all bursts was 29. Flows into the zone as recorded on waste water meters were reduced by about 17 per cent during the day and by 65 per cent at night. This was achieved without any deterioration in day time pressures but merely as a result of trimming excessive night heads." Later results in other zones confirmed the soundness of pressure reduction as a leakage controlling agent and such methods are of great importance in suitable supply situations.

Service reservoirs have normally been planned to serve an area or zone within defined pressure limits, but there are examples of excessive night pressures in reservoir controlled systems. Significantly undulating ground can nullify any consideration of using pressure reducing valves (PRVs) but systems should be checked periodically to ensure that pressures are not excessive. Similarly, consideration should be given to the reduction of delivery pressures at source works wherever possible.

When leakage detection is first carried out in a district and subsequent repairs completed, it may be found that pressure in the district has risen significantly, particularly at night. The incidence of leakage will therefore be perceptibly increased and positive pressure control may need to be exercised to correct this.

MISUSE OF WATER

Misuse of the supply is primarily a byelaw, inspectorate and publicity matter, with domestic and industrial consumers being prevailed upon to mend their ways.

However, excessive flushing of distribution systems when swabbing or air scouring, over-frequent backwashing of filters and disposal of sludge not sufficiently dewatered are amongst practices which authorities themselves could well more efficiently control to reduce waste.

DROUGHT AND EMERGENCY CONDITIONS

Drought and other long-term emergency conditions are likely to require substantially increased waste detection activity.

Where an area is supplied with relatively cheap water from a local impounding reservoir and a passive attitude to leakage detection has been adopted, remedial action will only begin when the reservoir water level begins to fall abnormally fast. This can result in stringent restrictions being applied within a comparatively short period whilst every available man is engaged in the search for and repair of leakage. The classic example of bolting the stable door after the horse has gone!

Liverpool Corporation many years ago tested the amount of leakage from relatively small holes in 0.5″ (13 mm) diameter lead pipe at a pressure of 45 lb/in^2 (31.6 m head). There have been many illustrations of the results and Fig. 12.1 shows one of these. It follows that a large number of relatively small leaks can be the cause of a speedy reduction of storage if the inflow to the system begins to fall off significantly.

If leakage control is already practised by district and/or waste metering of an area then, with the onset of drought conditions the long term supply situation is likely to be much better than where only passive control is exercised.

However, once it is apparent that drought conditions are likely, there are a number of measures which can be taken.

The prime control is the reduction of pressure throughout the system. This can be achieved by the partial closing of trunk main valves, reduction of pumping heads and by the setting up of small zones or districts fed through one or two connections at most. If PRVs are already in service, outlet heads might be further reduced and, if waste meter districts are in being, the districts should be set up by closing the boundary valves and feeding the district through the meter connection. Charts should be run from time to time so that some assessment of the savings can be made.

The degree of pressure reduction in any system is a matter for local decision, as at this stage undue inconvenience to the consumer is not envisaged.

Publicity should start at the same time, and industry and domestic consumers be warned of the situation and advised on self help measures that could be taken.

Further pressure reduction should follow if the drought or other emergency continues. Only as a last resort should shutting down the supply partially or entirely during particular times of the day or night be an option, or the closure of stop taps and the erection of stand pipes at various locations. The former course, if implemented, would inevitably lead to consumers drawing water for use during cut off periods, some of the water remaining unused and thus contributing to waste from the system.

Recharging of mains after shut off could result in contamination of the supply and in further leakage from the system, whilst the use of stand pipes would create a number of problems, not least for the old and the handicapped. It would be prudent temporarily to raise chlorine residual levels at source works in such circumstances.

The experiences of 1975 and 1976 confirm that the co-operation of all consumers in making water savings should be sought as early as possible if drought seems likely. Some industrialists made considerable savings in their use of water and in a number of cases never returned to their previous consumption, having assessed the financial savings to be of sufficient significance to justify continued reduced water usage.

With costs continuing to increase, the consumer may be less likely to exercise the care shown in 1975 and 1976, perhaps the more irresponsible taking the view that having paid for their supply they do not wish to be restricted. This is particularly relevant to garden watering and the use of sprinklers for that purpose and the industry will need to make extra efforts in future times of drought to carry the consumers with them in implementing restrictions on a voluntary basis.

Ultimate management of demand, having in mind recent developments, could be implemented by the use of electronic recording meters and the application of differential tariffs.

4. RECOGNITION AND DETECTION OF WASTE

ASSESSMENT AND MEASUREMENT OF WASTE

The terms used throughout this section are defined in the glossary in Report 26. In particular, the definition of waste is of prime importance: "Waste is that water which having been obtained from a source and put into a supply and distribution system and its consumers' installations, leaks or is allowed to escape or is taken therefrom for no useful purpose".

Various methods are available for assessing leakage and thereby waste. Measurement of the quantity of water passing into a system, area, zone or district, be it large or small, is a prerequisite for establishing the overall consumption from which assumptions and calculations can be made to give the relationship between input to the system, etc. and leakage from it in the form of waste.

Practically, the best measure of leakage from a distribution district is obtained by the operation of a waste meter from which, after clearing any leakage backlog, the minimum night flow (MNF) or night line can be determined from the meter chart, adjusted, if applicable, by subtracting any metered consumption within the district from the night line figure and thus deriving the net night flow.

Subsequent operation of the waste meter will indicate any variance in the night line, a rise usually signifying increased leakage which can normally be attributed to waste.

The net night flow, derived from the night line, can be expressed as a percentage of the average supply rate or of the maximum flow rate. In purely domestic districts the night line will coincide with the net night flow, and only in districts where industrial and business metered consumptions are taken into account will any adjustment be necessary to obtain the net night flow.

The results are best expressed in one of the following forms:

(1) as a flow rate—for example, litres per hour (l/h).
(2) as a flow related to mains length—for example, litres per kilometre per hour (l/km/h).
(3) as a flow rate per property—for example, litres per property per hour (l/prop/h).

Percentages and flow rates give information which can be shown graphically and comparison of ongoing results will give a leakage trend. Hopefully the trend will be level or downwards, the latter particularly during the early operation of newly established districts.

METERING OF DEMAND AREAS

It is essential to meter demand areas on a continuous basis. Such meters should be of a type from which the information can be obtained either on a chart or by the more modern methods of telemetry print-out or by the use of data loggers. Information can then be made available in the precise form required, principally to give:

(a) total daily consumption;
(b) maximum flows;
(c) average flows; and
(d) minimum flows (night lines)

In each area there may be a number of demand zones, for even if the supply to the area is derived from the same source, parts of the area will almost certainly be zoned off because of pressure limitations, this being particularly so in undulating areas.

It is often convenient to supply one zone from one or more service reservoirs. Pumped or boosted supplies will normally, because of their intrinsic nature, be operated on a zonal basis. Again, it is essential that zonal supplies within an area should be metered in similar fashion to the area of which they are a part. Indeed, it is usually the case that demand area meter records are obtained from summation of the demand zone meter records of that area.

The information derived from these sources is the basic reference point to which all subsequent effort in leakage detection and waste prevention is related.

Such meters should be regularly maintained and checked for accuracy though, in a properly monitored system, most defective metering equipment is likely to be pinpointed quickly because of non-conformation with a regular pattern of readings. Exceptions are Venturi and similar meters which may drift slowly from the norm.

Though not in all cases coming within the description of area demand meters, measuring devices at source works and aqueduct connections can be used to give similar information to that referred to earlier: certainly the total daily consumption figure is needed and again the metering equipment should be of the finest accuracy available and should be regularly maintained and checked.

Having derived the essential basic information, consideration must be given to the separate elements making up total consumption.

DISTRICT METERING

District meters, which may be demand zone meters or meters commanding districts within demand zones, are usually integrating meters of the Leeds Helix or similar type. Either by daily direct reading or from daily or weekly charts, comparison can be made with past trends and a rough assessment then made of the current position: many undertakings use or have used such a system and, properly monitored, some control of waste is thereby effected, increase in the night line being the signal to uprate the leakage detection effort in the relevant localities.

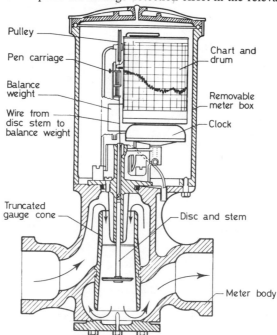

Fig. 12.2.   Deacon waste meter

Source: Metalock (Lancashire) Limited

However, by far the best method of detecting waste in selected districts has been by the operation of waste meters on a regular basis.

Types of Waste Meters

The two most widely used types of waste meter were designed by S. F. Deacon in 1873 and by George Kent in 1908.

The Deacon meter allows water to pass downwards through a diverging cone and then flow round a moveable disc centrally mounted in the cone. The downward movement of the disc is controlled by a counterweight and movement of the disc actuates a recording pen marking a chart which revolves with time (Fig. 12.2). This meter is available in sizes from 3 to 9 inch (75 to 225 mm) diameter, with respective maximum flow rates of 10 000 to 45 000 gallons/h (45 to 205 m³/h).

The Kent meter has a weighted gate, or plate, in front of an orifice, the gate being deflected from the vertical by the force of the flowing water. Increase or decrease of gate deflection depends upon increase or decrease in the flow. The deflection is transmitted by a linkage to a pen which records the flow rate on a chart moving with time and controlled by a clock (Fig. 12.3). The Kent meter is manufactured in sizes from 3 to 10 inch (75 to 250 mm) diameter, with respective maximum flow rates of 10 000 to 80 000 gallons/h (45 to 360 m³/h).

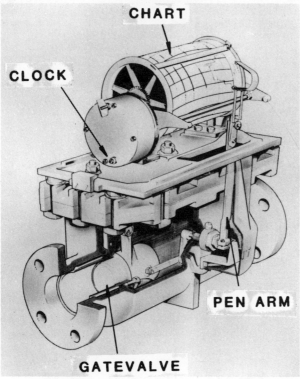

Fig. 12.3.   Kent gate type waste meter

Source: Kent Meters Limited

Recent Developments in Waste Meters and Ancillary Equipment

Recent developments give additional options, two examples of which are the Kent Helix 3000 meter (Fig. 12.4) and the Quadrina Waste Water Flowmeter (Fig. 12.5). These meters are of the turbine type and each can be used with data logging equipment.

Fig. 12.4.   Kent Helix 3000 meter

Source: Kent Meters Limited

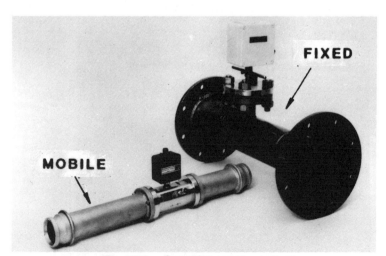

Fig. 12.5.   Quadrina waste meters

Source: Quadrina Limited

The Kent Advanced Flow Analyser System 3000 (AFA System 3000) comprises a meter with pulse unit, data logger, data port, micro-computer and printer with a software package for the computer. All data are conveniently stored on floppy disc and the software offers further operational advantages such as four compressed timescale ratios (2-5-10-20). The chart gives a permanent record of flow rates, digitally and graphically with total quantity on a real time basis.

The meter is manufactured in the following sizes:

Size	mm	40	50	65	80	100	150
Min. accurate capacity	m³/h	0.68	0.68	0.91	0.91	1.59	3.41
Max. peak capacity	m³/h	45	45	170	170	284	568

The Quadrina QW permanent waste flowmeter and the QXL portable hydrant flowmeter are both suitable for waste metering and are most effective when used with a suitable data recording system. The Quasette system is designed for use with any flowmeter in the Quadrina range of turbine flowmeters and incorporates a digital totaliser, digital rate of flow, real time clock and a selected sample period time where specified time periods are required. In addition to flow measurements the Quasette may be used in conjunction with the QRP range of pressure sensors to enable pipeline pressures to be monitored. It is not a data logging system but a fully portable, stand alone readout instrument which may be used with or without its recording facility in a very wide range of flow measurement applications.

The meters are manufactured in the following ranges:

QXL Portable Hydrant Flowmeter

Type		25J	32J	38J	50J	75J
Min. flow	m³/h	0.5	0.8	1.0	1.5	3.0
Max. flow	m³/h	20	30	45	80	160

QW Permanent Waste Meter

Type		3/2	4/2	4/3	6/3	6/4
Size	mm	75	100	100	150	150
Min. flow	m³/h	0.7	0.7	1.4	1.4	2.0
Max. flow	m³/h	70	70	140	140	200

The foregoing information is by no means exhaustive and with new developments coming along so rapidly, personnel within the water industry must be constantly assessing these developments and ensuring maximum use of the best of the new technology.

Location of Waste Meters

Waste meters can be sited in suitable chambers below ground or can be trailer mounted and moved from site to site.

Sites for permanent and for mobile waste meters must be chosen with care, having in mind particularly ground water problems and drainage of the meter chamber for permanent installations and taking particular note of traffic conditions and pedestrian safety in the case of mobile units.

Permanent meters should, wherever practicable, be so connected that they can serve two or more districts by the operation of valves and connections sited at or near the meter site. To a lesser degree, this also applies to mobile meter installations connected to suitably sited hydrants. It is, of course, necessary to use hydrants of fixed valve pattern in mobile installations.

Initial tests must show that sufficient supply at adequate pressure will be available to consumers within a waste meter district when the installation is in operation. In cases, hopefully few, where these criteria cannot be met, it will be necessary to operate the meter other than at peak flow periods which will still allow the determination of the night line.

Districts should, ideally, not have more valves than can be effectively operated during a step test. As the period during the night when step tests can be taken has decreased significantly in recent years, this may mean from three to four hours only after 0100 hours rather than the period from midnight to 0600 hours which was suitable in years past.

INDUSTRIAL AND DOMESTIC DEMAND, CALCULATED AND METERED

Industrial demand can be assessed principally from the meter readings of individual factories and businesses, as most consumers in this category are metered. Where for some reason such supplies are unmetered, assessment of the demand can be made from the number of employees and the number and type of fittings within such premises. Industrial estates are not normally waste metered, but with the provision of unmetered or bypassed fire supplies to some industrial premises, it would seem prudent to make provision for mobile waste metering of such sites as a check on possible leakage or misuse from the unmetered elements of premises supplied.

Though there is movement towards universal metering of shops and small businesses, it could be many years before all such premises are metered, so there will be the need for some years ahead to assess such supplies on the number of staff, the type of water use and the number of fittings individually applicable to such premises.

Domestic demand is normally the largest factor in the total demand of an undertaking. The Mansfield/Malvern study[24] which, unfortunately, did not take pressure into account, nevertheless gave an indication of *per capita* domestic consumption of greater accuracy than most of the previously assessed figures.

Since that study many undertakings have looked in greater detail at their domestic consumption figures and currently domestic consumption in one authority is assessed at 131 litres per head per day. This quantity contains an element for leakage and/or misuse from the consumer's installation and for unmetered consumption at the workplace. Further work needs to be done on this element in the demand equation as misuse and excessive use of water is included in consumer use.

In any particular period the total flow into a system is equal to the sum of the metered consumption and unmetered consumption (mainly domestic) and leakage. This approximates to the formula for unaccounted for water $u = s - (m + ap)$

where: u = unknown or unaccounted for quantities of water
       s = sum of all inputs into the system
      m = sum of all water accounted for by measure
      a = average domestic consumption per head of population plus an allowance for unmetered commercial use
      p = population supplied

A more accurate and reliable figure for leakage estimation is that based on total night flow measurements. This method deals with measured flow rates rather than quantities and domestic consumption is measured in terms of flow per property per hour rather than as an estimated average consumption per head of population supplied.

The equation thus becomes: $u^1 = s^1 - (m^1 + a^1n^1)$

where: u^1 = unknown or unaccounted for night flow rate
s^1 = sum of all input flow rates into the system (night line)
m^1 = total night flow rate of all industrial and commercial users
a^1 = average domestic night flow rate per property
n^1 = number of properties supplied

A method for converting into a total daily quantity, having in mind that night pressures are almost invariably greater than those applicable to daytime, is given in Report 26 (paras 5.07 to 5.10).

STEP TESTS AND AURAL SOUNDING

Ref. 11 and Report 26 give detailed information on the planning and setting up of waste districts and Refs. 8 and 9 should also be studied. However it is considered necessary to reiterate and comment on some of that information.

When a waste meter is first run it is usual for only the boundary valves isolating the district and the relevant meter valves, including the meter bypass valve, to be maintained prior to operation. A chart run for 24 hours under such conditions will give the daily pattern of flow in that particular district, including the initial night line which, before any other work is carried out on the district, will almost certainly have a significant leakage content. A typical district is shown as Fig. 12.6.

On completion of installation and when boundary valves are in proper condition, the initial open run should be carried out and the night line from the chart recorded. When the initial and future runs begin, after the district has been set up, the meter valve should be closed and the chart should then record zero flow, this being an indication that none of the boundary valves is passing. A pressure gauge installed downstream of the meter within the district should be used to confirm this test. Any metered supplies within the district should be noted and an assessed consumption made during the test to cover such consumers. Alternatively, by arrangement with the consumers, the metered connections can be shut out during the test. As soon as practicable after completion of the first open run, a step test should be carried out and again the chart results recorded. The policy should have been so drawn up that the acceptable leakage figure has been decided, say 6 litres per property per hour. Subsequent operations will decide where the acceptable leakage figure will ultimately lie.

The next stage in the process is again to set up the district as above and to close relevant valves within the system which will not interfere with supply but will reduce the number of valves to be shut during a step test. These valves within the district, shut before the test, are termed circulating valves. A 6 hour chart is normally used for step tests and the operation carried out during night conditions, say between 0100 and 0500 hours or marginally longer or shorter periods depending on local conditions and the prevailing pattern of consumer use after midnight.

Each valve in the district not already shut is then closed to a planned schedule, valves furthest from the meter first and that nearest the meter last. A minimum period of five minutes is usual between each closure, though shorter and longer periods of 2½ minutes and 10 minutes may be realistic. After completion of the test the valves are opened in reverse order, care being taken to operate valves slowly to guard against fracture of mains which may have emptied or partially emptied during the test.

The use of radio control during waste meter valving operations should result in more rapid completion of the exercise.

The chart so derived (examples of open run and step test charts are shown in Figs. 12.7 and 12.8) will indicate the roads in which leakage is likely to be taking place by the length of the vertical line shown on the chart, which will also be an indication of the amount of leakage.

Location and Repair of Leaks

Aural sounding then follows of stop taps, valves and hydrants in those roads where there is evidence from the chart that leakage is taking place. The use of electronic and other sounding devices may be necessary at this stage so that any leaks are accurately located and minimum excavation is necessary to carry out repair. It may be that some of the leakage is taking place on supply pipes and consumers' installations. These should also be located and the necessary action taken to ensure that consumers or property owners carry out effective repairs speedily.

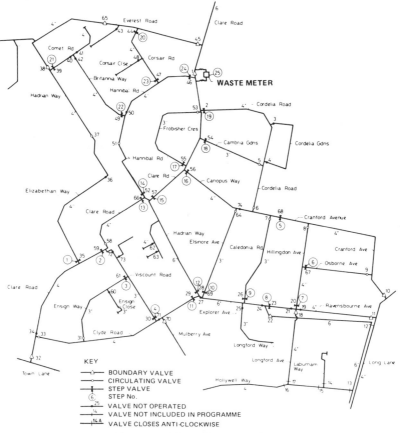

Fig. 12.6. Plan of waste district

Source: Water Research Centre[11]

Procedures vary in undertakings, but it is normal practice to serve a notice under the relevant byelaws on the consumers or owners concerned and to take follow-up action within a reasonably short period of time. Powers are available which allow undertakers to carry out the necessary repairs or to arrange for them to be carried out at the expense of the consumers or owners, the costs incurred being recovered from them in due course.

It is essential that all leakages located following the initial step test are repaired as quickly as practicable and a second 24 hour open run arranged immediately after completion of the repairs. The chart from this second open run will almost certainly

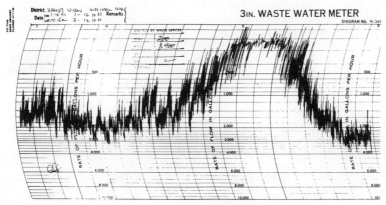

Fig. 12.7.   Waste chart open run

Source: STWA, Derwent Division

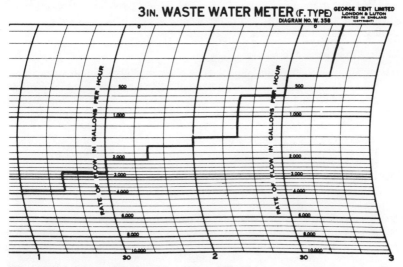

Fig. 12.8.   Chart showing step test with Kent gate type waste meter

Source: Water Research Centre[11]

show a reduced night line, maybe indicating a significant reduction when compared with the original.

Repetition of Step Test Metering

A second step test, which should then be carried out at the earliest practicable time, may still indicate leakage in the district. Again, follow up aural sounding and use of leak locating equipment should result in the leakage being repaired speedily.

A third 24 hour open run should be carried out, again as soon as practicable after repairs have been effected following the second step test. The chart from this run may give a further reduction of the night line and at this stage it may be that this indicates a figure of between four and six litres per property per hour (the number of properties within the district having been assessed during the planning of the district). This figure should be acceptable having in mind the nature of the district, the age of the mains within it and other factors. These factors include the daily pressure range, the type and age of property supplied, the presence of geological faults, mining subsidence and, in some areas, the number of domestic fittings fed from storage.

Further Action

From the waste meter records, it should be possible to arrange a cycle of operation for each waste meter, to be run on a monthly, bi-monthly, quarterly or other basis depending on the depicted change in night line over a period and the known conditions within each particular district.

Zonal and district meter information can often be an indication that the waste meters sited within that zone or district need to be operated. Easily retrievable zonal and district meter records are a necessity for the early recognition and subsequent detection of waste.

It will also be necessary to consider the origin of the supply to each district. The cost of supplying some districts may be much higher than the cost of supplies to others and the frequency of surveillance of districts may reflect these economic factors which will be discussed in detail when the economics of leakage detection and waste prevention measures are considered.

LEAKAGE DETECTION EQUIPMENT

Having assessed the amount of leakage and the rough location of leaks, it is then necessary to locate the positions of individual leaks and there are various ways in which this can be done.

Acoustic Methods

Acoustic methods are those relying on sounding directly on pipes and fittings or, indirectly, on the ground surface and involve the use of sounding sticks and apparatus depending on electronic amplification of the noise generated by the leak.

The stethoscope, or sounding-stick, is the simplest form of aural aid and can be most effective when used by a skilled inspector. The noise from the leak, transferred to the ground surface or fitting, is transmitted by way of the stick to the operator's ear. Unfortunately, not all leaks are noise producers. Leakage detection inspectors need to be selected carefully and, after thorough training and the acquiring of site experience, they are likely to be able to locate the point of leakage in the majority of cases—maybe more than 80 per cent by the more highly skilled inspectors. Practical guidance is given on this matter in Report 26, Section 8.

Additional sounding on the surface often then allows the leakage to be pinpointed and this sounding requires relative quietness and may need to be carried out at night.

Amplifying Devices

Electronic amplifying devices receive and amplify the noise generated at the leakage. These instruments allow a choice of certain frequency ranges from the leak noise for selective amplification so that outside noise interference can be partially reduced.

The 'Terrascope' and 'M-Scope' are two examples of this type of equipment and suitably experienced inspectors can successfully pinpoint leakage in a good percentage of cases using these aids. If the position of the main or service being scanned is known this assists the accuracy of the findings. With the increasing use of uPVC and the presence of AC mains, it is most important that mains records are accurate and comprehensive so that leakage detection, when necessary, is not made more difficult because the position of the main is not known or has been given erroneously.

Leak Noise Correlator

The leak noise correlator, first developed by the Water Research Centre and now produced commercially, is a powerful addition to the aids available to leak detection units and has been employed with great success in finding leaks which have not been pinpointed by other means. The apparatus is particularly effective in detecting leakage of low noise intensity or with high background noise levels.

The instrument makes use of the fact that sound velocity through a particular mains or pipe system is constant. By placing microphones on fittings on the main or on the main itself on each side of the suspected leakage the difference in time for the leak noise to reach the microphones can be measured. The distance between the microphones is known or can be measured and from this distance and the time difference the position of the leak may be calculated (Fig. 12.9). It may not be possible to use the correlator with full efficiency if the main under examination is of more than one material, such as iron and uPVC.

Full details of the equipment and guidance on its use are given in WRC TR 157[25].

The leak noise correlator is particularly convenient for use in urban areas where the number of valves, hydrants and stop cocks is greater than in rural areas. In the latter case it may be necessary to bar down to the main to allow access for the correlator equipment to be used.

A new Mark II instrument marketed in 1982 by the manufacturers Palmer EAE Ltd is microprocessor controlled and has electronic display systems. Previously, the time delay measurement and leak position calculation were manual tasks which, with the updated instrument, are now dealt with electronically. The machine size has also been reduced but it seems likely that operators will need more training to deal with the new model than was formerly the case.

Detection by Nitrous Oxide and Other Tracers

The use of nitrous oxide (N_2O) for leakage detection involves the gas being pressure injected in controlled quantities into the main or mains under inspection after withdrawal from service. The gas is soluble in water, non-reactive, non-toxic, chemically inert, odourless and tasteless. It can also be readily detected in small quantities and added advantages are its comparative cheapness and its availability in suitable cylinders. The procedure is for a scientist or other suitably trained person to inject N_2O into the main, a prerequisite being that the mains pressure must not be similar to or greater than the gas injection pressure. Injection can be made at a ferrule or other suitable point and water is then allowed to flow in the main at a measured rate until dosing of the length of main to be investigated is completed. The outlet from the main should then be closed and the mains pressure increased to the test pressure. As water leaks from the main, its pressure reduces to atmospheric and the nitrous oxide comes out of solution. Test holes are made along the length of the main on its known line and a probe is then inserted in each hole in turn, whence the air in the test hole is tested for nitrous oxide, presence of the gas indicating leakage at or near the relevant test hole. Details of dosing, precautions, etc. are given in WRA TP 109[11].

Other gases and tracers have been used, notably recently sulphur hexafluoride (SF$_6$) which has a number of advantages. WRC TR 80[26] gives full details of methods using sulphur hexafluoride.

The use of tracer methods has limitations, but the techniques are useful, particularly when dealing with trunk mains laid in non-urban areas and where the main can be isolated from normal supply.

Data Loggers and Telemetry

For those undertakings with some form of telemetry, continuous print out of information can be used, particularly during night periods, to observe on a day-to-day basis any significant change in night lines. Effort can thus be expended in areas or zones where such changes in night line have been noted.

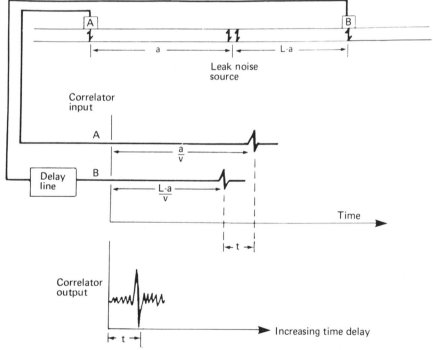

Fig. 12.9.   Diagram of leak/noise correlator
Source: Water Authorities Association[12]

Some undertakings are able to assess, from information similar to that outlined above, the particular district or districts which need attention because of increased leakage. Though fine control is possible in these cases, usually because the undertaking is small and relatively easily monitored, there is no reason why large undertakings should not achieve similar results by good technical innovation and sound management.

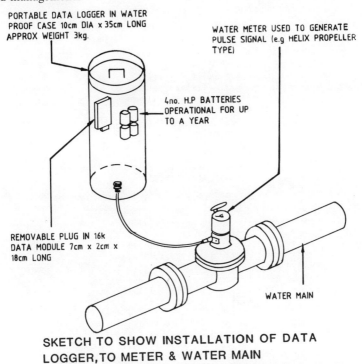

PORTABLE DATA LOGGER IN WATER PROOF CASE 10cm DIA x 35cm LONG APPROX WEIGHT 3kg.

WATER METER USED TO GENERATE PULSE SIGNAL (e.g HELIX PROPELLER TYPE)

4no. H.P BATTERIES OPERATIONAL FOR UP TO A YEAR

REMOVABLE PLUG IN 16k DATA MODULE 7cm x 2cm x 18cm LONG

WATER MAIN

SKETCH TO SHOW INSTALLATION OF DATA LOGGER, TO METER & WATER MAIN

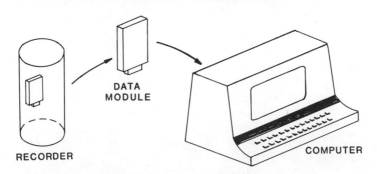

DATA MODULE

RECORDER

COMPUTER

INTERROGATED BY COMPUTER

Fig. 12.10.   Data logger as used for waste detection

Source: STWA, Avon and Derwent Divisions

Data loggers can of course be connected to most types of meter, though not currently to waste meters. The benefits to the industry as the data logging technique develops seem likely to be of significant value in distribution and leakage control, with many advantages over current methods of recording flow and

RECORD COMMENCED 15 : 22 : 0 BST ON Tuesday 30 June 1981

PERIOD ENDING	READING IN l/s	
15 : 32 : 0 BST	0.680	IIIIIIIIIIII
15 : 42 : 0 BST	0.680	IIIIIIIIIIII
15 : 52 : 0 BST	0.743	IIIIIIIIIIIII
16 : 2 : 0 BST	0.794	IIIIIIIIIIIIII
16 : 12 : 0 BST	0.842	IIIIIIIIIIIIIII
16 : 22 : 0 BST	0.901	IIIIIIIIIIIIIIII
16 : 32 : 0 BST	1.027	IIIIIIIIIIIIIIIIII
16 : 42 : 0 BST	1.093	IIIIIIIIIIIIIIIIIII
16 : 52 : 0 BST	0.926	IIIIIIIIIIIIIIIII
17 : 2 : 0 BST	0.866	IIIIIIIIIIIIIII
17 : 12 : 0 BST	0.725	IIIIIIIIIIIII
17 : 22 : 0 BST	0.725	IIIIIIIIIIIII
17 : 32 : 0 BST	0.741	IIIIIIIIIIIII
17 : 42 : 0 BST	0.741	IIIIIIIIIIIII
17 : 52 : 0 BST	1.019	IIIIIIIIIIIIIIIIIII
18 : 2 : 0 BST	1.065	IIIIIIIIIIIIIIIIIIII
18 : 12 : 0 BST	0.926	IIIIIIIIIIIIIIIII
18 : 22 : 0 BST	1.009	IIIIIIIIIIIIIIIIIII
18 : 32 : 0 BST	1.111	IIIIIIIIIIIIIIIIIIIII
18 : 42 : 0 BST	1.148	IIIIIIIIIIIIIIIIIIIIII
18 : 52 : 0 BST	1.112	IIIIIIIIIIIIIIIIIIIII
19 : 2 : 0 BST	1.075	IIIIIIIIIIIIIIIIIIII
19 : 12 : 0 BST	1.146	IIIIIIIIIIIIIIIIIIIII
19 : 22 : 0 BST	1.368	IIIIIIIIIIIIIIIIIIIIIIIIII
19 : 32 : 0 BST	1.587	IIIIIIIIIIIIIIIIIIIIIIIIIIIIII
19 : 42 : 0 BST	1.587	IIIIIIIIIIIIIIIIIIIIIIIIIIIIII
19 : 52 : 0 BST	1.448	IIIIIIIIIIIIIIIIIIIIIIIIIII
20 : 2 : 0 BST	1.190	IIIIIIIIIIIIIIIIIIIIII
20 : 12 : 0 BST	1.277	IIIIIIIIIIIIIIIIIIIIIII
20 : 22 : 0 BST	1.391	IIIIIIIIIIIIIIIIIIIIIIIIII
20 : 32 : 0 BST	1.391	IIIIIIIIIIIIIIIIIIIIIIIIII
20 : 42 : 0 BST	1.321	IIIIIIIIIIIIIIIIIIIIIIIII
20 : 52 : 0 BST	1.282	IIIIIIIIIIIIIIIIIIIIIIII
21 : 2 : 0 BST	1.156	IIIIIIIIIIIIIIIIIIIIII
21 : 12 : 0 BST	1.269	IIIIIIIIIIIIIIIIIIIIIII
21 : 22 : 0 BST	1.372	IIIIIIIIIIIIIIIIIIIIIIIIII
21 : 32 : 0 BST	1.319	IIIIIIIIIIIIIIIIIIIIIIIII
21 : 42 : 0 BST	1.042	IIIIIIIIIIIIIIIIIIII
21 : 52 : 0 BST	1.073	IIIIIIIIIIIIIIIIIIII
22 : 2 : 0 BST	1.111	IIIIIIIIIIIIIIIIIIIII
22 : 12 : 0 BST	1.228	IIIIIIIIIIIIIIIIIIIIIII
22 : 22 : 0 BST	1.049	IIIIIIIIIIIIIIIIIIII
22 : 32 : 0 BST	0.926	IIIIIIIIIIIIIIIII
22 : 42 : 0 BST	0.719	IIIIIIIIIIIII
22 : 52 : 0 BST	0.667	IIIIIIIIIIII
23 : 2 : 0 BST	0.699	IIIIIIIIIIII

EXAMPLE OF PRINT OUT FROM MODULE SHOWING TIME,DIGITAL AND ANALOGUE FLOW
(FLOWS RECORDED EVERY 10 mins FOR 14 DAYS DURATION ARE TYPICAL)

Fig. 12.11. Typical output from data logger

Source: STWA, Avon and Derwent Divisions

pressure information. A sketch of the equipment and a specimen print-out of information derived from an installation in use are shown in Figs. 12.10 and 12.11.

The logging of night lines for leakage detection purposes and the summation of flows over defined periods will be of particular use in the keeping of permanent records with consequent savings in administrative costs.

MANPOWER

It should be made clear that despite all the recent technological and electronic advances in the field of leakage detection and waste prevention, adequate manpower, properly trained and effectively deployed, will still need to be made available to ensure that systematic surveillance and repair of the system are assured. Of necessity some of the required measures will still require operatives to work at night, though probably under conditions and for periods less onerous than in past years. Manpower should not be withdrawn from leakage detection except in particular emergencies; it should not be regarded as a pool of labour for dealing with random tasks as and when these arise. Under drought and some other emergency conditions, however, additional manpower may be needed to deal with leakage as the overriding priority at such a time. The recommendations of the House of Lords Select Committee[13] should be referred to regarding manpower.

LEAKAGE FROM TRUNK MAINS

As indicated in Section 3 leakage from trunk mains is generally a less significant factor than leakage from the distribution system. However, it should not be ignored and there are a number of methods for locating leakage from trunk mains. These may be:

(i) walking and sounding the main;
(ii) measuring pressures at relevant points;
(iii) halving techniques using
    (1) WRC heat pulse flow meter
or (2) pairs of insertion turbine meters
or (3) sectioning.

Once leakage has been detected and isolated to a suitable length of main then the actual location may be found by sounding, by the use of SF_6 gas tracing techniques or by the leak noise correlator. Full information is given in Report 26 (Part 3, Section 10, paras 10.01 to 10.25).

Trunk main inspection and other costs are dealt with in Part 2 of the same publication.

5. RECTIFICATION

LEAKAGE CONTROL POLICY

The setting up and continuation of a leakage control policy which should lead to the speedy and effective repair of known leakage is a prerequisite of rectification.

The other essential factor is the prime importance of making a correct financial assessment before taking action and this aspect is dealt with in the last part of this Section.

For any leakage detection and waste prevention policy to succeed, management from the top and through all levels should give enthusiastic support to the implementation and continuance of that policy.

The three quotations given in the Introduction illustrate three points which should be noted. Firstly, the tendency to divert men to waste detection duties because of physical unfitness to carry out their normal work should be resisted, unless the operative concerned has the other qualities necessary to become a good waste inspector or waste supervisor.

In the second place, though it is good policy to advise consumers to exercise prudence and economy, these excellent exhortations will be rendered of little use unless the undertaking's waste policy is properly planned and efficiently and enthusiastically implemented in practical terms.

Finally, Thomas Hawksley's advice about fittings inspection was good for that time, but one must guard against appointing "one or two inspectors" (or ten or twelve) without first assessing the number really required to carry out the policy decided upon as right for a particular authority or for individual divisions or units within that authority.

Any leakage control policy must be based on measurement of flows in demand areas, zones and districts. Without such measurement only assessments of flows can

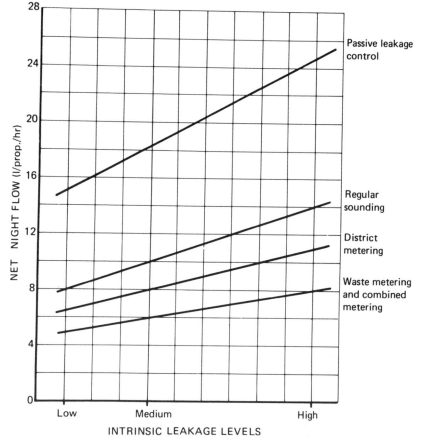

Fig. 12.12.   Prediction of net night flows

Source: Water Authorities Association[12]

be made which may be crude in the extreme. Even if only demand zone metering is employed, some idea of the position within each zone can be obtained from night lines and from checking service reservoir levels during off-peak periods. If only manual aural sounding is carried out, the results are not likely to approach those obtained by adequate demand zone, district and waste district metering. Even so, a system of minimal zonal metering backed up by manual aural sounding will give better results by far than the passive method of control, if control is indeed a term which can be applied to such a concept.

LEAKAGE CONTROL METHODS

The passive method is that whereby only waste causing concern to or complaints from consumers is actively pursued, except under drought or other emergency conditions. No attempt is made to measure or detect leakage but some aural sounding may be carried out where leakage breaks out on the surface but requires more definite locating. It is doubtful whether any undertaking is still following the passive method entirely and it is not one of the options which should be considered seriously if a leakage detection and waste prevention policy is to be effective.

Regular sounding is another option which should not be considered as the main component of leakage detection policy. Carried out on a systematic basis throughout an undertaking once or twice a year, it is obviously a better option in terms of results than the passive method. However, sounding, if non-selective, is wasteful of manpower and the best way of using manual aural sounding is by directing it to districts or parts of districts where leakage is known to be taking place.

This requires the operation of a comprehensive waste metering system where regularly produced charts show whether the leak detection team needs to move in and where step tests indicate the street locations where leakage is taking place. The maximum effort can then be directed to where it is needed—that is, converging on the leak(s).

Fig. 12.12 shows typical leakage levels for the four main methods of leakage control. For leakage in an undertaking using regular sounding techniques in the medium range, that is, net night flow of 10 litres/property/hour, the implementation of a full waste metering programme should produce net night flow of 6 litres/property/hour.

In setting up a leakage control policy it is rarely necessary to start from scratch. It will be prudent, however, to discuss the setting up and implementation of a policy from basics and this implies consideration of procedures which are already in being in many undertakings.

FLOW MEASUREMENT AND ESTABLISHMENT OF NIGHT LINES

Measurement of flows and quantities are necessary for all source and treatment works. Flows and quantities transmitted through trunk mains before and after treatment should be monitored and also the inlets to and outlets from service reservoirs.

It has been demonstrated that leakage from such installations is in general of much less significance than the leakage losses in the distribution system, that is, downstream of treatment works and service reservoirs.

Metering of all demand areas and demand zones is the first priority in establishing a waste policy. Edwards[27] has described an area and zonal metering system and given a diagram of the metering arrangements. Later, most of these meters were incorporated in a telemetry system which facilitated a complete review of the Derby and other area consumptions and reservoir levels over a very short time scale.

Such a metered system will give the basic information necessary to assess night lines for demand zones and modern electronics now give many added advantages in the type and frequency of print-out information which can be made available.

From such equipment it should be possible to establish night lines for each demand zone, and if district or waste meters are already installed in at least part of the zone then the more accurate the final net night loss calculation will be.

ESTABLISHMENT OF ZONAL AND DISTRICT PRIORITIES

The second stage in the process is the calculation of the unit cost of leakage for each demand zone. These calculations will point the way to where savings can be made more quickly and/or more economically. The first studies should give priority to pressure control where operating conditions are suitable. It is necessary to minimise pressures, particularly night pressures within each demand zone, and to consider the terminal pressure or the pressure at the zonal high point. These values should not be less than 10 to 15 metres head during periods of peak demand if and when pressure reduction takes place (Fig. 12.13).

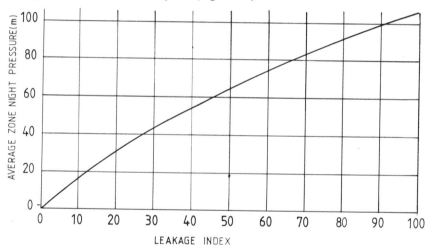

Fig. 12.13. Relationship between leakage (net night flow) and pressure
Source: Water Authorities Association[12]

Following this, the net night flow under the proposed pressure reduced conditions should be calculated and this can be converted into a daily quantity as previously mentioned. However, a good approximation for daily quantity is to multiply the night flow rate (per hour) by 20 times: the annual saving in cost can then be calculated. The economics and relevant costs of the policy generally will be considered in the final part of this Section.

After deciding where any PRVs, preferably flow related, are to be installed in the system the third stage of the exercise can proceed.

DISTRICT AND WASTE METERING ASSESSMENT

Demand zone metering may be sufficient basic cover for that part of a system so that waste metering could be adopted as the best means of local control rather than by installing a number of district meters with two or more waste meters installed within each district.

However, as the district meters ideally should serve between 2000 and 5000 properties and waste meters between 1000 and 3000 properties for urban areas, then three waste meters at the most within larger sized district meter areas and one or two waste meters within the smaller district meter areas would seem to be a satisfactory combination.

Smaller districts are more easily operated and larger districts may be marginally cheaper to operate. In compact urban areas 2000 properties/meter district is a good norm. For less densely populated areas, 1000 properties/meter district seems, on balance, to be best. Rural areas will almost certainly require special assessment with, in many cases, less than 1000 properties/meter district.

With the advent of the data logger and similar apparatus it may be possible to dispense with district meters, particularly for smaller districts, and to rely on demand zone metering with the requisite number of waste meters within the zone.

With regard to existing systems, many have district meters covering far more than 5000 properties and waste meters commanding fewer than the recommended lower figure of 1000 properties per meter. It could be that a re-examination of the existing system would result in some rearrangement of waste and district meter areas.

In the case of permanent waste meters a good proportion of these were designed to serve more than one waste meter district initially on the grounds of the cost savings made thereby. Districts could probably be replanned and most of the existing installations utilised but the cost of such an exercise should be carefully studied—the last state may be inferior to the first!

With larger numbers of properties included in waste meter districts the valve operations for step tests will require more careful study because of the increased number of operations involved.

Report 26 gives guidance as to the optimum number of properties to be included in waste meter districts, particularly in urban areas.

The rural position is rather less open to the assessments made for the urban scene. Each authority will need to consider such situations on an individual basis, though this does not mean that the rural areas and districts should be separated from the urban with regard to overall policy. However, in some rural areas, assessment of net night flow may be best related to litres per kilometre per hour (l/km/h) rather than to litres per property per hour (l/prop/h).

Again, the cost of district and/or waste metering must be assessed against the likely savings related to the reduction of leakage from the system. The benefits of any proposed pressure reduction and the cost of any PRV installations should be taken into account when assessing the metering costs.

PLANNING AND INSTALLATION OF DISTRICT AND WASTE METERS

The final stage in implementing the policy is the planning and installation of district and waste meters where such installations do not exist. The size of waste meter districts will depend upon local conditions but, wherever practicable, should be of size within the guidelines indicated earlier, that is, between 1000 and 3000 properties per waste district.

Work necessary for installation should begin on those districts where most savings are likely, such as high pressure districts (if not already dealt with), those with known high rates of leakage and those supplied from comparatively high cost sources.

Initially district boundary valves should be checked for tightness and requisite replacement or repairs be put in hand. The cost of such work on valves should be charged to general maintenance of the system and not to leakage control. Back log leakage should be similarly charged. The checking and maintenance of all valves within the district should follow as soon as practicable thereafter.

WASTE METER OPERATION AND RECORDING RESULTS

The initial open runs having been completed (see Section 4) a step test should be arranged.

The step test should indicate the particular roads in which leakage is taking place and manual aural sounding, backed up by more sophisticated equipment, should follow immediately. Once the leakages have been pinpointed, it is essential that repairs are carrried out quickly; on completion, a second open run should be arranged.

If the second open run gives a night line within the acceptable leakage figure then the district need not be re-run until it is scheduled. Districts should normally be run 3 to 4 times per year, though in mining subsidence areas and other known leakage-prone areas, monthly or bi-monthly runs should be programmed.

If, however, the second open run produces a night line above that for acceptable leakage in the district, then a second step test will be necessary followed by repair of leakage and one or more additional runs and step tests until the night line gives a satisfactory value.

During the initial open runs and step tests it is essential that sounding operations and repairs are organized to be carried out quickly. In established leakage detection organizations nothing lowers morale more than the same leakage being found second time round because repairs have not been effected from the previous operation.

The keeping of records of all waste meter district runs is another essential requirement if proper control of the policy implementation is to be maintained. It has been found that more than 70 per cent of leakage is found normally in less than 40 per cent of a waste meter district. There are exceptions to this, but it is important to realise that leakage does not take place on a conventionally even pattern throughout a waste meter district. The records will show, therefore, the black spots in any district so far as leakage is concerned. There is no justification whatever for finding leaks regularly in the same locations and continuing to repair them *ad infinitum*. Depending on whether the leakage is from joints or from actual main failure, information of this kind must be fed into mains renewal and reconditioning programmes. Similarly the actual locations of leakage from services must be recorded so that again, if needs be, the renewal of communication pipes can be given the proper priority.

With modern information storage techniques there is little excuse for not recording the relevant information on a waste district, road and property basis. Leakage detection and waste prevention policy must be all embracing, leading to discovery and repair of leaks and the recording of all necessary data. In addition it should ensure that renewal and reconditioning programmes are geared in priority to the areas of worst leakage. Though reconditioning of mains is generally meant to achieve a clean pipe barrel in some cases, in the short and mid-term, it can be advantageous to place comparatively thicker linings to remove or reduce leakage from joints and to give a limited further lease of life to, for example, mains affected by external "pepper-potting" corrosion.

The final point which needs to be made is that a leakage detection and waste prevention policy, once implemented, should be vigorously maintained. Any slackening of resolve or reduction in effort will see night lines increasing steadily until a major additional effort will be needed to retrieve the situation and to reestablish hard won gains (Fig. 12.14).

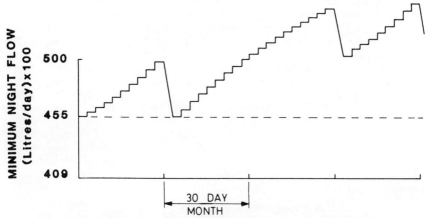

Fig. 12.14.   Effect of relaxing effort after situation under control
Source: Water Research Centre[11]

SUGGESTED PROCEDURE FOR SETTING UP AND OPERATING A LEAKAGE DETECTION SYSTEM

Each undertaking has its own method of work so that though operational targets may be generally similar there are a variety of ways of reaching such targets and the human condition ensures that some routes will be better than others.

Basic Data and Conditions

It is proposed to consider a hypothetical division or similar unit of an authority which is sufficiently similar to actual cases as to be relevant. The basic data are as follows:

Population—800 000. Area of supply—1800 sq.km
Consumption (average daily)—225 megalitres including unaccounted for water
No. of properties—300 000
Assessed current leakage figure—12 litres per property per hour

There are already source works and demand zone meters in operation; 42 in number and these are suitable for use either with telemetry computation or with data loggers, so that weekly or other scheduled readings can be taken. There is no pressure reduction or waste metering of the system and aural sounding is carried out as and when inspectors can be spared for such operations.

Considering the graph for prediction of net night flows (see Fig. 12.12) and assessing the leakage levels as in the medium range, then with aural sounding carried out as described above, the assessed figure for current leakage is taken as 12 litres/property/hour. With regular aural sounding an assessment of 10 litres/property/hour could be expected.

It is appreciated that undertakings will not all fall into this category but the philosophy behind the method for dealing with this case can be utilised to bring existing methods up to the proposed standard. There may even be a few undertakings who have already reached that standard or improved upon it.

The source works and demand zone meter figures should be entered into a suitable computer on a weekly or other agreed regular basis. The figures so derived from each demand zone should then be checked on the same schedule against domestic consumption, based on latest population statistics, plus measured industrial consumption, also updated and with an allowance for acceptable leakage of say 6 litres/property/hour.

The annual effect of the differences between the observed weekly figures and the assessed domestic consumption and acceptable leakage figures plus industrial metered consumption should be considered for each demand zone. This operation will indicate where most leakage could be taking place and will allow establishment of priorities.

At this stage it is essential to make a general financial assessment with particular reference to the probable savings in cost which can realistically be achieved. The cost of taking no action, the so-called passive method of leakage control, should be calculated along with consideration of the other more likely options. These, as already indicated are:

(a) Regular sounding (aural and electronic).

(b) The operation of district meters (with increasing use of data loggers).

(c) The operation of waste district meters usually in combination with demand zone meters and followed by selective sounding with increasing use of electronic equipment, particularly the leak noise correlator.

Though an intensification of leakage control methods will create an immediate backlog of repairs, the long-term average cost of repairs will not be significantly affected and should be ignored in comparative assessments. This point is fully covered in Report 26, paras 2.19 to 2.23.

From the original data, which gave in the hypothetical case assessed current leakage of 12 litres/property/hour, and the allowance of 6 litres/property/hour which is the target, the theoretical water saving per day is therefore:

$$\frac{6}{1\,000} \times 300\,000 \times 24 \times \frac{20}{24} = 36\,000 \text{ m}^3 \text{ or } 36 \text{ megalitres}$$

The rough pressure conversion allowing 20 hours at the night line hourly rate to give the daily quantity has been used.

If the average unit cost of leakage is assumed to be 3 p/m^3, then the annual financial savings if a loss from leakage of 6 litres/property/hour were achieved would be £36 000 $\times \dfrac{3}{100} \times 365 = £394\,200$.

For each undertaking the figure for average unit cost of water will vary, but obviously there will be a significant financial benefit in most cases. Further economic assessments will be made later.

Pressure Reduction

The next step should be to apply pressure reduction to those parts of the system which have been tested and shown to be adequately operable under lower pressure conditions. The cost of installing the necessary valves and other equipment must be taken into account. It may be that a relatively small number of large diameter PRVs will effect the planned reduction or a greater number of smaller diameter valves controlling local districts may be required. Most likely will be a combination of large and small diameter valves controlling local systems of various sizes.

A capital sum of some £30 000 is calculated to cover the cost of PRVs, which in operation are expected to effect overall reduction in consumption of 1 litre/property/hour. A pay back period of five years is suggested for this type of installation with annual maintenance costs of £400. The annual cost during the first five years of operation would therefore be some £6 400, well within the unit cost of the water saved (£65 700).

Waste District Metering

Having satisfactorily dealt with the pressure aspect attention can be turned to waste district metering and this should be arranged on a priority basis related to the demand zone weekly consumptions assessed as described previously. The installation of waste meters could be put in hand at the same time as or immediately after the pressure reduction installations are provided.

Guidance on optimum sizes for district and waste meter district sizes is given in Report 26. For the hypothetical division with 300 000 properties, plans will be made for one district per 1 000 properties on average. This means that urban areas will generally have from 1 000 to 1 500 properties per district and rural areas in many cases less than 1 000 properties per district. Because of local zoning and supply restraints in some areas and, in rural areas, because of the distances involved, the planning of districts with less than 1 000 properties within them will be acceptable.

In round figures some 300 districts will be needed throughout the division to achieve a percentage of meter cover as near to 100 per cent as practicable. Allowing for some meters commanding two or more districts it is likely that up to 225 meter installations will be needed. Of these some 80 per cent are likely to be mobile, the remaining 20 per cent being permanent installations. Permanent installations are best sited in urban areas with heavy traffic but traffic obstruction and vandalism can create problems. Every endeavour should be made to site such installations so that they can command more than one district and thus offset some of the additional initial cost inherent in permanent siting. In severe winters they may be operable when mobile meters are inoperable because of the conditions and allow an overall survey of leakage to be made in a very short period.

The provision of 36 mobile and 9 permanent meters annually should not cause undue strain on the normal labour force available to an organization of the size being considered, but it is essential that the work is properly planned and executed to tight time schedules to ensure that the meters can be operated at the earliest practicable time.

Meantime, the existing inspectorate should be reviewed and suitable personnel trained in the setting up and operation of waste meter districts and in the use of such leak detection equipment as is deemed necessary. The purchase of such equipment including a leak noise correlator should be provided for at the initial stage.

It will be necessary to consider the number of open runs and step tests likely to be needed in each year of operation and also the amount of back up aural sounding involved. This is part of the manpower element necessary to implement the policy and repair gang manpower must also be reviewed at this time. If a five year period of policy implementation has been decided on, then the manpower adjustments can take place evenly over the same period.

It will be prudent to allow three open runs and two step tests in the first weeks of each waste meter's operation. Thereafter, in the first year three further open runs and one further step test. In subsequent years, four open runs and one step test should be allowed for as an average. The relevant number of meter runs assumed for the first and sixth years of operation are given below:

Year One

Initial open runs	60×3	$= 180$
Quarterly open runs	$\dfrac{60 \times 3}{2}$	$= 90^*$
Total		270
Initial step tests	60×2	$= 120$
Further step tests	$\dfrac{60 \times 1}{2}$	$= 30^*$
Total		150

Year Six

Open runs	300×4	$= 1200$
Step tests	300×1	$= 300$

Note: *During each of the first five years, if meters come on stream steadily then those fitted during the last three months of the year will show only initial open runs and step tests and only in the sixth year onwards will this position clear.

With operation for fifty weeks annually, with three days reserved per week for the scheduled running of meters and step tests as indicated, then on each of those days it will be necessary to arrange for eight open runs and probably for four step tests when the scheme is fully operational. Such a schedule allows for any additional open runs or step tests to be arranged at short notice and for the sounding of stop-taps and other fittings in roads where leakage has been shown to be taking place. The manpower required for all this work can be assessed and costed.

Arrangements must be made for the retrieval of charts and the information obtained from them computerised for storage and for use as indicated earlier in the chapter. There are now a number of options open to undertakings which give the opportunity, by means of a suitable computer, to store, recall or use meter record information for distribution purposes other than leakage detection and waste control. The data logger, in particular, is a most useful tool now added to the distribution engineer's armoury.

Staffing

The appointment of a technical officer should be made at the start of policy implementation to co-ordinate the operational, administrative cost control aspects and to oversee the updating of requisite information, not least the position with regard to clearance of repairs required to deal with leakage discovered during metering and subsequent sounding.

The superintendents responsible for supervision of the inspectorate—their number would depend on the existing distribution depot arrangements for the undertaking—would be responsible for ensuring close liaison with repair gang supervisors if these gangs are under separate supervision. There is a case in some circumstances for a small number of repair gangs to be controlled by waste superintendents but the essential, whatever the supervisory methods employed, is to clear the waste by repair of leakage at the very earliest time practicable after discovery, the biggest leaks being dealt with first. Due regard should be given to the avoidance wherever possible or repairs outside normal working hours.

In distribution work there must be a good measure of flexibility though, with regard to leak detection, there is a case for not removing inspectors from their leakage detection duties unless in real emergency. This is only true, of course, when the initial work load has been properly assessed, as it should have been in this case.

Transport

Sufficient transport will be required for towing mobile waste meter trailers to site and for the general use of the inspectorate. Consideration should be given to the provision of suitable standard vehicles for the leak noise correlator and it is important to make available proper equipment and tools for use on site. The provision of radio communication for all such transport is essential.

ECONOMIC EFFECTS OF LEAKAGE CONTROL AND WASTE PREVENTION

An outline has been given of a suggested procedure for a hypothetical division of a water authority embarking for the first time on a fully active leakage control policy. Consideration of many options is given in detail in Report 26, which should be referred to by any water engineer wrestling with the problem of the economics of leakage control and waste prevention.

Unit Cost of Leakage

The first step is to determine the unit cost of leakage in p/m^3 and the procedure for determining this will be found in Report 26 (Chapter 4 and Appendixes B & C).

Operating Costs

The main factors in annual operating costs are:

(i) Pumping or boosting costs.
(ii) Water treatment costs.
(iii) Bulk purchase costs.

and these depend upon the quantity of water actually supplied.

If demand were to decrease because of leakage control, the decrease would vary between works as would the financial decrease. When savings are made at a number of sources then the unit operating cost is the average of the individual work costs suitably adjusted to the proportional reduction in demand obtained at each source. Only the relative elements of cost are relevant in this procedure.

Capital costs

The relevant capital costs from the future plan, usually over a five year period, are those costs most likely to be affected by changes in the demand trend and are as follows:

(1) Source works
(2) Treatment works

(3) Pumping and boosting stations
(4) Service reservoirs and water towers
(5) Trunk mains
(6) Reinforcement of distribution mains (not renewal)

The calculation for this element of the unit cost of leakage is complicated. It involves setting out the costs of those capital schemes which will be incurred in meeting future demands and making corrections to allow for future schemes beyond the five-year planning period. These costs are then discounted and summed to produce a total discounted capital cost for supplying future demand. The change in this aggregate cost, brought about by reduction in supply of one year's growth in terms of the quantity of the supply change, is the required unit capital cost (Fig. 12.15). The sum of unit operating cost and unit capital cost is the unit cost of leakage.

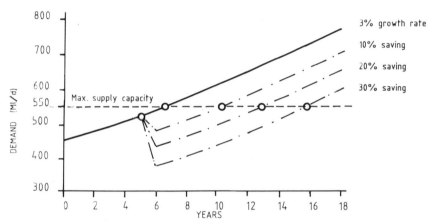

Fig. 12.15. Effect of progressive waste reduction upon deferment period
Source: Water Research Centre[11]

The use of the various tables and study of Report 26, Appendix C, should help the calculation of the unit capital cost. In considering the economic effects of applying the policy outlined earlier, the average unit cost of leakage quoted of 3 p/m³ is the sum of unit operating costs and unit capital costs calculated in similar fashion to the calculations explained in detail in Report 26.

The calculation of unit capital cost and the unit cost of leakage must be obtained for each individual undertaking and for each demand zone of that undertaking, thus allowing the preparation of a priority list for action, with implementation of the agreed policy first in those zones where most financial benefit will accrue.

Installation, Operational and Maintenance Costs

Taking the other side of the equation it is necessary to tabulate the costs of the main components of leakage control methods (see Table 12.I, taken in part from Report 26); the costs shown are for 1979. It should be emphasised that any undertaking implementing or continuing to operate a leakage control policy will need to ascertain the actual costs applicable to its own situation. It follows that costs must be revised regularly and at least once per annum.

TABLE 12.I.   Costs of Some Components of Leakage Control Methods

Operation	Mean cost (1979) £	Typical cost range (1979) £
Install a waste meter	1 400	840/1 600
Plan and set up a waste district	250	150/400
Record a night line (day and some night work)	36	18/54
Record a night line (night work only)	52	26/78
Perform a step test	85	60/110
Sound 1 000 houses	150	100/300
Read 100 district meters	80	60/100
Install PRV and set up pressure zone	1 750	500/3 000
Annual PRV maintenance	25	10/50
Locate leakage with leak noise correlator (per 200 m)	15	10/20
Repair backlog on introduction of leakage control per 1 000 properties	300	200/500

For the hypothetical undertaking, leakage initially has been assessed at 12 litres per property per hour and this is equal to a daily quantity of:

$$\frac{12}{1\,000} \times 300\,000 \times 24 \times \frac{20}{24} = 72\,000 \text{ m}^3 \text{ or } 72 \text{ megalitres}$$

The annual cost of this $= £72\,000 \times \dfrac{3}{100} \times 365 = £788\,400$

(based on average unit cost of leakage of 3 p/m^3)

so that the annual cost of leakage per property is:

$$£\frac{788\,400}{300\,000} = \textbf{£2.628 per property per annum}$$

The cost of PRVs has been given as £30 000 to be paid over five years with annual maintenance costs of £400, that is, an annual charge over the first five years of £6 400 reverting to £400 during the sixth and subsequent years. This gives a figure of **£0.021 per property per annum**.

Labour costs per hour, including overheads, were £4.20 on 1979 figures.

The cost of waste meter installation will rise by £63 000 per year with total expenditure of £315 000 over five years, this being for 225 meters at £1 400 each. The initial cost is expressed as an annual amount obtained by multiplying the initial cost by the chosen discount rate (i.e. 0.05 for a rate of 5 per cent). There is the additional cost applied to the relevant year for the planning and setting up over five years of 300 districts at 60 districts per annum at a cost of £250 each. The relevant data are shown in Table 12.II.

Planning and Setting Up Waste Meter Districts

The cost of planning and setting up waste meter districts at £250 per district for 60 districts each year for five years is £15 000 per annum, or **£0.05 per property per annum**.

Table 12.II. Costs of Waste Meter Installation

Year	Total initial cost £	Initial cost per property £	Annual costs £	Annual cost per property £
1	63 000	0.21	3 150	.011
2	126 000	0.42	6 300	.021
3	189 000	0.63	9 450	.032
4	252 000	0.84	12 600	.042
5	315 000	1.05	15 750	.053
6–20*	—	—	15 750	.053

Note: *Then reducing; completion in 24th year

Waste Meter and Allied Operational Costs

The first year costs of running the sixty districts commissioned during that period can now be calculated.

Waste Meter District Operational Costs

Initial open runs $60 \times 3 = 180$
Quarterly open runs $\dfrac{60 \times 3 = \ 90}{2}$

                      Total   270   @ £36   = £ 9 720

Initial step tests $60 \times 2 = 120$
Further step tests $\dfrac{60 \times 1 = \ 30}{2}$

                      Total   150   @ £85   = £12 750

Sounding Costs

Follow up 150 step tests say 50 per cent each district @ £150/1 000.

$$\text{Cost} = £150 \times 150 \times \frac{50}{100} \qquad\qquad = £11 250$$

Locate leakage using leak noise correlator at 400 metres/district @ £15/200 m.

$$\text{Cost} = £150 \times \frac{400}{200} \times 15 \qquad\qquad = £ 4 500$$

                              Total   £38 220

This cost will be repeated during the first five years as waste districts are commissioned at the rate of 60 per annum. During the second and subsequent years the cost of normal operation of meters commissioned in previous years will need to be added.

During the second year normal operation of waste districts, that is, those commissioned in the first year will cost:

Open runs $60 \times 4 = 240$ @ £36 =   £ 8 640
Step tests $60 \times 1 = 60$ @ £85   =   £ 5 100

Sounding costs following up the 60 step tests will amount to:

Sounding 50 per cent of 60 districts @ £150/1 000 properties.

$$\text{Cost} = £60 \times 150 \frac{50}{100} \quad\quad = \quad\quad £4\,500$$

Locating leakage using leak noise correlator at 400 m/district @ £15/200 m

$$\text{Cost} = £60 \times 15 \times \frac{400}{200} \quad\quad = \quad\quad £1\,800$$

Total cost   £20 040

The total cost of operating waste districts during the second year will be £38 220 + £20 040 = £58 260. The total operational costs for waste meter districts for the relevant years are shown in Table 12.III.

TABLE 12.III.   Costs of Operating Waste Meter Districts

Year	Costs £			Total operational costs	Cost per property £
1				38 220	0.13
2	38 220 + 20 040	=		58 260	0.19
3	58 260 + 20 040	=		78 300	0.26
4	78 300 + 20 040	=		98 340	0.33
5	98 340 + 20 040	=		118 380	0.39
6 onwards	(5 × 20 040)	=		100 200	0.33

The foregoing information will allow a final tabulation of the total costs of leakage and leakage control in terms of £/property/year (Table 12.IV).

TABLE 12.IV.   Annual Costs of Leakage and Leakage Control
(average unit cost of leakage 3 p/m^3)

Year	0	1	2	3	4	5	6
Leakage per property (litres/hour)	12	11	10	9	8	7	6
Annual Costs (£/property/year)							
Leakage	2.628	2.409	2.190	1.971	1.747	1.533	1.314
Pressure reducing valves	—	0.021	0.021	0.021	0.021	0.021	0.001
Waste meter installation	—	0.011	0.021	0.032	0.042	0.053	0.053
Waste meter operation	—	0.13	0.19	0.26	0.33	0.39	0.33
Prior to metering	0.15	—	—	—	—	—	—
Total for leakage control	0.15	0.162	0.232	0.313	0.393	0.464	0.384
Total for leakage plus leakage control	2.778	2.571	2.422	2.284	2.140	1.997	1.698

The annual savings at the sixth year in this case are £(2.778 − 1.698) × 300 000 = £324 000.

The results show that in this case waste metering allied to some pressure reduction is economically justifiable. If no allowance had been made for the cost of aural sounding prior to metering (this was calculated on the basis of half the division being sounded per annum) the figures still show a favourable balance even at year one. If average districts of 2 000 properties had been considered, the cost of meter installation would be almost 50 per cent less, say 120 installations for 150 districts. The operational costs would be marginally greater so that a slight reduction in the overall annual costs may have resulted. However, many undertakings are already partially waste metered, and if remaining areas are designed with the average district size recommended in Report 26, the sum for the undertaking may be more realistically applicable to the example quoted here.

It should be noted that there would still be financial benefit if a leakage figure of only 8 litres/property/hour were attained for then, at the fifth year, total cost of leakage and leakage control would be £2.211 per property per year and at the sixth year again £2.131.

Also, if the annual cost of leakage were based on an average unit cost of leakage of 1.5 p/m³, financial savings, albeit of a lower order, would be made in this particular case, as Table 12.V shows.

TABLE 12.V. Annual Costs of Leakage and Leakage Control
(average unit cost of leakage 1.5 p/m³)

Year	0	1	2	3	4	5	6
Leakage per property (litres/hour)	12	11	10	9	8	7	6
Annual Costs (£/property/year)							
Leakage	1.314	1.205	1.095	0.986	0.874	0.767	0.657
Pressure reducing valves	—	0.021	0.021	0.021	0.021	0.021	0.001
Waste meter installation	—	0.011	0.021	0.032	0.042	0.053	0.053
Waste meter operation	—	0.13	0.19	0.26	0.33	0.39	0.33
Prior to metering	0.15	—	—	—	—	—	—
Total for leakage control	0.15	0.162	0.232	0.313	0.393	0.464	0.384
Total for leakage plus leakage control	1.464	1.367	1.327	1.299	1.267	1.231	1.041

With unit cost of water at 1.5 p/m³ the annual savings at the sixth year would be £(1.464 − 1.041) × 300 000 = £126 900.

Some units in undertakings have already achieved leakage control rates of 5 litres/property/hour. It will be for each undertaking to establish targets, which may vary from unit to unit, though always ensuring that these targets are realistic and confer cost benefit.

Annual Workload

The annual workload can be assessed as follows:

1 200 open runs at 8 man hours = 9 600 man hours

300 step tests at 10 man hours = 3 000 man hours

Sounding following step tests at 20 soundings per hour =

$$300 \times 1\,000 \times \frac{50}{100} \times \frac{1}{20} = 7\,500 \text{ man hours}$$

Leak noise correlator at 4 hours per step test per district =
$300 \times 4 = 1\,200$ man hours

Total man hours annually $= 21\,300$
Allowing for 21 working days per month, man hours daily

$$= \frac{21\,300}{12 \times 21} = 80.5 \text{ man hours daily which corresponds to 10 men.}$$

The annual cost of some £9 500 per man should also cover the cost of transport as required and supervisory costs. In the first year only four men would be required, the labour force and transport being increased as necessary to the ultimate figure given above.

Discussion of Results

All the financial calculations are based on mid-1979 figures so that direct comparisons can be made with the various examples quoted in Report 26. It follows that adjustment of all the costs will be necessary to make current assessments of the figures.

The results of this hypothetical study have a symmetry which is most unlikely to be met in practice. However, by planning ahead in the manner shown, any slippage between planned and actual progress can be monitored and any discrepancy corrected in the next or subsequent years. It should be reiterated again that frequent monitoring of all costs, including overheads, is an essential factor in assessing real progress as the implementation of the leakage detection and waste control policy proceeds.

It should be emphasised that much more detailed information on most of the matter referred to in this chapter is available, particularly in Report 26.

Notwithstanding the detail of the above financial appraisal it is essential that calculations are undertaken using locally derived cost and performance data.

Finally, it should not be forgotten that although the main financial benefits have been covered in some detail there are others not so obvious. The implementation of a leakage control and waste prevention policy inevitably leads to better understanding and control of the distribution system, updated and more comprehensive records, fewer consumer complaints and closer control of labour. In short, more efficient and informed management.

6. PREVENTION OF WASTE

APPLICATION OF BYELAWS

Byelaws made for the prevention of waste, misuse or contamination of water have now been in operation for many years. On this subject reference should be made to Chapter 3, but any leakage detection and waste prevention programme must include the activities and draw on the skill and expertise of those engaged in the application of byelaws within each undertaking. Liaison will be necessary between the byelaws inspectorate and the leakage prevention supervisors and their respective section heads to ensure that maximum attention is paid to this very important aspect of water distribution.

ADHERENCE TO RELEVANT CODES OF PRACTICE

Again, this has been dealt with in other chapters, but there is need to ensure that the relevant Codes of Practice for mainlaying, plumbing and for central heating are strictly adhered to. Care should be taken particularly with the practices within the industry to ensure that the industrial or domestic consumer is set an example of how requisite work should be carried out. From the waste prevention aspect hydraulic testing of all new mains should be effected immediately or as soon as practicable after laying.

USE OF STANDARD MATERIALS, PIPES AND FITTINGS

Much of this topic is dealt with in Chapter 3. The universal use of properly accredited materials and fittings is a safeguard to all water users ensuring, so far as practicable in the light of current knowledge, comparatively trouble-free distribution, industrial and domestic installations.

INSPECTION OF CONSUMER INSTALLATIONS

Inspection of supply pipes and internal installations, be they domestic or industrial, ideally should be carried out before the installation becomes operative. Restrictions, usually financial, on the number of inspectors available to carry out such work may not allow the achievement of universal inspection, the ideal target. Nevertheless, inspection should be as widespread as practicable and should certainly include all new large industrial installations and building sites under construction by companies or builders new to the area.

Periodic inspection of consumer installations would require further manpower— inspection every five years in an undertaking such as that referred to in the example in the preceding section would mean dealing with 60 000 domestic premises and industrial premises additionally annually. Inspectorate resources should allow inspection to be made of industrial premises on a more frequent and recurring basis, particularly those with complex installations and those dealing with toxic products.

The plumbing inspectorate may also be involved in the final process of checking repairs to consumer installations carried out after serving of notice to rectify leakage or other defects.

This is an area which requires careful consideration, because the cost benefits in waste prevention alone could well cover the salaries of additional staff specifically trained in plumbing and able to deal effectively with contractors, builders and private plumbers.

PUBLIC RELATIONS

There is great scope for improvement in public relations at all levels. During the droughts of 1975 and 1976 many industrialists were visited by water authority officers and significant water savings made as a result. Domestic consumers also responded to the periodic advertisements in the national and local press and to television and radio broadcasts. Savings of a similar order were made during the national water strike of manual workers in 1983.

Many undertakings now have good contacts with the media and every opportunity should be grasped to put over the undertaking's viewpoint, particularly with regard to waste prevention. Arrangements should be made to name specific officers in the operational field so that the press, television and radio programmers can make speedy contact with such officers when needed. These officers should be the channels through which their colleagues ensure that matters needing explanation to consumers, or giving them warning of supply alterations and why these are necessary, reach the right publicity media at the appropriate time.

Arrangements should be made for responsible and informed officers to attend council and other relevant meetings, including public meetings when necessary. Waste prevention should be mentioned whenever and wherever possible. Often when this is done someone comes along to give details of leakage which has not been attended to for some reason and a positive response should be given to such complaints.

The showing of relevant films and slides with talks to organizations such as church fellowships, womens' institutes, senior citizens' organizations and schools should be arranged whenever requests for such information are made.

Particular attention should be paid to junior schools as it seems to be this age group which is most receptive to the information given. The provision of carefully prepared information, including brochures, should be used to stimulate interest and some effort should be made to persuade the education authority to include items on water use and its conservation in the school curriculum.

Local exhibitions and shows are other places where, by arrangement, information stands or displays can be sited. Other examples will be apparent in each locality, where publicity can be achieved at minimal or modest cost.

Finally the open day or days at selected works and visits to works by interested groups are useful publicity forums when the message of "waste not, want not" can be put across to consumers.

7. CONCLUSION

There are many facets of leakage detection and waste prevention, each having a part to play in keeping leakage from any water distribution system in check.

The industry must be seen to be dealing with leakage from its own apparatus in such a way that losses are reduced and kept to a minimum and, thereby, water charges may be more closely related to the minimum operational and funding costs; otherwise the industry is likely to lose credibility and the goodwill of the water rate payers.

The effort required in personnel and financial terms must be vigorously applied and maintained, otherwise within a comparatively short period of time most of the benefits of a leakage detection and waste prevention policy will be lost.

With an increasing number of electronic and technical aids becoming available the techniques of leakage detection and waste prevention will inevitably change and become more efficient.

Even so the industry will still need engineers, technicians, supervisors and a skilled inspectorate imbued with the enthusiasm and professionalism which some of their predecessors have shown in bringing leakage control to its present position of prime importance in the water distribution field.

8. REFERENCES

1. Wolverhampton Corporation Waterworks 1947 "The water supply of Wolverhampton", Wolverhampton Water Committee.
2. Feeney, A. 1880 "Descriptive sketch of the Company and works" South Staffordshire Waterworks Company.
3. Hawksley, T. 1888 "Report as to works" Derby Corporation Waterworks Committee.
4. Deacon, C. F. 1874/75 *Proc. ICE,* 42, Part 4.
5. Collins, E. 1893/94 *Proc. ICE,* 68, Part 3.
6. Kirby, O. J. 1896 *Trans. IWE,* 1, 160, Waste of water in its relation to lead service pipes.
7. Jenkins, A. J. 1900 *Trans. IWE,* 5, 79, The relationship between the cost of water wasted and the cost of detection and prevention of waste.
8. Clerke, R. W. G. 1949 *J. IWE,* 3, 515, The use and operation of waste water meters.
9. Gledhill, E. G. B. 1957 *J. IWE,* 11, 117, An investigation of the incidence of underground leakage and an improved method of waste control.
10. Institution of Water Engineers 1974 "Symposium on waste control: its importance in the planning and management of water supply systems", IWE, London.
11. Water Research Association 1974 "Waste control", Technical Paper TP 109, WRA, Medmenham.
12. Department of the Environment/National Water Council 1980 "Leakage control policy and practice", Standing Technical Committee on Water Regulations, Report No. 26, HMSO, London.
13. House of Lords Select Committee on Science and Technology 1982 "The water industry", Report, Vol. 1.
14. Dunstan, M. R. H. and Lawson, W. R. 1972 *J. IWE,* 26, 211, Analysing and planning a water distribution network in a developing country.
15. Phillips, J. H. and Kershaw, C. G. 1976 *J. IWES,* 30, 203, Domestic metering—an engineering and economic appraisal.
16. Beaumont, R. J. K. 1978 *J. IWES,* 32, 249, A practical approach to waste control.
17. Smith, R. J. and Males, D. B. 1978 *J. IWES,* 32, 423, A theoretical approach to the optimization of waste control expenditure.
18. Burch, R. H. and Marlow, K. C. 1978 *J. IWES,* 32, 443, Seven years' operational experience of computer-based telemetry and control applied to a water supply network.
19. Huntington, R. 1979 *J. IWES,* 33, 497, Resurrection of water supply distribution—new life for a faithful servant.
20. Willis, J. S. M. 1980 *J. IWES,* 34, 585, Leakage control policy and practice: short review of the DoE/NWC Standing Technical Committee Report No. 26.
21. West, J. W. 1982 *J. IWES,* 36, 405, The history of waste detection in Severn-Trent Water Authority, Derwent Division.
22. Bateman, J. F. LaTrobe 1884 "History and description of the Manchester Corporation waterworks" Day, T. J., Manchester and Spon, E. and F., London.
23. Reid, J. 1974 in Ref. 10, p. 113.
24. Thackray, J. E., Cocker, V. and Archibald, G. 1978 *Proc. ICE,* 64, 37, The Malvern and Mansfield studies of domestic water usage.
25. Water Research Centre 1981 "The location of leaks in water mains using the leak noise correlator", Technical Report TR 157, WRC, Medmenham.
26. Water Research Centre 1978 "Location of leaks in pressure pipelines using sulphur hexafluoride as a tracer", Technical Report TR 80, WRC, Medmenham.
27. Edwards, I. G. 1962 *J. IWE,* 16, 415, The reconstruction of the Derby Corporation waterworks.

Chapter 13

MANAGEMENT AND ADMINISTRATION

1. GENERAL INTRODUCTION

IN common with all other businesses, fighting to harness the best techniques of management and application of technology to contain costs, whilst maintaining acceptable levels of services, the water industry is increasingly questioning the viability of its activities.

No more is this so than in the management and administration of distribution systems. Recent years have seen the rise of consumer groups, making the consumer ever conscious of value for money and standard of service, the new Consumer Consultative Committees playing an increasing role in making the undertaker accountable for every penny paid for the service. Corporate aims of a water undertaking are now formulated and understood by all staff to ensure that 'value for money' means reaching well-planned goals effectively, and all proposals for expenditure are thoroughly vetted and appraised before competing for limited funds.

Increasingly, the treating of staff as a most valuable resource of the undertaking has lead to legislation, policies and procedures to govern their welfare, and the safety of the public at large as a result of their activities. When things go wrong, through industrial disputes, distribution staff may have to implement contingency measures in order to maintain supplies of wholesome water.

This chapter deals with the management and administration of these problems.

2. DEALING WITH THE CONSUMER

INTRODUCTION

Usually the only contact between the water undertaking and the consumer, (apart from receiving a bill for water charges) is through the consumer services section of the distribution department. If that consumer service is of the right quality, then the customer is well disposed to have a good opinion of all water undertaking activities. If the water inspector who calls is competent and courteous then confidence in water supply is increased.

The consumer needs to know of the existence and purpose of byelaws and how they are designed to make water supply safe. He needs information on water use, how to use water wisely, the effects of frost and thaw and the need for saving during periods of high demand and drought. If things go wrong he will need to know quickly and clearly the extent and duration of the trouble. For instance, if discoloured water issues from his tap it is important to show whether there is any risk to health, whether it is a widespread problem or caused by private pipework on his property; whether it·is likely to be repeated and how long it will last.

Providing all these services in an efficient and effective way occupy a large part of the distribution department's time and effort.

CONSUMER SERVICES

Byelaw Enforcement

Chapter 3 examines the purpose of and scope of water byelaws. Consumer

---

service staff must interpret those rules to the consumer and give guidance on their use. All water undertakings employ specially trained byelaw staff whose job is to ensure that the rules are complied with and who have to keep abreast of changes brought about, say, by the introduction of new materials.

They may work on a geographic basis, which works best where there is a concentration of heavy industry and the enforcement of byelaws is especially complex. In a more rural area it might be more appropriate for a water inspector to have a range of duties which include byelaw work. He will then usually be able to check and approve most development in his area but he will need the facility to call in a specialist should the need arise. The Backsiphonage Report[1] provides managers with a useful guide of the spectrum of pollution hazards and encouragement to use limited inspection resources in a priority manner.

Tap Washering

If thousands of leaking taps are left unattended the cumulative waste is significant and needs to be stopped. Equally, a 10 mile journey by a water inspector in a van to change a tap washer is hopelessly uneconomic.

Although a water undertaker has no specific duty to re-washer taps, practices vary, and one method is to provide a free tap washering service in cases of distress or need but not to publicise this facility. Free tap washers are sometimes issued in small quantities to people who enquire, as a good method of promoting the message to use water wisely and repair leaks.

Meter Reading

The water industry meters most non-domestic supplies. All industrial water users take metered systems and most commercial users are now fed via a meter rather than on a rateable value basis. Most water undertakings now offer the option of a meter to householders (see Section 5).

Thus meter reading is an increasing activity which will take up more time and manpower until technical advances make remote reading viable. Generally, water undertakings are moving away from using inspectors in favour of full time meter readers, who may be employed within the finance or the distribution department.

Large consumers with high water usage usually have their meter read monthly and receive a monthly account to provide a proper cash-flow for the transaction. Intermediate users are read quarterly and small users half yearly. Meter readings are organized into "walks" to minimise the activity time.

The time, the place and the date of meter readings need to be recorded accurately, especially in cases of dispute about the amount of water used. The Water Acts give legal standing to the meter readings as *prima facie* evidence of water consumption. Therefore, a formal, clear and precise set of meter readings records is necessary. These have to be passed to the computer for account processing.

A good working knowledge of water consumption in the area is valuable for interpreting how trends in demand are varying. An alert distribution inspector will notice a disproportionate change in a consumer's demand which might well indicate an undetected leakage. The consumer needs to be advised quickly so that he does not continue to pay for unused water, and the water undertaking needs the leak to be repaired to prevent wastage.

Meter readings are an excellent indication of the way demand varies. They can be correlated to trends of growth or decline, climate and seasonal variations, each being a vital input in the planning of the water supply system, its water sources, plant and mains capacity. They also form an important part of waste detection and prevention, since the assumption is made that water flowing through the meter is a legitimate demand for which the consumer is paying. Waste detection calculations are based on "night line flow" exercises, when the water flowing at night is assumed to be wastage after known proper demands have been deducted. This means that major metered consumers have the meter read before, during, and after the night flow test because that water is taken to be genuine usage. (An approximation to the consumption of smaller meters during a night flow test is assessed).

Water meters are notorious for difficulty in reading. They remain the property of the water undertaker but may be situated within the consumer's property. The location may have been accessible when the meter was first installed but in changing circumstances may be hidden or in a deep pit prone to flooding. Such meters can now be replaced by a magnetic headed meter allowing remote reading.

Meters deteriorate with age and usually begin to under read, or their size may become inappropriate for current demand. If demand has declined, water will pass without turning the meter mechanism and, if it has increased markedly, the meter will thrash until it fails. It is good practice to exchange old meters and to relocate them on a phased basis in a safe accessible position.

Chapter 11 covers meter installations and options.

Serving of Notices

Much of the work of the distribution department is governed by statute and codes of good practice (see Chapter 2 for legal aspects). For instance, it is mandatory that proper notice for mainlaying work in highways is served under PUSWA.

Other notices are advisory only, for example a frost precaution leaflet or a warning of mains flushing work.

It is sensible to keep a reference catalogue of all the printed or standard notices a distribution department needs, ready to hand and consciously updated on a regular basis. This would include:

(1) Water byelaws made under s.17, Water Act 1945 (WA 45).
(2) The 28 day, 7 day and emergency PUSWA notices.
(3) Notices to lay mains under s.19, WA 45.
(4) Formal easement documents for mainlaying in private land.
(5) Defective fittings notices under s.63, WA 45.
(6) A comprehensive dossier of Safety at Work information.
(7) The terms and conditions under which the water undertaker offers a ss.36 and 37, WA 45 "revenue guarantee" for the payment for new mains. (See Section 5).
(8) Electrical earthing notices (although water undertakers are not liable to provide continuous earthing for electrical apparatus through the water service pipe, on old properties this was often done. Printed advice on good safe practice is therefore usually issued, for the protection of both householders and workmen).
(9) Frost and thaw publicity pamphlets.
(10) "Turn-off" notices to advise consumers of a planned interruption of water supplies.
(11) Notices to warn of flushing, or other operations which will cause a temporary disturbance and discoloured water.

(12) Service pipe application form bearing the terms and conditions which govern their laying.
(13) Water meter application form and the terms including conditions which apply to industrial, commercial or domestic meters.
(14) Explanatory information concerning mains reconditioning works.

Response to Calls for New Connections

Section 41, Third Schedule, WA 45 prescribes that the water undertaker shall lay and charge for the communication pipe part of the service pipes, and subsequently take over the pipe between the main and the stop tap usually positioned near the highway boundary. Unless the water undertaker does the work within 14 days of it being paid for it can be prosecuted, although this hardly ever happens in practice. A building developer needs the water supply connection to his house to be timed for the vendor moving in, and before footway reinstatement. The water undertaker needs to plan a continuous workload for service layers, and to arrange unimpeded access to the main and footway on site.

The undertaker's inspector and the building site foreman should meet and exchange information on site in advance of the work being required, to monitor site conditions and so that the arrival of the service layer can fit in with both his work schedule and site progress.

Undertakers usually require written orders and pre-payment for a water service connection and should also stipulate that all private pipework (both above and below ground) is laid and byelaw approval given before the communication pipe is connected.

Standard fixed charges for a service pipe connection save administration costs and are designed to be cost effective overall. The charges would however be applied in categories for, say, a pipe in a grass verge or a metalled footway. Also they would normally carry the proviso to do the work on a cost plus basis where particular circumstances merit it.

When an industrial consumer applies for a new large supply of water for which mains reinforcements are necessary, the water undertaker offers appropriate terms under s.27, WA 45 (see also Section 5). For further reading on the legal position, see Chapter 2.

Organizing Rechargeable Work

This type of work covers:

(a) Service repair work, stop taps etc.
   Costs of repair work are apportioned between the undertaker and consumer, depending on the location of the defect. The undertaker is responsible for apparatus in the highway, the boundary with private property normally being the 'back of footpath'. Where the main stop tap lies just within the curtilage and as reasonably close to the boundary as is practicable, the water undertaker is responsible. Otherwise, repair work on private property is generally chargeable to the owner.
   Difficulties arise in the apportionment of costs between consumers, particularly in repair of supply pipes feeding multiple properties. Undertakers may differ in their approach, some equalising costs between all parties and others adopting a user cascade apportionment.
(b) Damage to apparatus (by third party)
   Attempts are made to recover the cost of repairing damage occasional to an undertaking's apparatus.

(c) *Fire hydrant installation, marking and repair*
Fire authorities agree the location of hydrant installations (Fire Services Act 1947), and are charged with all or part of the costs involved and of their upkeep. Provision of marker posts may be carried out directly by the water undertaker or by the fire authority with the agreement of the water undertaker.

(d) *PUSWA, mains diversion etc.*
PUSWA regulates the interference to a water undertaker's apparatus by road improvement schemes. Agreement is made with the highway authority on the effects of disturbance and, in the case where essential re-location works are carried out, the cost may be recharged to the highway authority. Such cost must allow for "financial benefit" due to deferment of renewal of the apparatus, using DoE tables based on estimated plant life, and "betterment", which is an allowance for increasing plant capacity in the system.

An accepted formula is in use by some highway authorities to calculate a sum due to the water undertaker to defray possible future maintenance, the object being to avoid unjustified diversion costs. This is occasionally applied when additional cover is placed upon existing apparatus.

Recovery of Charges

Oncosts are applicable to the direct costs, but care must be taken to ensure their correct attribution.

Prompt recovery of costs is important and in the case of phased work, interim accounts should be considered.

Disputes may arise through a misunderstanding of who pays, the extent of the work carried out, or the charging of oncosts. Careful presentation and explanation may be the key to ending the dispute.

Public Liability Insurance (PLI)

Claims upon a water undertaking are normally dealt with through PLI. Examples include damage to the apparatus of other undertakings, and claims by consumers alleging damage occasioned by the water supply (stained laundry, etc.). The Water Act 1981 places a clear responsibility upon undertakers for any damage occasioned by flooding and other consequences of burst mains, although case law may determine otherwise (see Chapter 2).

Cut-offs

One of the difficult aspects of dealing with consumers is the sealing-off of consumers' supplies following non-payment of water rates. Serious cases of debt recovery may be dealt with by physical cut-off of the supply pipe. A charge is made for subsequent reinstatement.

Redundant services should be cut-off at the main.

CONSUMER COMPLAINTS

Enquiries in General

Every water undertaking must have a first-class system for responding to an outsider's enquiry. With the availability of computers, systems can be developed to:

> (i) Recognise the consumer and his status, i.e. provide a record of previous dialogue, and of payments made.

   (ii) Provide a responsive method of acting on the enquiry.

   (iii) Provide statistics from which to evaluate the service given.

The maintenance of such systems allows the public quick response to their enquiries by way of both information and action, and provision of statistical information for management.

A well-designed consumer enquiry system provides a basis for service performance indicators (see Section 6 and Chapter 4) and for justifying expense on the associated network maintenance, analysis and planning.

Consumer Consultative Committees

Following the publication of a Monopolies & Merger Commission report on certain aspects of performance of a water authority, the Water Act 1983 allowed for authorities with smaller memberships, and, in order to cater adequately for consumer representation, set up machinery for the establishment of Consumer Consultative Committees (CCCs). See Chapter 2 for details.

Source and Types of Complaint

A complaint may be received by telephone, by letter, written across a water bill or via a third party, for instance a member of parliament, local councillor, or Citizens' Advice Bureau. It may be received by word of mouth by a mainlayer or a water inspector or it may be given in good faith but to the wrong address, area or department. Coordination of supply complaints from such diverse sources is the responsibility of the distribution function.

Types of complaints are dealt with in Chapter 4.

Accepting, Recording and Dealing with Complaints

Guidelines should be issued to telephonists and response centre staff on how to obtain accurate facts from complainants, and how to give advice on remedying simple domestic problems.

Every complainant must have his complaint accepted, recorded, summarised and assessed for urgency. An assurance on the action to be taken must be given.

A computer system or standard pre-printed form should be used and the consumer's details (and complainant's if different), including name and address, property reference etc. recorded.

A modern computer system should ensure that the details are transferred instantly for action. Where pre-printed forms are used it is equally vital to ensure the speediest communication and for the report to be assimilated by an officer who will exercise judgement on the manner and priority of action, and deal with the response to the complainant.

Interpreting Complaints

Consumer complaints require categorisation by type, location and frequency in order to find their source and solution. Thus an outbreak of severe but transient discoloured water complaints might be the result of a large burst whereas persistent trouble often means that a main (or mains) are internally corroded and need flushing, swabbing, relining and even renewing. Good management demands that the worst mains have to be treated first and properly codified complaint information is a component in deciding the priority of mains requiring attention. Again the computer can help and a good data base technique can interrogate the data quickly without the tedium of a manual information retrieval method.

Discoloration complaints point to corrosion in the mains system or perhaps a water treatment inadequacy (for instance a coagulation floc carry over), whereas low pressures noted over an area may indicate excessive frictional loss in the distribution mains and, often, the need for mains improvement.

Isolated complaints usually mean that the communication pipe or the individual private service pipework is the source of the trouble. Complaints arise from consumers sharing a common service pipe, either because of its inadequate sizing for present-day peak use, or due to the deteriorated state of old pipes—usually of lead or galvanised iron. (See earlier for rechargeable repairs). Separate supply pipes have every advantage except their initial cost and should be encouraged wherever they can be laid as a replacement of old common supply pipes.

Replying to Complaints

When complaints have been dealt with it is important to ensure that the undertaker confirms this, usually in writing. It may be that a point of law is concerned, damages are involved or there are allegations concerning a member of staff. In these cases it is essential to record matters in correspondence.

Key factors in replying to consumer complaints are:

(1) Establish the *facts* in dates, times, people and property.
(2) Tell the truth.
(3) Be clear, be concise.
(4) Be courteous.
(5) Respond quickly.
(6) Keep other staff informed (for example, scientists on water quality complaints).

Call-out Charges

A small call-out charge may be levied by undertakings for attention to consumer problems outside normal working hours. The charge is waived when inspection reveals public safety hazards, proven undertaker's responsibility or cases of hardship.

Who Should Meet the Consumer?

The water undertaker's employees may enter consumer premises under the provisions of the Water Acts to check byelaws, meters, water wastage and similar matters. Generally these duties will be performed by uniformed staff each with proper credentials to show he/she is a *bona fide* employee.

Because of possible impersonation of statutory officials, the credentials should include a photograph sealed within the document and an extract or summary of the relevant parts of the law.

PUBLIC RELATIONS

Introduction

Good public relations[2] are a necessity for any large enterprise, including water undertakings. Distribution department public relations begins with the undertaker's personnel who meet the consumer and the public, that is the supervisors, inspectors and trench grades. They form the point of contact with the consumer who pays the bill. They need to know in broad terms the objectives and obligations of the water industry and the salient and current concerns of the distribution function.

Classic circumstances occur when internally corroded water mains are to be descaled and relined. During this operation the water supply to consumers will be interrupted and despite every precaution being taken there will be dirt and upset to the water supply. Thereafter things will be improved; there should be less trouble from discoloured water, better pressure and flow and the life of the main is extended. And of course all this can be achieved without excavating all the metalled surface of the footway and at about one-third of the cost of relaying the water main. It is very much in everyone's interest to tell consumers all this beforehand. Then they will know of the problems, their probable duration and the reason for the work being undertaken.

Follow these principles:

(a) Speak with authority.
(b) Be sincere.
(c) Be enthusiastic.
(d) Be courteous.

The Press and Media

In the absence of information from a water undertaker the press will seek a story from wherever they can get it. If the consumer is prepared to talk to the press then they will listen. Therefore it behoves the water undertaker to inform the newspapers both consciously and conscientiously about what is happening. A regular rapport with pertinent journalists may pay dividends.

Equally, radio and television contacts should be cultivated to keep them aware of developments in the water industry. Local radio stations welcome this. Many will say that the British water industry's publicity efforts through television have not been effective and that only during the 1975/76 drought and 1983 strike was public interest and sympathy sustained.

The coming of cable television and other means of telecommunication already offer the opportunity for addressing particular districts or even individual households on any message which concerns the undertaker and the consumer.

Imparting information to individuals, groups or the media is a skilled art. To do it effectively basic professional techniques have to be acquired. Communication skills for distribution department personnel should therefore be taught.

It is in order to ask for time to gather information but it is seldom wise to say nothing or to delay a reply.

Advice on Water Use

The printed word is an important facet of public relations, be it by an individual letter, a public notice or an information sheet. Good clear sentences are necessary which avoid jargon and obscure phraseology. In some communities, foreign translations may be necessary.

One successful message which was promoted was "help us to help your neighbour—use water wisely".

Indiscriminate use of hose pipes for garden watering exacerbates the situation during drought, consumers not knowing the high cost of water transmission, nor appreciating that their coincident usage can deprive other consumers on a mains system quite adequate for normal demands.

Warning of frost and good burst prevention techniques should be by the issue of clear sound advice in newspapers during the first cold snap in, say, early November.

See Section 5 for reference to the effect of water use on charges and Chapter 5 for references to demand management.

Talks to Public Bodies and Groups of Consumers

Talks to public bodies, local organizations, and commercial and social groups form a regular part of a distribution department's activities. This might be in response to a specific scheme of work or may be a more general enquiry for information. "There's a lot behind your tap" is a typical title for a talk about water supply and distribution. If the speaker is informed, prepared and skilful, then each member of his audience will know more about his water supply by the end of the evening. At the start they might think "the rain is free why should we pay for water". They should leave knowing the story of water supply from raindrop to consumer's tap, with an understanding of the time, effort and money it necessitates to bring a safe and plentiful supply to them.

Knowing your audience is always excellent advice. It is important to find out about local supplies before giving information to a parish council. Of what material are the mains, when were they laid, when did they last burst, is discoloration a problem? Be well prepared beforehand.

Summary

Perhaps public relations is as much about reminding as informing—the need to explain regularly what the job of the water industry is and how it seeks to accomplish it. In the absence of a repeated statement of these objectives it is too easy for public relations to become negative and defensive of a lost position. Failure-based communication between the undertaker and the consumer can occur where one waits for the receipt of a consumer complaint, say.

3. PLANNING FOR EMERGENCIES

'NORMAL' EMERGENCIES

Definitions and Procedures

Before discussing emergency procedures it is perhaps worth attempting to identify 'normal' emergencies. To most consumers a burst pipe within their premises could be classed as an emergency. To a water undertaker anything from a burst service pipe to a treatment plant failure could be so classed. It is important for the undertaking to classify those works which are considered to constitute an emergency, to prepare plans for dealing with the situation and to keep informed all those operational personnel who will be involved. In many cases, undertakers will issue to those employees involved a set of operating procedures or instructions. In other cases it may be that the procedures have evolved from a series of instructions from management, whether they be verbal or written or a combination of the two. Naturally, a laid down procedural document has great advantages when training new staff and standardising procedures but one can never hope to cater for every eventuality and, in such situations, one has to rely on the experience, training and 'know-how' of those employees involved.

Reporting Centre

Looking at emergency procedures in detail, the first link in the system is the undertaker's reporting centre, and/or control room. In small organizations the emergency call may be received at the standby inspector/superintendent's home. In larger organizations the emergency receiving centre may also be both the radio communication centre and the pumping station and reservoir control centre. Where such duties are not combined there will generally be a direct link between centres carrying out the various functions. Such centres are normally manned continuously and, to minimise the levels of manning, they may be centralised to cover extensive areas outside or even during normal working hours.

In the reporting centre it is essential that the undertaker employs personnel who are quickly able to ascertain the degree of severity of an occurrence which is reported by a member of the public. It will be his decision, whilst usually following a set of guidelines, as to what type of assistance is needed. Site inspection may be necessary to verify the report before expensive remedial measures are put in hand. In most organizations, procedures outside normal working hours differ considerably from those during normal hours.

Emergency Repairs

Many undertakers operate standby and/or call-out systems so that operatives are available for duty outside normal working hours. The arrangements for such systems are widely varied throughout the industry and are generally subject to local agreements and conditions.

As an alternative, contractors may be utilised not only for routine mainlaying and emergency works during the day but also to provide emergency cover outside of hours.

Some undertakers, however, operate a shift system of working so that there are emergency crews on duty at all times of the day. With such a system, the emergency gangs can then be directed and re-directed as and when necessary.

Special arrangements may also be necessary for the drawing of stores, plant and equipment for emergency work or, as an alternative, small emergency stores may be made available without the need to refer to the general stock.

Maintaining Supplies

Having provided the labour required to carry out the emergency repairs it is likely that mains will have to be isolated and it may be necessary for alternative supplies to be arranged. The 'level of service' given may govern the procedure which distribution staff will follow in dealing with emergencies. For example, if less than a certain number of properties are affected, it may be the undertaker's policy to isolate the main until the next working day and provide standpipe supplies, tankers or bowsers as a temporary measure. Such an arrangement may be considerably cheaper than the cost of employing a repair gang outside normal hours but must, of course, be balanced against the inconvenience to members of the public who may be without water for some considerable period.

Where trunk mains are affected by emergencies there should preferably be laid down procedures for providing alternative supplies (see later).

SOME CAUSES OF A MAJOR EMERGENCY

All water undertakings in this country have at some time experienced a major emergency situation, and as a consequence have either developed new, or updated existing contingency plans.

Industrial action in any of the service industries or the vagaries of the weather have produced situations where, unless adequate plans are made in advance, serious supply deficiencies would occur. Contingency plans must therefore be tailored to a variety of situations, which may include:

(i) Failure of major plants.
(ii) Adverse weather conditions.

(iii) Industrial action.
(iv) External agencies.

Failure of Major Plant

The inability of a treatment works to cope with water quality changes, failure of pumping plant or of the electricity supply, pollution of the contents of a service reservoir, the loss of a critical trunk main or a concurrent breakdown during a carefully planned maintenance operation, are examples of such failure.

Many of the above problems can be obviated by good system management. Plans should be laid to combat changes in raw water quality, dependent on risk.

Standby pumping plant and provision of a standby diesel alternator at small or medium output source or booster stations may be viable, dependent again on risk. For diesel plant, fuel stocks should be risk assessed.

Service reservoirs should be adequately sealed, inspected and cleaned at regular intervals and good hygiene practices strictly observed.

Trunk mains fittings should be regularly inspected and maintained, repair materials should be available and stocks of couplings, etc. replenished when drawn upon.

Adverse Weather Conditions

The two periods of maximum demand in the water industry are during the summer period of hot weather, commencing with the bedding plant season, and a period in the winter which follows sub-zero temperatures.

It is vital that trends are clearly monitored to assist in the prediction of a deteriorating situation, which if allowed to continue may present grave problems in maintaining supplies.

The 1975/76 drought taught engineers to avert problems by thinking ahead all the time of how the situation might develop and taking prompt action.

The risk of pollution is always present during flooding and sub-zero emergencies and it is wise to increase the vigilance on water quality sampling at these times.

Plant and equipment subject to flooding, particularly air valve installations, must be made secure.

Industrial Action

This can affect the industry from within or without and may have a direct, or indirect, effect upon the water supply.

The first priority in any situation of this nature is the need for a satisfactory dialogue with trade union representatives and the establishment of a liaison committee in order to protect public health and safety. These arrangements must be clarified at an early date.

In the event of industrial action in the water industry the demand for water could increase astronomically in the early stages as consumers take their own reserves of water. Such increased demands can exacerbate the situation when pumping and booster stations overload and trip-out. The danger of mains becoming de-watered increases the risk of pollution and water quality control measures must be fully provided for.

Sympathetic and unofficial strike action can present problems with deliveries of essential supplies and strategic reserve stocks of these must be fully maintained.

External Agencies

Arrangements must always be made to safeguard supplies against pollution and aquifers, rivers and lakes from the spillage of dangerous substances, by accident or sabotage.

It is normal for water undertakings to have established procedures for reporting spillages. Offenders can be prosecuted under The Rivers (Prevention of Pollution) Acts, 1951-1961, with each offence carrying a maximum penalty of £1 000.

Problems arising from sabotage or war should be included in the organization's security arrangements and procedures and the water supply function is a major aspect of regional Civil Defence plans.

MAINTAINING SUPPLIES IN A MAJOR EMERGENCY

The statutory water undertaker has a duty to meet the reasonable demands of consumers, and, whatever problems occur, every endeavour must be made to do so.

Switching Supplies

Distribution systems should be designed with flexibility to allow re-distribution of supplies in the event of failure of any part, subject, of course, to degree of risk.

Plans should be available to divert alternative sources of supply to support affected areas and to share available storage. It must be assumed that any water supply system has been designed to accommodate a short period of major source loss and local plans prepared to deal with individual situations.

Mobile pumps may be required to transfer or boost supplies into depleted areas or those without standby plant. It is wise to examine the system and install branches for mobile pumping plant which may be used to advantage at short notice.

Water Rationing

If full supplies cannot be maintained appeals for economy in water use may be made. Should the appeals fail and the situation deteriorates to the extent that water rationing is contemplated, it is advisable to have plans prepared well in advance. Water rationing can be carried out by pressure reduction, alternate day street isolation, use of standpipes or street bowsers.

It will always be preferable to keep trunk feeder mains charged with water, but if standpipes were restricted to their proximity, carrying distances may be too great and dangerous situations may arise from queuing.

Where potable water bowsers are to be used they should be clearly marked to distinguish them fron non-potable containers, with consumer instructions, for example, a "boiling notice", affixed. In farming communities, mobile tankers may be required.

It is advisable to make provisional arrangements with tanker hire companies, breweries and bulk transportation companies to use their resources if the need should arise.

Priorities

In order to guard against the extreme circumstances of having to shut off selected supplies, the undertaking must know its critical consumers and how they would be affected by a cessation of supply. Health service industries, industrial processes and employment may be affected and a list of priority consumers should be made in order to govern water rationing procedures.

Domestic supplies should be given priority, whilst the specific locations of renal dialysis patients must be notified to control centres and local uniformed staff.

Priority of remaining users may vary from area to area, but most lists should nominate:

(1) hospitals;
(2) food and drink manufacturers;
(3) water and sewage plants;
(4) power stations;
(5) other utilities;
(6) water-using industrial processes; and
(7) schools, etc.

See later for the procedure in dealing with the termination of supplies.

Assistance to Neighbouring Undertakings

During the 1939-45 war, interconnections were made between adjoining undertakings' distribution systems to provide interchange of emergency supplies. Many of these remain in service and there have been numerous additions. These are quite naturally in fringe areas and in some instances of limited value. It is important, however, to remember that in times of emergency any support is welcome and these small supplies could be augmented by boosting.

In reviewing contingency supply plans there are many locations today that could be interconnected and a review of the matter should be undertaken.

COMMUNICATION

In implementing any changes in the continuity or quality of the supply it is fundamentally important to keep the consumer and any other affected party fully informed.

Consumer Notification

Section 80, Third Schedule WA 45 requires undertakers to give notice to all consumers where supplies are likely to be materially affected by repairs or other maintenance work. Whilst Section 80 precludes work of an emergency nature, it is generally considered "good public relations" for those people affected to be informed at an early stage that supplies have been interrupted and, if possible, the alternative measures which are being taken. Such information may be disseminated either by written notices to each consumer, announcements through mobile public address systems or by contact with the local press and radio. Above all other needs, it is of utmost importance that the reporting centre is made aware of the situation, the measures which are being taken and that it is clearly advised of the information which is to be given to customers. Many of the general public's criticisms of the water industry's handling of publicity matters originate from inadequate and inaccurate statements issued by poorly briefed personnel.

Temporary Cessation of Supplies

The organization is entitled to take reasonable steps to meet any emergency which arises, but this is no excuse for negligence in maintaining supplies. In the event of a decision being made to cease supplies to any consumer legal advice should be sought, but any action must be kept to a strictly practical level.

In the event of a developing situation likely to result in a failure of supply where no alternative exists, the following action should be taken:

(a) Provide a bowser or standpipe supply.
(b) Arrange for affected consumers, especially listed priority consumers, to be warned as soon as possible if the water supply is critical to their function.

(c) Arrange with hospitals for the re-location of renal dialysis patients.
(d) Draft a statement of policy for consumers who make telephone enquiries.
(e) Draft a press statement.
(f) Draft a notice for the withdrawal of trade supplies.
(g) Draft a notice for the withdrawal of piped domestic supplies.
(h) Arrange extended manning of telephone switchboards.

Use of the Media

The media can greatly assist in getting quick messages to consumers. Fuller notes on making best use of local media were given in Section 2.

Liaison with Outside Organizations

In an emergency situation there is a need to maintain effective contact with numerous outside authorities and it is essential that an emergency committee is set up to deal with this. The Local Authority Environmental Health Officers, Medical Officers of Health and hospital authorities, particularly the renal units, have a specific interest in the water supply.

The social services and the local government departments can be of considerable service in times of difficulty and contact with the police, fire and highway authorities must be reinforced.

4. SERVICING DISTRIBUTION ACTIVITIES

VEHICLES, PLANT AND EQUIPMENT

The provision and maintenance of suitable vehicles, plant and equipment are essential to the efficient operation of an undertaking's distribution section. The responsibility for the provision, maintenance and administration of such items might rest with the distribution staff in small organizations, whereas in larger ones responsibility is normally assigned to full time transport and plant engineers and/or managers.

Vehicle Fleet Administration

Water undertakers are required to obtain an operator's licence from the licensing authority if utilising goods vehicles over 3.5 tonnes gross vehicle weight. This is normally the case where transport is provided for direct labour teams. A qualified officer will need to be employed, who must satisfy the licensing authority's requirements that vehicle defects are reported, and Road Traffic regulations are heeded. The licence will relate to specific listed vehicles, which requires updating, and records must be kept to ensure that licensing, plating, MOT tests etc. are carried out on the due date.

Vehicle Selection

Selection of vehicles is an integral part of the viability of a direct labour team[3]. Modern day practice may commit the water undertaker to a heavy medium-term investment in vehicles, which should only be undertaken after a close appraisal. Vehicles for direct labour teams may be mass-produced or customer designed. Some features to consider are:

(i) Driver capabilities and training.
(ii) Craneage, tipping or towing features.
(iii) Stowage of tools and materials.

(iv) Integral, skid or towed power source.
(v) Working facilities on board.
(vi) Personnel to be carried.
(vii) Their health and welfare requirements.
(viii) Operational and size limitations.

Organization and method study into site and transport requirements may be desirable to assist in vehicle selection. Field trials of new vehicles should be carried out to obtain widespread views of supervisors and operatives. Undertakers carrying out vehicle appraisal can benefit from the experiences of other operators from the water, gas and similar utilities. Competent evaluation will take into account capital and running costs calculated over the total vehicle life, and comparisons made between purchase, lease and hiring arrangements.

Vehicle Operation

Close liaison is necessary between distribution and transport staff to plan for maintenance and inspection schedules and minimise downtime. However, labour standing time is more costly than vehicle standing time, so an economic level of spare vehicles is necessary. The economies of providing in-house maintenance facilities and holding spares must be considered against the contracting-out option.

Mobile and Ancillary Plant and Equipment

The maintenance of mobile and ancillary plant involves maintenance schedules, optimum plant utilisation and flexibility as well as cost allocation.

The selection of mobile and ancillary plant and equipment is largely governed by the same factors as vehicles, although for smaller items greater emphasis is placed on the operative's needs, capabilities and safety requirements. Where major changes are envisaged, field trials again prove invaluable in providing the most effective use of financial resources.

Small plant and equipment may be based on a standard issue for all employees within the group, thus it is important that the most suitable item is chosen.

A policy of preventative plant maintenance should yield much the same results as for vehicles. As it is important that operator standing time be reduced to the minimum possible, plant and equipment serviceability is of utmost importance.

For further reading see:
Lowe, D. 1982 "The transport manager's handbook", Kogan Page.

STORES MANAGEMENT

Coordination

An adequate supply of materials and equipment is essential to the efficient management of a water undertaking.

Close liaison is required between the stores and distribution staffs in the determination of those items to be stocked and the appropriate stocking levels. The aim must be to provide an effective level of service at the minimum cost.

Stock Categories

Stock items may be treated in different ways depending on their future use.

Strategic items intended for emergencies—for example, major burst mains, may be held in a separate location, remote from the normal stores holding, but must be included in the recording system.

Some items may be on "free issue"—for example, minor transport spares, or others may be eligible for self picking on a "supermarket" approach when the storekeeper would record the issues on the way out.

The stores system can also be used to hold 'non-stock' items until they are required for particular projects. These items are not entered into the stock system and should be held separately.

Selection of Stock Items

The user must be consulted on the stock levels to be provided and on which items should be held in stock to avoid the frequent need for *ad hoc* purchases. It is good management to reduce stock holding to the minimum value commensurate with an acceptable level of service; joint agreement with the users is required for the need to hold in stock any particular items.

Standardisation can often reduce the number of different items to be stocked without affecting the users' flexibility.

Regular reviews of those items held in stock are necessary to avoid redundant items.

Purchasing and Stock Levels

Annual purchasing contracts may be used to regulate the purchase of fast turnover or high value stock items.

Stock levels are evaluated in weeks' normal usage, and re-order levels and quantities are set by making an allowance for the anticipated demand prior to receipt of an order such that the minimum holding is maintained.

It is useful to periodically consider the ratio of the value of stock held to stock issued per annum. This will give a guide to the effectiveness of control over stock levels.

Stores Catalogue

It is essential that users know what is available from stock. Manually produced stores catalogues can be used, but computer printed catalogues or on-line systems providing instant access to the current stock position through visual display units are increasingly being adopted.

Receipt, Inspection, Handling and Storage

All receipts or returns from users must be entered into the stores recording system.

Items received for stock should be inspected, and if necessary tested, to establish acceptability before placing in pipe bays, storage racks etc.

Appropriate facilities are required for the safe handling and storage of many different commodities, and an allowance must be made for compliance with health and safety, fire and security provisions.

Requisitioning and Issue

On receipt of an authorised requisition bearing the correct financial coding information, the stores staff would make the issue and enter the transaction into the system.

Stocktaking and Security

Routine stock checks are required by persons unconnected with the operation of the stores on a pre-determined cycle—for example, annually.

Stock discrepancies must be reported and rectified on the stock records.

Care must be taken to avoid losses due to inappropriate storage, theft or vandalism. Stock should be covered by insurance and the insurance company may require certain security provisions.

Further Reading

The following books and articles would provide further, more detailed, information:

1. British Standards Institution, BS 5729 "Guide to stock control".
2. Bailey, P. and Farmer, D. 1970 "Materials management handbook", Gower Press.
3. Bailey, P. 1970 "Successful stock control by manual systems", Gower Press.
4. Morrison, A. 1974 "Storage and control of stock", 2nd revised edition, Pitman.
5. Monopolies and Mergers Commission 1981 "Report on the Severn-Trent Water Authority, East Worcestershire Waterworks Company and The South Staffordshire Waterworks Company", HMSO, London.

RECORDS OF MAINS AND SERVICES

Statutory Requirements

There is a statutory duty placed upon all water undertakers to record upon a map not less than 6 inches to 1 mile (1:10560), the positions of all pipes, except service pipes, within six months of their being laid or altered. This statutory duty is imposed by both the Waterworks Clauses Act of 1847 (s.19) and s.12, Third Schedule, WA 45.

The Health & Safety at Work etc. Act 1974 imposes a duty upon the undertaker to ensure, in so far as is reasonably practicable, the health, safety and welfare of its employees and others who may be affected by his operations. As there is, therefore, an obligation for undertakers to protect their employees and the public from the hazards which might exist in water mains systems, the maintenance of an adequate records system is a prerequisite.

The onus of protecting the undertaker's installations within the highway, which is imposed upon other statutory undertakers and authorities by PUSWA, is eased by the availability of water undertakers' mains records.

Uses and Benefits of Providing Record Systems

Whilst there are statutory requirements for mainlaying records systems, there will be operational and future planning requirements which will justify the needs for providing a system which, in general, will be of a higher standard than that required by statute.

The uses which might accrue from a records system include the design, maintenance and operation of distribution systems, response to emergencies, dealing with planning applications, asset valuations, exchange of PUSWA notices and site location of apparatus.

The benefits accruing from a sound records system include reduction in time and cost on design works, trial holing, mains location, excavation and reinstatement work and mains plotting for other utilities, and improvement in management of the distribution network and efficient running of the undertaking.

Records Required

Currently most undertakers record mains on 1:1250 Ordnance Survey scale plans in urban areas and 1:2500 plans in rural areas. In some remote areas Ordnance Survey information is only available at 1:10000 scale.

Unfortunately Ordnance Survey 1:1250 or 1:2500 plans are of too small a scale to allow record information to be plotted with any great degree of accuracy and it is usually necessary for these plans to be used as a guide with additional location plans being utilised as accurate reference information. Such plans might be in the form of field books and sketches, separate trunk mains records, waste district plans, major connections sketches and enlargements, overall network diagrams, as well as many other detailed drawings of pumping stations and reservoir inlet and outlet arrangements.

Where such enlargements or details are in existence, clearly marked reference to these should always be made on the master 1:1250 or 1:2500 plan, in order to allow for simple retrieval. It is essential that such details are made easily accessible to operational staff if site records are to be efficiently utilised.

Records Systems in Use

(a) Conventional Systems
Many records are derived from field books, some dating back to the early 19th century. Drawn on site, they show detailed information of joints and fittings, as well as location and depth. The details may have been transferred to paper or transparent Ordnance Survey maps. A more advanced use of transparent Ordnance Survey plans utilises a transparent overlay upon which the mains records are plotted. Additional transparencies and paper prints may be produced from flat bed copies. The major advantages of this system are the ease of updating either the overlay or the Ordnance Survey sheet, without laborious re-plotting and the ability to provide planning or maintenance information on additional overlays.

(b) Digital Mapping System
The Ordnance Survey produce maps in digital form for use within computerised systems. Mains records can then be digitised from existing records through the computer which overlays the details on the Ordnance Survey data base tape, and which can then be recalled in various views (overlays) at any selected scale. An instant hard copy for small areas can be taken or for larger and more accurate details a plotter is used.

In addition to mains records, other details can be stored in data form within the computer such as: size, lengths, class, year laid, renovation, grid reference, nodes on reference points, fittings, 'C' values etc.

Information is stored in data files which can be extracted separately from the map base and sorted into size, dates, locations etc. as required.

The use of this system is limited by the availability of Ordnance Survey digital map tapes, which at present cover only a small percentage of England and Wales. It is practicable however to digitise mains records into the system without the digitised map base, and overlay plots on to existing paper maps.

Standard Detailing

For a records system to prove efficient to those personnel using it, certain conventions are required regarding the type and quantity of information which is to be 'stored' on the plan.

DoE Report No. 25[4] gave recommended standards for sewer and water main records, which extended to the use of computerised systems. The adoption of these standards within the water industry, following an earlier IWES report[3], is now quite widespread.

Records Maintenance

It is essential that the upkeep of records is given priority within an undertaking. Whilst this may be a repetitive task, its nature dictates that records will need to be continually updated.

Storage and Retrieval Systems

Historically, plans have been stored in horizontal form and sometimes bound in book form but more recently transparencies and paper prints have been maintained on vertical systems to enable easier retrieval. In most undertakings a set of master copies is also retained in a secure location to guard against loss by fire or other cause.

Microcopying of records has the advantage of reducing storage space. Additional microcopies in conjunction with viewers and copiers may then be utilised by design, operations and planning personnel. In general, the use of microcopying will be an accompaniment to map based record systems but will not be used in place of them.

It is essential that systems of storage are easily accessible to all operational, design and planning staff and that retrieval systems can be simply interrogated by all levels of staff.

Digital mapping systems allow immediate access to information from many locations. Plots (prints) at various scales can be obtained from a centralised plotter.

Storage required will be local to the computer and will require considerably less space over conventional systems.

Accessibility of Records to Other Bodies

The Water Act 1945 only requires the undertaker to keep available for inspection apparatus records. Most undertakers do, as a matter of courtesy, transfer this information on to developers' own plans or provide copies of their and other utilities' mains records. Difficulties arise if plotting errors occur and thus a disclaimer is normally added to most information.

Two trials have been initiated by the National Joint Utilities Group (NJUG) where the exchange of information between utilities in Bradford was carried out on microfilm and in Edinburgh on a freephone basis (SUSIE).

A third trial is now under way in Dudley (South Staffordshire Waterworks Company) where the exchange of records is being carried out on a computerised system, using digital mapping with each utility having access to the other utilities' mains records. The information given for exchange however is limited to mains location, size and material.

Use of Pipe Location Equipment

Whilst every effort will be made to maintain accurate records, drafting and plotting errors, unrecorded alternatives and highway modifications will have introduced some inaccuracies into mains records systems. In such situations, electronic pipe location equipment is of assistance in locating installations. A skilled operator will provide accurate plots in the majority of cases. In some organizations, pipe location equipment is regularly used by surveying staff where mains records have been found inaccurate.

5. HOW THE CONSUMER PAYS FOR SERVICES

CHARGING FOR SERVICES

The effect which the Water Act 1973 has had on current charging policy is comprehensively covered in Chapter 2. Distribution staff, however, may assist the financial controllers of water undertakings in many ways.

Availability of the Supply System

In making available sufficient capacity in the trunk and distribution network, a potential peak of demand has to be met. (Insofar as this peak may be controlled see p. 423 "Unrestricted Demand"). The associated costs tend to vary with potential demand rather than actual consumption of water. The costs arise from:

(i) Interest on capital works.
(ii) Depreciation of the works.
(iii) Repair and maintenance of the system.
(iv) Inspection of the system and waste prevention.

The costs attributable in making available the supply can then be allocated, to metered and unmetered consumers, in relation to share of capacity. Whether share of capacity is best indicated by such a basis as connection size or meter type and size is theoretically questionable but authorities have their own methods of recovering these costs.

Leakage

In specifying the quantities of water distributed from source, care must be taken to recognise that leakage from the system takes place. Account should be taken of an apportionment of estimated leakage taking place within the system and that within unmetered properties (that is, downstream of the highway boundary) and, also, within the system, apportionment of the leakage 'contribution' between measured and unmeasured consumers. Few undertakings would have reliable figures for these apportionments, however, due to the wide variation in circumstances and user performance.

Meter Accuracy

The ability of both meters within the system and on premises to register consistently within acceptable tolerances must be considered. Whilst efforts are made to ensure appropriate meters for the appropriate task, their limitations, particularly in registering quantities outside their normal range of flow rates, should be recognised. Slow filling of tanks through ball valves is a particular case in point.

CHARGES FOR PROVIDING A SUPPLY

Revenue Guarantee Agreements

A Revenue Guarantee Agreement is the method by which the cost of providing water mains of the required capacity for a site of domestic dwellings, under ss.36 or 37, WA 45 [and relevant Water (Scotland) Act], is covered (see also Chapter 2).

Cost of Off-site Works

Disputes have arisen where apportionment of an off-site mains scheme for domestic supplies has been included in the overall cost of the revenue to be guaranteed, within the meaning of s.37(1), WA 45 (see Chapter 2, Section 5).

Phasing of Large Sites

In recent years, larger sites are fewer, and those which exist may take longer to develop, or may be split between different developers. This is causing increasing concern to undertakings wishing to ensure that final mains distribution designs are adequate, whilst financial cover is forthcoming for all the costs of phased construction.

Industrial Supplies

Cover for provision of source works and the distribution capacity to cater for new or extended industrial demand for water is a matter of negotiation between the water undertaker and the developer. Various formulae and costing methods, perhaps with regard to the financing of capital for phased construction, have been developed, but each case needs to be considered on its merits.

For reading on use of industrial water, see reference 6.

EFFECT OF WATER USE ON CHARGES

General

As the component uses of water receive more attention, so does the consideration of its value to the consumer, and of the amount of water genuinely needed for given purposes. When combined with the total cost of providing all water demanded and at the precise moment of demand, particularly at coincident times, the charging structure and management of consumer demand have their place.

Unrestricted Demand

The capital cost of providing system capacity to meet unrestricted demand is becoming prohibitive. Likewise, coverage of system risk of plant or resource failure requires economic appraisal. Such evaluations may justify enforcement of system pressure control or flow restriction measures, publicity on use of water, compulsory metering or peak charging.

There are a number of uses which the consumer makes of his water supply which are more time-based than quantity-based, such as rinsing under a sink tap. Flow restriction measures within the incoming supply, either by pipe sizing or by throttling the stop tap, are possible but not always practical. Control of the mains pressure is generally practicable and many undertakings have installed schemes with lucrative short pay-back periods to this end. Refer to Section 6 and Chapter 12 for further notes on the correlation between pressure and leakage, and to Chapter 5 for comprehensive reference to demand management.

The Credit and Load Management System (CALMS)

As an example of a system designed to investigate demand management possibilities and meter reading interrogation, reference is here made to the CALMS trials. In particular, South Staffordshire Waterworks Company is participating, in conjunction with the Water Research Centre, the Midlands Electricity Board and British Telecom, in a trial for the two-way transmission of data from consumers' water and electricity meters in the Kingswinford area.

CALMS utilises an electronic unit containing a micro-processor which replaces the electricity meter within the property and which is in communication with the utility, using idle time on the telephone line. The "interrogation" will be controlled by a small computer at the telephone exchange.

The Kingswinford area as a whole is remotely monitored for pressure and flows using pressure transducers and zone meters which compare overall consumption with that of the selected properties. Consumptions are examined whilst adjusting pressure through six PRVs controlling parts of the area.

Other purposes for which the CALM system could be used include:

1. Display of charges and costs which would encourage conservation.
2. Peak flow reduction.
3. Distribution system telemetry.

The WRC are currently involved with three other trials at Milton Keynes, Guildford and Ilkeston. Milton Keynes has a Thorn-EMI Mainsborne signalling system, whilst the others are using CALMS.

Bulk Supplies

Lastly, the use to which bulk supplies of water from a neighbouring undertaking are used and charged for, particularly in fringe areas, can have quite an effect on the local cost of providing supplies and hence on the overall cost of supply. The reorganization of the water industry in England and Wales, in 1974, drastically reduced the number of undertakings, and therefore the number of bulk transfers of water supplies from one undertaking to another. Nevertheless a number of such transfers still exist. Charges for bulk supplies may be regulated by historical agreements, but modern water supply management should ensure that bulk supply arrangements are appropriate in the regional context, and to local conditions. Charges should be marginal in order to inhibit unnecessary capital works which mitigate against overall consumer benefit.

6. DISTRIBUTION MANAGEMENT

CONTROL OF EXPENDITURE

With a revenue expenditure for the water industry in supply alone well in excess of £1 000 million, an immediate perspective is placed on the importance of managing costs and obtaining value for money. A good proportion of this sum is attributable to distribution and in particular to manual employees' wages and to power consumption. Two areas of vital importance are:

(a) Justification and appraisal of capital and maintenance works.
(b) The effectiveness of supervision and the work force employed.

JUSTIFYING EXPENDITURE

There are five areas of management now given more attention than hitherto:

(i) Network strategy.
(ii) Appraisal of new works.
(iii) Renewal, maintenance and inspection of the network.
(iv) Leakage policy and system pressure.
(v) Electricity tariffs and pumping strategy.

Network Strategy

Most undertakings have now embarked on network analysis (Chapter 5), indeed some have used networking techniques since the 1960s. In its use, a model is set up which forms a ready vehicle for applying alternative strategies for the future. Although this may rest on a large element of the unknowns, it can be updated at any time with the best information available. The requirements may be in the form of security needs, planning strategies, industrial changes, population predictions, elements and behaviour in demand etc. In relation to larger works, such as sources, service reservoirs and trunk mains, this model is essential to give the lead-in to maintenance or renewal of existing plant and siting of new works. It must be sensitive to the many changes which may arise in an uncertain economic environment.

Appraisal of New Works

It is fundamental that all new works proposals are financially appraised using datum values with reliable inflation and discount rates and incorporating all relevant funding and running costs. See Chapter 5 for further reading.

Renewal, Maintenance and Inspection of the System

From corporate policy objectives on the constancy of supply, water quality and service in general will come a justified frequency for maintenance and inspection of the system. More specifically this may cover service reservoir cleaning programmes, maintenance of accessible valves and their chambers, painting pipe bridges etc. Renewal, either by major refurbishment or total replacement, must be based on sound reasoning to meet the corporate objectives, and be taken in the context of the network strategy.

Alternative measures should be drawn out and financially appraised. The best system information should be obtained, using network surveys and obtaining physical pipe and water samples where appropriate. It is surprising how often schemes may be postponed, amended or cancelled by adhering to these principles. Such aids also assist in priority rating, competing for funds and in forming meaningful expenditure programmes.

Leakage Policy and System Pressure

A DoE/NWC report[7] provides a reference for determination of leakage control policy.

In order to attain maximum economic benefit, the leakage policy must be developed in conjunction with a total system strategy referred to earlier (see also Chapter 12).

Optimisation of system pressures is a feature of both leakage control and pumping optimisation policies, and must again be developed in conjunction with a total system strategy (Chapter 5 covers this more fully).

Electricity Tariffs and Pumping Strategy

Hourly variations in the demand for electrical power have led electricity boards to offer all consumers a variety of tariffs designed to even output. Large consumers are offered the additional attraction of load management schemes, where for a given 'risk' of load shedding at short notice, consequent savings in unit costs are offered. Water undertakings with pumped supplies are taking increased interest but are finding again that as such options become more sophisticated towards the economic benefits of both power generation and water supply, so this can influence total pumping strategy.

Example

Earlier paragraphs will now be drawn together into an illustration. An undertaking may find that a new proposal for a low level service reservoir may suit the requirement to lower system pressures, thereby reducing waste, hence saving damage from leakage, waste detection and water quantity pumping costs, and reduce power costs from lower pumping heads. It may also provide additional security of supply in the event of emergencies, and still be self financing as a pumped storage scheme by taking up attractive electricity tariffs or load management options. The proposal may obviate the need for expensive system renewal, may stand competitive appraisal against other falsely attractive schemes, yet still remain within the context of a network strategy.

Corporate Plan

Any large organization, such as a water undertaking, should have a corporate plan which allows employees to know its medium and long term aims and targets. This will promote more objective decision making in the short, medium and long terms in all technical manpower and financial matters. Such a plan will represent a corporate view of the important issues to be tackled over the next few years, and provides a vehicle for advising managers of the main direction of planned activities and for assessing achievements of goals. A single source of reference can provide the opportunity for significant improvement in management and an aid to providing defined levels of service at minimum cost to the consumer. The network strategy referred to above can be part of the undertaking's corporate plan.

PERFORMANCE AIMS AND INDICATORS

Introduction

The water industry is preparing indicators of performance on common bases. The levels of service, and range of standards to which they relate, cover quality, quantity, availability and other services, the procedures and processes by which these are achieved and measured, the costs incurred and changes that might arise if those standards are varied. It must be appreciated that each undertaking has its own particular characteristics and problems which are reflected in the costs incurred. At the outset, differing accounting systems are used, but the interest generated by performance indicators may well lead towards standardisation of common elements. The indicators cannot, and must not, be used as a "league table", therefore, but provide a year by year comparison of company, authority and division performance and encourage, by cross fertilisation, the adoption of better management concepts, particularly those arising from detailed analysis of the "high" indicators.

Legal and Other Aspects

The legal and other requirements must be understood as a basis to the indicators. The statutory responsibilities in relation to the provision of services are contained in the Water Acts 1945 and 1973, and the Water (Scotland) Act 1946 and subsequent adaptions. However, the two important words "wholesome" and "sufficient", which appear in s.31, Third Schedule, WA 45 are not defined and reference to a dictionary is appropriate.

Water quality is subject to mandatory EC directives where these exist, unless waivers or an interim period for implementation have been agreed with the DoE.

A water undertaking may incorporate in its corporate plan specific aims, such as minimum standards relating to the adequacy and security of supply.

Levels of Service

The reader will be directed to performance indicators commonly in use, or may derive his own. As an example, an indicator relating to the adequacy of supply will be given.

Sufficiency, not being defined, is referred to in quantity terms in The Code of Practice for Water Supply (CP 310) which recommends that not less than three gallons per minute be available from a tap connected to the rising main. For pressure, in consumer protection terms, the requirements of ss.39 and 60, Third Schedule WA 45 appear vague, but in practice most undertakers endeavour to provide a minimum pressure in the main of between 15 m and 18 m head.

A DoE suggested indicator is as follows:

$$\frac{\text{Connected population experiencing inadequate pressure}}{\text{Total connected population at beginning of year}} \times 100 \text{ per cent}$$

Such an indicator may be derived for any division, geographical area or zone. Internal study of the results can lead to investigations of burst main history, refurbishment and renewal justification, presure control schemes etc., they may lead to savings in costs or to improved levels of service, or both, and give a sound basis for the priority allocation of future capital and renewal investment on the distribution system.

An approach to further indicators of levels of service is given in Appendix A, whilst parameters and a selection of more general indicators relating to distribution are shown in Appendix B.

For further reading see Slater[8].

BUDGETS AND THEIR CONTROL

Each undertaking has its own regulations governing the limits of responsibility for financial authority for each department and nominated officer. Forward planning for capital and revenue expenditure is necessary in plenty of time for appraisal of proposals and priority rating of schemes. Undertakings differ in defining qualifications for expenditure to be apportioned to a capital or a revenue account but broadly the capital account covers new works and major renewals of plant, equipment and buildings, and the revenue account covers the normal running of the organization and routine maintenance of its plant, equipment and buildings.

Capital programmes are normally prepared on a rolling 5 or 10 year basis, whilst revenue budgets are prepared in advance at the start of each financial year, allowing time for the essential balance between likely income and proposed expenditure. The major part of the former of course is that accruing from water rates and meter income and external constraints will almost certainly tie down the undertaking to modest levels of expenditure which in turn place pressure on management for heavy scrutiny of all items. A prerequisite to estimating the levels of proposed expenditure is an objectively based programme of works and an associated manpower plan. Capital works will find themselves competing for limited funds, which is a prime reason for their careful appraisal and rating of priority.

When forward revenue expenditure is agreed, budgets are built up along with the necessary reporting systems to allow the responsible officers to examine financial control alongside the management of the work programmes. Flexibility of modern systems should allow managers to receive financial information in a form which best suits them, and which they fully understand and are motivated to respond to.

Early prediction of budget disparity is therefore automatic, allowing sufficient opportunity for alteration of programmes or virement of budgets.

EXPENDITURE ANALYSIS

A good manager will memorise the general levels of expenditure for which he is responsible. He is then in a better position to react to budget adherence or variation, as presented periodically. Expenditure information should be promptly reported, there being nothing as 'dead' as overdue historical costs. Analysis can be subjective, such as costs of plant, labour, materials; or objective—for example, the cleaning of service reservoirs, refurbishment of mains, exchange of meters. Units of work carried out should be collated with costs in order to provide unit costs. For example, costs of washing out hydrants, or of replacing stop-taps in tarmac footpaths, can be compiled. The results can be used to compare depot with depot, undertaking with undertaking, or more importantly, direct labour rates with contractor's competitive rates, partly to ensure economic methods of working, but ultimately to ensure maximum benefit of expenditure in the consumer interest. Whilst direct labour competition for projects is more widespread in local government, its limited use as yet in the water industry has stimulated a healthy review of uneconomic site practices. Handled carefully, such an approach will normally be welcomed by the unions, who will not favour reduction in the scale of their direct labour force.

ROLE OF THE SUPERVISOR

The actual manager of costs incurred is the supervisor. The first essential is to appoint to supervisory posts only persons of natural ability, suitably trained or capable of training in both the technical field and in management. The quality of leadership is paramount, involving responsible personal attitudes to performance and standards of work and their reflection by his employees.

The supervisor must be totally aware of the objectives of the undertaking and the required standards of workmanship, water hygiene, maintenance of vehicles and equipment, health and safety and administration. He must appreciate his role in controlling direct and indirect costs, and of recognising and achieving economic operation.

The supervisor must understand target levels of unit costs and use financial information available to minimise project costs.

Above all, the good supervisor understands the human element of his employees, the need to balance skills and levels of training, to ensure good workmanship, knowledge of procedures and care of plant and equipment. When the occasion arises he has to maintain discipline, listen to grievances, understand personal problems, and maintain good working harmony and industrial relations.

The effectiveness of the supervisor is fundamental to the importance of managing the undertaking's expenditure and giving the consumer value for money. Markham[9] has covered this more fully.

7. THE PERSONNEL FUNCTION

INTRODUCTION

The personnel function in the water industry, not least in distribution, is an integral part of management. It must have the closest links with organized unions and seek to ensure that different branches or levels of management have a consistent approach to similar problems. It can do this by adopting the following aims:

(1) Determine, interpret and implement personnel policies and procedures.
(2) Develop methods, procedures and agreements best calculated to promote the most efficient organization and management of manpower.
(3) Advise managers and employees of personnel policies and procedures, and assist in ensuring consistency in their application.
(4) Ensure an adequate supply of competent and suitable personnel at all levels through efficient manpower planning and development.
(5) Ensure that personnel systems are efficiently developed and managed and conform to all statutory requirements (see Appendix C).
(6) Develop, implement and monitor a comprehensive welfare programme.

In a growing number of organizations, the payroll function is now an integral part of the personnel function.

INDUSTRIAL RELATIONS

Personnel staff are generally responsible for:

(a) disseminating information on employment legislation and conditions of service agreements;
(b) advising on the consequences of changes of industrial relations practices; and
(c) establishing and maintaining procedures.

Within the industry, the main framework of the relationship between employers and employed is provided by the 'Conditions of Service' which are negotiated in part nationally and in part locally. Apart from Chief Officers and a few other senior staff of the industry, most employees are covered by one of the following national joint negotiating bodies:

(i) The Joint National Council for Water Industry Chief and Senior Staff (JNC).
(ii) The National Joint Staff Council for Water Service Staffs (NJSC).
(iii) The National Joint Craft Committee for the Water Service (NJCC).
(iv) The National Joint Industrial Committee for the Water Service (NJIC).

Agreements for the NJIC and NJSC are normally bound together, and updated in a collective document.

Following the abolition of the NWC on 30th September 1983, various aspects of the Conditions of Service, formally agreed nationally, are determined locally.

The future role of the regional joint negotiating machinery is, at the time of writing, uncertain.

Consultative committees and Health and Safety committees provide opportunities for appropriate dialogue between employees and unions. The framework of these is of a national, regional and local nature, and their constitutions may include local variations. However, they generally operate in a similar way to the other consultative bodies with both management and employer representation and with the work of the committees being organized by joint secretaries.

MANPOWER PLANNING

The water industry recognises the importance of manpower planning in its drive for efficiency.

This is achieved in the short term by preparing and recommending overall training and development policies in the light of requirements. In the longer term, the aim of a manpower plan is to assess and review the likely future structure, staffing and manning needs, in accordance with policy objectives.

TRAINING

The Water Act 1973 places a responsibility on employers to provide appropriate and proper training for their employees.

Training is not open-ended and the priority is to give the necessary knowledge and skills to enable postholders to carry out their present jobs satisfactorily. Although not necessarily compartmented, it can be grouped into the categories below.

Training for academic, managerial or professional advancement may be taken at appropriate colleges or course centres.

Training specific to the water industry can be undertaken at one of the training centres run by the Water Industry Training Association, which has developed a wide range of specialist courses in the techniques and skills covering manual work, and operational engineering, administrative, scientific, financial and legal subjects.

Water undertakings provide varied "in-house" training and short instructional courses, as well as "on-the-job" experience, all designed to improve day to day work and efficiency.

WELFARE

Within the industry welfare is normally related to the employee at work, his protective clothing, eating facilities, shelter from bad weather and similar matters, although there is a growing awareness of the broader aspects of welfare, including pre- and post-retirement counselling, advice and help.

Matters such as protective clothing, eating facilities etc. are often discussed by local Joint Consultative Committees, and it is usual for there to be an agreed issue of clothing and level of facilities. In some cases the employer has a statutory obligation to provide safety equipment, shelter and eating facilities and the advice of specialists such as the safety officer is normally obtained before radical alterations are made, to ensure compliance with the relevant regulations.

8. REFERENCES

1. Department of the Environment 1974 "Report of the Committee on Backsiphonage in Water Installations", HMSO, London.
2. Young, J. A. 1976 *J. IWES*, 30, 313, Public relations and consumer service in a crisis economy.
3. McAllister, T. J. 1982 "The development of a mainlaying and service laying vehicle at the South Staffordshire Waterworks Company", Paper presented to IWES Midlands Section.
4. Department of the Environmental/National Water Council 1980 "Sewer and water mains records", Standing Technical Committee on Sewers and Water Mains, Report No. 25.
5. Institution of Water Engineers 1972 "Organization and procedure for maintaining records of distribution mains", Final Report of Research Panel No. 12.
6. Thackray, J. E. and Archibald, G. G. 1981 *Proc. ICE*, 70, 403, The Severn-Trent studies of industrial water use.
7. Department of the Environment/National Water Council 1980 "Leakage control policy and practice", Standing Technical Committee on Water Regulations, Report No. 26, HMSO, London.
8. Slater, R. J. 1982 "Standards of service and cost implications", Public Works Congress, Paper No. 7.
9. Markham, W. A. 1979 "The role of the supervisor as an effective manager of costs", Paper presented to AWO Midlands Area.

APPENDIX A. FURTHER INDICATORS OF LEVELS OF SERVICE

Levels of Service

Costs also related to levels of service provided.
   Who sets the standards?

      Legislation—obligations
      International/National recommendations—mandatory
      Company policy—optional

Who measures them and the role of the consumer?

   Areas to be considered:

      Quality
      Quantity
      Reliability/Constancy
      Service

Indicators

Type	Standard	Measure	Indicator
Quality	Report No. 71. WHO Standards. EEC Directives.	Bacteriological samples complying. Chemical samples complying.	Both expressed as a percentage of the total number of samples in each category.
Quantity	Water Acts as interpreted by the undertaker. CP 310.	Consumers receiving water at satisfactory pressure. Consumers receiving sufficient water.	Both under normal peak conditions and expressed as a percentage of total number of properties supplied.
Reliability/ Constancy	Water Acts as interpreted by the undertaker	Consumers experiencing a supply failure exceeding a stated period of time.	Expressed as a percentage of the total connected properties depending on standard/s adopted: e.g. less than 4 hours, between 4 and 8 hours and over 8 hours.
Service	Water Acts.	Connecting supply pipes within stated period or by agreement.	Assumed 14 days, or as agreed, expressed as the percentage of the total number of properties connected during the year.
	Water Acts.	Laying mains within the stated period.	Assumed 3 months, or as agreed; DoE use cumulative totals in calculating the indication.
		Consumer quality complaints.	Expressed as a percentage of total connected properties. May be sub-divided into type of complaint.
		Genuine consumer service complaints such as unfair treatment, unsatisfactory service, etc.	Expressed as a percentage of total connected properties. May be sub-divided into reasons for complaint and also complaints taken to outside bodies, e.g. member of parliament, Ombudsman.

APPENDIX B. PERFORMANCE INDICATORS RELATING TO DISTRIBUTION

Choice of Indicators:

Output   Volume abstracted
           treated
           supplied
           consumed   (allowance made for transmission losses)
   Static population
   Equivalent population   (to allow for metered consumption and holiday/commercial beds)
   Properties   (as defined, e.g. separately rated hereditaments plus meters, excluding garden meters).

Input   Costs
        Manpower   (adjusted for rechargeable and capital work)
        Financing   (interest and dividends paid less received and depreciation)
   Other costs
      Power
      Chemical
      Abstraction
      Rates
      Sewerage
      Purchase of water
      Contract services
      Materials purchases

Examples of:

Indicators "Of Difficulty"

Properties/km of main
Properties/sq. km of area
Average day peak week/average day (annual)
Sources—per cent surface water
Treatment—per cent disinfection only
Average pumping head

Derived Indicators

Costs per megalitre
Costs per property
  manpower
  other costs
  financing
  total (adjusted for exports)
Cost of pumping 1 megalitre/100 m lift

APPENDIX C. Statutory Instruments Relating to Personnel in the Water Industry

Disabled Persons (Employment) Acts 1944 and 1958
Factories Act 1961
Offices, Shops and Railway Premises Act 1963
Young Persons (Employment) Acts 1964
Redundancy Payments Act 1965
Transport Act 1968
Equal Pay Act 1970
Attachment of Earnings Act 1971
Contracts of Employment Act 1972
Water Act 1973
Employment and Training Acts 1973 and 1981
Trade Union and Labour Relations Acts 1974 & 1976
Health & Safety at Work etc. Act 1974
Juries Act 1974
Rehabilitation of Offenders Act 1974
Sex Discrimination Act 1975
Employment Protection Act 1975
Race Relations Act 1976
Safety Report and Safety Committee Regulations 1977
Unfair Contract Terms Act 1977
Employment Protection (Consolidation) Act 1978
Employment Act 1980
Social Security and Housing Benefits Act 1982
Employment Act 1982
Industrial Training Act 1982
Water Act 1983
Data Protection Bill
Ethnic & Sex Monitoring } Under consideration
Truck Act

(*above*) **60 in diameter steel pipe bridge, Hampton Loade**
(*South Staffordshire Waterworks Company*)

(*right*) **Cockfosters water tower, capacity 251 000 gal**
(*Lee Valley Water Company*)

INDEX